MIRANDA
Lee

IT STARTED WITH A LOOK

IT STARTED WITH
COLLECTION

October 2015

November 2015

December 2015

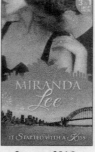

January 2016

Miranda Lee is Australian, and lives near Sydney. Born and raised in the bush, she was boarding-school educated, and briefly pursued a career in classical music before moving to Sydney and embracing the world of computers. Happily married, with three daughters, she began writing when family commitments kept her at home. She likes to create stories that are believable, modern, fast-paced and sexy. Her interests include meaty sagas, doing word puzzles, gambling and going to the movies.

Published in Great Britain 2015
by Mills & Boon, an imprint of Harlequin (UK) Limited,
Eton House, 18-24 Paradise Road, Richmond, Surrey, TW9 1SR

IT STARTED WITH A LOOK © 2015 Harlequin Books S.A.

At Her Boss's Bidding © 2002 Miranda Lee
Bedded by the Boss © 2004 Miranda Lee
The Man Every Woman Wants © 2011 Miranda Lee

ISBN: 978-0-263-91565-5

011-1015

Harlequin (UK) Limited's policy is to use papers that are natural, renewable and recyclable products and made from wood grown in sustainable forests. The logging and manufacturing processes conform to the legal environmental regulations of the country of origin.

Printed and bound in Spain
by CPI, Barcelona

AT HER
BOSS'S BIDDING

MIRANDA LEE

PROLOGUE

SHE was perfect, Justin thought from the first moment Ms Rachel Witherspoon walked in to be interviewed.

Perfectly plain and prim-looking, dressed in a very unsexy black suit, mousy brown hair severely scraped back and anchored in a twist. No make-up and no perfume, he realised with relief, the absolute opposite of the blonde bombshell who'd been wiggling her way around his office for the last month, pretending to be his personal assistant.

No, that was probably unfair. The girl had been efficient enough. The company who'd sent her over straight away after his previous PA quit on short notice didn't have dummies on their books.

But she'd made it clear within a few days that her services could easily extend beyond being just his PA. She'd used every opportunity—and every weapon in her considerable physical arsenal—to get this message across. He'd been bombarded with provocative clothes, provocative smiles and provocative comments till he couldn't bear another second. When she'd come in last Monday, showing more cleavage than a call-girl, Justin had cracked.

He didn't sack her as such. He didn't have to. She was just a temp. He simply told her that this would be her last week, saying that he'd hired a permanent PA and she was starting the following Monday.

A lie, of course. But a necessary one for his sanity.

Not that he was sexually tempted by her. Oh, no. It

was just that every time she came on to him, he was reminded of Mandy and what she must have got up to with that boss of hers. What she was *still* getting up to every single day, jet-setting around the world and being his personal assistant in every which way there was.

Justin's jaw clenched down hard at the thought. It had been eighteen months since his wife had confessed what had been going on, then added the shattering news that she was leaving him to become her boss's mistress.

Eighteen months! Yet the pain was still there. The pain of her betrayal and deception, plus the sharpest memory of the hurtful things she'd said to him that final day. Cruel things. Soul-destroying things!

Most men who'd been so savagely dumped might have soothed their battered egos by going out and bedding every female in sight. But Justin hadn't been to bed with a single woman since Mandy walked out. He simply hadn't wanted to. Just the thought of being physically intimate with another female made him shudder.

Of course, none of his male friends and colleagues knew that. You didn't confess such things to other men. They would never understand, or sympathise. His mother had an inkling, though. She knew how hurt he'd been by Mandy's deception and desertion. She kept telling him that someday he'd meet a really nice woman who'd make him forget about Mandy.

Mothers were eternal optimists. And incorrigible matchmakers.

So when his mum—to whom he'd been complaining about his office situation—rang last weekend to say that she had the perfect PA for him he'd been understandably wary. Only after he'd struggled without a secretary for a week, and been repeatedly reassured that this Rachel was nothing like his temptation of a temp, did Justin agree to interview Ms Witherspoon.

And here she was. In the flesh.

What there was of it.

She was so thin! And terribly tired-looking, with huge black rings under her eyes. Nice eyes, though. Nice shape. And an interesting colour. But so sad.

She was supposed to be only thirty-one, according to the birthdate on her résumé. But she looked closer to forty.

Understandable, he supposed, after what she'd gone through these last few years. Sympathy for her washed through Justin and he decided then and there to offer her the job. He already knew she had the qualifications, even if she might be a bit rusty. But someone as smart as she obviously was would have no trouble brushing up on her secretarial skills.

Still, he supposed he had to go through the motions of a proper interview, otherwise she might think it a bit fishy. Nobody liked charity. Or pity.

'So, Rachel,' he said matter-of-factly once she'd settled herself in the chair. 'My mother has told me a lot about you. And your résumé here is very impressive,' he added, tapping the two-page work history which had been faxed to him the day before. 'I see you were finalist in the Secretary of the Year competition a few years back. And your boss at that time was very high up in the Australian Broadcasting Corporation. Perhaps you could tell me a little about your work experience there…'

CHAPTER ONE

'THIS is just like old times, isn't it?' Rachel said to Isabel as she jumped into bed and pulled the pretty patchwork quilt up to her chin.

'True,' Isabel returned, and climbed into the matching single bed, her memory racing back to those old times.

Rachel and Isabel had attended the same boarding-school, and become best friends from day one. After Rachel's parents were killed in a freak train accident when Rachel was only fourteen, the girls had grown even closer. When Rachel's upbringing had been taken over by her mother's best friend, a nice lady named Lettie, Isabel had been thrilled to discover that Lettie lived in the same suburb of Sydney as her parents did. During the school holidays Rachel had often slept over at Isabel's. Sometimes, she'd stayed for days. Lettie hadn't minded. The girls had become inseparable, and liked nothing better than to lie awake in bed at night and talk for hours.

Rachel smiled over at Isabel. 'I feel like fifteen again.'

Well, you don't *look* like fifteen, Isabel thought with an inner sigh. Rachel looked every one of her thirty-one years, and then some. Which was a real pity. She'd once been drop-dead gorgeous, with glossy auburn hair, flashing eyes and a fab figure which Isabel had always envied.

But four years of nursing her terminally ill foster-mother had taken its toll. Rachel was a mere shadow of her former self.

Isabel had hoped that Lettie's finally passing away— the poor love had been suffering from Alzheimer's— and Rachel getting back into the workforce would put some oomph back into the girl.

But that hadn't happened yet.

Still, it had only been a few weeks.

She *had* put on a couple of pounds, which was a start. And when she smiled as she had just then you could catch a glimpse of the vibrant beauty she'd once been.

Hopefully, tomorrow, at the wedding, she'd smile a lot. Otherwise, when she saw the photographs of herself at a later date she'd be in for a shock. Isabel knew that she herself was looking her very best. Love suited her. As did pregnancy.

She was glowing.

Isabel was glad now that she'd taken *some* measures to make sure her chief bridesmaid didn't suffer too much by comparison.

'Promise me you'll let my hairdresser have his wicked way with you tomorrow,' Isabel insisted. 'Red hair will look much better with your turquoise dress than brown. And its bare neckline needs curls bouncing around on your shoulders. None of that wearing your hair pulled back like you do for work. Or up in any way. Rafe hates hair worn up on a woman, anyway. I've also hired a make-up artist to do our faces and I don't want to hear any objections.'

'I won't object. It's your day. I'll do whatever you want. But just a temporary rinse in my hair, please. I don't want to show up at the office on Monday morning with red hair.'

'Why not?'

'You know why not. One of the reasons Justin hired me as his PA was because I was nothing like my predecessor. She'd been flashy and flirtatious, remember? Alice told us all about her.'

Isabel rolled her eyes. 'I don't think a bit of red dye in your hair constitutes flashy and flirtatious.'

'Maybe not, but I don't want to take any chances. I like my job, Isabel. I don't want to do anything to risk losing it.'

'You know, when I first heard about Justin McCarthy I thought he was being sensible, not wanting a glamour-puss secretary who obviously had the hots for him. Office affairs rarely end well, especially for the woman. Now I'm beginning to agree more with Rafe's opinion of him. He says any divorced guy who fires a beautiful PA for flirting with him has to either be paranoid about women, or gay.'

'He did not fire my predecessor,' Rachel said, rather defensively, Isabel thought. 'She was just a temp. And Justin is not at all paranoid about women. He's very nice to me.'

'You said he was difficult and demanding.'

Rachel sighed. 'That was only on the day I somehow stupidly deleted a file and it took him six hours to recover it. Normally, he's very even-tempered.'

'Not all bitter and twisted?'

'I don't see any evidence of it.'

'OK, that leaves gay. So, what do you think? Is your boss gay? Could that be the reason his wife left him?'

'I honestly don't know, and quite frankly, Isabel, I don't care. My boss's private life is his own business.'

'But you said he was good-looking. And only in his

mid-thirties. Are you saying you're not attracted to him, just a little?'

'Not at all. *No*,' Rachel repeated firmly when Isabel gave her a long, narrowed-eyed look.

'I don't believe you. You told me a little while back that you were so lonely you'd sleep with anything in trousers. Now here you are, working very closely with a handsome hunk of possibly heterosexual flesh and you're telling me you don't have the occasional sexual fantasy about him? You might be a bit depressed, Rach, but you're not dead. This is me you're talking to, remember? Your best friend. Your confidante in matters up close and personal over the years. I haven't forgotten that you lost your virginity at the tender age of sixteen, and you were never without a boyfriend after that till Eric dumped you. You might not like men much any more, given what that bastard did, but—'

'Oh, I still like *some* men,' Rachel broke in. 'I like Rafe,' she added with a cheeky little grin.

'Yes, well, all females like Rafe,' Isabel returned drily, 'even my mother. But since darling Rafe is already the father of my babe-to-be, and about to become my husband tomorrow, then you can't have him, not even on loan. You'll have to find some other hunk to see to your sexual needs.'

'Who said I had sexual needs?'

'Don't you?' Isabel was startled. She must have after four years of celibacy!

'I don't seem to. I rarely *think* about sex any more, let alone need it.'

Yes, that was patently obvious, now that Isabel came to think about it. If Rachel felt like sex occasionally, she'd do herself up a bit, and to hell with her paranoid boss. There were plenty of other secretarial jobs in the world, and plenty of other men to go with them. The business district of Sydney was full of very attractive men of all ages. Of course, with her looks on the wane, Rachel might not be able to catch herself a seriously gorgeous hunk like Rafe, but there was no reason for her to be lonely, or celibate.

'Actually, I'm not sure I ever did need it, as such,' Rachel went on thoughtfully. 'Sex was just another facet of my being in love. Losing my virginity at sixteen wasn't a sexual urge so much as an emotional one. I'd fallen in love for the first time and I wanted to give myself to Josh.'

'But you enjoyed it. You told me so.'

'Yes, I certainly did. But it wasn't just sex I was after. It was that lovely feeling of being loved.'

Isabel smiled. 'You know, it's possible to have very good sex without love, Rach.'

'Maybe for you, but not for me. When I said I'd sleep with anyone after Lettie died, that was just my grief and loneliness talking. I can't just sleep with anyone. I have to be in love and, quite frankly, since my experience with Eric I don't think I'm capable of falling in love any more. I just don't have the heart for it. Or the courage. Eric hurt me more than I could ever explain. I honestly thought he loved me as much as I loved him. But, looking back, I don't think he loved me at all.'

'He didn't, the selfish rat. But that doesn't mean that one day you won't meet a man who will love you the way you deserve to be loved.'

'You're only saying that because you were lucky enough to find Rafe. Not so long ago, you didn't have such a high opinion of the male sex.'

'True.' Isabel couldn't deny that she'd been a classic

cynic for ages where men were concerned. She'd spent most of her adult female life falling in love with Mr Wrong. She knew where Rachel was coming from and, honestly, she couldn't blame her for feeling the way she did. Eric had treated her shamefully, dumping her after he found out Rachel was quitting her job to look after Lettie. That, coming on top of Lettie's own husband heartlessly abandoning his increasingly vague wife, must have been the final straw. It was no wonder Rachel's faith in the male sex had been seriously dented.

'I'm quite happy as I am, Isabel,' Rachel went on, '*without* a man in my personal life. I'm really enjoying my job. It's very interesting working for an investment consultant. I'm learning a lot about the stock market, and money matters, which hasn't exactly been my forte till now, as you know. I'm thinking of going to university at night next year and doing a business degree, part-time. I have plans for my life, Isabel, so don't you worry about me. I'll be fine.'

Isabel sighed. That's what she always said. Rachel was one brave girl. But a rather unlucky one. When Lettie died they'd both thought she'd at least have some financial equity in Lettie's house, despite it being mortgaged. Rachel was the sole beneficiary in Lettie's will, made after Lettie's husband had deserted her. Rachel had been going to sell the house and put a deposit on an inner-city apartment with the money left over after the loan had been repaid. So she'd been shattered to find out the house was still in Lettie's husband's name.

When Rachel went to the solicitor who was looking after Lettie's estate and explained that she'd personally paid the mortgage for the past four and a half years with money she'd earned doing clothes alterations at home, the solicitor had countered that Lettie's ex had paid the mortgage for fifteen years before that and had no intention of giving her a cent.

She was also informed that Lettie's ex was thinking of contesting Lettie's last will as well, since it was made after she was diagnosed with a mentally debilitating illness. Rachel was advised she could go to court to fight for a share of the house and contents if she wished, but her case was shaky. Even if she won, the amount of money she'd be awarded would undoubtedly be exceeded by her court costs.

So Rachel had walked away with nothing but a few personal possessions, her clothes and a second-hand sewing machine.

She'd temporarily been living with Isabel in her town house at Turramurra, and had agreed to house-sit whilst Isabel and Rafe were away on their honeymoon. Isabel had offered her the use of her place on a permanent basis for a nominal rent, since she was moving into Rafe's inner-city terraced house on their return, but Rachel had refused, saying she would look for a small place of her own closer to the city.

Silly, really, Isabel thought. She should let her friends help her in her hour of need. But that was Rachel for you. Independent and proud. *Too* proud.

But the nicest person in the world.

Isabel hoped that one day a man might come along worthy of her. A man of character and sensitivity. A man with a lot of love to give.

Because of course that was what Rachel needed. To be loved. Truly. Madly. Deeply.

Just as Rafe loves me, Isabel thought dreamily.

God, she was so lucky.

Poor Rachel. She did feel terribly sorry for her.

CHAPTER TWO

RACHEL hurried down the city street the following Monday morning, anxious not to be late for work. She'd caught a slightly later train than usual, courtesy of the longer time it had taken her to get ready for work that morning. Now she was trying to make up for lost time, her sensibly shod feet working hard.

Turning a corner into a city street which faced east, Rachel was suddenly confronted by the rays of the rising sun slanting straight into her eyes. But she didn't slacken her pace.

The day was going to be warm again, she quickly realised. Too warm, really, for a black suit with a long-sleeved jacket. Spring had been late coming to Sydney this year, but it was now here with a vengeance. October had had record temperatures so far and today looked like no exception. Not a cloud marred the clear blue sky, making the weather forecast for a southerly change today highly unlikely.

There was no doubt about it. She'd have to buy some new work clothes soon. What she'd been wearing would not take her right through the spring till summer. She should never have been stupid enough to buy all long-sleeved suits to begin with. She'd buy something other than black next time too, though nothing bright or frivolous. Something which would go with black accessories. Light grey, perhaps. Or camel. That colour was very in.

Unfortunately, such shopping would have to wait till

Isabel got home from her honeymoon in three weeks' time. Rachel didn't have a clue where the shops were that Isabel had taken her to last time, and which catered brilliantly for the serious career girl. Admittedly, a large percentage of the clothes in those shops was black, but they also had other colours.

Till then, however, she was stuck with black. And long sleeves.

Thank heaven for air-conditioning, she thought as she pushed the sleeves up her arms and puffed her way up the increasingly steep incline.

A sideways glance at her reflection in a shop window brought a groan to her lips. Her hair was still red, despite several washings yesterday and a couple more this morning. Maybe not quite as bright a red as it had been for the wedding on Saturday, but bright enough. She wished now she'd gone out yesterday and bought a brown hair dye. But at the time she'd been hoping the colour would still wash out.

If Isabel hadn't already been winging her way overseas on her honeymoon, Rachel would have torn strips off her mischief-making best friend. That hairdresser of hers must have used a semi-permanent colour on her hair, Rachel was sure of it.

Admittedly, she'd ended up looking pretty good for the wedding. From a distance. Amazing what a glamorous dress, a big hairdo and a make-up expert could achieve. But that was then and this was now, and bright red hair did not sit well with Rachel's normally unmade-up face, or her decidedly *un*-glamorous work wardrobe.

She was thankful that the repeated washings yesterday had toned down the colour somewhat. Hopefully, the way she was wearing it today—scraped back even more severely than usual—would also minimise the effect. She would hate for Justin to think that she was suddenly trying to attract his attention in any way.

As she'd told Isabel the other night, she liked her job. And she didn't want to lose it. Or even remotely risk the good relationship she'd already established with her boss, which was very professional and based on mutual respect. Justin had told her only last week what a relief it was to come into work and not be overpowered by some cloying perfume, or confronted with a cleavage deep enough to lose the Harbour Bridge in.

Rachel was out of breath by the time she reached the tall city office block which housed the huge insurance company where she worked.

When she'd first heard about the job as Justin's PA Rachel had been under the impression that Justin was an AWI executive. That wasn't the case, however. He was an independent hot-shot financial analyst under contract to AWI to give them his exclusive financial advice for two years, after which Justin planned on starting up his own consultancy company. Preferably in an office away from the inner-city area, he'd explained to her one day over a mutual coffee break, ideally overlooking one of the northern beaches.

Meanwhile, AWI had given him use of a suite of rooms on the fifteenth floor of their building, which was high up enough to have a good view of the city and the harbour.

But the view wasn't the only good thing about this suite of rooms. The space was incredible. Rachel had sole occupancy of the entire reception area, which was huge, and boasted its own powder room and tea-cum-store room, along with a massive semicircular work station where three secretaries could have happily worked side by side without being cramped.

Justin's office beyond was just as spacious, as well as having two large adjoining rooms, one furnished for meetings, the other for relaxing and entertaining. Rachel had never seen a better-stocked bar, not to mention such a lavish bathroom, tiled from top to bottom in black marble, with the most exquisite gold fittings.

Justin had confided to her during her first interview that this suite of rooms had previously been occupied by an AWI superannuation-fund manager who'd re-decorated as if he owned the company, and been subsequently sacked. No expense had been spared, from the plush sable carpet to the sleekly modern beech office furniture, the Italian cream leather sofas and the impressionistic art originals on the walls.

Clearly, Justin being allotted this five-star suite of rooms showed how much his skills were valued by his temporary employers.

Rachel valued him as her boss, too. She admired his strong work ethics and his lack of personal arrogance. Most men with his looks and intelligence possessed egos to match. Justin didn't. Not that he was perfect, by any means. He did have his difficult and demanding moments. And some days his mood left a lot to be desired.

Still, Rachel already knew she'd like nothing better than to go with him when he left to set up his own company. He'd already implied she could, if she wanted to. He seemed as pleased with her as she was with him.

A shaft of sunshine lit up Rachel's red hair again as she pushed her way into the building's foyer through the revolving glass doors. The top of her head fairly glowed in the glass and she groaned again. She would definitely be going out at lunch time and buying that brown dye. Meanwhile, she would explain to Justin the reason behind her change of hair colour, and that it was as good as gone. Then he couldn't jump to any wrong conclusions.

No one gave Rachel a second glance during the lift ride up to the fifteenth floor, which was because none of the smartly dressed men and women in the lift even knew her. Few people who worked in the building knew her. Justin worked alone, with only the occasional fund manager actually dropping in for advice, face to face. Mostly they contacted Justin by phone or email, and vice versa.

So far, he hadn't held a single meeting around the boardroom-like table in his meeting room, and only once to her knowledge had he entertained an AWI executive in the other room. Sometimes, he had a nap in there on one of the two sofas after he'd been working all night. He did attend monthly meetings upstairs with all the fund managers, but he never attended the company's social functions, and he resolutely refused to become involved in AWI's internal politics.

The truth was her boss was a loner.

Which suited Rachel just fine.

She'd found that since her lengthy stay-at-home absence from the workforce—and the outside world in general—she'd become a bit agoraphobic. She liked the insular security of her present office situation, plus the little contact with strangers which her working day held. She no longer seemed to have the confidence she'd once had to make small talk with lots of people. She'd actually become quite shy, except with her very close friends, like Isabel and Rafe, which wasn't like her at all. She'd once had a very outgoing personality.

Isabel kept saying she'd get back to her old self eventually.

But Rachel was beginning to doubt it. Her experiences over the last few years had definitely changed her. She'd become introverted. And serious. And, yes, plain.

That was one of the biggest changes in her, of course. She'd lost her looks. And dying her hair red wasn't going to get them back. All it made her feel was foolish.

The lift doors opened and Rachel bolted down the corridor, hopeful of still arriving before Justin. He worked out in the company gym every day before work, and occasionally lost track of time. Hence his tardy arrival at the office on the odd morning.

The door from the corridor was still locked, heralding that this was one of those mornings. Rachel sighed with relief as she found her key, already planning in her mind to be sitting at her desk, looking coolly composed and beavering away on her computer when Justin finally came in.

She was doing just that when the door burst open fifteen minutes later. Her heart did jump, but not for any sexually charged reason, as Isabel had fantasised the other night, just instant agitation. What would her boss say when he saw her hair?

Justin strode in, looking his usual attractive but conservative self in a navy pinstriped suit, white shirt and bland blue tie. His damp dark hair was slicked back at the sides, indicating that he'd not long showered. He had the morning papers tucked under one arm and was carrying his black briefcase in the other. He was frowning, though not at her, his deeply set blue eyes quite distracted, his thick dark brows drawn together over his strong, straight nose in an attitude of worried concentration.

'Morning, Rachel,' he said with only the briefest sidewards glance as he hurried past. 'Hold the coffee for ten minutes, would you?' he tossed over his shoulder as he forged on into his private sanctuary. 'I have something I have to do first.'

When he banged the door shut behind him Rachel glared after him, her hazel eyes showing some feminine pique for once.

'Well!' she huffed at the closed door. 'And good morning to you, too!'

So much for his having noticed her red hair. It came to Rachel that she could have been sitting there stark naked this morning, and Justin would not have noticed.

Not that her being naked was anything to write home about these days. Despite having put on a couple of pounds during the past month, she was still thin, her once noteworthy breasts having long ago shrunk from a voluptuous D-cup to a very average B plus. She'd complained about it to Isabel on Saturday when they were getting dressed before the wedding.

'You still have bigger boobs than me,' Isabel returned as she surveyed Rachel in her underwear. 'OK, so you're thin, but you're in proportion. Actually, you look darned good in the buff, girl. You've surprised me.'

Rachel had laughed at the time. She laughed now, but with a different type of self-mockery. What on earth was she doing, even thinking about what she looked like naked? Who cared? No one was going to see her that way, except herself.

Again, it was all Isabel's fault, putting silly thoughts into her head about Justin and sex.

Sex! Now, that was a subject not worth thinking about.

So why was she suddenly thinking about it?

Rachel filled in the next eight minutes trying to work through her irritability, before giving up and rising to go pour Justin a mug of coffee from the coffee maker, which she kept perking all day. Justin liked his coffee. She figured that ten minutes would have passed by the time she carried it in to him. Any further delay was unacceptable. The sooner he noticed her red hair, and the sooner she explained the reason behind it, the sooner she'd be able to settle down to work, and put aside the fear of looking ludicrous in her boss's eyes.

'Come in,' Justin snapped when she tapped on his office door exactly ten minutes after his order.

She entered to find him sitting at the bank of computers which lined the far side of his U-shaped work station. His back remained to her as he rode his swivel chair down the long line of computers, peering at each screen for a couple of seconds as he went. His jacket was off and his shirtsleeves rolled up. His tie, she knew without being able to see it, would be loosened.

As Rachel made her way across the room Justin slid down in front of the furthest computer on the right.

'Just put it down here,' he directed, patting an empty spot next to his right elbow without looking up.

Grimacing with frustration, Rachel put the coffee down where ordered and was about to leave when she stopped.

'Justin…'

'Mmm?'

He still didn't look up.

She sighed. 'Justin, I need to talk to you,' she said firmly.

'What about?' Again, no eye contact.

'I wanted to explain to you about my red hair.'

'What red hair?' He spun round from the computer, his eyes finally lifting. He frowned up at her, his head tipping slightly to one side. 'Mmm. It's a bit bright for you, isn't it?'

Rachel winced. 'It looked all right for the wedding on Saturday,' she said, her pride demanding she say something in her own defence.

His blue eyes widened. 'Wedding? What wedding? My God, Rachel, you didn't go and get married on the weekend without telling me, did you?'

Rachel almost laughed. As if.

'I don't think you need worry about that ever happening, Justin,' she said drily. 'No, I was a bridesmaid at my best friend's wedding on Saturday and she insisted on having my hair dyed red for the day. It was supposed to wash out afterwards but, as you can see, it didn't. I just wanted to reassure you that I'm going to dye it back to brown tonight.'

He shrugged his indifference, then picked up his coffee. 'Why bother?' he said between sips. 'It doesn't look *that* bad. And it'll wash out—or grow out—eventually.'

Rachel's shoulders stiffened. It would take two years for it to grow out. Did he honestly think she had such little personal pride that she'd walk around with half-red, half-brown hair for two *years*?

Clearly, he did.

'It looks dreadful and you know it,' she said sharply, and whirled away from him before she did something she would regret.

Rachel could feel him staring after her as she marched towards the open doorway, probably wondering what was wrong with her. She'd never spoken to him in that tone before. But when she turned to close the door behind her he wasn't staring after her at all. Or even thinking about her. He was back, peering at the maze of figures on the computer, her red hair—plus her slight outburst—clearly forgotten.

Rachel didn't realise the extent of her anger till she tried to get back to work. Why she was so angry with Justin, she couldn't understand. His indifferent reaction to her hair should have made her happy. It was all rather confusing. But there'd been a moment in there— a vivid, *violent* moment—when she'd wanted to snatch the coffee out of his hands and throw it in his face.

It was perhaps just as well that her boss didn't emerge for the rest of the morning, or call her for more coffee to be delivered. Clearly, he was steeped in something important, some sudden programming brainwave or financial crisis which required his undivided attention.

In the month she'd been his PA, Rachel had discovered that Justin was a computer genius as well as a financial one, and had created several programs for following and predicting stock-market trends, as well as analysing other economical forces. Aside from her general secretarial duties, Rachel spent a couple of hours each day entering and downloading data into the extensive files these programs used. They needed constant updating to work properly.

She was completing that daily and slightly tedious area of her job shortly before noon, when the main door from the corridor opened and Justin's mother walked in.

Alice McCarthy was in her early sixties, a widow with two sons. She'd been one of Rachel's best customers during the four years she'd made ends meet by using her sewing skills at home. A tall, broad-shouldered woman with a battleship bust and surprisingly slender hips, Alice had difficulty finding clothing to fit off the peg. But she loved shopping for clothes, rather than having them made from scratch, and had more than enough money to indulge her passion. Mr McCarthy had been a very successful stockbroker in his day, and, according to Alice, a bit of a scrooge, whereas Alice veered towards the other extreme. Consequently, she was in constant need of a competent seamstress who could cleverly alter the dozens of outfits she bought each season.

Till recently that person had been Rachel, whom Alice had discovered when Rachel had distributed brochures advertising her sewing skills through all her local letterboxes. Alice lived only a couple of streets away from Lettie's house.

Despite the thirty-year age gap, the two women had got along well from the start. Alice's natural *joie de vivre* had brought some brightness into Rachel's dreary life. When her foster-mum passed away and her friends thought Rachel needed a job working outside of the home Alice had been generous enough to steer her into her present position, despite knowing this meant she had to find another person to alter her clothes. Fortunately, a salesgirl in one of the many boutiques Alice frequented had recommended an excellent alteration service in the city, run by two lovely Vietnamese ladies who were extremely efficient as well as inexpensive.

After Rachel had gone to work for her son Alice had

rung her at the office a couple of times to see how she
was doing, but this was the first time she'd made a
personal appearance.

'Alice!' Rachel greeted happily. 'What a lovely surprise. You're looking extremely well. Blue always
looks good on you.'

Alice, who was as susceptible to a compliment as
the next woman, beamed her pleasure. 'Flatterer.
Nothing looks all that good on this unfortunate figure
of mine. But I do my best. And my, aren't you looking
a lot better these days? You've put on some weight.
And you've changed your hair colour.'

Rachel's hand went up to pat the offending hair.
'Not for long. It goes back to brown tonight. I had it
dyed for Isabel's wedding on Saturday. You remember
Isabel, don't you? You met her at Lettie's funeral.'

'Yes, of course I remember her. Very blonde. Very
beautiful.'

'That's the one. She wanted my hair red for the day.
Of course, it wasn't done like this. It was down and
curled. I also had more make-up on than a supermodel
on a photo shoot.'

'I'll bet you looked gorgeous!'

'Hardly. But I looked OK for the occasion. And for
the photographs. I'm well aware this colour red doesn't
look any good on me normally.'

'But it might, you know, Rachel, if you wore some
make-up. It's just that against your pale skin it looks
too bright. And without any colour in your face that
black suit you're wearing is too stark, by contrast.
Now, if you were wearing blue,' she added, her own
blue eyes sparkling, 'like the blue I've got on, and a
spot of make-up, then that red hair just might be perfect.'

Rachel really wasn't in the mood for another woman to start trying to make her over. Isabel had been bad enough on the weekend. On top of that, she was still upset over Justin ignoring her this morning.

He wouldn't ignore her, however, if she started seriously tarting herself up. He'd think something was really up and then there would be hell to pay.

'Alice,' she said, slightly wearily. 'You were the one who told me about my predecessor, that flashy, flirtatious temp your son was so relieved to eject from his office. The reason Justin gave me this job is because he *likes* the way I look. He *likes* me *au naturel*.'

Alice rolled her eyes. In her opinion, no man liked women *au naturel*, even the ones who said they did. They all liked women to doll themselves up. You only had to watch men's eyes when a glamour-puss walked into a restaurant, or a party. Justin was simply going through a phase, a post-Mandy phase.

The trouble was, this phase was lasting far too long for her liking. It wasn't natural. Or healthy, either, for her son's mind or his body.

'That boy doesn't know *what* he likes any more,' she grumbled. 'That bitch of a wife of his certainly did a number on him. If ever I run into her again I'd like to…'

Whatever it was Alice was about to vow to do to her son's ex-wife was cut dead when the door to Justin's office was suddenly wrenched open, and the man of the moment appeared.

'Mum! I thought I heard a familiar voice. What are you doing here? And what were you talking about just then? Not gossiping about me to Rachel, were you?'

Alice's cheeks flushed but she managed not to look

too guilty. 'I never gossip,' she threw at her son defiantly. 'I only ever tell the truth.'

Justin laughed. 'In that case, why are you here? And no white lies, now. The truth, the whole truth and nothing but the truth.'

Alice shrugged. 'I came to the city early to do some shopping, didn't see a single thing I liked and decided on the spur of the moment to pop in and take you to lunch. Rachel too, if she'd like.'

'Oh, no, no, I can't,' Rachel immediately protested. 'I have some shopping that I simply have to do.' Namely, some brown hair dye.

'And neither can I,' Justin informed his mother. 'There was some unexpected bearish rumblings on the world stock markets last night and I have to have a report ready for the powers that be here before trading ceases today. So I'll be working through lunch. I was going to get Rachel to pop out and bring me back some sandwiches.'

'Poor Rachel,' Alice said. 'I thought the days of secretaries doing that kind of menial and demeaning job were over. I dare say you have her bring you coffee twenty times a day as well. I know how much you like your coffee. What else? Does she collect your dry-cleaning too?'

Justin looked taken aback. 'Well, yes, she has collected my dry-cleaning. Once or twice.' His eyes grew worried as they swung towards Rachel. 'Do you object to doing that kind of job, Rachel? You've never said as much.'

Rachel sighed. Of course she didn't object. If Alice thought those jobs were menial and demeaning, let her try changing urine-soaked sheets every morning.

'No, I don't mind at all. Really, Alice,' she insisted when Justin's mother looked sceptical. 'I don't.'

Now it was Alice's turn to sigh. 'No, you wouldn't. Just make sure you don't take advantage of Rachel's sweet nature,' Alice warned her son.

Rachel wished Alice would simply shut up.

Justin's eyes met hers again and she knew by their exasperated expression that he was thinking exactly the same thing. Rachel gave him a small smile of complicity, and his blue eyes twinkled back.

'I would never take advantage of Rachel,' he told his mother. 'I value her far too much to do anything to risk losing the best PA a man could have.'

Rachel's cheeks warmed at his flattering words.

She didn't realise at the time how ironic they were.

CHAPTER THREE

MOST city singles loved Friday afternoons. Their moods would lift as the working week drew towards an end, anticipation building for that wonderfully carefree moment when they poured out of their office buildings and into their favourite bars and drinking holes for the traditional Friday-night drinks-after-work bash. Even the non-drinkers liked Fridays, because there was still the weekend to look forward to, two whole days without having to sit at their desks and their computers; two whole days of doing exactly as they pleased, even if that was nothing.

Rachel was one of the exceptions to the rule. Since coming back to work she hated the week to end because she hated the prospect of two whole days of doing just that. Nothing.

As she made her way to work the following Friday morning Rachel began thinking she might have to go shopping by herself this weekend after all, just for something to do. Last weekend had been OK, because of Isabel and Rafe's wedding. But this weekend was going to be dreadful, with Isabel away and that strangely soulless town house all to herself.

She could hardly fill the whole weekend with housework. She already kept the place spotless on a daily basis. She could read, of course, or watch television. But, somehow, indoor activities did not appeal. She felt like getting out and about.

It was a pity that the town house didn't have a garden. Unfortunately, the courtyard was all paved and the few plants dotted around were in pots. Rachel liked working with her hands. That was why she'd first taken up sewing as a teenager.

But sewing was on the no-no list for Rachel nowadays. She never wanted to see her sewing machine again. It was packed away at the back of a cupboard, never to see the light of day again. After the funeral, whenever she looked at it she thought of Lettie's illness, and all that had happened because of it. No nice associations at all.

Sometimes, she wished Justin would ask her to work overtime on the weekend. She knew he went into the office on a Saturday, so surely there was something she could do. Extra data entry, perhaps. Justin often had to farm some of that work out to an agency.

But he never asked, and she wouldn't dream of suggesting it. He might see her offer as evidence of a desire for more of his company, rather than the result of chronic loneliness.

Rachel glanced up at the sky before she entered her building. The clouds were heavier than the day before, the southerly change predicted earlier in the week having finally arrived yesterday, bringing intermittent showers.

The thought of more rain over the weekend dampened Rachel's enthusiasm for shopping by herself. Maybe she would wait till Isabel returned. There was no real hurry, now that Sydney's weather had changed back to cooler. Her black suits would do a while longer.

Yes, she decided as she swung through the revolving glass doors. Her shopping expedition could wait.

Justin was already in when she arrived. Surprisingly,

he'd put on the coffee machine and was in the act of pouring himself a mugful when she walked into the tea room. He was wearing one of her favourite suits, a light grey number which looked well against his dark hair and blue eyes, especially when teamed with a white shirt and blue tie.

'Morning,' he said, throwing her a warm smile over his shoulder. 'Want me to pour you one as well?'

'Yes, please,' she answered, her spirits lifting now that she was at work. She shoved her black bag and umbrella on the shelf under the kitchen-like counter, then took the milk out of the fridge, preferring her coffee white, though she could drink it black, at a pinch. Justin always had his black.

'What's it like outside?' he asked, and slid her mug along the counter to where she was standing.

'Overcast,' she said as she added her milk.

'Not actually raining, though?' he queried just before his mug made it to his lips.

'Not yet. But it will be soon.'

'Mmm.'

Rachel detected something in that 'mmm' which made her curious.

'Why?' she asked. 'Do you have something on this weekend which rain will spoil?'

He took the mug away from his mouth. 'Actually, no, just the opposite. I won't be here in Sydney at all. I'm flying up to the Gold Coast this afternoon to spend the weekend at a five-star ocean-front hotel.'

'Lucky you,' she replied, wondering who he was spending the weekend with.

'No need to feel jealous. You're coming with me.'

Rachel was grateful that she hadn't lifted her own

coffee off the counter, because she surely would have spilt it.

Justin chuckled. 'You should see the look on your face. But don't panic. I'm not asking you to go away with me for a dirty weekend. It's for work.'

Rachel closed her mouth then. Well, of course it was for work. How could she, even for a split-second, imagine anything else?

Silly Rachel.

'What kind of work?' she asked, finally feeling safe enough to lift her coffee off the counter and take a sip.

'A different kind of investment advice from my usual. Apparently, this holiday hotel—it's called Sunshine Gardens—is on the market and all potential buyers—of which AWI is one—are being flown up free of charge so they can see and experience first-hand the hotel's attractions and assets. Generally speaking we can do our own thing, except for tomorrow night, when we'll be wined and dined by management, after which there'll be a video shown, along with a presentation of facts and figures to con everyone into believing the hotel is a rock-solid investment. Guy Walters was supposed to go, but he can't, so he asked me to go in his place.'

Rachel frowned. 'Guy Walters. Who's he? I can't place him.'

'You must know Guy. Big, beefy fellow. Fortyish. Bald head. Exec in charge of property investments.'

Rachel searched her memory. 'No. No, I don't think I do. I'd remember someone who looked like that.'

Now Justin frowned. 'You're right. Guy hasn't been down here to see me personally since you started. Anyway, I do weights with him every morning. When I arrived this morning he wasn't there. He raced in half an hour later and explained that he was off to the airport to fly to Melbourne because his dad was ill, after which he explained about where he was supposed to be going and begged me to go in his place. Apparently, the CEO of AWI is super-keen on buying this place and is expecting a report on his desk first thing Monday morning, no excuses. Guy said I was the only one he could ask to go in his place whose opinion he would trust. He said he knew an old cynic like me wouldn't be blinded by surface appearances and would look for the pitfalls. At the same time, he also wanted a woman's opinion. He said women see things men don't always see.'

'So what woman was *he* going to take? His secretary? Or a colleague?'

'No, actually, he'd been going to take his wife. When I pointed out I didn't have a wife he said that shouldn't present a problem for a man-about-town like me, and I got all that male nudge-nudge, wink-wink crap. Guy's always implying I must have a little black book filled with the phone numbers of dozens of dollybirds available for dirty weekends at a moment's notice.'

Rachel stopped sipping her coffee, her curiosity piqued. 'And you don't?'

'God, no.' The distaste on his face was evident. 'That's not my style.'

Rachel didn't know what to think. Maybe he simply didn't like women. Or maybe he just had old-fashioned principles and standards.

The thought that he might be right off sex—and women—was swiftly abandoned. The sceptic in Rachel couldn't see any heterosexual male of Justin's age and health being totally off sex no matter what. It went against everything she and all her female friends had come to believe about the human male animal.

'I told Guy I would be taking my valued and very astute PA,' Justin added. 'If you're available to go, of course. Are you?'

'Yes, but...'

'But what?'

'What about the accommodation? If this chap had been going with his wife, then...'

'I've already thought of that and there are no worries there. AWI's been allotted a two-bedroom apartment with two separate bathrooms, so there's no privacy issue. Also, you don't have to spend every minute of every day with me. You're free as a bird. I'd expect you to accompany me to the dinner on the Saturday night, however.'

'Er—what would I have to wear to something like that?'

'Guy said it's black tie. Lord knows why. Someone's being pretentious as usual. Probably their PR person. Do you have something suitable in your wardrobe? If not, I'm sure AWI can spare the expense of a dress. You could buy one up there tomorrow. Tourist towns usually have loads of boutiques.'

'No, I've got something suitable,' Rachel returned, thinking immediately of her bridesmaid dress, which Isabel had chosen specifically because it was the sort of dress you could wear afterwards. At the time, Rachel hadn't been able to imagine where, but it would be ideal for wearing to this dinner. As much as Justin might not like her coming into the office done up to the nines, surely he wouldn't want her to accompany him to a dinner looking totally colourless and drab.

A tiny thrill ran down her spine as she thought of

how surprised he might be if she wore her hair down and put on a bit of make-up. Nothing overdone, of course. A classy, elegant look.

'Great. And don't forget it's going to be a lot warmer up there at this time of year,' Justin went on. 'You'll need very light clothes for day wear. Very casual, too.'

Rachel saw the expression in his eyes as they flicked up and down the severely tailored black suit she was wearing.

'It's all right, Justin,' she said wryly. 'I do have some other more casual clothes.' Again, thanks to Isabel.

When Isabel's ex-fiancé broke off their engagement earlier this year Isabel had given Rachel her entire honeymoon wardrobe, bought to be worn on a tropical island. Rachel had thought at the time she would never have an opportunity to wear any of them, same as with the bridesmaid dress.

Now, suddenly, she did. What a strange twist of fate!

'So when is the flight?' she asked.

'It departs at four, which doesn't leave all that much time to do what has to be done here before we go. Unfortunately, I can't abandon my other work today entirely. I still need to check last night's markets and you'll still have to update the files. So, let's see, now…you live at Turramurra, don't you?'

'For the moment.'

He frowned. 'What do you mean, for the moment?'

'It's my friend's place. I've been staying with her temporarily since my foster-mum's funeral. Don't you remember? I told you all about Lettie and her illness at my interview.'

He slapped his forehead with the ball of his free hand and shot her an apologetic glance. 'Of course you did. You also said you'd be selling her old house and buying yourself a unit closer to the city. Sorry. I did listen to you that day. Honest. I'd just forgotten for the moment. So how's all that going? Found a buyer yet?'

Rachel sighed. 'Unfortunately, things haven't worked out the way I thought they would. Lettie did will me everything she owned, but it turned out she didn't own the house and contents in the first place. It was all still in her husband's name. I could have taken the matter to court but I just didn't have the heart. The solicitor said I probably wouldn't end up with much, anyway.'

'He's right there. Litigation is to be avoided at all costs. But gee, Rachel, that's a damned shame. And not fair, after all you did for your foster-mum. But then, life's not fair, is it?' he added with the bitterness of experience in his voice. 'So what are you going to do about a place to live?'

'Well, I'm house-sitting Isabel's town house whilst she's on her honeymoon. She won't be back for another fortnight. But I plan on renting a place of my own closer to the city after she does get back.'

'Flats near the city are expensive to rent,' Justin warned. 'Even the dumps.'

'Tell me about it. I've been looking in the paper. I can only afford a bedsit. Either that, or I'll have to share.' Which was a last resort. The idea of moving in with strangers did not appeal at all.

'Can't see you sharing a place with strangers,' Justin said, startling Rachel with his intuition. 'Can't you stay where you are in your friend's place? She won't be needing it, now that she's married.'

'She did offer it to me for a nominal rent.'

'Then take it and don't be silly,' he pronounced

pragmatically. 'So, how long do you think it would take you to go there, pack, then get back to the airport? I'll pay for taxis both ways, of course.'

'I don't think I could do it in less than two hours, and that's provided I don't hit any traffic snags. It is Friday, you know.'

'True. That means you'll have to leave here by one at the latest. Guy gave me the plane tickets, so I'll give you yours before you go and we'll meet at the allotted departing gate. OK?'

'Yes. OK.'

Justin smiled over the rim of his coffee mug. 'I knew I could count on you not to make a fuss. Any other woman would have had hysterics about how she'd need all day to get packed and changed, but not you.'

Rachel gave a rueful little laugh. 'I'm not sure if that's a compliment or a criticism.'

'A compliment,' Justin said drily. 'Trust me. Come on, let's get back to work. I want to have a clear desk and a clear head by the time that plane takes off this afternoon. I don't know about you, but I'm rather looking forward to having a break away from this office, not to mention this rotten weather. I've always been partial to some sun and surf. Which reminds me. Don't forget to pack a swimming costume. Even if you don't like the surf, the hotel has a great pool, I'm told.'

He plonked down his empty mug and marched off, leaving Rachel to stand there, staring after him, her stomach revolving as she recalled the bright yellow bikini amongst the clothes Isabel had given her.

The thought of swimming in a bright yellow bikini in front of her boss sent her into a spin.

'Hop to it, Rachel,' he threw over his shoulder.

She hopped to it, but she still kept thinking about

that bikini. Though modest by some standards, it was still a bikini. That, combined with the colour, would not present the non-flashy, non-flirtatious image Justin had of her and which he obviously felt comfortable with. She knew it was a stretch of the imagination that he would ever be sexually attracted to her—especially if he didn't like women—but in the end Rachel decided that the bikini would be accidentally left at home. She had a good thing going with her job and she didn't want to risk changing the status quo.

With this thought in mind, she decided not to wear her hair down for the dinner tomorrow night, either. It could go up as usual. And her make-up would be confined to a touch of lipstick. That was all she owned, anyway. It would be crazy to race out and buy a whole lot of stuff for one night. For what? Just to satisfy her feminine pride? Because that was all that was at stake. *Her* pride. Nothing to do with Justin. He obviously didn't give a damn how she looked.

Feeling much better with these decisions, Rachel put her mind to her job. At one o'clock on the dot she was off, the taxi making good time to Turramurra. Packing was a breeze. Isabel's discarded honeymoon gear was already in a very nice suitcase. It was just a matter of taking some things out, and adding some, namely her bridesmaid gear, along with her toilet bag. She did also add some white sandals from Isabel's wardrobe, knowing her friend wouldn't mind.

She didn't have time to change but she did put a simple white T-shirt on under her black jacket so that she could take the jacket off once they reached Coolangatta.

By two-ten she was back in a taxi, heading for Mascot, but this time the going was slower, because it had started to rain quite heavily. They fairly crawled down the Pacific highway. There was an accident at an intersection at Roseville, which caused a back-up, and they moved at a snail's pace again right down to Chatswood, after which the flow of traffic improved, courtesy of the new motorway. But her watch still showed five after three when she climbed out at the domestic terminal at Mascot. By the time she'd waited in line, been booked in and gone through Security, it was twenty-five to four, only ten minutes from the scheduled boarding time.

As she hurried along the long corridor towards the nominated gate Rachel hoped Justin wasn't worrying. She knew he'd already arrived because the lady on the check-in counter had been left instructions on her computer to give her the seat next to him.

Gate eleven came into sight at last, and so did Justin. He was sitting on a seat at the end of a row in the waiting area, reading an afternoon newspaper, and not looking at all anxious, though he did glance up over the top of the pages occasionally. When he spied her walking towards him he folded the newspaper, smiled and patted the spare seat beside him.

'You made it,' he said as she dropped down into it.

'Just. The traffic back into town was horrendous. I was wishing I had a mobile phone to call you and tell you my progress.'

'No worries,' he said. 'You're here now.'

'Yes. Yes. I'm here now.' Breathless, relieved and quite excited, now that she wasn't stressing about her clothes, or how she would look at tomorrow night's dinner. It had been years since she'd gone anywhere for the weekend and here she was, flying off to the Gold Coast in the company of a very attractive man.

OK, so he was only her boss, and there was nothing remotely romantic between them. But other people didn't know that. Other people might look at them and think that they *were* going off for a dirty weekend together.

Not likely, you stupid girl, a quite savage voice reprimanded inside her head. *Just look at him. He's gorgeous! The epitome of tall, dark and handsome. And just look at you. Talk about drabsville. A few years ago, things might have been different. You were a real looker then. Now you're a shadow of your former self. No, not even a shadow. A shell. That's what you are. A cold, empty, sexless shell!*

Rachel sagged back against the seat, a huge wave of depression swamping her earlier excitement.

'I think this trip'll do you good,' Justin said suddenly by her side.

'Oh?' she replied wearily. 'Why do you say that?'

'You've been a bit down-in-the-mouth since your friend's wedding last weekend. I dare say you're missing her. And it can't be much fun, working for a workaholic bore like me.'

She stared over at him. 'You're not a bore. I like my job. And I like working for you.'

He smiled at her. 'And I like you working for me. You are one seriously nice woman. Which is why what my mother said the other day has been bothering me. Tell it to me straight, Rachel. Do you object to bringing me coffee and running little errands for me? If you do, then I want you to say so. Right now.'

'Justin, I don't mind. Honestly. It's a change sometimes to get up and do something physical instead of just sitting at the computer, updating files.'

He frowned. 'That's a good portion of your job, isn't

it? Updating the files. That *must* be boring for someone of your intelligence. I should involve you more in what I do, explain my programs, show you how to analyse the data yourself, make proper use of that good brain of yours. Would you like that?'

'Oh! I…I'd *love* it! If—er—you really think I could do it, that is,' she added, her chronic lack of confidence not quite keeping up with her instant enthusiasm over his proposal.

'Of course you can. That way, when I set up my own company, I'll promote you to being a proper personal assistant with a salary to match, and we'll hire another girl to work on Reception and data entry.'

'Justin! I…I don't know what to say.'

'Just say yes, of course.'

She beamed at him. 'Yes, of course.'

'That's another thing I like about you. You don't argue with me. Aah, there's the boarding announcement. Come on, let's be one of the first on board. Then I can settle back to reading the newspaper and you can read that book you've got in your bag.' He was on his feet in a flash and off.

'How do you know I've got a book in my bag?' she asked after they'd been through the boarding-pass check and were striding down the tunnel towards the plane.

'Rachel, give me credit for *some* powers of observation,' he said drily. 'I do realise I have my nose buried in computer screens most of the day but I'd have to be a total moron not to notice some of your habits. You read every single lunch-hour. And I imagine every day on the train to and from work. Am I right?'

'Yes.'

'What kind of books do you like?'

'Oh. All kinds. Thrillers. Romances. Sagas. Biographies.'

'I used to read thrillers obsessively when I was at uni,' he said in a happily reminiscent tone. 'But I have to confess my reading rarely extends beyond the newspapers and business-based magazines these days.'

'I think that's a shame. Reading's a great pastime. And a good escape.'

'A good escape, eh? Yeah, you're right. It is. Maybe I should try it,' he muttered under his breath, 'instead of the gym.'

Rachel just caught this last possibly meant-for-his-ears-only remark, and wondered what he was trying to escape from. The memories of his marriage?

If his mother was to be believed then his ex-wife had been the bitch from hell. But if that was the case, then why would Justin have married her in the first place? He didn't strike Rachel as being a fool, or a pushover.

Relationships were a minefield, Rachel mused as she trailed after Justin past the welcoming flight attendants and into the body of the plane. And most marriages were a right mystery to all but the people involved. Justin's mother would naturally blame her son's wife for their break-up, but did she really know what had happened between the pair of them?

Justin stopped abruptly next to row D and turned to her. 'You have the window seat,' he said. 'I don't mind sitting on the aisle. Actually, it gives me a bit more leg room.'

'Thanks,' she said gratefully, and slid into the window seat. She liked to see where she was going.

Once settled, Rachel took out her book then stowed her black shoulder bag under the seat in front of her,

ready for take-off. 'I hope it's not raining up there too,'
she said as she peered out at the rain-soaked tarmac.

Justin looked up from the newspaper. 'It isn't according to the radar weather map I looked up on the
internet just before I left the office. It's fine on the Gold
Coast today with a top temperature of twenty-seven
degrees. And more of the same is forecast for the weekend.'

'Sounds lovely,' she said with a happy sigh.

When Justin resumed reading his newspaper, Rachel
opened the family saga she'd been reading the last couple of days. It wasn't riveting so far, but she liked the
author and trusted her to get her in eventually.

Soon, she was off in that imaginative world of the
story, so she didn't see the man who boarded the plane
shortly afterwards. Or his female companion. If she
had, Rachel would have recognised both of them.

She missed seeing them again at Coolangatta
Airport, as it was so easy to do in crowds. Though,
admittedly, she had been occupied chatting away with
Justin at the luggage carousel and hadn't looked round
at the other people waiting to collect their bags. She
missed them again in the foyer of Sunshine Gardens,
because she and Justin were already riding the lift up
to their ocean-view apartment by the time they arrived.

Rachel might not have seen them at all till the following night at the dinner—which would have been an
even greater disaster—if she hadn't discovered on
reaching the door of their apartment that her door key
didn't work.

'It must be faulty,' Justin said when his worked fine.
'I'll call the front desk when I get inside and they can
bring you up another one.'

'No, I'll go back down now and get one myself,' Rachel said. 'You saw how busy they were.'

'Rachel, you're much too considerate sometimes.'

'Not really. I've always found it's quicker and less irritating to just do things myself, rather than wait for someone else to do it.'

'True. That's why I carried the luggage up myself instead of leaving it to the porter. I'm like you, I think. I can't stand waiting for things. When I want something I want it *now*. Off you go, then. I'll put your case in your bedroom and find the coffee-making equipment. Or would you rather I pour you a drink drink?'

'Coffee for now, I think. But you don't have to make it.'

'I know that. Call it repayment for services rendered.'

'Justin, you are much too considerate sometimes,' Rachel quipped as she hurried off, smiling when she heard his answering laugh.

Rachel had no sense of premonition as she rode the lift down to the ground-floor level again. Why should she have?

The lift doors opened and she walked out into the terracotta-tiled foyer, glancing around again at the décor as she made her way over to the reception desk.

Actually, this hotel reminded her of an island resort she'd gone to once with Eric. High ceilings, cool colours and glass walls overlooking lush green gardens with lots of water features.

Eric...

Now, there was a right selfish so-and-so if ever there was one. If she'd known how shallow he was she'd never have fallen in love with him in the first place, let alone agreed to marry him.

Rachel gave herself a swift mental shake. She wouldn't think about Eric. Ever again.

But, perversely, when she walked up to the reception desk the man booking in reminded her strongly of Eric, despite only viewing him from the back. He had the same sandy blond hair. The same way of holding his shoulders. The same elegance.

The attractive brunette standing next to him seemed familiar as well. Rachel listened to them chatting away together as they checked in, their voices horribly familiar.

And then, suddenly, they both turned around.

CHAPTER FOUR

JUSTIN was suitably impressed the moment he stepped inside the apartment. It had a cool, comfy feel, with plenty of space, even to having its own foyer, which was unusual in hotel apartments.

As he dropped their two suitcases next to the hall stand—a sturdy yet elegant piece with a smoked-glass top and carved oak base—Justin caught a glimpse of himself in the matching mirror above. His hair, which possibly needed a cut, was all over the place. That's what happened when you had to walk across windy tarmac, as they had at Coolangatta airport. No tunnels to spoil you.

Straightening, Justin smoothed back the wayward top and sides with the flat of his hands, then moved a little closer to the mirror to peer at the bags under his eyes.

Could do with a good eight hours' sleep, he thought as he turned and went over to slot his room key into the gizmo beside the door. The lights came on automatically, as did the air-conditioning. That done, Justin strode into the main living area, where he stripped off his jacket and tie, tossed them over the back of one of the nearby dining chairs then took himself on a quick tour of the rest of the apartment.

Absolutely everything met with his approval, even the crisp citrus colours they'd used on the walls and soft furnishings. Normally, lime and yellow and orange would not be to his taste but the brightness was offset

by the wall-to-wall cream carpet, the cream woodwork
and the extensive use of pine. The kitchen was all pine,
with white counter-tops and white appliances, and the
bathrooms—thank heaven—were white as well. Justin
had had about enough of that all-over black marble in
the hideously pretentious bathroom at his office.

He contemplated giving Rachel the main bedroom,
then decided she would only protest, so he put her bag
in the second bedroom, which suffered little for size.
Both bedrooms also had access to the balcony that
stretched the full length of the apartment and had a
view that looked pretty spectacular, even from inside.

How much better would it look from the balcony
itself?

Justin decided to find out before making the coffee,
and wasn't disappointed. You could see for miles, from
Tweed Heads on his right to Surfer's Paradise in the
northern distance with its tell-tale skyline of skyscrap-
ers. The sea was looking breathtakingly beautiful, even
now, with the sun having set and the sky darkening
from its earlier bright blue to a dusky grey. Admittedly,
first thing in the morning the sun might be a bit too
brilliant as it rose over the horizon and slammed
straight into the windows behind him, but in the afternoon and evenings it would be wonderful to sit outside
here in one of the deckchairs, sipping some chilled
white wine.

'I wonder if Rachel likes white wine,' he said to
himself, and seriously hoped so, because the scenario
he'd just pictured in his mind didn't seem quite so appealing on his own. He would ask her when she got
back, and if she did he'd see about having Room
Service send up a bottle or two. Then later he'd take
her to the swankiest restaurant in the place for dinner.

Hotels like this always had at least one à la carte eating establishment.

Rachel deserved a bit of spoiling, he decided, after all she'd been through these past few years.

Justin breathed in the refreshing salt-sea air for thirty seconds longer before returning to the living area and going in search of the coffee-making equipment. It crossed his mind whilst he rummaged around in the cupboards that Rachel was taking a good while. Presumably, the front desk was still busy. Or maybe they couldn't find another key to this room. He made a mental note to find out what had actually happened. Guy would want to know what he thought of the service. The last thing a new owner needed to do was to have to sack staff then find replacements. Far too expensive and time-consuming an operation.

The electric jug found, Justin filled it and put it on, then set about emptying a small packet of—wow!—*quality* coffee into each of the two white mugs he'd located. No cheap muck. That was good. Very good. He hated hotels that supplied low-grade products. He'd have to remember to ask Rachel what the shampoo and conditioner were like. He could actually never tell the good from the bad in that department, but a woman would know. Guy was right in that regard.

The water had boiled and Justin was standing there, deciding whether to pour his or wait for Rachel to come back, when there came a knock on the door. He hurried over to answer it, tut-tutting to himself on the way.

'You don't have to tell me,' he said when he wrenched open the door to find Rachel on the other side. 'They didn't have another key.'

Rachel just stood there, her face ashen, her eyes anguished, her hands clutched tightly in front of her.

Justin, despite not being the most intuitive male in the world, was quick to appreciate her distressed state.

'Rachel!' he exclaimed. 'What is it? What's happened?'

'I...I...'

Clearly, she could not go on, her throat making convulsing movements as she struggled for control.

'Come inside,' Justin said and, taking her left elbow, steered her quite forcibly into the apartment. Her hands remained clutched tightly in front of her and she looked as if she was going to burst into tears, or faint.

Once Justin had kicked the door shut behind them, he guided her over to the three-seater opposite the television and plonked her down into the middle cushion, then sat on the pine coffee-table, facing her.

'Rachel,' he said softly, taking her still clasped hands within his. 'Tell me what happened?'

She gave a small laugh that held a decided edge of hysteria.

'What happened?' she repeated. 'They didn't recognise me, that's what happened. *He* didn't recognise me. Can you believe that?'

'Who's he?'

'Eric.'

'Who's Eric?'

'My fiancé,' she choked out, 'till I told him I was leaving my job to stay home and mind Lettie.' She started shaking her head as though still not quite believing the situation she found herself in. 'I thought I knew why he broke our engagement,' she went on in shaken tones. 'I thought he didn't love me enough, or care enough to support my decision. It never crossed my mind that there might have been another woman in the wings all along, and that I'd given him the perfect excuse to call our wedding off.'

'What makes you think there was another woman at the time?'

'Because I've just seen the bitch,' she said, surprising Justin with the unexpected flash of venom. 'She was downstairs just now, checking in with him.'

'And she is...?' Justin probed, knowing it couldn't be Rachel's best friend, since she was overseas on her honeymoon. Thank God.

'The real-estate agent who sold him the fancy unit which was supposed to be our marital home,' she elaborated bitterly.

'I see. And are *they* married now?'

'No. Living together, I presume from the conversation I overheard at the desk. Either that or they just go away together on what he called weekend junkets associated with her job.'

'I see,' Justin said again, trying to think of something to say to pacify her. But he knew how hard that was, when your emotions were involved. 'Look, you don't really know he was carrying on with this woman before he left you, Rachel. You're just jumping to conclusions.'

'No, I'm not. I know I'm right. I had a feeling about them at the time but I ignored it. I told myself that I was imagining the intimate little looks which used to pass between them, and the many excuses he made to meet up with her at the unit when I was busy at work. Eric's a top lawyer, you see, and can pretty well come and go as he pleases.'

'OK. So he's a two-timing rat as well as a shmuck.

What does it matter now? You can't possibly still be in love with him. Not after…how long ago was it?'

'Four years, give or take a month.'

'See? Now, if you'd said a year maybe, or eighteen months…' like in his case with Mandy '…then I'd understand why you're so upset.'

'Love doesn't stop simply because you want it to, Justin. Even if I didn't love Eric any more, I wouldn't be human if I didn't hate seeing him with another woman like that. But I'm doubly upset because neither of them *recognised* me!' she finished on a strangled sob.

Sympathy *and* empathy consumed Justin as he realised what she was saying. Her hurt was not solely because of this Eric's former betrayal, but because he hadn't recognised her physically.

Justin understood that type of humiliation well and his heart went out to her.

'Maybe he wasn't really looking at you,' he tried excusing. 'Maybe he was off in another world.'

'I wish. But no. He bumped into me when he turned away from the check-in desk. Almost knocked me over. He actually grabbed my shoulders and looked right at me for a second or two. He saw me well enough and there was not a hint of recognition. *She* didn't recognise me, either. Though I can't really blame her. She didn't know me all that well. We only met a couple of times. And I know I've changed a lot. But Eric should still have known me. We were lovers, for pity's sake!'

'Did you say something to him? Call him by name?'

'*Speak* to him? No.' She shuddered. 'I bolted into the ladies' room in the foyer and stayed there till I was sure they'd have left the area and gone up to whatever floor they're staying on. That's what took me so long.'

What probably took her so long, Justin believed, was the time she'd spent in there, weeping and looking in the mirror to see what it was this Eric had seen, and *not* seen.

'Do you think he…um…might have been pretending not to know you?'

'No. There was nothing like that in his eyes. Just blankness. He didn't recognise me.'

'Have you changed *that* much in four years, Rachel?'

Her shoulders sagged, her eyes clouding to an expression of utter misery. 'I guess I must have.'

'So what do you want to do?' he asked, his own spirits sagging at the realisation that this weekend wasn't going to be such a happy or relaxing getaway after all.

'About what?' she asked wearily.

'Presumably this couple will be at the dinner tomorrow night. That must be the junket you heard mentioned.'

Horror filled her face at the prospect.

'You don't have to go,' he said quickly.

'Are you sure? I mean…I don't like to let you down but I…I don't think I could bear it. Eric might recognise me after I do myself up a bit. But, there again, he might not. Either way, I'm going to be terribly uptight, and very poor company with few powers of observation.'

'It's all right, Rachel. Truly. I'll go by myself.' He let her hands go and straightened.

She stared up at him, and he realised her hazel eyes were really quite lovely. How could that fool have not recognised her, if he'd been her lover? Eyes were the one thing which never changed. How many times would this Eric have stared down into Rachel's eyes when they'd been in bed together?

Hell, Mandy's beautiful blue eyes were imprinted on his brain!

His sigh carried a wealth of emotions of his own. 'I'll go finish making us that coffee.' And he stood up.

'You are such a nice man,' she choked out, then burst into tears, burying her face in her hands.

Smothering a groan, Justin sat himself down next to her and took her into his arms, cradling her weeping face against his shirt front.

'No decent human being,' he said gently as he stroked her back, 'could be anything but nice to you, Rachel. This Eric is scum. You're better off without him.'

'I know that,' she sobbed. 'But it still hurts to see him with another woman.'

'I'm sure it does,' Justin murmured soothingly. God knows how *he'd* react if he ever ran into Mandy with that swine who'd stolen her away from him, he thought. Murder was too good for the pair of them.

'Maybe seeing him again like that is a good thing,' he tried, though not quite believing it himself. 'It should give you the motivation to forget him once and for all and get on with your own life. After all, life isn't too bad for you now, is it? You have a job you like, with a considerate boss. Or so you said,' he added wryly. 'And soon you'll have an even better job with enough of a wage coming in to afford a seriously nice place to live in of your own. What more could you possibly want?'

'To still be beautiful,' she mumbled into his chest.

Justin reached down and took her hands away from where they were jammed under her chin, then tipped her face up so that their eyes met. 'You *are* still beautiful, Rachel,' he said softly. 'Where it counts.'

'Right,' she said ruefully. 'Pardon me if I don't get too excited by that compliment. I've found that beauty on the inside is highly overrated as an asset, especially when it comes to the opposite sex.'

'Not all men are as shallow as your Eric,' he countered, confident that he didn't judge a woman so superficially.

'Is that so? Might I ask you a rather personal question?'

'Shoot.'

'Was your ex-wife beautiful?'

Justin opened his mouth, then closed it again. Mandy had been drop-dead gorgeous, there was no doubt about it. She had a very pretty face, big blue eyes, long blonde hair. A *great* figure. And she'd known how to showcase herself to perfection, from the top of her glossy blonde head to the tips of her pink-painted toes.

Rachel, on the other hand, was a far cry from drop-dead anything. Yet she wasn't ugly. She couldn't even be called plain. Aside from having genuinely lovely eyes, she had regular features in her oval-shaped face and an interesting mouth, now that he bothered to really look. Wide, and tilted up at the corners, with a very full bottom lip.

It was just that she always looked so colourless, like a picture that had faded badly. The black suits she wore to work looked extra-drab on her, as did the clunky mid-heeled black shoes.

As for her hair...

He could not think of a good thing to say about her

hair, except that it was far better not red, as it had been last Monday, because any attention brought to it could only create a more negative impression.

'Case closed,' Rachel said succinctly, and stood up. 'God, I feel terrible. I must look terrible too. I think I'll go and have a shower and change. Which way to my room?'

'What about coffee?'

'Thank you but I don't feel like it just now.'

Me neither, he thought. He needed something much more potent in the drinks department. Some food was in order as well. Time was getting on and he hadn't had anything to eat since breakfast except that on-board snack. He wouldn't mind betting Rachel hadn't had any lunch either. No wonder she was so thin.

Though not *that* thin, he'd realised when he was holding her close just now. She had some reasonable breasts hiding there underneath that black jacket. Either that, or she'd been wearing a padded bra.

'Showering and changing sounds like a good idea,' he agreed, determined not to spend all weekend wearing a suit. Bad enough he had to tog up in a tux tomorrow night. 'Your room's on the right down that hallway. The bathroom's opposite on the left. I left your case at the foot of the bed. I'm going to pop into the shower too, but first I'll order us something to eat from Room Service, since going out to dinner tonight is out of the question now. You wouldn't want to run into yours truly and his lady-love. And no, please don't say again what a nice man I am.'

She gave him a faint smile. 'All right.'

'Go, go, go.' He waved her off.

Once Rachel went, he crossed to the desk, which held the leather-bound folder that listed all the hotel's services, plus the in-house menu. He ran his eye swiftly down and decided on something cold. A platter of mixed seafood and a couple of different salads, followed by strawberries and cream, all washed down with a bottle of their best white wine.

Most women liked white wine and Rachel needed cheering up.

Frankly, so did he.

He always did after thinking about Mandy.

Room Service arrived half an hour later, with Justin able to answer the door totally refreshed and dressed in beige cargo shorts and a dark red polo shirt. His feet he'd happily left bare for now. With the food safely deposited in the fridge, and the waiter tipped and dispensed with, Justin set about opening the bottle of wine, a Chablis, after which he popped it in the portable wine cooler provided.

The wine glasses supplied weren't exactly top-drawer crystal but they were nice enough. He placed two of them in the fridge to chill then wandered down the hallway to see how Rachel was progressing. He'd heard her shower going for ages earlier on.

'You ready yet, Rachel?' he asked, stopping in the hall between both shut doors, her bedroom and the bathroom. He didn't know which room she was in.

'Not really.' Her voice came from the bedroom.

'What do you mean, not really?'

'I have a slight problem.'

'What's that?'

'I—er—washed my smalls in the shower before I realised I'd forgotten to pack any more.'

Justin had to struggle not to laugh. But Rachel without underwear was so *un*-Rachel. 'That's OK. Just put on a robe for now. They'll dry by morning, then you can go shopping for more.'

'Er...'

'Don't tell me you didn't pack a robe, either.'

'No, no, I do have a robe but it's a bit...um...'

'What?'

'Nothing. I suppose I'm silly to worry,' she muttered.

'Put it on, then, and get yourself out here. Your pre-dinner drink awaits.'

'OK. I...I'll just be a minute.'

'I'll be out on the balcony, waiting. Don't be too long. I hate drinking alone.'

Justin was lounging back in a deckchair, sipping his wine and thinking life wasn't too bad after all, when he heard the glass door slide back from down Rachel's end. His head turned just in time to see her step out onto the balcony.

Justin did his best not to do a double take, or to stare. But, hell, it was hard not to.

The robe Rachel was wearing was not a modest little housecoat by any means, but a very sexy emerald-green satin number which clung as only satin could. Admittedly it had sleeves to the elbow and did reach down to her ankles. And she *had* sashed it tightly, but this only seemed to emphasise the surprisingly shapely and obviously naked body underneath it.

Clearly, she hadn't been wearing a padded bra earlier, Justin realised as his gaze took in the natural fullness of her breasts, which were very nice indeed. Actually, her body was very nice all round. She had a deliciously tiny waist and enough curve to her hips to look very feminine and, yes, almost sexy.

Amazing what had been hiding underneath those awful black suits she'd been wearing to the office!

Amazing what that awful hairdo had been hiding as well. Having her hair down and curling damply onto her shoulders took years off her face. There was some much-needed colour in her complexion as well, possibly from the heat of the shower, which gave him a glimpse of what she might look like with some make-up on.

Maybe still not a beauty queen but one hell of a lot better than her usual colourless façade. With the right kind of dress she could look quite fabulous. That figure of hers was a knock-out.

When she started coming towards him the robe flapped back at the knees, revealing a full length matching nightie underneath, which was perhaps just as well. He didn't want to stare too much or she was sure to get embarrassed. Even so, it was a very sexy outfit and not the sort of lingerie Justin would have expected Rachel to own, let alone wear.

Still, seeing her in it gave him an idea which just might salve some of Rachel's pride and give him some personal satisfaction as well. He already hated this Eric creep for what he'd done to such a nice woman. Dumping her was bad enough, but fancy not recognising her!

Of course, Rachel was her own worst enemy when it came to her appearance. Obviously, she could look a whole lot better than she did every day.

If she'd do what he was going to suggest, however, then, come tomorrow night, dear old Eric was bound to recognise her. And Rachel would never have to scuttle off and hide in a ladies' room again, weeping with hurt and humiliation. She'd be able to hold her head high in any company and show her pathetic ex-fiancé that he'd made a big mistake in dumping her.

A *big* mistake.

Just as Mandy made a big mistake dumping you? came the dark and caustic thought. *Is it vengeance for Rachel you want here, or some vengeance for yourself?*

Mandy, he thought angrily. Always, it came back to Mandy!

CHAPTER FIVE

WHEN Rachel saw Justin's sudden scowl she stopped walking towards him. She hadn't minded his surprise on first seeing her dressed as she was. Surprise was fair enough. But a scowl was another matter entirely.

'I...I think I'd better go back and find something else to put on,' she said. 'This just isn't appropriate, is it?'

'Certainly not!' he exclaimed, then astonished her by laughing. 'No, no, that's not what I meant. I meant don't go back inside and change. You look perfectly fine as you are. Heavens, Rachel, you're wearing more clothes than most girls wear walking down the street up here. Here, sit down and get some of this wine into you.' He swept up a bottle of white wine from the portable cooler standing by his chair and poured her a glass.

'I hope you like Chablis,' he said as he placed the glass on the white outdoor table and pushed it across to where she was settling herself in one of the matching white chairs.

'Yes, I do. Thank you.' Rachel was grateful for the drink, but more grateful to be sitting down, and no longer on show. That short walk along the balcony had felt like a million miles. Talk about embarrassing!

The whole situation was embarrassing. Fancy forgetting to bring any underwear.

She picked up the wine glass, cradled it in both her

hands to stop them shaking and took a sip. 'Oh, yes,' she sighed. 'This *is* good.'

'It ought to be,' Justin said with a smile in his voice. 'It cost a small fortune. But no sweat. Everything's on the house, according to Guy. I aim to take full advantage of it. And so should you. Which gives me an idea. Wait here.'

He put down his wine and levered himself up from the chair. 'Won't be long,' he said, and hurried back inside through the sliding glass doors, leaving Rachel to do a spot of staring of her own.

It was strange seeing her boss in a bright top, casual shorts and bare feet. She'd always known he sported a nice shape and tan, but she'd never seen so much of it before. Even his bare feet were brown, which made her wonder what a man who wore shoes and socks all week did to achieve that. Lie in one of those sunbeds at the gym? Or swim a lot in an outdoor pool? If so, where? She knew he lived in a high-rise apartment in an exclusive complex down on the harbour foreshore at Kirribilli, so it probably sported a pool. Exclusive ones usually did.

'I thought as much,' Justin was saying as he returned through the open glass doors, carrying an open black leather folder. 'They do have a beauty salon in this place.'

'A…a beauty salon?' Rachel repeated, not sure what Justin was getting at.

'Yes. Seeing you wearing that gorgeous green and with your hair down has shown me, Rachel Witherspoon, that you have been hiding your light under a bushel. I don't know if anyone has ever told you before but black does nothing for you, and neither does the way you wear your hair to work. You also have a damned good figure, which your working wardrobe doesn't show to advantage. With a different hairstyle, some make-up and the right clothes, Rachel, you could look more than good. You could look great.'

'But…'

'But what?'

'But I thought you didn't want me looking great, especially at work.'

'What?'

'Your mother told me all about your previous PA long before you ever did.'

He grimaced. 'Oh, God, she didn't, did she?'

'Afraid so.'

He frowned over at her. 'So you *deliberately* made yourself look like a plain Jane to get the job.'

Not really, an amazed Rachel was thinking. She'd just come *au naturel*. She *was* a plain Jane. But she wasn't about to say so. She rather liked the thought that Justin believed she'd been down-playing a whole host of hidden attractions.

'Well…' she hedged, not sure what to say at this juncture.

'Oh, Rachel, Rachel, you didn't have to do that. I'd have given you the job, anyway, because I saw right from the start that you were nothing like that other girl. It wasn't just the way she dressed, you know, but the way she acted. Like some oversexed vamp all the time. She drove me insane.'

'So you wouldn't mind if I did myself up a bit for work?'

'Why should I mind?'

'I was worried that if I suddenly came into the office with a new hairdo and a new wardrobe you might think I was…um…'

'Tarting yourself up for me?'

'Yes,' she said sheepishly.

He laughed. 'I would never think that of you. Silly Rachel.'

Rachel tried not to be offended. But she was, all the same. Yes, silly, *silly* Rachel.

'Which brings me right back to my original suggestion,' he went on. 'Now, tomorrow I want you to go down to that beauty salon and get the works. Facial, massage, pedicure, manicure, waxing, hair, make-up. The lot. It says here they do all that.'

'That seems excessive.' Even for me, she thought ruefully.

'No, it's not. It's necessary.'

'Oh, thank you very much,' came the waspish comment.

'Now, now, this is no time for over-sensitivity, Rachel. The truth is you've let yourself get into bad habits with this plain-Jane nonsense. I can understand that you might not have bothered with your appearance much when you were at home all the time, but I'll bet there was a time when you went to a lot of trouble with your hair and make-up and clothes.'

'We-ll…'

'*Well?*' he probed forcefully.

'I always suspected I didn't become a finalist in the Secretary of the Year competition on my office skills alone,' she said drily.

'I don't doubt it. I'll bet you were a looker back then.'

'I was…attractive.'

'And you never wore black.'

'Not often.'

'How did you wear your hair?'

'Down,' she admitted. 'With auburn highlights.'

'No wonder people from your past didn't recognise you today. But, come tomorrow night, Eric the Mongrel will recognise you all right.'

'Eric the Mongrel?' she repeated on a gasp.

'Yeah. That's what I've nicknamed him. Do you like it?'

'Oh, dear. I *love* it.'

'So you'll do it? Come to the dinner with me?'

Rachel swallowed. It would take every bit of courage she owned to face Eric and that woman once more, even if she was dolled up to the nines. But, by God, she would!

'Yes,' she said, and Justin beamed.

'Fantastic. Here. A toast is in order.'

He held his glass out towards her and she clicked it with hers.

'To the comeuppance of Eric the Mongrel,' Justin pronounced.

Rachel's stomach flipped over. 'Comeuppance?'

'Oh, yes. Your ex deserves a few serves. And I'm just the man to deliver them!'

Justin paced up and down the living room, impatient for Rachel to make her appearance. She'd stayed hidden ever since her return from the beauty salon around five, letting herself in whilst he'd been in the bathroom, shaving. Now it was getting on for seven and he was dressed in his tux and ready to go down for the cocktail party that preceded the dinner at eight, an arrangement Rachel was well acquainted with. They'd discussed it last night.

So when seven came and went without her showing,

Justin strode down the hallway and knocked firmly on her door.

'Enough titivating in there, Rachel. It's seven o'clock. Time you faced the music.'

'Coming,' she called back. But nervously, he thought.

The door opened and Justin's blue eyes rounded.

'Wow, Rachel. You don't just look great. You look fabulous!'

Even that was an understatement. Where had his plain-Jane PA disappeared to? In her place stood a striking creature. No, a stunning creature. No, a striking, stunning, *sexy* creature.

Justin found himself standing there, just staring at her, trying to work out what she'd done to cause such a dramatic transformation.

It couldn't just be her hair, though it was very different. And very red, he noted wryly. Cut in layers, it fell from an off-centre parting to her shoulders, framing her face and her *eyes*, her always lovely eyes, which now looked not just lovelier but larger. Was it the smoky eye make-up which had achieved this effect, or some other subtle change? Whatever, when he looked into her face he couldn't stop looking at her eyes.

They looked back at him, heartbreakingly hesitant. She still didn't know how beautiful she was. How amazingly, incredibly beautiful.

'You honestly think so?' she asked. 'You don't think I look...foolish?'

'Foolish?' he echoed in disbelief. 'In what way could you possibly look foolish?'

'My hair colour bothers me for starters. It's too red,' she said, touching it gingerly with her equally red nails.

'Honey, you can carry off red now,' he reassured softly.

'Oh…' She blushed prettily. 'But don't you think the make-up girl put too much foundation on me? I look like a ghost.'

'No, you don't. That's the fashion. You know, that's the slinkiest bridesmaid dress I think I've ever seen,' he remarked, shaking his head as his gaze ran down the dress again.

It was a turquoise silk sheath, with thin shoulder straps and a fitted waist that showed off Rachel's nice bustline and tiny waist to perfection. The skirt was straight and slender, and fell to mid-calf, with a slanted hem from which hung strands of crystal beads. Under this rather provocative feature her legs were bare, yet looked as smooth and shiny as they would if covered in the most expensive stockings. Her feet were shod in turquoise high heels, which matched the colour of the dress and had open toes, showing scarlet-painted toes. She smelled faintly of jasmine, possibly from a scented oil used to massage her skin. Her arms, Justin also noted as his eyes travelled back up to her face, looked as soft and shiny as her legs, probably the result of a full body massage today.

That beauty salon deserved a medal for the miracle it had managed in one short day. Not that he'd tell Rachel that. Despite her fab new look, her self-esteem was still wavering, which was a problem. Frankly, he'd been looking forward to exacting some well-deserved revenge on rotten exes tonight, and he needed Rachel's full co-operation to achieve that end. Clearly, her confidence still needed some more boosting.

'You look good enough to eat, Rachel. Eric the

Mongrel is going to be jealous as sin when I walk into that dinner party with you on my arm.'

'I think it's Eric's girlfriend who might be the jealous one,' Rachel returned as she looked him up and down.

Justin was surprised but pleased that she thought him attractive. It would make his plan for the evening run smoother. 'Yes, we've both cleaned up rather well, haven't we? Come on, let's go and put a cat amongst the pigeons. Do you have a bag?'

'No, I don't.'

'No need. It's not as though we have to go outside. There'll be no wind to mess up your hair. If you feel in the need for any repairs during the night you can always whip up here in the lift. I'll have my key card with me.'

'Yes, I might need to do that after dinner. I always eat off my lipstick, though the make-up girl who did me up said this particular brand is renowned for not coming off. She said it's the one the actresses use who make blue movies.'

Justin laughed and started shepherding Rachel towards the door. 'That's handy to know. So if you disappear under the tablecloth at any time tonight I'll feel confident you'll resurface still looking immaculate.'

When she looked scandalised Justin tut-tutted. 'Come, now, Rachel, try to get with the spirit of this occasion. Remember, I'm not just your boss for tonight. I'm your lover as well.'

'*What?*' She ground to a startled halt.

Justin was taken aback. 'I thought you understood that was part of my plan. Look, how else are we going to get up Eric the Mongrel's nose, unless he thinks we're a hot item? We want him to believe you haven't missed him one bit, that you've survived his callous dumping; you did your duty to Lettie like the angel you are and are now moving on to a much more exciting and fulfilling life than you would have had married to him. You're looking better than ever. You live in a fantastic town house at Turramurra. And you have this great new job, with a handsome, successful, besotted boss who can't keep his hands off you.'

'But…but I wouldn't *like* having a boss like that!'

'You might not, but it's some men's fantasy. And some women's. Trust me on that. I would imagine it was right up Eric the Mongrel's alley.'

'You have to stop calling him that or I'm going to giggle all night.'

'That's all right. Giggling's good.'

'But it's not *me*.'

'It can be. You can be anything you want to be tonight. The point of this exercise is to show your ex that he doesn't know you at all, if he ever did. And to make him want the new you like crazy!'

'I…I don't think…'

'Now, thinking's a definite no-no for this evening as well. Thinking rarely does anyone any good. Just follow my lead, honey, and everything will be fine.'

When he took her elbow he felt her resistance and stared down at her. She stared back up at him.

'You called me honey.'

'Well, I'm not going to call you Rachel all the time. Sounds far too platonic. OK, so honey's out. How about the occasional darling? Yes, that's much better. Much classier. Come along, Cinders, darling,' Justin said with a rueful smile. 'It's time to go to the ball.'

CHAPTER SIX

RACHEL stood silently by Justin's side in the ride down in the lift, her stomach twisted into nervous knots.

How could she possibly carry this charade off? It was…beyond her. She might be looking good on the outside but inside she was still the same Rachel who'd run into Eric yesterday and bolted like a frightened horse. Fear rippled down her spine and invaded every pore in her body. The thought of confronting her ex with his new lady-love held nothing but a sick-making apprehension.

'I…I can't do this, Justin,' she whispered just as the lift stopped at one of the floors on the way down to the lobby.

'Yes, you can,' he reassured firmly.

The lift doors whooshed back and there, waiting for the lift, were the objects of her fear.

Rachel sucked in sharply.

'I gather that's Eric the Mongrel,' Justin whispered.

'Yes,' she choked out, not feeling at all like giggling at the silly nickname this time. Eric the Magnificent would be more like it. He really was a drop-dead gorgeous-looking guy, especially in a dinner suit. Charlotte was no slouch in the looks department, either, the passing years seeming to have enhanced her darkly striking beauty. Tall and supermodel-slim, she was chic personified with her concave-cut dark brown bob and elegant black dress.

'Charlotte, come on,' Eric said impatiently, stepping

70

forward to hold the lift doors open whilst not giving its occupants a second glance.

Charlotte, who'd been checking her hair and make-up in the hall mirror when the lift doors opened, finally swung round. 'Keep your shirt on, lover,' she said. 'These things never start on time.'

As Charlotte walked past Eric into the lift he glanced up over her shoulder and finally noticed Rachel in the corner, his face registering instant recognition this time, plus considerable shock.

'Good lord!' he exclaimed. 'It's Rachel. You remember Rachel, Charlotte. Rachel Witherspoon.'

Rachel would later wonder where her courage—and her composure—came from. Possibly from the look of surprise on that bitch's face as she surveyed Rachel from top to toe.

'So it is,' Charlotte said. 'Fancy seeing you here, of all people.' Her sexily slanting black eyes soon slid over to Justin. Women like Charlotte never looked at other women for long when there were attractive men around.

Meanwhile, Eric kept staring at *her* as though she were a little green man from Mars.

'I was just thinking the same about you two,' Rachel returned, proud as punch of her cool control. 'I gather you're together? This is my boss, Justin McCarthy,' she swept on, not giving either of them the chance to answer. 'Justin, these are friends of mine, Eric Farmer and Charlotte—er—sorry. I can't seem to recall your second name, Charlotte.'

'Raper.'

'Oh, yes. Raper…' A ghastly surname. 'So what brings you two up to the Gold Coast this weekend? Business, or pleasure?'

Eric muttered 'Pleasure' the same time as Charlotte said 'Business'. After Charlotte shot him an angry look he changed his answer to 'Both'. But he looked far from happy.

Rachel had to smile at having rattled Eric so easily. Justin was right. A spot of revenge was a good salve for old wounds. But she still wasn't sure about pretending she and Justin were lovers.

'And you?' Eric finally thought to ask. 'Are you here for business or pleasure?' He too was assessing Justin on the quiet, Rachel noticed. And perhaps not feeling his usual male superiority. For, as glamorous as Eric still looked at first glance, up close there was some evidence he was beginning to go to seed. He was becoming jowly, his crowning glory was thinning on top and his stomach was no longer athletically flat.

Frankly, he was looking a bit flabby. Of course, he had to be going on forty nowadays, whereas Justin was in his earlier thirties. Justin was taller than Eric, too. Taller and fitter and possibly more attractive, Rachel was surprised to discover.

'We're just here on business, aren't we, Justin?' she said, and touched him lightly on his nearest arm, her eyes pleading with him not to say differently.

Justin covered her hand with his and gave it an intimate little squeeze. 'Oh, absolutely,' he agreed, whilst his glittering blue eyes gave an entirely different message. 'Rachel's my new PA, and such a treasure. Only been with me for five weeks or so, but I already wouldn't know what I'd do without her.'

Oh, God, Rachel agonised. Somehow, without saying a word to that effect, Justin was making it sound as though their relationship extended way beyond the office.

'Really,' Eric said coldly, one eyebrow arching as he stared at her cleavage.

Rachel could feel heat gathering in her cheeks because it was perfectly clear what Eric was thinking.

'Eric,' Charlotte said sharply. 'Will you please move your butt inside the lift so that the doors can close?'

He flashed his lover a caustic glance but took a step inside.

'Have you known Rachel long?' Justin asked him whilst they waited for the lift to resume its ride down.

Rachel immediately tensed over what answer he would give.

'We were engaged once a few years back,' Eric bit out. 'But things didn't work out at the time, did they, Rach?'

Everything inside Rachel tightened further at his use of that once affectionate shortening of her name. But she'd be damned if she'd show any reaction on her face other than indifference to the role he'd once played in her personal life. 'Oh, I think things worked out just fine, Eric,' she said with a casual shrug. 'I did what I had to do and you did what you had to do. Anyway, there's no point in talking about the past. You've obviously moved on, and so have I.'

The lift doors closed at that juncture, as though emphasising her point.

'You still let a good one get away,' Justin remarked on the way down. 'But your loss is my gain.'

'I thought she was only your PA,' Eric shot back.

'Oh, she *is*. But a good PA these days is worth her weight in gold. Rachel leaves the girl I had before her for dead. She's not only beautiful but bright as a button, and such a sweetie. Just think, if you two hadn't broken up Rachel would be your wife by now. Instead, she's working for me, making my life run like a breeze. Amazing the little twists and turns in life, isn't it? Aah, here we are at the lobby.'

Rachel did her best not to flinch when Justin slid a highly intimate arm around her waist and steered her smoothly from the lift in Eric and Charlotte's wake. *They* weren't touching at this point, Rachel noted. They weren't even holding hands. Charlotte's body language showed anger, and so did Eric's.

Rachel tried to be scandalised with what Justin had just done, and she was a bit, but at the same time she felt a strange elation. And some vengeful satisfaction. Now she knew what Justin had meant by putting a cat amongst the pigeons.

'I presume you're going along to the special presentation dinner tonight?' Justin asked Eric before he could make his escape with Charlotte.

'Yes, we are. Charlotte's in real estate and is here representing a wealthy client of hers.'

'I can speak for myself, Eric,' Charlotte snapped. 'Actually, my client is more than wealthy. He's a multi-multimillionaire. Trust me, if he decides to buy this place whoever you're working for won't stand a chance. What this man wants he gets. So who is it that *you* work for, anyway? And what is it that you actually do?'

Justin delivered an intriguingly enigmatic smile. 'Now, that would be telling, wouldn't it? I can confess to being an investment adviser, but, as I'm sure you are aware, client confidentiality is important in matters such as this. Property-development deals are rather like a game of poker. You don't ever put all your cards on the table, not till after the game has been done, or won.'

'My client never bluffs,' Charlotte said smugly. 'He

doesn't have to. When he wants something he simply makes sure he's the top bidder. Money overcomes all obstacles.'

'Is that so? Your client might not ever bluff, but if he keeps making business decisions that way he might end up with a house of cards rather than a solidly based portfolio. One day, it'll come crashing down around him.'

'Well, that's no concern of mine,' Charlotte said with an indifferent shrug of her slender shoulders. 'He's just a client. As long as I get my commission on a sale, I don't care what happens afterwards.'

'Spoken like a real-estate agent,' Justin said with a dry laugh.

She didn't bat an eyelid at the barb. 'Property's a tough business.'

'But you're well up to it.'

'Oh, I'm not *that* hard,' she returned. 'Not once you get to know me.' And she flashed him an almost co-quettish smile.

Rachel could not believe it. Charlotte was making a play for Justin right in front of her and Eric's eyes!

But what's new? she realised bitterly. That was what she'd done with Eric when he'd been engaged to her.

A quiet fury began to simmer within Rachel. Charlotte had seduced Eric away from her, but no way was Rachel going to let Charlotte get her claws into Justin! He might only be her boss but he was far too nice a man for the likes of that alley cat to play with.

'I hate to interrupt this conversation,' she piped up with a saccharine smile, 'but we really must be getting along, Justin. The dinner starts at eight and you promised to meet Mr Wong at the main bar at seven-fifteen. And it's way past that now.'

'You're right. See what I mean? What would I do without her? No doubt we'll run into each other again during the dinner. Maybe we can even sit at the same table. Mind us a spot if you can. Meanwhile, I must away and meet my—er—meet Mr Wong. And no, don't ask me who he is, sweetheart,' he threw at Charlotte, then pressed his index finger to his lips. 'Client confidentiality, remember.'

'Who the hell is Mr Wong?' he whispered to Rachel after a sour-faced Eric grabbed Charlotte's arm and started steering her forcibly past Reception in the direction of the main conference room, the venue for the dinner.

'No idea,' Rachel confessed. 'I made him up.'

'But why? The idea is to stay in Eric and Charlotte's company if we're to achieve our aim for the night.' And nodded towards the departing couple's backs.

'She was flirting with you,' Rachel pointed out indignantly.

'So? That was good, wasn't it? It'll make Eric the Mongrel jealous and insecure.'

'I was afraid you might be liking it.'

'I was. But not the way you're thinking. I wouldn't touch that cold-blooded bitch in a million years. God, Rachel, you don't know me very well if you'd think that.'

'But I *don't* know you very well, do I? You have an unexpectedly wicked streak in you, Justin McCarthy. Yet before tonight I thought you were…um—er—er…' She struggled to find a word other than 'nice'.

'Staid?' he suggested drily. 'Boring?'

'No! Never boring. Maybe a little staid. No, you're not really staid, either. Oh, I don't know what I mean. I guess I just didn't think you'd ever conceive of something so devious as to make them think we're lovers even whilst you're claiming we aren't. That was incredibly conniving of you, and manipulative.'

'If you can't beat 'em, then join 'em, Rachel. People like Eric and Charlotte are devious, and conniving, and manipulative. They're also shallow and selfish and truly wicked. They don't care who they hurt or betray. All they care about is themselves and what suits them at the time. If you think I'm the first man Charlotte has flirted with, then think again. She hasn't been faithful to your Eric, nor he with her. That's the way they both are.'

'Maybe, but not *everyone* is like that, Justin,' she pointed out, unwilling to embrace the self-destructive philosophy of total cynicism. Isabel had been like that with men for ages, till she met Rafe. And, really, Rachel hadn't admired that about her one bit. She was a much nicer person now that she was living her life with love and hope in her heart.

'True,' Justin said, his gaze softening momentarily on her. 'Some people are decent and kind. But the two people we were unfortunate enough to fall in love with *weren't*. Eric treated you abominably, Rachel. And he shouldn't be allowed to get away with it!'

Rachel stared up into her boss's bitter blue eyes and realised he wasn't only talking about Eric. He was talking—and thinking—about his wife. Justin was deeply wounded.

Rachel wanted to ask him about his wife and what she'd done to him, but knew it was not the right time, or the right place. For one thing, his wounds were still way too raw. Maybe there would never be a right time or a right place. Maybe he'd loved her far too much, and would never get over her.

At least *she* had the comfort of knowing she no longer loved Eric. Seeing him again tonight had at least proved that to her once and for all. He might be successful and superficially handsome, but 'handsome is as handsome does', she'd discovered first-hand this evening. He was welcome to the likes of Charlotte. They were made for each other, in her opinion.

'Promise me you won't flirt with Charlotte when we finally get to that dinner?' she asked.

Justin laughed. 'I promise. But you shouldn't worry about me, you know, Rachel. I can take care of myself where female vampires are concerned. How are *you* doing, meeting up with lover-boy again? Does he still turn you on with those smooth, golden looks of his?'

'God, no.' She half laughed, half shuddered. 'No, not at all.'

'I suspect he still has the hots for you.'

She blushed. 'Don't be ridiculous!'

Justin frowned. 'You think it's ridiculous for a man to have the hots for you, especially the way you look tonight?'

'Well, no... I mean...yes... I mean... Look, I still can't compare with Charlotte. She's one seriously sexy lady.'

'She's about as sexy to me as a dead skunk.'

Rachel was startled. 'Really?'

'Really. But to ease your concern I will consign all of my flirting for the rest of the evening to yours truly. Make Eric the Mongrel's teeth gnash some more.' He glanced at his watch. 'Mmm. Twenty to eight. Look, let's go to that main bar you mentioned, where I'm supposed to be meeting the mysterious Mr Wong. We can fill in the time till eight with a couple of pre-dinner drinks.'

Rachel bit her bottom lip. 'Oh, I—er—made that up about the main bar as well. I have no idea if there is such a place.'

Justin grinned. 'And you said I had an unexpectedly wicked streak in me. I think you're the one who has the unexpectedly wicked streak, Ms Witherspoon. Come on, we'll go ask at Reception where the bars are located. They have to have at least one or two in a place this size.'

They had three, one connected with the à la carte restaurant on the mezzanine level, one on the first floor in the disco-till-you-drop room and a third up on the top floor, which had a more sedate dance floor and a view to die for, or so the clerk behind the desk said. It also wasn't open to the public, just the clientele of Sunshine Gardens and their guests.

Ten minutes later they were sitting at a table on an open-air terrace, sipping Margaritas by moonlight and drinking in that view to die for, which was spectacular, even at night. Most of the buildings along the foreshore were lit up, outlining the curved sweep of the coastline for as far as the eye could see. The night air was still and balmy, with Rachel's bare arms and shoulders not proving a problem.

'This is so lovely,' she said with a wistful sigh. 'But we won't have time for a second drink. Not if you want us to make that dinner on time.'

Actually, she hated the thought of going down to that dinner now. As much as she'd enjoyed her moment of vengeance in the lift, she didn't want to keep pretending she and Justin were lovers, or to have Justin acting like some sleazebag boss who couldn't keep his hands off her. She knew he meant well, but in a way it was demeaning for him to act out of character like that.

'What if I said we'd skip the presentation dinner entirely, and order some food to have right here?' he startled her by suggesting. 'They do serve light meals. They're listed on the other side of the drinks menu.'

'But don't you *have* to go to the dinner?'

'It's not strictly essential. They're making a video of the promotional presentation after the dinner for potential buyers who couldn't make it tonight. I'll buy a copy in the morning and view it when I get home tomorrow night, in case there's anything remotely informative in it, which is doubtful.'

'But what about Eric and Charlotte?'

'What about them? You said you didn't give a toss about Eric any more.'

'I don't.'

'Well, then we've done what we set out to do,' he said. 'Made Eric the Mongrel see you've survived without him. Also made him see he gave up a truly fine and, might I say, very attractive lady for a total bitch like Charlotte. Frankly, it could prove a more successful and devious strategy not showing up to the dinner at all. Eric will stew over the thought that I've whisked you back up to our room for a long night of hot sex, and darling Charlotte will worry her material little heart out that my mysterious Mr Wong might be some mega-rich businessman from Singapore who'll bid more for Sunshine Gardens than the ego-maniacal fool she's representing. Your revenge is already complete, Rachel. Why risk spoiling it?'

'But...'

'You have a penchant for buts, Rachel. There are no buts in this case, not even business buts. I guarantee I won't get into trouble over not going to that dinner. I made my own private enquiries around town today and I won't be recommending that AWI buy this place, anyway. Reliable sources tell me the occupancy rate here is way down, except in peak tourist season, and even then not a patch on a couple of their nearby competitors. Another little birdie told me that, despite the quality of the building and the décor, the management here is less than the best and staff turnover is very high.'

'What reliable sources? What little birdie?'

'The people who live here in Coolangatta, and work here. Shop owners. Suppliers. Taxi drivers. They have no reason to lie, whereas the present owners of Sunshine Gardens have every reason to misrepresent the truth.'

'I see.'

'So what do you say? We miss the dinner and stay up here?'

'Yes, please,' Rachel said eagerly as relief overwhelmed her.

Justin smiled his own pleasure at the change of plan. 'We'll order a bottle of wine with our dinner,' he suggested on picking up the menu. 'And then we might have a dance or two. That dress has dancing written all over it.'

Rachel's heart jolted. She hadn't danced in years. The last time had been with Eric, the week before he'd broken off with her, and the day before she found out the awful news about Lettie. They'd been to a Christmas party and she'd got very tipsy on the punch. He'd whispered hot words of love and desire in her ears whilst he danced with her, holding her very close, making her want him to put his words into action.

When she'd been beyond resisting him he'd whisked her into the bathroom and made love to her up against the door.

Or so she'd thought at the time. Now she knew he hadn't been making love at all. He'd just been having sex. Because he'd never really loved her.

'I...I haven't danced in years,' she said, her voice shaking a little at the memory. As much as she no longer loved Eric, the damage he'd perpetrated on her female psyche was still there.

'You didn't dance at your friend's wedding?' Justin asked on a note of surprise.

'No.'

'Why not? I'll bet you were asked in that dress.'

'Yes, I was.'

'Why did you say no?'

'I...I just didn't want to.' In truth, she'd felt far too emotionally fragile at the time to do something as potentially destructive as dance with a man. When she'd watched the bride and groom dance their first dance together she'd been consumed with a pain so sharp, and a misery so deep, she'd fled into a powder room— one of her favourite escapes—and cried for ages.

Justin frowned. 'This has something to do with Eric the Mongrel, hasn't it?'

Her smile was sad. 'How did you guess?'

'You told him in the lift you'd moved on, Rachel. And you told me just now he no longer mattered to you. I think it's time you put your feet where your mouth is. You're going to dance with me tonight and I don't want to hear another word about it. I won't take no for an answer.'

'Yes, boss,' she said, rather amused by his tough-guy attitude. It was so un-Justin. Same as with his earlier pretending to be a sleazebag boss.

'That's a very good phrase,' he pronounced firmly. 'Practise saying it.'

'Yes, boss.'

'Again.'

She laughed. 'Yes, boss.'

He grinned. 'By George, she's got it!'

CHAPTER SEVEN

JUSTIN sat there, watching Rachel really enjoy herself, possibly for the first time in years. She'd relished the food, despite the meal being a simple one, and she'd certainly swigged back her fair share of the wine. Now she was looking totally relaxed, leaning back and peering up at the stars.

He'd just ordered their after-dinner coffee but it probably wouldn't arrive for a while. Whilst the setting and ambience of the bar was great, the service was slow. The place was clearly understaffed, especially for a Saturday night. Management were probably cutting costs to make their profit margin look better, a common strategy when a business was for sale.

Time to ask Rachel to dance, Justin decided. The music coming from inside the bar was nice and slow, the rhythm easy to follow.

He rose to his feet, walked round her side of the table and held out his hand towards her. 'Shall we take a turn around the terrace, Ms Witherspoon?' he asked with feigned old-fashioned formality.

She smiled up at him. Such a lovely smile she had. Pity she didn't use it more often. Still, maybe she would after tonight.

'Why, thank you, Mr Darcy. Oops. Mr McCarthy, I mean.' When she stood up she swayed back dangerously on her high heels. He grabbed her upper arms and pulled her hard against him.

84

'Oh,' she gasped, her eyes startled as they jerked up to meet his.

'Methinks you've had too much to drink, Ms Witherspoon,' he chided gently. 'Just as well you find yourself in a gentleman's company this evening, or you might be in a spot of bother.'

'Yes. Just as well,' she murmured even whilst her eyes remained locked to his and her woman's body stayed pressed up against him.

Justin could not believe it when his own male body suddenly stirred to life. Neither could Rachel, by the look on her face.

Nevertheless, she didn't move. Or say a word. Just stared up at him with those lovely eyes of hers, her lips still parted. Yet for all that, she didn't look disgusted, or repelled by his arousal. Neither did she attempt to push him away, not even when his arms developed a devilish mind of their own and stole around her waist, one hand settling in the small of her back, the other sliding down to play over the soft swell of her buttocks. Instead of wrenching away from him in outrage, her own arms actually slipped up around his neck, and she sank even more closely against him.

'Rachel,' he breathed warningly.

'Yes, boss?' she said in a low, husky voice, her hazel eyes having gone all smoky.

'You're drunk.'

'Yes, boss.'

'Maybe dancing together isn't such a good idea.'

'Just shut up, boss, and move your feet.'

Her uncharacteristic assertiveness surprised him, but he shut up and moved his feet. Still, he'd been right. It wasn't a good idea. The slow, sensual rhythm of the music got further into his blood, as did the scent—and softness—of the woman in his arms. Of course, it didn't help that her fingertips started stroking the back of his neck in a highly provocative fashion, or that she kept gazing up at him with eyes full of erotic promise. By the time the music stopped he was in agony, his erection straining against the fly of his suit trousers.

At least he had a jacket on.

'I need to go to the gents',' he ground out after depositing her back in her chair. Fortunately, their coffee had finally arrived. A potful, as ordered. Hopefully, after a couple of strong cups Rachel might sober up and stop trying to seduce him.

His normally very proper PA was going to hate herself in the morning, Justin thought ruefully as he strode back inside the bar and over to the gents'. Alcohol could make even the most sensible woman behave a bit stupidly. Add her tipsy state to all that had happened earlier this evening, and he had a very different Rachel on his hands tonight.

Of course, he had to shelve some of the blame himself. He hadn't realised when he'd encouraged her to make herself over today that her transformation would be quite so dramatic. When a woman looked as seriously good as Rachel did tonight she was apt to find her flirtatious side.

Still, what was *his* excuse for responding so powerfully? Since he didn't fancy Rachel in that sense, he could only conclude he was suffering from acute frustration.

Maybe his male body was finally rebelling against its long stint of celibacy. Possibly it was time for him to search out an accommodating female who'd give him regular sex without any emotional strings involved. *Definitely* no strings involved. The last thing he wanted was a serious relationship. Or being told he was loved.

Definitely not. Sex was all he needed, something that was painfully obvious when he went into a cubicle in the gents' and confronted his wayward flesh.

Justin sighed and waited till the worst had subsided. But he was still aroused when he emerged from the cubicle to wash his hands. The sight of a condom dispenser on the wall next to the basins immediately caught his attention, with temptation not far behind.

Before he could think better of it, he dropped a couple of single dollars in the slot provided and slipped two condoms in his trouser pocket. Who knew? He might come back up here after Rachel was asleep. It was still only early. He'd already noticed an attractive redhead sitting all by herself at the bar, who'd given him the eye as he walked past. He just might return and take her up on her none-too-subtle invitation, since getting to sleep tonight in his present state of mind and body might prove difficult.

Difficult? More like bloody impossible!

Once Justin left her alone, Rachel's conscience—and common sense—returned with a vengeance. What on earth did she think she was doing, flirting with her boss and dancing with him like that, winding her arms around his neck like a clinging vine and moulding her body to his like some neglected nymphomaniac?

Justin's getting turned on wasn't his fault. He was just a man after all, a man who possibly hadn't had sex for some time. His leaving her to race off to the gents' had been too embarrassing for words.

Rachel cringed with humiliation, and guilt. If she could have bolted back to her hotel room right now without consequences she would have. If Justin hadn't been in possession of the door key she might have. As things stood, she had no alternative but to sit there and wait for his return, when she would apologise for her appalling behaviour, and beg his forgiveness and understanding. She would blame the wine, then throw herself on his mercy by explaining that she wasn't herself tonight.

Not her recent self, anyway. The Rachel Justin had employed would never have acted as she just had. In a way, it amazed her that she'd had the gall. Being sexually aggressive took courage, and confidence. Either that, or being turned on to the max.

This last thought bothered her the most. Because during those moments when she'd felt his hardness pressing into her stomach she'd wanted him in the most basic way; wanted to feel him, not against her but inside her. It was a startling state of affairs for a girl who'd always believed she had to be in love to want to be made love to. Clearly, she'd come to a point in her life when that wasn't the case any more. Perhaps that was what happened to a single woman when she got to a certain age, or when she'd been so lonely for so long that any man would do.

Rachel hated that idea but she could not deny it just might be true.

Crossing her arms with a shiver that had nothing to do with being cold, Rachel peered anxiously through the plate-glass window into the more dimly lit bar, both wanting and fearing Justin's return.

But there was no sign of him. He was certainly taking his time.

Desperate for distraction from her increasing agitation, she poured herself some coffee and gulped it down, black and strong. Unfortunately, this only served to sober her up and make her agonise further over the folly of her earlier actions.

She was refilling her empty cup when her boss finally showed up, but he didn't sit back down. He stayed standing by the table, his expression grim as he frowned down at her.

'I think I should take you back to the apartment,' he said abruptly. 'What you need is sleep, not coffee.'

'I'm not *that* drunk,' she replied sharply before remembering that being intoxicated was to be one of her excuses for behaving badly.

'I didn't say you were. But you've had a long and emotionally exhausting day. Come along, Rachel, be a good girl, now, and don't argue with me.'

Perversely, Rachel now felt like arguing with him, his patronising tone having really rubbed her up the wrong way. Any thought of apologising went out of the window.

He'd been equally to blame for what had just happened, she decided mutinously. If he hadn't insisted she tart herself up she would never have had the confidence to do any of the things she'd done tonight. *He'd* never have asked her to dance, either. When she'd been a plain Jane he hadn't given her a second glance.

She'd be damned if she was going to feel ashamed of her behaviour. Considering how long it had been since a man had taken her in his arms, it was no wonder she'd lost her head there for a while. She was only human.

A soon-to-be unemployed human, if you keep this attitude up, came the dry voice of reason.

With a sigh of surrender to common sense over rebellion, Rachel put down her coffee-cup and levered herself carefully out of the chair. This time, she was much more steady on her feet.

'I didn't think Cinderella had to go home till midnight,' she muttered with a glance at her watch. 'It's only half-past ten. Still, if you say it's time for me to go to bed then it's time for me to go to bed. You're the boss after all.'

Justin wished she hadn't said that, his mind immediately filling with various lust-filled scenarios associated with his taking this particular Cinderella to bed, none of which involved his playing the role of Prince Charming. More like the Black Prince. When he went to take her arm he thought better of it, deciding to keep his hands to himself till she was safely ensconced in her bedroom. *Alone.*

'Let's go, then,' he grated out, and stepped back to wave her ahead of him.

Unfortunately, Rachel walking ahead of him in that highly provocative dress stimulated him further. If she'd had eyes in the back of her head she'd have been disgusted by his suddenly lascivious gaze as it gobbled up her rear view, which, whilst not quite as delicious as her front, had the bonus of its owner not being aware of being ogled. He could ogle to his heart's content.

Justin didn't even notice the redhead at the bar this time as he passed by, his attention all on Rachel's *derrière* in motion. The tinkling sounds of the crystal-drop hem brushing against her legs dragged his eyes down to her shapely calves, then further down to her slender ankles and sexily shod feet.

Justin didn't normally have a shoe or foot fetish, but that didn't stop him imagining Rachel walking in front of him in nothing but those turquoise high heels. Nothing. Not a stitch.

His stomach crunched down hard at the mental image, blood roaring round his body and gathering in his nether regions. The end result was an erection like Mount Vesuvius on the boil. It surprised him that there wasn't smoke wafting from his trousers.

Their ride down in the lift was awkward and silent, Justin keeping his hands linked loosely over his groin area in a seemingly nonchalant attitude, but inside he was struggling with the most corrupting thoughts.

She probably wouldn't stop you if you started making love to her. She wants it. You know she does. Understandable under the circumstances. She probably hasn't been to bed with a man since Eric the Mongrel left her. And she certainly hasn't looked this good since then, either. She wants you to want her. That's why she was stroking your neck like that. And that's why she wasn't all that happy a minute ago when you brought her Cinderella night to an abrupt halt. You'd be doing her a favour if you slept with her. You'd be delivering the whole fantasy. A man in her bed for the night. A man wanting her again. A man finding her beautiful and desirable and, yes, sexy.

Which he did find her tonight. What man wouldn't? She looked gorgeous.

But what about in the morning, Justin? What about next week when you have to work with her? What then?

Justin smothered a groan. He couldn't do it. No matter what. It was unacceptable and unconscionable and just plain wrong. She might not be dead drunk but she was decidedly tipsy, and extra-vulnerable tonight. She needed compassion, not passion. Understanding, not underhanded tactics.

'You're angry with me, aren't you?' she said wretchedly when they finally made it into the apartment, neither having said a word since they'd left the bar.

Justin sighed. 'No, Rachel, I'm not angry with you.'

'You're acting as though you are.'

'I'm sorry if it looks that way. If you must know, I'm angry with myself.'

She blinked her surprise. 'But why? I'm the one who's been behaving badly.'

'That's a matter of opinion. If you could see into my head right now then you wouldn't think that.'

She stared at him and he stared right back, his conscience once again raging a desperate war with his fiercely aroused body. He tried to recapture the gentle and platonic feelings Rachel usually engendered in him; tried to recall how she'd once looked. But it was a losing battle. That sexless creature was gone, and in her place was this incredibly desirable woman. All he could think about was how she'd felt in his arms upstairs and how she'd feel in his bed down here.

'This is an even worse idea than dancing with you,' he muttered as he stepped forward and cupped her startled face with his hands. 'But I haven't the will-power to resist. Don't say no to me, Rachel. Not tonight.'

He was going to kiss her, Rachel realised with a small gasp of shock. No, not just kiss her. He was going to make love to her.

She almost blurted out 'no', his carnal intentions fuelling instant panic. But before her mouth could form any protest his lips had covered hers in a kiss of such hunger and intensity that she was totally blown away.

His tongue stabbed deep, his fingers sliding up into her hair, his fingertips digging into her scalp as he held her mouth solidly captive under his. It was a brutally ravaging, wildly primitive, hotly demanding kiss.

And she loved it, her moans echoing a dazed, dizzying pleasure.

'No, don't,' she choked out ambiguously when his head lifted at long last, leaving her mouth feeling bruised and bereft. She actually meant, No, don't stop. But he naturally took it another way.

'I told you not to say that,' he growled, and swept her up into his arms. 'There will be no "no"s tonight.'

He kissed her again as he carried her down to his room, then kissed her some more whilst he took off all her clothes. Once she was totally, shockingly naked, he spread her out on the bed and kissed every intimate erogenous part of her body.

And she never once said no. Because she never said a word. She was beyond words. Beyond anything but moaning with pleasure.

Yet she didn't come. He seemed to know just how much she could endure without tipping over the edge. Time and time again she would come incredibly close, and tense up in expectation of imminent release. But each time he would stop doing what he was doing, and she'd groan and writhe with frustration. As often as not he'd just smile down at her, as though he was enjoying her torment.

By the time he deserted her to strip off all his own clothes she would have done anything he asked. But he didn't ask. Instead, he drew on one of the two condoms he pulled from his trouser pocket, and just took. Swiftly and savagely.

'Oh,' Rachel gasped, coming within seconds of his

entering her. She'd never climaxed as quickly as that before, her flesh gripping his as he continued to thrust wildly into hers. He didn't last long, either, his back arching as his mouth gaped wide in a naked cry of primal release. Afterwards, he collapsed across her, his chest heaving, his breathing raw.

Rachel just lay there under him, stunned and confused. For a woman whose body had just been racked by a fierce and fantastic orgasm, she didn't feel at all satisfied, just primed for more.

'Don't talk,' he commanded when he finally withdrew and scooped her still turned-on body up in his arms. 'Talking will only spoil everything.'

His *en suite* bathroom was as white and spacious as hers, with a shower cubicle built for two. Holding her with one strong arm, he adjusted the water on both shower heads then deposited her in there before leaving to attend to the condom.

Rachel stood under the warm water and watched him through the clear glass of the shower cubicle, thinking that he really had a fabulous body. When he'd undressed earlier she'd been too caught up with her own excitement and apprehension to notice him in detail. Now her eyes avidly drank in his perfect male shape; the broad shoulders, slender hips, tight buttocks. Muscles abounded in his back, arms and legs. He also sported an all-over tan, except for the area that had been covered by a very brief swimming costume. Justin was built very well indeed. His wife certainly hadn't left him because he was inadequate in that department. Or in the lovemaking department either. He knew what to do with a woman's body all right. He made Eric's idea of foreplay look pathetically inadequate.

Thinking of Justin's wife and Eric reminded Rachel

that what she was doing here—and what Justin was doing here—had nothing to do with love and relationships, and everything to do with need. Need for sex, and the need to be needed, even if only sexually.

At least, that was the way it was for her. Justin's wanting her, even for this one night, had done more for her feminine self-esteem than all the physical makeovers in the world. He'd brought out the woman in her again. If nothing else, after tonight she could not go back to being that pretend plain Jane who'd been playing the role of his prim PA in such a piteous fashion.

Even if it meant having to resign, she would truly move on from this point, and live her life as she once had. There would be no more wimpishly making the least of herself. No more hiding behind dreary black suits and spinsterish hairdos. Definitely no more being afraid of other people, and men in particular. That sad, lonely chapter in her life was over.

'You're thinking,' Justin grumbled as he joined her under the water and turned up the hot tap.

'And you're talking,' she reminded him as she lifted her hands to slick her dripping hair back from her face.

'That's my prerogative. I'm the boss. Keep your arms up and your hands behind your head like that,' he ordered thickly. 'Lock your fingers together. Keep your elbows back.'

Rachel was staggered by his request. But she obeyed, and found the experience an incredible turn-on. By the look in his eyes, Justin did too. His gaze roved hotly over her body, which felt extra-naked and extra-exposed as she stood there like that. The now steaming water kept splashing over her head and running down her face, into the corners of her by now panting mouth. Down her neck it streamed, forming a rivulet between her breasts, pooling in her navel before spilling down to the juncture between her thighs, soaking the curl-covered mound and finally finding its way into the already hot, wet valleys of her female flesh.

'Beautiful,' he murmured, his voice low and taut. 'Now close your eyes and don't talk. Or move.'

Her eyes widened but then fluttered closed, as ordered. Rachel was far too excited to even consider not obeying him. She'd never played erotic games before, and the experience was blowing her mind.

Now, within her self-imposed prison of darkness, she could only imagine how she looked, standing there so submissively, with her elbows back and her breasts thrust forward, their nipples achingly erect. Was he looking at her and despising her for her unexpected wantonness, or delighting in her willingness to play slave to his master?

The shocking part was she didn't seem to care, as long as he looked, and touched, and satisfied her once more. By the time his hands started skimming lightly over her body, she was already craving another climax, her mind propelling her forward to that moment when he'd surge up into her, filling her, fulfilling her.

She moaned softly when something—not his hand—rubbed over her nipples. Soap, she soon realised. A cake of soap. He wasn't washing her as such, just using the soap, caressing her with its slippery surface, making her nipples tighten even further. Every internal muscle she owned tightened along with them. When the soap started travelling southwards Rachel sucked in sharply.

No, not there, she wanted to warn him. But before her tongue could formulate her brain's protest the soap was between her legs, sliding back and forth, back and forth, back and forth. She tried to stop the inevitable from happening, but it was like trying to stop a ski-jumper in mid-jump. When her belly grew taut and her thighs began to tremble she knew the struggle for control had been futile.

She came with a violent rush, her knees going to jelly and her arms falling back down to her sides. She might have sunk into a wet heap on the floor had he not snapped off the water and swept her back up into his arms. Her eyes must have conveyed her shocked state as he carried her back to his bedroom, but he just ignored them and spread her dripping body face down across the bed, pushing a pillow up under her hips.

Was she too shattered to stop him at that moment? Or was this what she secretly wanted as well? For him to take her like that. For him to take her over and over in every position imaginable. To make her come again and again. To show her…what?

That she could be as wickedly sexy as the next woman? As Charlotte, perhaps?

When he didn't touch her—or take her—straight away an impatient Rachel glanced over her shoulder, only to see he was busy with a condom. She was tempted to tell him that he didn't really have to use protection. Not unless he was a health risk. Perversely, she was on the Pill for reasons which had nothing to do with contraception. It simply stopped her from having dreadful PMT, which she hadn't been able to cope with on top of the stress of minding Lettie.

She didn't tell him, in the end. Not right then. She wasn't *that* brazen. But she told him later, after she realised he had no more condoms and she'd moved way beyond brazen, way beyond anything she thought she could ever be.

CHAPTER EIGHT

JUSTIN stared down at the sleeping woman in his bed with disbelieving eyes. Was that really his prim and proper PA lying there in the nude, looking wickedly sexy with a sheet pulled suggestively up between her legs? And had it been himself who'd ravaged and ravished her amazingly co-operative body all night long?

The answer was yes, to both questions.

He groaned, his hands lifting to clap each side of his face then rake up into his hair. Whatever had possessed him? With Rachel, of all women!

Bosses who seduced their secretaries were top of his most despised list of men.

But seduce Rachel he had. The fact that she'd enjoyed herself enormously in the end had little bearing on the fact that initially he'd taken advantage of her drunken and vulnerable state, blatantly using his position as her boss to pressure her into sex. When he thought of the things he'd asked her to do in the shower his mind boggled. That she'd done everything he wanted, without question, was testament to her not being her usual sensible self. It was a particularly telling moment when she'd confessed later in the night to being on the Pill. No girl these days made such a rash revelation, not unless they were totally out of their minds with lust!

Which Rachel had been by then. No doubt about it.

Astonishing, really. He would never have believed it of her. Not with him, anyway. Still, given the circumstances, possibly any man would have done last night. He'd known that subconsciously. Hell, no, he'd known it *consciously*. He'd thought about her vulnerable state *before* he'd crossed the line. And what had he done? Still crossed that line, then wallowed in her unexpected sensuality and insatiability, urging her on to arouse him repeatedly with her mouth till he was ready to take her in yet another erotically challenging position.

His body stirred just thinking about it. Groaning, Justin dragged his eyes away from Rachel's tempting nudity and headed straight for the bathroom, plunging his wayward flesh into the coldest of showers.

She'll have to go, he began thinking, despite the icy spray doing the trick. I can't possibly work with her. She'll make me feel guilty all the time. Or worse.

The prospect of spending every weekday having cold showers at lunch time would be untenable. Aside from the constant distraction and frustration, it would remind him of Mandy, and what Mandy was up to on a daily basis with that bastard boss of hers.

Yet to sack Rachel would make him an even bigger bastard of a boss. Justin was trapped by the situation. Damned if he did and damned if he didn't!

'Bloody hell,' he muttered, and slammed his palms hard against the wet tiles.

Rachel woke with a start, her eyes blinking as she tried to focus on where she was. She didn't recognise the ceiling. Or the walls. Or the bed, for that matter.

And then, suddenly, she remembered.

Everything.

'Oh, God,' she moaned.

The sound of the shower running was some comfort,

because it gave Rachel the opportunity to jump out of the bed, gather up her clothes and escape back to her own room without having to face Justin, naked, in his bed.

Grimacing, she dived into a shower of her own without delay, where she stayed for some time, doing her best to wash away all the evidence of what she could only describe as a night best forgotten.

But forgetting the way she'd acted was nigh on impossible when she was constantly confronted with the physical consequences of her amazingly decadent behaviour. Her nipples ached. Her mouth felt like suede. And she probably wouldn't be able to walk without discomfort for a week.

As much as she hadn't felt ashamed of her behaviour last night—she'd blindly viewed it as an exciting liberation from her drab, lonely and celibate existence—in the cold light of day she could see that having her own private orgy with her boss had not been a good career move.

He would not be pleased, she knew, either with her or himself.

Rachel was sitting on the side of her bed half an hour later and wishing she were dead, when a knock on the door made her jump.

'Rachel,' Justin said through the door in a business-like voice. 'Are you dressed?'

'Not quite,' she croaked out. A lie, since she'd just pulled on an outfit from Isabel's discarded resort wardrobe, white capri pants and a matching white and yellow flowered top, *with* underwear, thank God. She'd bought a couple of bra and pants sets the previous day. But her hair was still wrapped in a towel and she hadn't a scrap of make-up on.

Despite regretting going to bed with Justin, no way was she going to revert to plain-Jane mode again. If nothing else, yesterday's make-over had propelled her out of that pathetic state.

'We have to talk,' Justin went on. 'And we have to eat. In case you haven't noticed, it's after eleven and the breakfast buffet downstairs has long closed.'

'I'm not very hungry,' she said wretchedly.

'Maybe not, but you still have to eat something. We'll only get a snack on the flight home this afternoon. Look, why don't I order sandwiches from Room Service whilst you get dressed? Then we can talk over brunch on the terrace. We have plenty of coffee and tea in the room, so a hot drink is no problem. See you out on the terrace in, say…half an hour?'

'All right,' she agreed, thinking with some relief how very civilised he was sounding. Maybe he wasn't going to sack her after all.

Any hope of Justin's that she might appear dressed in dreary black again was dashed when she stepped out onto the terrace looking delicious in tight white trousers and a bright yellow top that hugged her breasts. For a girl he'd recently thought of as skinny, she had some surprising curves.

And some surprising moves, he recalled, doing his best not to stare at her pink glossed mouth.

Gritting his teeth, he waved her to her seat at the table, then got straight down to brass tacks. No point in putting off the unpleasant.

'Before you say anything,' he began, 'let me immediately apologise for my appalling behaviour last night. I have few excuses, except possibly eighteen months of celibacy and half a bottle of wine. Then, of

course, there was the way you looked last night…' Not
to mention the way you look this morning, he could
have added when his gaze swept over her again.

On top of the figure-fitting clothes, her hair was
swinging around her face in a sleek, sexy red curtain,
and her scarlet-painted toes were peeping out at him
from her open-toed white sandals. She also smelled like
fresh green apples, a scent he'd always liked.

'I owe you an apology as well,' she returned with
what sounded like relief in her voice. 'I led you on
when we danced together. I know I did. And I certainly
didn't say no at any stage. I guess I must have been
drunker than I realised.'

Justin was happy to play it that way, if it made her
feel better. It certainly made him feel better. Or did it?
Was she implying she must have been plastered to go
to bed with him? Did she need reminding just how
many times she'd come last night? And how often
she'd begged him not to stop, long after the effects of
that wine had worn off?

She'd been drunk all right. Drunk on desire.

You wanted me, baby, was on the tip of his tongue.

But, of course, he didn't say that.

'Fine,' he said instead. 'We're both to blame. That's
fair. So let's forgive each other, forget last night ever
happened and just go on as before.'

He saw her shoulders snap back against the seat and
her chin jerk up in surprise. She fixed frowning eyes
upon him. 'You can really do that? Forget last night
ever happened?'

*Not with you sitting next to me, sweetheart. And
looking good enough to eat.*

Justin shrugged. 'Yes, why not? It didn't mean anything to either of us. You needed a man and I needed

a woman. It was simply a case of being in the wrong place at the wrong time. It's obvious that both of us need to get out more,' he finished up with a bitter little smile.

'So you're not going to sack me?'

'Sack you! Of course not. The thought never occurred to me.'

Which was possibly only the first of a host of lies he'd be telling Rachel in future.

'I...I was worried that you might. Isabel always says that to have an affair with the boss is the kiss of death, job-wise. The girl always ends up being given the boot.'

Not always, he wanted to say. Not when the woman in question is my beautiful blonde ex-wife. She's been her boss's assistant-cum-mistress for two years and they're still together, at it like rabbits on desks and in private jets and on yacht decks.

'But we're not having an affair, are we?' he reminded Rachel ruefully. 'We made the mistake of going to bed together. *Once*. But we won't be making that mistake again, will we?'

'What? Oh, no. No, certainly not,' she said firmly, but her eyes remained worryingly ambivalent.

Justin knew then that she was experiencing at least a little of the leftover feelings which were still haunting him.

Damn, damn and double damn! His own dark desires he could cope with. And hide. But he was a goner if she started coming on to him again.

'One thing, though,' he went on brusquely.

'Yes?'

'Your appearance...'

'Yes?'

Justin wasn't sure if what he was about to say would work. But it was the only way out of the bind he'd got himself into.

'I—er—wondered if you're intending to dress differently for work from now on. I mean...I'm only human, Rachel, and I wouldn't want you coming into the office in clothes which I might find...distracting.'

She closed her eyes for a few seconds and pursed her pretty lips. 'Justin...' Her eyes opened again and her chin lifted in what could only be described as a defiant gesture. 'I'm sorry,' she said firmly, 'but I refuse to go back to the way I used to look. I couldn't. I'd rather resign than do that.'

'There is no question of your resigning!' he pronounced heatedly. Surprising, when this was what he'd been trying to make her do. Resign. But the moment she said she might he knew that was not what he wanted. He wanted Rachel to stay on, working for him. He wanted... God, he didn't know what he wanted any more.

He smothered a weary sigh before it left his lungs. 'You can wear what you like,' he said. 'Within reason, of course.'

'I've *never* been the type of girl to dress provocatively at work, Justin. I simply won't be wearing those awful black suits again, except perhaps tomorrow. I don't have any other work clothes till I buy some more. I'll pop out and buy a couple of brighter outfits during my lunch hour.'

'Not too bright, I hope,' he muttered, dreading anything which would constantly draw his eyes and rev up his hormones. 'What about your hair?'

'What about it? Don't tell me it's too bright as well.'

No, just too damned sexy the way you're wearing it today.

'Would you consider wearing it back up again?' he suggested in desperation. 'I've always thought that a suitable look for work.'

She sighed. 'Very well, I'll put my hair up.'

'And not too much make-up.'

'I have *never* worn too much make-up, either. I only have lipstick on at this moment.'

'Really?'

He would have sworn she was wearing much more. Her skin looked so pale and clear, yet her cheeks were glowing. As for her eyes... He'd always known they were her best feature but had they always had such long lashes?

'Don't worry, Justin,' she said with more than a touch of irritation in her voice. 'I won't waltz in to work looking like the office slut. And I promise I'll wear underwear.'

His stomach jolted at the thought of her walking around the office without anything on underneath her clothes. What a shockingly appealing idea!

Justin suppressed a sigh and wondered how long it would be before Rachel stopped being the object of his sexual fantasies. A week? A month? A year?

Damn, but he wished he'd resisted temptation last night. And he wished he'd never suggested that bloody make-over. He wanted his old Rachel back. She didn't stir his blood or challenge his conscience. She was sweet and kind and calming. This new Rachel was anything but calming. Even now, he wanted to say to hell with all this conciliatory chit-chat, let's just go back to bed and stay there all day. And to hell with underwear in the office as well. I *want* you buck-naked under your clothes. And no bra. Never a bra. I want your beautiful breasts accessible to my touch at the flick of a button. I want to be able to lift your skirt at any time and lean you over my desk and just do it. I want...

Justin's fantasies were really running away with him when a sudden appalling realisation reined them in. What he wanted to do with Rachel was exactly the sort of thing Mandy's rapacious boss had been doing with her!

Justin's blood ran cold at the thought, which was good. Very good. And very effective.

His burgeoning arousal ebbed away immediately.

That was what he'd do in future. Think of Mandy whenever these unacceptable desires struck. Pity he hadn't thought of the bitch last night. But better later than never!

Rachel realised that her attempt at a little joke about her underwear had backfired when Justin's back stiffened and his face took on an icily disapproving expression. Truly! It was getting difficult to remember him as the red-hot lover who'd made her do all the deliciously wicked things he'd made her do last night.

All of a sudden, he was acting like some prude!

Still, maybe that was what he basically was. A prude. Maybe he *had* been drunker last night than he seemed at the time.

Whatever, it was clear he deeply regretted having sex with her and was doing his level best to return their relationship to its previous professional-only status, even going so far as to want her to go back to looking much the same as she used to.

Fat chance of that, buster, she thought with private mutiny. If you want me to revert to plain-Jane mode, how about you doing something about *your* looks?

Why don't you stack on twenty kilos, and put a paper bag over your head for good measure? Oh, and start wearing grotty, nerdy clothes, none of those super-suave suits you wear into the office, or that coolly casual outfit you've got on at the moment. After all, sexual attraction—and distraction—was a two-way thing.

From the moment she'd set eyes on him again this morning, her heart had quickened and her eyes had surreptitiously gobbled him up. Frankly, it had been an effort so far not to keep staring at him in those smart beige trousers and that sexy black open-necked shirt. She supposed she should be grateful that he wasn't wearing shorts, but she was still brutally aware of what lay beneath his clothes. All that working out in the gym had produced a fantastic body. Talk about toned and honed! She hadn't been able to stop touching it last night.

In fact, she *hadn't* stopped touching it. If truth be told, she wanted to touch it again. Right now.

Rachel gave herself a savage mental shake and rose to her feet.

'I'll make us some coffee to go with this food,' she said, glancing resignedly at the two plates of mixed sandwiches that were sitting on the table. She still didn't have any appetite and would definitely need help in washing bread down her throat.

'You don't have to wait on me,' he said curtly, and rose to his feet as well. 'I'll help.'

Getting the coffee together was awkward. When Justin brushed her arm Rachel jumped away as though she'd been stung by a bee. When he glared at her she winced inside.

Lord, but she was like a cat on a hot tin roof around him. The lightest of touches and her skin felt scalded.

Rachel could only hope that time would lessen this sudden and intense physical awareness. After all, last night *was* still fresh in her mind. And her body was still harbouring some solid reminders as well. She felt tender in some places and rock-hard in others. On top of that, her whole system was suffering from a general feeling of agitation, which was perverse, since all that sex should at least have relaxed her nerves, not fired them up.

Hopefully, things would improve when they were back into their normal working-day routine. It wasn't helping that they were still alone together in this hotel, well away from their real lives. Perhaps that was another reason why they'd both acted so out of character last night. A romantic setting was well-known for undermining people's sexual defences. A woman's, anyway.

Rachel's hand shook as she picked up her cup and saucer, some coffee slopping into the saucer. Justin shot her another impatient look, which irked her considerably.

'OK, so I'm clumsy this morning,' she snapped. 'We can't all be perfect all the time.'

'I would have thought that was obvious after last night,' he retorted, and carried his coffee back to the terrace without spilling a drop.

Rachel fumed as she followed. What a pig, she began thinking. And she'd always imagined him to be kind. Why, he was nothing but a typical male. Trying to put the blame on her for last night. He'd been the one to kiss her first! He was the one to open Pandora's box. And now he was trying to shove her back in there again and close the lid.

Well, she was not going to go. She was free now.

Free of Eric. Free of the past. Free to be the woman she wanted to be.

Which was not some mealy-mouthed creature who was too afraid to speak up or be herself lest she lose her job. There were plenty more PA positions to be had. And plenty more men out there who could turn her on. She didn't need Justin McCarthy to provide her with either a salary *or* sex.

Despite her disgruntled state, Rachel decided that in deference to having to tolerate Justin's constant company for the next few hours, she would hold her tongue for today. But, come tomorrow, if he started pressuring her to be something she wasn't she'd start looking around for another job.

Because there was no going back after this. The die had been cast and she intended to roll with it!

CHAPTER NINE

JUSTIN could not believe it when he walked into work the following morning—a cowardly half an hour late—and found Rachel wearing what he'd always thought her dreariest black suit, yet looking so sexy, it was sinful.

The severely tailored jacket with its long sleeves and lapelled neckline seemed tighter, and more shapely, hugging her small waist and full breasts. Had she taken it in at the seams? She'd definitely taken the skirt up, he realised when she brought in his morning coffee, the hem now a couple of inches above her knees instead of sedately covering them. And she was wearing black stockings. Not the thick, opaque, sexless kind. The sheer, silky, sexy kind which drew a man's eye and made him picture them attached to suspenders.

When he started wondering just that he wrenched his eyes back up to her face, which wasn't much help. OK, so she *had* put her hair up, as he'd requested. But not the way she'd used to, scraped back severely into a knot. It was caught up very loosely with a long black easily removable clip. Several strands had already escaped its ineffectual clasp to curve around her chin, drawing his gaze to her mouth, a mouth which bore no resemblance to Rachel's usual workaday mouth. It was more like that mouth which had tormented and teased him on Saturday night. Blood-red and full and tempting. Oh, so incredibly tempting.

Justin clenched his teeth hard in his jaw and dropped

110

his gaze back to his work. 'Just put the coffee down there, thank you, Rachel,' he said brusquely, nodding to a spot near his right hand.

When she lingered in front of his desk without saying a word he was finally forced to look up. 'Yes?' he said sharply. 'What is it?'

'Could I have a longer lunch hour than usual today, Justin?' she asked. 'I have some clothes shopping to do. I'll work late to make up for it.'

Justin no longer cared what clothes she bought. She couldn't look any sexier to him if she tried, anyway.

'Yes, yes.' He waved her off impatiently. 'Take all the time you need.' *The rest of my life, preferably.*

'Are you sure?'

'Yes, Rachel,' he bit out. 'Quite sure. Now, if you'll excuse me, I have to write this report for Guy.'

'Did I hear my name mentioned?' the man himself said as he strode in.

Justin welcomed the distraction. 'Aah. You're back from Melbourne earlier than I expected,' he said, glad to have an excuse to ignore Rachel. 'How's your father?'

'Much better. It was one of those nasty viruses. He was rotten on Friday and Saturday but on the improve by yesterday. So what did you think of Sunshine Gardens?'

'Take a seat and I'll tell you. Close the door as you go out, would you, Rachel?'

Justin noticed that Guy's eyes followed her as she did so.

He gave a low whistle after the door clicked shut. 'So that's your new PA,' he said, with meaning in his voice. 'You lucky dog, you. I *love* pretty women in black. Though, of course, I prefer them in nothing at all.'

'There's nothing between Rachel and myself,' Justin lied staunchly, his face a stony mask.

Guy chuckled. 'That's your story and you're going to stick to it. Wise man. Office affairs are best kept behind closed doors. And hotel-room doors. So how was your weekend junket? Everything to your satisfaction?' And he grinned lecherously.

Justin decided to ignore Guy's none-too-subtle innuendoes and plunged into giving him a brisk report on the hotel as a property investment. Naturally, he didn't mention their not having been to the presentation dinner. He let Guy think they had. Justin had watched the video last night and hadn't changed his mind about the place, despite the glowing marketing spiel.

'So that's my professional opinion,' Justin finished up. 'Added to the fact I think it's a lemon, I also gleaned some valuable inside information from a lady real-estate agent there for the free weekend. Apparently, the client she was representing is intent on purchasing the hotel at any price. I never think it's a good idea to get into a bidding war with that kind of buyer.'

'This agent could have been bluffing.'

'Yes, but I don't think so.'

'Mmm. Do you happen to know who this interested party is?'

'No. Just that he's filthy rich and has an ego the size of his cheque-book.'

'I heard a whisper that Carl Toombs is thinking of going into the property market up that way.'

Justin struggled to keep his face unreadable. No one at AWI knew the circumstances behind his divorce. No one knew that his ex-wife was Carl Toombs' secret mistress. No one except him and Mandy and his mother.

Justin's own ego had kept their secret for them.

So of course he could not be seen to react to Carl Toombs' name in any way other than a professional one.

'The man certainly fits the description the agent gave of him,' he said coolly. 'She said her client always gets what he wants, money no object.'

And wasn't that the truth? He'd set his sights on a married woman who'd been deeply in love with her husband at the time—Justin still believed that—and totally corrupted her, with his money, his charisma and his supposed sexual prowess.

Justin hated the man with a passion. As did quite a lot of other people in Australia, people who'd invested in some of his previous entrepreneurial get-rich-quick schemes. Some had succeeded, but a good few had failed. Yet somehow Toombs always managed to extricate himself with his own fortune intact. He had brilliant lawyers and accountants, and the best of contacts, both in the political and social scene. Married twice, with an adult daughter from his first marriage and two teenage sons from his present wife, Carl Toombs was in his early fifties, but looked a lot younger, courtesy of his personal dietician, trainer and cosmetic surgeon.

When Mandy had first gone to work for Carl Toombs she'd made jokes about his vanity and massive ego. Justin had joined in. But the joke had been on Justin in the end. Carl Toombs had come out on top. Literally.

Thinking about that swine and Mandy inevitably put Justin in a foul mood. 'I hope Toombs buys the place,' he went on testily. 'And I hope he loses a packet. Of his own money for a change.'

Guy looked taken aback. 'Sounds as if you lost some of your money in one of his famous ventures.'

Justin gritted his teeth. He'd lost something he valued much more than money. 'Let's just say he wouldn't want to meet me in a dark alley on a dark night.'

Guy laughed. 'And there I've been, thinking you'd never put a foot wrong financially.'

'We all make mistakes, Guy. That's how we learn.'

'And what did tangling with Toombs teach you?'

'Never to underestimate a man who has more money than I have.'

'True,' Guy said, nodding sagely. 'OK, so you don't suggest that I recommend Sunshine Gardens to the CEO.'

'Not if you value your job.'

Guy laughed, then stood up. 'See you tomorrow morning at the gym?'

'Absolutely.'

'Don't work too hard.'

'You don't really mean that.'

Guy smiled. 'Nope. I hope you work your butt off. Profits have been up since you came here. I even sleep at night sometimes.'

'Get out of here. And tell Rachel to bring me another coffee when you go past, will you? This one's gone cold.'

'Will do. I might stay and watch her do it, too. That girl has an incredible walk. And a *derrière* to die for. But I suspect you already know that, McCarthy,' he threw over his shoulder as he walked towards the door. 'No wonder you work out every morning till you're ready to drop. Can't be easy keeping your hands off that nice piece of skirt out here.'

Justin groaned. 'For pity's sake, Guy, keep your voice down. She might hear you. Haven't you heard of sexual harassment in the workplace?'

Guy shrugged and put his hand on the door knob, but he didn't turn it. 'I could be mistaken, mate, but I caught a glimpse of something in your PA's very lovely eyes a few minutes ago which indicated she might not be averse to a little sexual harassment from you.'

'Don't be ridiculous!'

'I'm not being ridiculous. I studied body language when I did a sales and marketing course recently, and she fancies you, mate. I guarantee it. But I guess if you're not interested, then you're not interested. Poor girl. I guess she'll just have to go find herself some other tall, dark, handsome jerk to give her a bit. Pity I don't fit the bill. I'd give her one, I can tell you. OK, OK, you don't have to say it. Get lost. And I won't forget the coffee on my way out.'

He didn't. Unfortunately. Soon, Rachel was undulating towards his desk with the coffee and Justin found himself mentally stripping her again. Oh, God. This was how it all began back there in that bar, with him watching her walk in front of him and imagining her without any clothes on. The trouble was, this time he *knew* what she looked like without any clothes on. And the reality far surpassed the fantasy his imagination had conjured up. She was all woman. And she could be all his, according to Guy.

Was he right? Did she really fancy him, not as some rebound substitute for Eric the Mongrel, but as a man in his own right? Was she secretly hoping he'd keep their affair going?

The thought both excited and worried him. He didn't love her. He'd never love her. He wasn't capable of that kind of love any more. He wasn't capable of any relationship of any depth. All he would want—or need—from any woman for a long time was what she'd given him the other night. Sex without strings.

He watched her put the coffee down then glance up at him, her face expectant. 'Is that all for now?'

Was it? What would she do, he wondered, if he told her to go close the door, then lock it?

A shudder of self-loathing—or was it arousal?—ricocheted through him. He could not do it. *Would* not.

'Rachel…'

'Yes?'

'Nothing,' he bit out. 'That's all. You can get back to your work. Oh, and you can take the whole afternoon off for your shopping, if you like.'

'The whole afternoon?' she echoed in surprise.

'Yes, why not? You deserve it after the weekend.'

He'd meant she deserved some time off because, technically, she'd been working overtime. But when her face darkened he immediately saw how his words could be interpreted.

'You mean in exchange for services rendered?' she threw at him.

'No, of course not. Look, if you're going to bring that up all the time, I'm not sure we *can* go on working together.'

Justin didn't need to have studied body language to gauge her reaction to that charming little announcement. Her whole body stiffened, and her eyes…her eyes stabbed him right in the heart.

'I see,' she said frostily. 'It's nice to know where things stand. You'll have my resignation on your desk *before* I leave at lunch time. And yes, I will have the whole afternoon off, thank you very much.' Spinning on her heels, she stalked from the room, banging the door behind her.

Justin slumped back into his chair with a groan. He'd done it now. And he'd never felt lower in all his life. He dropped his head into his hands and called himself every name under the sun.

Rachel could not sit down at her desk and go calmly back to work. She paced the outer office for a couple of angry minutes, then marched into the tea room and poured herself a fresh coffee, more for something to do than because she wanted it. In fact, the steaming mug remained untouched on the counter whilst she just stood there, tapping her foot and trying to gather herself.

Isabel had been so right about office affairs. Not that she needed her best friend to tell her that. Hadn't it always been the case in the workplace? The male boss got away with sleeping around and the female employee got the push.

She had an urge to go back in there and give Justin a piece of her mind. But pride wouldn't let her. Pride and common sense. Given her lack of recent work experience, she needed a reference. Not that Justin would dare not give her a reference. She could make real trouble for him over this, if she had a mind to.

But Rachel had no stomach for such an action. No, she would simply resign and to hell with Justin McCarthy. In fact, to hell with him for the rest of the day. She was going to write out her resignation right now and leave. And then she was going to go out and spend every cent in her savings account on a brand-new wardrobe!

Leaving her coffee still untouched, Rachel stormed back to her desk and set to work on her resignation letter.

Justin was in front of one of his many computer screens, pretending to work, when his office door was flung open and Rachel marched in with flushed cheeks and her head held high.

'There's my resignation,' she announced, and slapped a typed page down in front of him. 'I'll work out my notice and I'll expect a glowing reference, though lord knows how I'm going to explain leaving my present position after so short a time. But I guess that's my problem. Oh, and I'm taking the rest of the day off, starting right now!'

'Rachel, don't...'

'Don't what?'

'Don't resign,' he said wearily.

'Too late,' she snapped, and Justin winced. 'And please don't pretend this isn't what you want. You've been working towards this moment ever since you woke up yesterday morning and found me in your bed.'

Justin could not deny it.

'I'm beginning to wonder if the same thing happened with your previous girl. Or do you only screw the plain ones?'

'Rachel, I didn't mean t—'

'Yes, you did,' she broke in savagely. 'You screwed me good and proper. But I'll survive. I'm a survivor, Justin McCarthy. Watch me.'

He watched her walk with great dignity out of his office, and he'd never admired her more. But he didn't call her back, because she was right. He had screwed her good and proper. And he wanted to do it some more.

Best she leave before he really hurt her.

Best he crawl back into his celibate cave, and best he go back to work!

Rachel felt tears begin to well up in the lift ride down to the lobby. Her anger was swiftly abating and in its place lay a misery far greater than she had anticipated. At the heart of her dismay lay the fact she'd really liked Justin. And she'd really liked working for him.

And you *really* liked having sex with him, came another quieter but more honest voice. That's why you're feeling so wretched. All your silly female attempts to look attractive for him this morning were a big waste of time. You vowed you'd never get that horrible sewing machine out again and what did you do last night? Hauled the damned thing out of the bottom of the wardrobe and worked till midnight practically remaking this wretched suit.

And what did he do? Hardly looked at it, or at you. He doesn't want you any more. He never really did. How could you possibly have started imagining he might? You were just there, when he needed sex. He said as much yesterday. And now you're a nasty reminder of behaviour he'd rather forget.

Rachel's eyes were swimming by the time the lift doors opened, so she fled to the ladies' room in the lobby and didn't come out till she was dry-eyed and back in control.

But she no longer felt like shopping for clothes. What did it matter what she wore around Justin?

Hooking her black carry-all over her shoulder, she headed for the exit. Straight home, she decided.

'Rachel!' a male voice shouted, and her heart jumped. 'Wait.'

Her heart began to race as she turned.

But it wasn't Justin hurrying towards her across the lobby.

It was Eric.

CHAPTER TEN

'ERIC!' Rachel exclaimed, startled. 'What…what are you doing here?' Possibly a silly question when he'd always worked in the Central Business District in Sydney. It was inevitable that one day, now she was working in the city, she might run into him.

But to run into him only three days after running into him on the Gold Coast seemed to be stretching coincidence too far.

'I was looking for you,' he explained. 'I asked around about your boss and found out he worked in this building.'

'How enterprising of you,' she said coolly.

'I am, if nothing else, enterprising,' he returned, and smiled what she'd once thought of as such a charming smile.

She no longer thought anything about Eric was charming.

She no longer thought he was all that gorgeous, either, despite his grooming still being second to none. His sleek black business suit would have cost a fortune. And he would have spent half an hour blow-drying his hair to perfection this morning. It must be killing him, she thought a bit spitefully, to find that it was receding at a rapid rate.

'Why were you looking for me?' she asked in a less than enthusiastic tone.

'I was worried about you.'

She could not have been more surprised if he'd proposed marriage.

'Good lord, why?'

'Can we go somewhere and talk in private? There's a coffee shop just off the foyer facing the street. How about in there?'

She shrugged with seeming indifference. 'If you insist.'

He didn't enlighten her till the coffee arrived, and she refused to press, despite being curious. The days when she'd hung on Eric's every word had long gone.

'You didn't come to the dinner on Saturday night,' he began, throwing her slightly. What to say to that? Rachel cast her mind back to the night in question and decided to go with the fiction Justin had created.

'We had no need after my boss met with his client.'

'Mr Wong decided against Sunshine Gardens?'

Rachel maintained her cool. 'You don't honestly expect me to discuss my boss's business with you, do you? If that's why you've come, to pump me for inside information for your girlfriend, then you've wasted your time. *And* the price of this coffee.'

'That's not the reason,' Eric said hastily when Rachel made to rise. 'I came to warn you. About your boss.'

Rachel sat back down, blinking. 'Warn me. About *Justin*?'

'Look, I know I hurt you, Rachel. I'm not a fool. The way you look at me now...you probably hate my guts and I can understand that. But I don't hate you. In fact, I think I made a big mistake breaking up with you. You are one special lady and you deserve better in life than getting tangled up with the likes of Justin McCarthy.'

Rachel opened her mouth to deny any involvement with Justin, but after their performance on Saturday night it would be difficult to claim they weren't lovers. Not that it was any of Eric's business who she slept with.

'I don't know what you're talking about,' she said stiffly. 'Justin is a wonderful boss, and wonderful in every other way. What could you possibly be warning me about where he's concerned?'

Eric laughed. 'I have to give him credit. He puts on a good act. But he's not in love with you, Rachel. He's just using you.'

'How kind of you to tell me that,' she said, struggling now to control her temper. 'Might I ask what right you have to say that, what evidence? Or is it just that when you look at me you see a pathetic, foolish woman that no man could really love?'

'There's nothing pathetic or foolish about you, Rachel, and you know it. You're still as beautiful and bright as you always were. But you do have one fatal female flaw. You fall in love with bastards.'

'I am *not* in love with my boss,' she denied heatedly.

But when Eric's eyes searched hers she felt her face flame.

'I hope not,' he said. 'Because he's one bitter and twisted guy. Not that he doesn't have a right to be. I'd be bitter and twisted if my wife did to me what his wife did to him.'

Rachel's mouth went dry. 'What…what did his wife do?'

'I thought you wouldn't know about that. It's not the sort of thing a man would spread around. Charlotte didn't put two and two together on Saturday night when you first introduced him. After all, his is not such an unusual name. But she got to thinking about it last night and made some discreet enquiries, and bingo, he was the one all right.'

'Eric, would you kindly just say what it is you've come to say?'

'Your boss's ex-wife has been Carl Toombs' personal assistant for a couple of years now. And I mean *very* personal. He pays for her apartment and she travels everywhere with him. Their relationship is a well-kept secret but that's the reason she left her husband, to shack up more often with her high-profile boss. You do know who I'm talking about, don't you?'

'Yes, of course I do,' Rachel snapped. 'I might have been out of the workforce for a few years, but I wasn't dead. I don't know of anyone in Australia who wouldn't know who Carl Toombs is.'

'OK, OK, don't get your dander up. Anyway, Toombs is Charlotte's client, the one who wants to buy Sunshine Gardens. Because of their business association, Charlotte's had quite a bit to do with his beautiful blonde PA over the past few weeks, and you know girls. They like to chat. Anyway, the ex-Mrs McCarthy confided in Charlotte over lunch and a few Chardonnays the other day. Apparently, darling Mandy is still suffering great gobs of guilt over her ex-hubby. She told Charlotte how cut up he was when she left him. She confessed she said some pretty dreadful things so that he would hate her and forget her, but that *she'd* never forget the look on his face when she told him she'd been having sex with Toombs for some time. She said she did love her husband and he was mad about her, but she simply couldn't resist Carl's advances. She said Carl wanted her and nothing was going to stop him having her. She said she thinks she broke her husband's heart.'

Rachel didn't say a word. She was too busy absorbing the full ramifications of Eric's news.

'From what I gather he's one very bitter man,' Eric went on. 'Knowing you, Rachel, you probably think he's in love with you. You're not the type of girl to jump into bed idly. But it's not love driving your boss these days. More like revenge.'

'You don't know what you're talking about, Eric. For one thing, I'm not in love with Justin. And I don't imagine for one moment that he's in love with me.'

Eric frowned. 'Then...what is it between you two?'

'That's my business, don't you think?'

'You are sleeping with him, though.'

'That's my business, too.'

'Look, I've only got your best interests at heart, Rachel. I care about you.'

She laughed. 'Since when, Eric? Are you sure you didn't seek me out today to tell me this because you're getting bored with Charlotte and think you might have a bit more of what you once used to take for granted?'

'I never took you for granted, Rachel. I loved you in my own way. I just couldn't see our marriage working with you becoming a full-time home carer. I'm a selfish man, I admit. I wanted more of your time than that. I need a wife whose first priority is me.'

'Then you chose a strange partner in Charlotte. Her first priority is her career. And her second priority is herself.'

'I always knew that. Why do you think I didn't marry her? It was you I wanted for my wife, Rachel. I still do...'

'Oh, please. Spare me. Thank you for the coffee,'

she said, rising without touching a drop. 'And thank you for your very interesting news. You might not know this but you did me a huge favour in telling me about Justin's ex. It's made everything much clearer.' Which it had. She might not know the full details of Justin's thoughts and feelings. But it wasn't revenge driving him. Revenge would have acted very differently at the weekend, and today. Revenge *would* have used her.

Rachel walked away from Eric without a backward glance, her mind wholly and solely on Justin. Alice hadn't exaggerated. Her son's wife certainly was a cold-blooded bitch. Either that, or terribly materialistic and disgustingly weak.

He was better off without someone like her in his life. The trouble was…did he realise that yet?

Maybe. Maybe not. Clearly, he'd been deeply in love with this Mandy. Possibly, he still was. It was hard to say.

Still, time did heal all wounds. Just look at herself. She'd once thought the sun shone out of Eric. She'd been devastated by his dumping her. Today, she hadn't turned a hair at his declaring he still wanted her as his wife. The man meant nothing to her any more, and being free of him felt marvellous.

Rachel suspected, however, that Justin was not yet free of his ex. His beautiful blonde ex, Eric had said. Naturally, she would be beautiful. *Very* beautiful. Men like Carl Toombs didn't take ugly women as their mistresses. They chose exquisite creatures with perfect faces and figures, women with a weakness for money and a fetish for the forbidden.

It was no wonder Justin had an aversion to sex in the office. Rachel understood completely. But it was time for him to forget the past and move on, as she had decided to do.

Of course, she'd had four years to come to her present state of heart and mind. Justin's wife had betrayed and abandoned him much more recently. Only two years ago. And she'd said truly dreadful things to him, according to Eric.

What kind of things? Rachel wondered during the lift ride back up to the fifteenth floor. Had she criticised his skills in bed? Hard to imagine that. Justin left Eric for dead as a lover. And every other boyfriend she'd ever had. Perhaps the wretched woman had told him he wasn't rich enough, or powerful enough? Who knew?

Rachel didn't dare ask him, but she dared a whole lot more. She dared to go back and tell him she'd changed her mind about resigning. She dared to stay. And she dared to go after some more of what they'd shared on Saturday night.

If truth were told, she couldn't stop thinking about it. Surely he had to be thinking about it, too. Rachel could be wrong but she suspected she was the first woman Justin had had sex with since his wife left him.

The thought amazed, then moved her to anger. Selfish people like Eric and Mandy had a great deal to answer for. But you couldn't let them get away with trampling all over your emotions, and your life. You had to stand up and fight back. You had to stop playing the victim and move on. There were other people out there. Other partners. But you had to be open to finding them. You had to embrace new experiences, not run away from them.

Rachel left the lift at her floor and hurried along to her office, her new-found boldness waning a little once she approached the door she'd slammed shut less than an hour ago. Suddenly, she was biting her bottom lip and her stomach was churning. Was Justin still there behind that door, sitting at his computers, slaving away? Probably. It wasn't lunch time yet, and her boss had no reason to go home. He had nothing in his life except his work, a bruised ego and a broken heart.

Till now, that was. Now he had *her*. Her friendship and companionship. Her body too, if he still wanted it.

Her hand was shaking by the time she summoned up enough courage to knock. But it was a timid tap. Annoyed with herself, she didn't knock again. Instead she turned the door knob and went right in.

'Oh, no,' she groaned, her gaze darting around Justin's empty office.

Rachel was battling with her disappointment when she heard a banging noise coming from inside one of the adjoining rooms, the one with the bar and the sofa in it. Before her courage failed her again she marched over and flung open the door.

Justin almost dropped the ice-tray he was holding. He hadn't expected to see Rachel again. Not that day, anyway. After she'd left he'd tried to work, but he'd been too distracted, and too depressed to concentrate. In the end, he'd come in here in search of some liquid relaxation.

'What on earth do you think you're doing?' she threw at him.

Her accusing tone—plus her unexpected reappearance—didn't bring out the best in him.

'What does it look like I'm doing?' he countered belligerently. 'I'm getting myself some ice to put in my Scotch. But the bloody stuff's stuck.'

'But...but you never drink during the day!'

'Actually, you're wrong there,' he said drily. 'I often drink during the day. Just not usually during the week.' He gave the ice-tray another bang on the granite bar-top and ice cubes flew everywhere.

'Don't do that!' he roared at her when she hurried over and began picking up the ice cubes. Damn it all, the last thing he wanted was for her to start bending over in front of him.

She ignored him and picked them up anyway, giving him a good eyeful of her *derrière*-to-die-for. 'You shouldn't drink alone, you know,' she said as she straightened and dropped several cubes into his glass.

'What do you care?' he snapped, irritated by her presence beyond belief. 'You're not my keeper. You're not even my PA any more.'

'I am, if you still want me to be. I came back to tell you I don't want to resign. I want to keep working for you.'

He laughed. 'And you think that's good news? What if I said I don't want you working for me any more? What if I said your resigning was exactly what I wanted?'

'I don't believe you.'

'She doesn't believe me,' he muttered disbelievingly, and quaffed back a mind-numbing mouthful of whisky. 'So what do I have to say to *make* you believe me?'

'There's nothing you can say,' she pronounced, and gave him one of those defiant looks of hers. Damn, but she had a mouth on her. What he wouldn't like her to do with it!

He tossed back another decent swig and decided to shock her into leaving again.

'What if I told you that since Saturday night whenever I look at you I'm mentally undressing you? What if I confessed that after you made that joke about you not wearing any underwear it became my favourite fantasy, you not wearing any underwear around the office? What if, when you accused me of having screwed you good and proper, my first thought was that I hadn't screwed you nearly enough?'

She just stared at him, clearly speechless.

'That's only the half of it,' he went on after another fortifying swallow of straight Scotch. 'When you brought me that coffee this morning after Guy left it wasn't coffee I wanted from you but sex. I wondered what you'd do if I asked you to lock the door and just let me do it to you right then and there across my desk. From behind,' he added for good measure.

Her eyes grew wider but she still hadn't said a word. She seemed rooted to the spot, frozen by his appalling admissions.

The trouble was, giving voice to his secret sexual fantasies about her had also had the inevitable effect on his body. Or was it just her, standing there in front of him, within kissing distance?

'Well? What *would* you have done?' he demanded to know, his raging hormones sparking more recklessness.

She finally found her tongue. 'I...I don't know,' came her astonishing answer.

'What do you mean, you don't know?' he shot back, floored by such an ambiguous reply.

'I mean I don't know. I was angry with you back then. Why don't you ask me now?'

My God, she meant it. She actually meant it.

His hand tightened around his glass and his head spun. So that was why she'd come back, was it?

Because she wanted him to seduce her again. He'd suspected this might be the case when she'd come in this morning looking good enough to eat, but he'd been hoping he was wrong.

Any hope of that, or that he could keep resisting temptation disappeared as swiftly as the rest of his Scotch. Emptying the glass, he banged it back down on the bar-top and faced his nemesis.

'Would you go and lock the door, Rachel?' he asked in a gravelly voice. 'Not the one that separates this room from my office. Or the one separating my office from yours. The one out in your office. The one that lets the outside world in.'

She did it. She actually did it. Justin's mind reeled with shock. But nothing could stop him now.

'Now come here to me,' he ordered thickly when she reappeared in the open doorway, looking both beautiful and nervous.

She came, her cheeks flushed with excitement and her eyes glittering brightly.

'I've been wanting to do this,' he growled, and reached up to release the clip. As her hair tumbled down around her face and shoulders Justin knew that he wasn't simply crossing a line here, he was about to propel them both into a world from which there was no turning back, a word where lust ruled and love was nothing but a distant memory. She had no conception of the demons in his mind, or the dark desires that had been driving him crazy since Saturday night. She probably thought he loved her.

Now, that was one transgression he would not be guilty of. Deception. The games he wanted to play with her were sexual, not emotional.

'You do realise I don't love you,' he said as he flicked open the buttons on her jacket.

'Yes,' she surprised him by admitting, though her voice was trembling and her eyes had gone all smoky.

'I will *never* fall in love with you,' he added even as his hands slipped inside her jacket to play with her breasts through her bra. God, but her nipples were hard. So incredibly hard.

And so was he.

'I...I don't expect you to,' she replied somewhat breathlessly.

'You don't have to do anything you don't want to do,' he told her before his conscience shut down entirely.

'But I want you to,' she choked out.

'Want me to do what?' he murmured as he slipped the jacket off her shoulders and let it fall to the carpet.

'Wh...whatever,' she stammered.

Justin suspected she was too turned on to know what she was saying. He was rapidly getting to the point of no return himself.

For a split-second, he almost pulled back and saved her from herself. And from him. But she chose that moment to reach round and unhook her bra herself. Blood roared into his ears as she bared her beautiful breasts to his male gaze. And then she did something even more provocative. She dropped the wisp of a bra on the floor then reached up and rotated her outstretched palms over her rock-like nipples.

Any hope of salvation fled. He was lost, and so, he realised when he looked down into her dilating pupils, was she.

CHAPTER ELEVEN

THE phone was ringing when Rachel arrived home that night around seven. She raced to answer it, thinking—no, *hoping*—it might be Justin.

'Yes?' she said as she snatched it up to her ear.

'Rach, I was just about to give up and hang up.'

'Isabel!' Not Justin. Of course not. Silly Rachel. 'What…what are you doing, ringing me on your honeymoon?'

'Oh, don't be silly, Rach. We can't have sex *all* the time.' And she laughed.

Rachel almost cried.

'Not that we haven't given it a good try,' Isabel burbled on. 'I think I've worn him out. The poor darling's having a nap so I thought I'd use the opportunity to give you a call and find out how things are going at home. I've already rung Mum and Dad, so don't start lecturing me.'

'I never lecture you, Isabel. Not any more. The boot's on the other foot these days.'

'You could be right there. But you need lecturing sometimes. So tell me, how's things with your job?'

'Fine,' she said with pretend lightness.

'You still getting along with grumpy-bumps?'

'Justin is not a grumpy-bumps. He's just serious.'

And how, Rachel thought with a shiver, trying not to think about the day she'd spent with him.

'In that case, he's probably not gay,' Isabel pronounced. 'Gay men are never serious.'

'Justin is definitely not gay,' Rachel said, her tone perhaps a tad too dry.

'Really? Is that first-hand experience speaking there?' her best friend asked suspiciously.

Rachel decided that some sarcastically delivered truths would serve her purpose much better than heated denial. Because no way could she ever tell Isabel what was going on between herself and her boss. Isabel would be scandalised. She was pretty scandalised herself!

'Yes, of course. Didn't I mention it? He can't keep his hands off me. We've been doing it everywhere. On the desk. In the little-men's room. On the boardroom table. Standing up. Sitting down. Frontwards. Backwards. Haven't tried it upside-down yet. But give it time.'

'OK, OK,' Isabel said, sighing exasperatedly. 'I get the drift.'

No, you don't, Rachel thought with an erotically charged shiver. I'm telling you the shocking truth. 'But let's not talk about me,' she went on hastily. 'Can I know where you went on your honeymoon now?'

'Yes, of course. Hong Kong. And we're loving it. The clothes shopping is fantastic. I've been such a naughty girl. Bought a whole new wardrobe. But you know Rafe. He likes me to dress sexily, and all my clothes at home are a tad on the conservative side.'

Rachel had never thought Isabel's wardrobe at all conservative. Just classy.

'You can have them, if you like,' Isabel offered.

'What? All of them?'

'Everything I left behind. Provided you wear them, of course. That's the deal. You have to wear them. To work as well. It's time you bit the bullet and threw out those dreary black suits. I'm sure your boss could cope. It's not as though any of my old outfits are provocative. You can even have the shoes to go with them. We're the same shoe size.'

'Yes, I know. But are you sure, Isabel?' she asked, amazed by her friend's generosity.

'Positive. Actually, there's nothing in that place that you can't have. Take the lot. Handbags. Jewellery. Make-up. Beauty products. Whatever you can find. I won't be needing any of it.'

'You can't mean that, Isabel. You used to spend a small fortune on all your accessories. As for cosmetics and skin products, both bathrooms here are chock-full of them.'

'And I don't need any of it. Look, I brought everything I really like with me, and that includes my best jewellery. The stuff I left behind is just costume jewellery, bought to go with the clothes I've just given you. You're welcome to whatever you can find. If you don't use them they'll only go to waste. I have a new look now, from top to toe. Speaking of new looks, I've also bought some great maternity clothes for when I begin to sprout. Oh, I can't wait to get home and show everything to you.'

'So when exactly will you be home?'

'Next Saturday week. The flight gets in around midday. I'll ring you when we arrive home at Rafe's place and you can come over that evening for dinner.'

'But you won't want to cook after travelling.'

'Who said anything about cooking? We'll order something in. Is that all right by you?'

'Perfect.' There was no worry that she'd be spending any time with Justin on a Saturday. That was one of the many stipulations he'd made during their marathon afternoon of sex and sin. He wasn't offering her a real relationship. He didn't think it was fair to her to build her hopes up in that regard. Meeting each other's sexual needs was what they were doing. But dating was out. So was going to each other's places. Sex was to be confined to the office, but not till after five in future. Today was an exception.

She'd agreed to stay behind after work for a while every day till they were both satisfied. She'd agreed that he would not take her out to dinner afterwards, or take her home. She'd agreed that they wouldn't see each other at weekends.

In hindsight, Rachel could see she would have agreed to anything at the time.

But she knew, deep down in her heart, that she was skating on thin ice where Justin was concerned. She had underestimated the extent of his broken heart, and the darkness that had invaded his shattered soul. If Eric had hurt her, Justin could very well destroy her. But she felt helpless against the power of her need to have him make love to her as he had today. Primitively. Erotically. Endlessly.

There was nothing she wouldn't agree to to continue their sexual relationship.

'Uh-oh, I'd better go, Rach. The lord and master is stirring. Now, don't do anything I wouldn't do till I get home,' Isabel said happily, and hung up.

'No worries there,' Rachel muttered ruefully as she replaced the phone in its cradle. 'Whatever you're doing with Rafe, I'm doing one hell of a lot more with Justin. Much, much more.'

An image flashed into her mind of her straddled over Justin's lap, her back glued to his chest, her arms wound up around his neck. They were seated on his

office chair, their naked bodies fused and beaded with
sweat, despite the air-conditioning. He was making a
pretext of showing her how his programs worked
whilst he idly played with her breasts. If he'd expected
her to learn anything, he was sadly mistaken. All she'd
learned was that she was rapidly becoming addicted to
his brand of sex, and rapidly becoming obsessed with
him.

If Isabel thought Rafe's body was great, then she
hadn't seen Justin's. She quivered just thinking about
how he felt, all over. She couldn't get enough of touching him. And whatever else he wanted her to do.

And he'd wanted her to do everything today. There
wasn't an inch of his beautiful male flesh that hadn't
enjoyed the avid attentions of her mouth, or her hands.
She'd been shameless. Utterly shameless.

Yet shame wasn't her overriding emotion when she
thought of the woman she became in his arms. The
memory evoked the most intoxicating excitement. Her
heart thundered and a wave of heat flushed her skin.

There was no way she could voluntarily give up having sex with Justin. No way she could quit now and
get another job. She was his, till he decided otherwise.
His to admire and desire. His to have and, yes, to hold.

But never to marry, she reminded herself.

Her heart twisted at this last thought. But that didn't
stop her racing down to Isabel's walk-in wardrobe and
seeing what was there for her to wear for Justin tomorrow. Something classy but sexy, she wanted, her
eyes scanning the long rows filled with outfits, most of
them suits in pastel shades. She pulled out a pale blue
silk trouser suit, then put it back. Trousers did not appeal. She needed something with a skirt, either long
and floaty, or short and tight. Something that would

draw Justin's eye and recharge his hormones. She wanted him well and truly fired up by five. She wanted him as desperate for her as she already was for him.

A cream linen suit caught her eye, matched with a mustard-gold camisole. The jacket still had long sleeves but that didn't matter yet. Sydney's weather was still overcast and cool.

She laid it across the bed then rummaged around till she found matching cream shoes and bag. The jewellery box on the dressing table revealed a pearl choker with matching earrings. Not real pearls, of course, but still classy-looking. This time she would put her hair up in a more severe fashion, showing her throat and ears. To compensate, she would wear more make-up, paying particular attention to her eyes and mouth. Rachel knew she had nice eyes. And Justin seemed fascinated with her mouth.

Oh, and she would wear perfume. One of the expensive French fragrances Isabel had always favoured. Rachel had already noticed several not quite empty bottles in the wall cupboard above the main vanity unit. She would experiment with a new one each day and find out which one Justin seemed to like the most, then go and buy herself a bottle.

Stripping down to her underwear, she tried on the cream linen suit, pleased to see that it fitted very well, a surprise, considering she was considerably slimmer around the hips and waist than Isabel. Perhaps Isabel had bought it last year when she'd been dieting. The cami was much too tight around the bust, however, so Rachel took it off, discarded her bra and tried it on again.

With her full breasts settled lower on her chest the top felt less tight, but, as Rachel walked over to check her reflection in the cheval mirror on the back of the wardrobe door, the satin rubbing over her naked nipples had them puckering into pebble-like peaks. She winced at the sight of their provocative outline, which screamed her lack of underwear, plus her constant arousal. Would she dare wear it like this? And would she dare take off her jacket?

Oh, yes, she accepted as another wave of heat flooded her body.

She dared.

She would dare anything after today!

CHAPTER TWELVE

JUSTIN glanced up at the office wall clock for the ump-teenth time that afternoon. Almost five. His pulse quickened at the thought that soon he could abandon any pretence of working and do what he'd been desperately wanting to do all day: have sex with Rachel.

Just the thought of it sent his blood racing through his body.

But then another less happy thought intruded. It was Friday again. For the next two days he would not see Rachel at all; could not thrill to the exquisite anticipation of knowing that at the end of the day she would let him remove all her clothes to draw her naked and trembling into his arms.

Last weekend had been almost unendurable without her. This weekend would probably be worse. Justin resolved to keep her with him later than usual tonight. She wouldn't mind. She enjoyed what they were doing just as much as he did, a fact that soothed his conscience somewhat. If he ever thought that what they were doing together was hurting her in any sense he would have to stop.

But *could* he stop, even if his conscience demanded it? That was the question. He had difficulty at the moment doing without her for two days. The prospect of never having sex with Rachel again was an idea he didn't want to address.

Another glance at the clock showed it was finally five o'clock.

His heartbeat took off.
It was time.

Rachel's head snapped up from her computer with a
gasp when Justin wrenched open his office door right
on the dot of five. She'd been pretending to herself that
she hadn't noticed the time, pretending to be working.

But that was all it was. Pretence. She lived for this
moment every day. It was what she dressed for. And
undressed for. It was why each afternoon at four-thirty
she rose to lock the outside door, then go to the ladies'
room to make preparations for just this moment. For
the last half-hour she'd been sitting there with her panties stuffed in her top drawer and no underwear of any
kind covering her bare buttocks and upper thighs. Stay-
up stockings had long replaced her pantyhose. She also
rarely wore a bra these days, having quickly grown
addicted to the feel of silk linings against her bare skin,
plus the aphrodisiacal effect of knowing she was naked
underneath her clothes.

Their eyes locked across the room and her surroundings slowly began to recede. Suddenly there was only
him, and the way he was looking at her.

'Get yourself in here, Rachel,' he ordered, his impatience echoed in the tightness of his neck muscles.

Her legs felt like lead as she levered herself up from
her desk and walked, like some programmed robot, into
his office. Yet inside she was anything but a cold-
blooded machine. She was all heat and hyped-up nerve-
endings. Her head was spinning like a top and her heart
was pounding behind her chest wall.

The speed with which he yanked up her skirt then
hoisted her up onto his desk punched all the breath
from Rachel's body. He was between her legs in a

flash, unzipping his trousers and freeing his rather an-
gry-looking erection. Her body was ripe and ready for
him, needing no foreplay. His hands grasped her hips,
his fingertips digging into her skin as he scooped her
bottom to the very edge of the desk and drove into her
to the hilt. With a grunt of satisfaction he set up a
powerful pumping action, his eyes grimacing shut, his
lips drawing back over gritted teeth. Rachel leant back
and braced herself by gripping the back edge of the
desk, but even so her bottom slid back and forth across
the smoothly polished desk-top.

Something—possibly the fact he hadn't even kissed
her first—got to Rachel, and suddenly she wanted him
to stop.

The trouble was…her body didn't want him to stop.
It had a mind of its own. Frantic for release, it was.
And ruthlessly determined in its quest, pushing aside
any gathering qualms and ignoring the danger warnings. Her libido remained recklessly separated from her
heart as pre-climactic sensations began to build and the
need to come became all-consuming.

Her belly tightened. As did her thighs. Her bottom.
Her insides. He groaned in response to her involuntary
squeezing and then they were both splintering apart,
their cries of erotic ecstasy echoing in the stillness of
the room. His back arched back as he shuddered into
her whilst she gripped the edge of the desk so hard her
fingers went white.

But the spasms of pleasure passed, as they always
did, and this time Rachel came back down to earth with
a terrible thud.

The reality of what they were doing together could
no longer be denied. It was beneath her, carrying on

like this. So why was she settling for such an arrangement? *Why?*

The reason was obvious, she accepted with considerable anguish. The reason had always been obvious, if she'd looked for it. The reason was at this moment still inside her body, his arms wound tightly around her waist, his head resting between her sweat-slicked breasts.

It was then that she started to cry.

CHAPTER THIRTEEN

'I THOUGHT you said you were never going to take me out to dinner,' she said with curiosity—and something else—in her voice. Was it hope?

Rachel's unexpectedly breaking down into tears after the episode on the desk had jolted Justin out of his selfish desires, and made him take a long, hard look at what he'd been doing. He wasn't a complete fool, or a bastard, even if he'd been acting like one. It didn't take him long to realise that a woman of Rachel's standards and sensitivity couldn't indulge her sexual self indefinitely without her emotions—and her conscience—eventually becoming involved. She claimed she was all right, and that she often cried after she came.

But she never had before.

She'd said through her sobs that she didn't want him to stop, but to continue in the face of her distress was something he simply could not do. He hadn't sunk *that* low.

So he'd comforted her as best he could, then announced that he was starving and couldn't possibly go on till they'd eaten, adding that he didn't want any of the take-away muck they sometimes had delivered to the office. He wanted a decent meal. And decent wine.

Despite a momentary look of surprise, she hadn't made any protest, so he'd booked a table in a nearby restaurant whilst she'd made whatever repairs needed to be made after sex, and retrieved her panties from where she always put them in her top drawer. Fifteen minutes later, here they were, sitting opposite each other at a candlelit table, with Rachel finally giving voice to what was a very fair question over his changing the rules of their arrangement.

He stared across the table at her and thought how lovely she looked in the soft candlelight. The simple mauve dress she was wearing was very classy and elegant. There again, all the clothes she wore to work these days were classy and elegant.

'So I did,' he said quietly. 'But things change, Rachel. I thought it was time we talked.'

Was that panic in her eyes? Or fear? Fear of what, for pity's sake? Of his stopping the sex? Or changing the rules?

Maybe she hadn't been lying to him when she said she was all right. Maybe she liked things the way they were. Maybe she'd become as addicted to his body as he was to hers.

Such thinking threw him. He didn't want her feeling nothing but lust for him. He wanted… He wanted… What *did* he want, damn it?

He wants to call it quits, Rachel was thinking.

Oh, God, she couldn't bear it if he did that. Which was perverse, considering. It should be her telling him that, yes, things *had* changed, and that she wanted out. Out of his office and out of his life.

But she stayed silent and waited for him to say what he had to say, nausea swirling in her stomach at the thought he might not want her any more.

'We really can't go on like this, Rachel,' he said, and a great black pit opened up inside her.

'Why's that?' she said, struggling to sound calm and reasonable whilst her world was disintegrating.

He sighed. 'Look, it's been fantastic. I grant you that. Every man's fantasy come true. But I can see things are in danger of becoming...complicated.'

'In what way? I've done everything you asked.'

He stared at her. 'Yes, you certainly have. Just excuse me for a moment whilst I order the wine.'

She sat there numbly, with Justin and the wine waiter's voices nothing but distant murmurs. Her mind was going round and round and so was her stomach. What was she going to do when he told her it was over? How would she survive?

'Rachel...'

'What?' She blinked, then made an effort to gather herself.

'The waiter's gone.'

'Oh. Yes. So he has.'

'The thing is, Rachel, I don't want to continue with what we've been doing.'

She nodded, her mouth as dry as a desert. 'Yes, I rather gathered that.' Her voice sounded dead. Hollow.

'I want to try something a little more...normal.'

Her head snapped back, her eyes rounding.

'I know I said I didn't want a real relationship with you, and I meant it at the time. And, to a degree, that still holds true. Love and marriage are not on my agenda, so I won't pretend I am offering you any hope of that. But I do want you in my life, Rachel, not just as my PA and not just for the sex. I want to go out with you and, yes, go home with you sometimes. My weekends are terribly lonely. Last weekend was... intolerable.'

'Mine too,' she agreed readily, her spirits lifting with what he was suggesting.

'So I was thinking, if you'd like, that we could try that kind of a relationship.'

She struggled not to cry.

'I...I'd like that very much,' she managed, and found a smile from somewhere.

He smiled back. 'I can't promise not to ravage you occasionally in the office.'

'I won't mind.'

He laughed. 'You're not supposed to say that.'

'What am I supposed to say?'

'*No* might be a good start.'

'You're not much good with no.'

'It's not my favourite word, I confess. Not where you're concerned. But it really isn't right, you know, doing it on my desk. I'm finding it increasingly hard to concentrate on my work.'

'Poor Justin,' she said.

'You don't sound all that sympathetic.'

'I'm not.'

'Would you believe I've actually been feeling quite guilty?'

'Not guilty enough to stop, though,' she pointed out with a wry little smile.

He smiled back. 'No. Not nearly *that* guilty.'

The arrival of the wine gave Rachel a few moments to hug her happiness to herself. Justin might not be offering her the world, but being his special lady friend was a big improvement on the role of secret sex slave.

'This is the best wine,' she said after the waiter left and she took a sip.

'Hunter Valley whites are second to none,' Justin replied, sipping also.

'Can...can I tell Isabel about us?' Rachel asked tentatively. 'She'll be home from her honeymoon tomorrow.'

'If you want to. But I'd rather you didn't mention what we've been up to these past two weeks.'

'Heavens, I wasn't going to tell her about *that*!' she exclaimed.

Rachel doubted Isabel would be shocked as such. But she would be furious. With Justin, for treating her best friend in such a fashion. At least now Rachel would be able to say that she was Justin's proper girlfriend. They might even be able to go out with Rafe and Isabel sometimes as a foursome.

Justin's head tipped to one side as he searched her face. 'You have enjoyed what we've been doing, haven't you, Rachel?'

'How can you ask that?' she exclaimed, blushing now. 'You know I have.'

'And your tears tonight... Did you tell me the truth about them?'

She swallowed, then looked him straight in the face. 'Why would I lie?'

'I was worried you might think you're in love with me.'

'Not at all,' she said without batting an eyelid. And it wasn't really a lie, because she was *sure* she was in love with him. 'I...I confess I was bit upset because you hadn't kissed me first. You just...you know...'

He grimaced. 'You're right. It was unforgivable of me. But I refuse to take all the blame. That perfume you're wearing today should be banned. I just couldn't wait.'

Rachel made a mental note to buy a king-sized bottle

of that one. If she couldn't have Justin's love, she could at least ensure his ongoing lust.

'So when are we going on our first date?' she asked eagerly.

'We're on it now.'

'Oh. Yes. So we are. And where to after dinner?'

'I thought I'd take you home to my place for the night.'

Now Rachel was seriously surprised. When he'd said he would like to come home with her sometimes she'd thought he was still keeping his own place out of bounds.

'If you like, that is,' he added.

'I'd like it very much.'

'I lease a furnished apartment at Kirribilli,' he went on. 'No point in buying a place when I plan on setting up my future business out of the city. I'd like to buy some building with a couple of floors and then I can live above the office. I resent the time I waste travelling to and from work. Not that Kirribilli is all that far from here. Just over the bridge. But you know what I mean. Parking in the CBD is appalling and public transport is the pits.'

'I know just what you mean. I don't mind my train trip too much when I get a seat. But that's not always the case. So what's it like, your place in Kirribilli?'

'Very modern. Very stylish. But a bit on the soulless side. Could do with a spot of colour. Everything's in neutral shades.'

'Sounds like the place I live in. It's all cream and cold. I much prefer warm colours and a cosy, almost cluttered feel to a room. That's why I'd like my own place, eventually, no matter how small. Then I could decorate it exactly as I want, with lots of interesting pictures on the walls, and knick-knacks galore.'

'Sounds like Mum's place. Truly, there's hardly a spare space on the walls, or on any of the furniture. She's a collectorholic. You'll have to come over and see her collection of teapots one day. They fill up two china cabinets all by themselves.'

Rachel blinked her surprise. 'You mean you're going to tell Alice about us?'

'Is there any reason you want to keep our friendship a secret?'

'No. I guess not. But you know mothers. She might start thinking we'll get married one day.'

'I can't worry about what she might think,' he said a bit sharply. 'She should know me well enough to know that is never going to happen. Now, why don't you think about what you're going to order for dinner? The waiter's on his way over.' And he picked up his menu.

Rachel was happy to do likewise, aware that her face had to be registering some dismay over his curt remark that he would never marry her. As much as Rachel tried telling herself that she was pleased with the kind of relationship Justin was offering her, deep down in her heart she knew it was a second-rate substitute for marriage and a family.

Isabel would think her a fool for accepting such a go-nowhere affair. What on earth are you doing, Rach, she'd say, wasting more of your life on another man who's never going to marry you or give you children? You're thirty-one years old, for pity's sake. Soon you'll be thirty-two. Grow up and give him the flick. And get yourself another job whilst you're at it.

Easier said than done.

Love made one foolish. And eternally hopeful.

Even whilst cold, hard logic reasoned she *was* wasting her time, Rachel kept telling herself that maybe, one day, Justin would get over his ex-wife and fall in love with her. Maybe, if she was always there for him, he'd wake up one morning and see what was right under his nose. A woman who loved him. A woman who would never leave him. A woman who'd give him a good life. And children, if he liked.

He would make a wonderful father, she believed. And she...she would dearly love the chance to be a wonderful mother.

'So what do you want?' he asked, glancing up from the menu.

You, she thought with a painful twist of her heart. Just you.

CHAPTER FOURTEEN

RACHEL woke mid-morning to the sun shining in the bedroom window and the smell of fresh coffee percolating. Justin's side of the bed was empty, but she could hear him whistling somewhere.

He sounded happy. And so was she. Relatively.

Spending last night in his bed had given her some hope that Justin hadn't changed the rules of their relationship just so he could have more of what he'd been having at the office. When he'd brought her back to his apartment after dinner he'd been incredibly sweet, and his lovemaking incredibly tender. He'd held her in his arms afterwards, stroking her hair and back. Strangely, she'd felt like crying again at the time, but she'd kept a grip on herself, thank the lord. Justin wouldn't have known what to make of that. She'd finally fallen asleep and here she was, totally rested and...totally surprised.

'Goodness, breakfast in bed!' she exclaimed as a navy-robed Justin carried one of those no-spill trays into the room.

Sitting up, she pushed her hair back from her face and pulled the sheet up around her nakedness just in time for him to settle the tray down across her lap.

'My, this is lovely,' she murmured, eyeing the freshly squeezed orange juice and scrambled eggs on toast, along some fried tomato and two strips of crispy bacon on the side. 'I usually only have coffee and toast. So what are you having?'

'I've already had it,' he said, sitting down next to her on the side of the bed then leaning across where her legs were lying under the bedclothes.

He looked marvellous, she thought, despite the messy hair and dark stubble on his chin. His vivid blue eyes were sparkling clear, with no dark rings under them. He must have slept as well as she had.

'I'll bet you didn't have anything as decadent as this,' she chided.

'I surely did. And I enjoyed every single mouthful. I'm going to enjoy watching you eat yours, too. You need a bit of fattening up, my girl.'

'Oh? You think I'm too thin?' she asked, that dodgy body image raising its ugly head again.

'Not unattractively so, as I'm sure you are aware. But you don't have anything much in reserve.'

'But if I put on weight I won't fit into my lovely new wardrobe. And my boobs will start sprouting. That's where fat always goes on me first.'

'Nothing wrong with a bit more weight on a woman's boobs. Though yours are already a gorgeous handful. Pity any extra weight I gain doesn't go where it would do me the most good. It usually becomes entrenched around my middle.'

'How can you say that? You don't have an extra ounce of fat on you.'

'You didn't see me eighteen months ago. I was the original couch potato with a sprouting beer gut.'

'I don't believe you. You have the best body I've ever seen on a man in the flesh, with a six-pack to envy. And you certainly don't need any extra inches in that other department. You have more than enough for me.'

His laugh carried a dry amusement. 'Being with

someone like you seems to have made a permanent difference to the size of my equipment.'

'So I noticed. But you know what they say. Size doesn't matter. It's what you can do with it that counts. And I certainly have no complaints over what you do with yours.'

'So I noticed. You are seriously good for my ego, do you know that?'

As opposed to his ex-wife, Rachel guessed. Justin's revelation about being a bit overweight and less than fit eighteen months ago gave rise to the speculation that the vain puss he was married to might have criticised him over his physical appearance, as well as his sexual performance. Rachel recalled Justin once implying he thought himself staid, and boring. Had that woman undermined Justin on every level, simply to excuse her own disgusting and disloyal behaviour?

More than likely. Guilt in a human being often searched for any excuse for their own appalling actions.

As much as Rachel understood how such criticisms would have been crushing, Justin must surely now know the woman never really loved him. True love wasn't based on superficial things like gaining—or losing—a few wretched pounds. Or on knowing every position in the Kama Sutra.

Again, she wanted to ask him what Mandy had actually said when she left him, but once again this wasn't the right moment. Hopefully, in time, he might confide in her himself. Meanwhile, she had to play a waiting game.

Wrapping the sheet more firmly around her bare breasts, she tucked into the breakfast whilst Justin watched her with a self-satisfied smirk on his face.

'You're really enjoying that, aren't you?' he said and she nodded, her mouth full of egg.

'I'm brewing some very special coffee for afters.'

She swallowed the last mouthful of egg and smacked her lips. 'If it tastes half as good as it smells, I'll be in heaven.'

'That's what I was thinking about you all yesterday,' he said drily, and she laughed.

'I aim to buy a really big bottle of that perfume this very day.'

He groaned. 'Sadist.'

'Takes one to know one. Now you know how I've been feeling every day in that office, waiting for five to come round. Only a sadist would make a rule like that.'

'Trust me, it was much harder for me, with the emphasis on ''harder''. Hopefully, we might both have a bit more control at work if we spend every night together.'

Rachel blinked her surprise. '*Every* night?'

'Too much for you?'

She wanted to say no, of course not. But she didn't want to be that easy. She'd been far too easy with Justin so far. Men never appreciated women who were easy.

'Yes, I'm afraid so,' she said. 'We women do have personal things we have to do sometimes, you know. Also, once Isabel gets back I will want to spend some time with her. She's my best friend, after all. Actually, I'm having dinner with her and her husband tonight. Her husband, Rafe, has a terraced house in Paddington. He's a photographer.'

'I see,' Justin muttered, his face falling.

Rachel decided that faint heart never won fat turkey.

'You can come too, if you like,' she said, and was rewarded with a startled smile.

'Seriously?' he asked.

'Of course. There's no way I'm going to be able to keep you a secret from Isabel. I wouldn't even try.'

'But won't she mind having someone extra thrust upon her on such short notice?'

'No, and she's ordering food in anyway.'

'I would have thought she'd be too tired to entertain on the first night back from an overseas honeymoon.'

'I said much the same thing to her on the phone but she insisted. I guess it's not all that long a flight from Hong Kong and I dare say they'll have flown first class. Probably slept all the way. But I'll check with her when she calls me. Which reminds me, I will have to go home this morning to await her call and get fresh clothes.'

'I'll drive you,' he offered.

'Gosh, you mean you have a car?' she teased. 'I thought you lived in trains and taxis.'

He certainly did have a car, a nice new navy number. Not overly flash; more of a family car, with easily enough room for two adults and two children.

Rachel wished she'd stop having such thoughts about Justin, but it was impossible not to dream.

They pulled up at the town house in Turramurra shortly after one, Justin accompanying Rachel inside as she knew he would. And they ended up back in bed, as she knew they would. So much for her resolve not to be easy! But it was so hard to resist him once he started kissing her. They were still in bed together when Isabel's call came shortly after three p.m.

'Yes?' Rachel answered in a slightly croaky voice.

'Rach, is that you?' Isabel asked, sounding doubtful.

'Yes, yes, it's me. Justin, stop that,' she hissed under her breath. 'I have to talk to Isabel.'

'Is that the TV on in the background, or are you talking to someone?' Isabel asked.

'I...um...I'm talking to someone.'

'Oh? Who?' Now she sounded surprised.

Rachel gave Justin a playful kick and he laughed before climbing out of bed and heading for the bathroom, Rachel wincing at the sight of the red nail marks she'd dug into his buttocks. Truly, she'd turned into a wild woman in bed!

'Sounds like a man,' Isabel said.

'It is.'

'Oh, my God, you've gone and got yourself a boyfriend!'

'You could be right.'

'Who? Rafe, Rafe, Rachel's got herself a man!' she called out before returning her attention to her friend. 'Where did you meet him? What's he like? Have you been to bed with him yet?'

Rachel had to smile. Trust Isabel to get down to the nitty-gritty straight away. 'I met him at work. He's gorgeous. And yes, I've been to bed with him.'

'Oh, wow, this is such great news. How old is he?'

'Early thirties.'

'Presumably, he works for AWI.'

'Yes.'

'What's he look like?'

'Tall, dark and handsome.'

'What's he like in bed?'

'Makes Eric look like a moron.'

'Single or divorced?'

'Divorced.'

'Oh. Pity. But you can't have everything, I suppose. So, does Casanova have a name?' she added.

Rachel's stomach swirled. This was going to be the sticky part. 'Um…Justin McCarthy.'

Dead silence at the other end for at least ten seconds. Hearing Justin switch on the shower was a blessing. He wouldn't be returning for a while. Time enough, hopefully, to smooth things over with Isabel.

'Justin McCarthy,' Isabel finally repeated in her best I-don't-believe-you-could-be-such-an-idiot voice. 'Your boss. You're sleeping with your boss. Your obviously not gay but pathetically paranoid boss.'

'Um… Yes.'

'But why? How? *When,* for pity's sake?'

Rachel did her best to explain the circumstances leading up to their first going to bed together, as well as where their affair had gone since then, without it all sounding as though she was desperate and Justin was simply using her for sex.

Her friend's sigh told it all. 'You are just setting yourself up for more hurt, love,' Isabel said.

'Maybe. Maybe not. Either way, it's my choice.'

Isabel sighed. 'True.'

'He's really a very nice man.'

'I suppose I'll have to take your word for that.'

'No, you don't. If you'll let me bring him over to dinner tonight then you can judge for yourself.'

'What a good idea,' she said in a tone that worried the life out of Rachel.

'Promise me you won't say anything sarcastic.'

'Who? *Me?*'

'Yes, you, Miss Butter-wouldn't-melt-in-your-mouth. You've got a cutting tongue on you sometimes.'

'I'll do my best to keep it sheathed.'

'You'd better.'

'Where is lover-boy at the moment?'

'In the shower.'

'Good, because I have something I want to say to *you*.'

Rachel rolled her eyes. Here it comes. 'What?'

'Now, don't take that tone with me, Missy. Someone has to look after your best interests and that someone is me. I know you, Rach. You probably think you love this man. But I seriously doubt it. It's just a rebound thing after running into Eric like that. You've also been very lonely. And loneliness can make a girl do incredibly stupid things. From the sound of things, your boss has been very lonely too, not to mention having had the stuffing kicked out of him. Not too many men could come through an experience like that without a seriously damaged soul. How do you know he's not living out some sort of sick revenge, doing to you what he imagines Carl Toombs is doing to his wife? Have you thought of that?'

'Yes.'

'And?'

'It doesn't fit his character. He's too decent for that.'

'Decent! Reading between the lines, he's been screwing you silly all over your office. I haven't forgotten that little joke you made during our last phone call. Only that wasn't a joke, was it? That was the truth!'

'Sort of. But things have changed.'

'Huh. He's just changed the scene of his crimes, that's all. He's probably afraid you'll slap a sexual-harassment suit on him if he keeps doing it on his desk. He's thinking ahead.'

'Thinking ahead to what?'

'To that day when he gets bored and gives you the bullet.'

'He's not like that.'

Isabel groaned. 'You *do* think you love him.'

'I do love him, OK? So shoot me.'

'For pity's sake, girl, it could just be lust, you know. Even on *your* part.'

'Like it was on yours? With Rafe?'

'That was different.'

'How?'

'It just was.'

'Wait till you meet Justin. Then tell me if you still think that.'

'All right. I will!'

CHAPTER FIFTEEN

'I STILL can't believe it,' Isabel said to Rafe as the returned honeymooners made the after-dinner coffee together in the kitchen.

'What can't you believe, darling? That you've come back home to find Rachel looking utterly gorgeous and glowing? Or that her creep of a boss—the one you've been ranting and raving about all afternoon—is actually a genuinely nice guy?'

'Both. Frankly, I don't know what to think any more. If I didn't know Justin McCarthy's history I'd say he just might be in love with her. The way he looks at her sometimes... As for Rachel, I've had to abandon any desperate hope I was clinging to that she might only be in lust with the man. She's obviously mad about him.'

Rafe glanced over the kitchen island at the woman *he* was mad about. 'Then why are you still so worried?' he said.

'I just couldn't bear to see her get hurt again. She's had such a rotten deal in life so far, Rafe. She deserves to be happy.'

'I know, sweetheart,' Rafe said soothingly. 'I know. But she's a grown woman. She has to make her own choices and decisions in life. You can't make them for her. Even if you could, what would you say? Leave him before he leaves you? You saw for yourself the physical transformation in her. Whatever happens between them in the end, that can't be a bad thing.'

'No… No, you're right. If nothing else, falling for
Justin McCarthy has done wonders for Rachel's looks.
It's difficult to believe she's the same girl who was
worried about having a bit of red dye put in her hair
three weeks ago today. I wonder what Alice makes of
all this.'

'Alice?' Rafe frowned.

'Justin's mum. She was the one who got Rachel the
job as Justin's PA in the first place.'

'Aah, yes. I remember now. Well, maybe Alice
doesn't know that her son's new Girl Friday has been
promoted to Girl Saturday and Sunday as well.'

'If she doesn't then that would be telling, don't you
think? You told your mother about us quick smart.
Maybe I'll try to find out over coffee.'

'Isabel,' Rafe said sharply. 'Don't interfere.'

'But…'

'No buts, darling, except butt out. It's their life.'

'Oh, don't be so typically male! The trouble with
you is you don't really care. Rachel's not *your* best
friend.'

'No. She's not. Which is possibly why I'm a better
judge of what you should and shouldn't do. Now, let's
take this coffee out to our guests and finish this very
pleasant evening chatting about non-inflammatory subjects.'

'Such as what?'

'How about Rachel's new look? That should keep
you two girls going till after midnight, talking about
hair and make-up and clothes.'

'Very funny.'

'Justin and I could discuss manly things, such as
money and football and sex.'

'You're a male chauvinist pig, Rafe St Vincent.'

'Not at all. Just a typical male, as you so cleverly pointed out. And, speaking of typical males, I wonder if Rachel would consider accidentally on purpose getting pregnant to the marriage-shy Mr McCarthy. It's amazing how the thought of your own cute little baby-to-be can focus even the most commitment-phobic people.'

Isabel's eyebrows arched. 'Now, that's an idea. But a bit too soon, I think. Though I might mention it to her later on. Trust you to come up with that one,' she finished ruefully.

'All brilliantly successful ideas should be shared. Come along, darling. If we don't get out there with this coffee, it'll be stone-cold!'

Rachel knew Isabel was out there in the kitchen gossiping to Rafe about her and Justin. But nothing her friend could say would stop her from continuing with her relationship with Justin. The more time she spent with him, the more deeply she fell in love with him. And it wasn't just the sex bewitching her. It was definitely the man. He was everything Eric had never been. Kind. Considerate. Caring. And funny, when he wanted to be. She'd been amazed at what a witty conversationalist he'd been over dinner with people he hadn't met before. It was obvious Rafe liked him. And Isabel too, if she'd put aside her personal prejudice long enough to admit it.

'I like your friends,' Justin said whilst they were sitting there at the dining table alone, waiting for the coffee. 'And I like their house,' he added, glancing around the cosy dining alcove which came off the main lounge room upstairs.

'They'll probably buy a bigger place after their baby is born,' Rachel remarked.

'They're expecting a baby?'

'Didn't I say so? I thought I had. Yes, Isabel was already expecting before they got married. But that wasn't why they got married. They planned it that way. Or Rafe did. Actually, Isabel wasn't going to get married at all. But she wanted a baby. Oh, dear, I'm not explaining this very well. It's a bit complicated.'

Justin smiled. 'It sounds it.'

'Let me try to explain it better. Now, let's see…a few months back Isabel decided to have a baby using artificial insemination, then raise it by herself, because she was sick to death of falling in love with Mr Wrong. You know the kind. Not exactly good husband or father material. She'd already tried the idea of marrying with her head rather than her heart, and was engaged to this really nice architect who felt the same way, but two weeks before their wedding he fell head over heels for another girl and called the wedding off. It was around this time—only a couple of months back really—that Isabel met Rafe. He was going to be her wedding photographer. Right from their first meeting, she was very attracted to him. No, that's understating things. She fancied him like mad. So much so that when she found out he was single and unattached she asked him to go away with her on her pre-booked and pre-paid honeymoon, on a strictly sex basis with no strings attached. Naturally, Rafe agreed.'

'Naturally,' Justin said laughingly.

'Well, yes, what man wouldn't?' Rachel concurred. 'Isabel's drop-dead gorgeous. Anyway, to cut a long story short, Rafe fell in love during their fling and didn't like the idea of Isabel having a baby all by herself. So he set about deliberately getting her pregnant

without her knowing, hoping that then she'd marry him.'

'How on earth did he get her pregnant without her
knowing it was on the cards?'

'I gather he doctored the condoms.'

'That was an extremely bold move.'

'Love can make you bold, I guess. And wanting
something badly enough.'

'I guess,' he said, his eyes clouding over, then drift-
ing off somewhere distant.

'Did you want children when you were married,
Justin?' Rachel asked before she could think better of
it.

'What?' He stared at her for a second as though he
had no idea what she was talking about. But then his
eyes cleared. 'Yes, yes, I did. Mandy did, too, till
she…' He broke off abruptly. 'Can we discuss something else, please?'

Isabel and Rafe's return with the coffee was a blessing, though Isabel's intuition antennae seemed to pick
up on something straight away, and she flicked Rachel
a frowning glance.

Rachel gave a little shake of her head and dredged
up a covering smile. 'You haven't shown me all the
lovely things you bought in Hong Kong yet,' she said
brightly.

'I was just saying that to Isabel,' Rafe replied. 'Why
don't you two girls take your coffee into the bedroom
and do just that? We two men can stay here and talk
about man stuff.'

Isabel rolled her eyes as she handed the stylish blue
and white mugs of steaming coffee around. 'In that
case, you have a deal. Two arrogant, self-opinionated
males exchanging macho bulldust is not my idea of a

fun time. Come on, Rach, let's get out of here and leave these two to play one-upmanship all by themselves.'

'I'll have you know that I never play one-upmanship!' Rafe called after the girls as they retreated, mugs in hand.

Rachel and Isabel's laughter lasted till the bedroom door was safely shut behind them.

'What happened out there?' Isabel asked straight away. 'You were both happy as larks when Rafe and I left to go make the coffee, and as tense as anything when we came back.'

Rachel sighed. 'The conversation came round to you and Rafe expecting a child and I stupidly asked him if he'd wanted children when he was married.'

'*Stupidly* asked!' Isabel exclaimed, her expression one of outrage. 'What's stupid about a normal question like that? Truly, Rachel, you're not going to turn into one of those women afraid to ask their boyfriend anything about his past. Or your future together, for that matter. I, for one, would like to know *exactly* what his intentions are towards you.'

Rachel had to smile. Dear Isabel. She really was a good friend. When she wasn't playing bossy mother. She didn't know it but she was just like her own mother in some ways, a fact which would pain Isabel if she realised it.

'He wants me to be his lover, his friend and his PA,' Rachel answered patiently. 'But not necessarily in that order of priority. He doesn't want me to be his wife. And obviously not the mother of his children. He doesn't love me. Neither does he want to remarry. He told me so upfront. He's been very honest with me,

Isabel, and I have no right to cross-question him, or try to change the status quo.'

'Oh, Rachel, that's just so much crap.'

'No, it's not. I've gone into this affair with my eyes wide open. I know the score. Justin doesn't want my love. He wants my friendship, my companionship and my body.'

'And you can live with that?'

'For the time being. That doesn't mean I don't have a very different long-term agenda. I'm not that self-sacrificing. I love Justin more than I ever loved Eric and I aim to marry him one day.'

'Wow. Now, that's more like my old Rachel. So what are you going to do? Get pregnant accidentally on purpose after a little while?' Isabel asked excitedly.

Rachel was taken aback. 'Are you insane? That strategy would never work with Justin.'

'How do you know? Rafe said it's a winner if the guy cares about you at all, and you obviously think he does.'

'Yes, I do. But he hasn't totally got over his wife yet. I'm hopeful he will, though, the same way I eventually got over Eric. Time does heal all wounds, you know.'

'No, it doesn't,' Isabel countered sharply. 'Sometimes people get gangrene. On top of that, it took you damned years to get over that rotter, my girl. By the time Justin is ready to move on from his slutty ex, you might be too old to have children. Don't wait, I say. Take a chance and get preggers and see what happens.'

'Uh-uh, Isabel. That worked for you and Rafe because you loved each other. Justin doesn't love me yet. He wouldn't marry me at this point in time and I don't want to be a single mum. I want any child of mine to have it all. Both parents who love him or her, and who love each other.'

Isabel frowned, and cocked her head on one side. 'Are you sure he doesn't? Love you, that is?'

'What? Look, what are you playing at now, Isabel?'

'Just looking at the situation from a different angle. To be honest, if I didn't know Justin's personal history I would have said he was quite besotted with you.'

Rachel could feel herself blushing. 'You really think so?'

'Absolutely. He might very well be in love with you. He just doesn't know it himself yet. Rafe didn't realise he loved me for ages. So tell me one thing. Is Justin going to tell his mother about you, or is your sleeping together to be kept a tacky little secret?'

'Funny you should ask that. I thought he'd want to keep our affair a secret. But no, he's already told Alice over the phone and we're going to her place for lunch tomorrow. Apparently, he has lunch with his mother practically every Sunday.'

'Well, well, well,' Isabel mused. 'That's good news. That's very good news indeed.'

'I thought so too.'

'We have reason to hope, then, don't we?' Isabel said, feeling more optimistic over this relationship than she had all evening.

'We do, Isabel,' Rachel agreed and smiled at her best friend. 'Now, no more talk about Justin. I want to see all the goodies you brought back from Hong Kong.'

CHAPTER SIXTEEN

'WHAT are you thinking about?' Rachel asked dreamily.

They were in bed together, post-dinner with Isabel and Rafe, post-coitus, both on their backs, both staring up at the bedroom ceiling.

Justin didn't answer immediately, since the truth was out of the question. How could he possibly tell her he was thinking that if she wasn't on the Pill they might have just made a baby together, or, even more amazingly, that he wished that were the case?

Ever since Rachel had told him that story tonight about Rafe deliberately getting Isabel pregnant to get her to marry him, he'd been having the most incredible thoughts. He knew he didn't love Rachel. Hell, how could he when he still loved Mandy? Yet here he was, wanting her to be the mother of his child. And maybe even his wife!

Was he losing his mind? Or had Rachel's also asking him if he'd wanted children when he was married to Mandy made him realise just how much he *had* wanted children? Losing the woman he loved to another man didn't mean he had to lose the chance of having a family of his own, did it?

Another remark of Rachel's tonight came back to tantalise his mind, and torment his conscience.

Wanting something badly enough can make you bold.

Would it be bold to tell Rachel he'd fallen in love

with her and wanted to marry her? Or was that just plain bad?

'Justin?' Rachel prompted, but Justin closed his eyes and pretended to be asleep. Better not to answer right now. The lies could wait. Till the time was right.

He heard Rachel eventually sigh, then turn over and go to sleep, but he didn't sleep for quite a while. He was too busy planning his strategy for getting Rachel to fall in love with him.

Taking her to his mother's for lunch tomorrow was an excellent first move. But it would only be the first of many.

Justin hadn't realised till that moment how bold he could be when he wanted something badly enough. Or how ruthless.

'Rachel, my dear!' Alice exclaimed shortly after opening her front door to them. 'I hope you don't take offence but you look simply marvellous! I can hardly believe it.'

Rachel laughed and didn't take offence. 'It's a bit of an improvement from the last time you saw me, isn't it? No more dreary black for starters.' In deference to Alice's suggestion that blue would suit her, she was wearing a blue silk trouser suit that did look very well against her colouring. Her hair had taken ages to do that morning, and so had her make-up, but it was worth it to see the expression of surprise and pleasure on Alice's face.

'And Justin, love,' Alice said, her gaze swinging over to check out her son from top to toe. 'You're looking ten years younger yourself. Whatever you've been doing with Rachel, keep it up.'

'Mum. *Really.*'

'Oh, don't go all prudish on me. You know I can't stand it when you do that. It reminds me of your father, who, might I add, was not in any way prudish behind closed doors. He just liked to act that way in public. Come along, you two. Come through to the back terrace. I've got a nice cold lunch all set out there, with a couple of delicious bottles of Tasmanian wine for us to try.'

'Like father, like son,' Rachel whispered to Justin when he took her arm and guided her down the long central hallway.

'Behave yourself,' he rasped back. 'Or I'll put you over my knee when I get you home tonight.'

She shot him a cheeky look. 'Would you? You promise?'

'Have some decorum,' he said, but smilingly. 'We're at my mother's.'

'What are you two whispering about?' Alice shot over her shoulder.

'I was telling Justin how much I like your house,' Rachel said.

'Which reminds me, Mum. I want you to show Rachel your teapot collection later. She's into pottery and knick-knacks.'

'Oh, wonderful. I'll take her to a few auctions with me. We'll have such fun.'

They emerged onto the sun-drenched back terrace that looked like a new addition to the house, which was federation-style and inclined to be a little dark inside with smallish windows. Cosy, though, from what Rachel had glimpsed during her journey down the hallway. The terrace, however, looked like something that belonged to an Italian villa, with a lovely vine-covered pergola overhead and large terracotta tiles providing an excellent floor for the rich cedar-wood outdoor setting.

The lunch set out on the table looked as if it would feed an army, with all sorts of seafood and salads, and two already opened bottles of white wine resting in portable coolers. The wine glasses waiting to be filled were exquisitely fine, with small bunches of grapes etched into the sides.

'I'll just get the herb bread out of the oven,' Alice said. 'Justin, pour the wine. I don't mean to rush you into eating but a storm's been forecast for this afternoon and I'm worried it might spoil everything. We haven't seen the sun for some time and I wanted to take advantage of it whilst it was there.'

She hurried off, leaving Rachel to openly admire the rest of the huge back yard with its large tract of lawn and neat garden beds along the side and back fences.

'You were lucky to have such a lovely big back yard when you were growing up,' she commented. 'My parents were inner-city apartment people. Career people, too. Frankly, I often felt like the odd man out. I wasn't surprised when they sent me to boarding-school. I was often in their way. Of course, I was upset when they were killed, but it wasn't till I lived with Lettie that I knew the kind of love and attention that a child cherishes. She wanted me. She really did. She was always there when I needed her. I never felt that with my parents. So it was impossible to let her down when she needed me.'

A wave of sadness hit her as she thought of Lettie and the cruel illness that had taken her. She didn't realise Justin was there till he took her into his arms. 'You are the kind of person who would never let any person down,' he said softly. 'A very special person. I am so lucky to have found you, Rachel.' He tipped up her chin and kissed her so tenderly that it brought a lump to her throat.

Was this the kiss of love? Could her heart's desire be coming true this quickly?

Alice clearing her throat had them pulling apart, but Rachel didn't feel at all embarrassed. She was too happy for that. Alice looked happy too. Perhaps she was also hoping for what Rachel was hoping for.

Rachel didn't have the opportunity to find out till after lunch was finished. With Justin retreating to the family room to watch the final round of a golf tournament on TV, Alice was able to draw Rachel into the living room on the pretext of showing her the famous teapot collection. But the conversation soon turned from pottery to personal matters.

'Has he told you about Mandy yet?' she asked quietly.

'He won't speak about her at all. Or his marriage.'

'Typical. His father was like that. Would never speak of emotional matters or past hurts. So, do you really love my son, Rachel? Or is this just an affair of convenience?'

'I love him with all my heart,' Rachel confessed. 'But I daren't tell him that. He told me right at the start he didn't want my love. Just my companionship.'

'Oh, is that what prudes are calling sex these days?' Alice said with a dry laugh. 'Companionship.'

Rachel just smiled. 'I don't dare ask him about Mandy, either. Although I do know who she left him for. It was Carl Toombs. But I don't know why. I can only guess.'

'I see. Well, if he won't tell you what happened then I will,' Alice pronounced firmly. 'That cruel bitch.

There is no other word for her! She told my son that the reason she was leaving him for another man was because he was no longer physically attractive to her. Just because he'd put on a few pounds. At that time he was a dealer, working crippling hours. And slaving away on his own private projects with every spare minute, just to give her the best of everything. When he combined a sedentary job with take-away food and no energy to exercise then of course Justin put on some weight. But he was far from fat. Still, that's what she called him the day she dumped him. Fat and flabby. And boring to boot. She also complained about their sex life, but what time did he have for fun and games when he was beating himself to death making himself rich enough for her? Not that Justin could ever have been rich enough for her, not compared to Carl Toombs. She wanted to justify her appalling behaviour and to do that she sacrificed my son's self-esteem. It was wicked what she did to him that day. Wicked.'

'Poor Justin,' Rachel murmured.

'He was shattered afterwards for a long, long time. His only refuge was in work and exercise. God knows the hell he's been through as a man, emotionally and mentally. I can't tell you how happy I am that he's finally met a decent girl like you, a girl who can truly appreciate the fine man he is. You *do* really love him, don't you?'

'Alice, I'm crazy about him. As for Mandy, she had to be stupid not to appreciate what she had.'

'That's the strange thing. I honestly thought she did. She seemed to love Justin when she married him. And she always said she'd have a baby as soon as they were financially secure. Frankly, when she did what she did I was almost as shocked as Justin. She didn't seem that sort of girl. Of course, she *is* the sort men always made a play for.'

'She's really that beautiful?' Rachel asked, her heart twisting with jealousy.

'I have to admit she's stunning to look at. And she has a captivating manner as well. A real charmer, no doubt about that. I'm not surprised that the likes of Carl Toombs went after her. What did surprise me was that he succeeded in getting her. I honestly thought she loved my son. Obviously, she had us both fooled. Maybe she was always a little gold-digger at heart. Though, to give her some credit, she didn't take a cent from Justin when she left him. Guilty conscience, probably. Though I dare say she was already getting enough money out of her wealthy lover. Mistresses of men like that don't want for anything. Still, if she thought he was going to leave his wife and marry her then she's been sorely mistaken.

'But Justin will marry you,' Alice added, and Rachel's heart jumped.

'Why do you say that?'

'Because he'd be crazy not to. And my son is not crazy. You wait and see. I suppose you haven't told him you love him.'

'No way. Why? Do you think I should?'

'Not yet. Men like to think love and marriage are their idea entirely. It's a male-ego thing. And, speaking of male ego, I think we should rejoin said male ego before it begins to feel neglected.'

Both women were chuckling away when they entered the family room, only to be shushed into silence by said male ego watching male stuff. They looked at each other and pulled appropriate faces, then withdrew to the kitchen to make afternoon tea and exchange the exasperated view that they didn't know why women bothered falling in love with any man in the first place!

CHAPTER SEVENTEEN

RACHEL insisted Justin drop her off home after the luncheon at his mother's. Without his coming in.

'I have washing to do,' she told him. 'And a host of other little jobs to organise myself for the coming week. I'm sure you do, too,' she added firmly when he looked as though he was going to argue.

He sighed, then went.

The following morning Rachel was so glad she'd taken that stand. Glad she was alone and travelling on the train to work. Very glad she'd got a seat and she could read the front-page story in the daily newspaper privately.

TOOMBS FLEES AUSTRALIA, the headlines screamed. TYCOON IN INVESTMENT SCANDAL.

The details were a bit sketchy, but it seemed Carl Toombs had finally done what many people had forecast for him. He'd gone bust, and taken a lot of creditors and investors with him. The journalist writing the article implied it was only his company that had gone belly-up. On a personal basis, Toombs himself was probably still as rich as Croesus. Being a conscience-less but clever crook, he would have siphoned money off into Swiss bank accounts, or other anonymous off-shore establishments, before doing a flit at the weekend, minus his family.

There were photos of his wife and children at the gate of his harbourside mansion, plus the classic comment from the wife saying she knew nothing about her husband's business dealings, and had no idea where he was. She claimed to be as devastated as his employees and business colleagues, who'd all been left high and dry without their entitlements etc etc etc.

Did that include his PA-cum-mistress? Rachel wondered. Or had she vanished with the disgraced tycoon?

Only time would tell, she supposed. But how would Justin react to this news? Rachel couldn't even guess. This was one area where she still didn't have all the answers, despite what Alice had told her the previous day. The subject of Mandy was *verboten* with Justin.

Rachel arrived at work in a state of nervous anticipation over Justin's mood. No use hoping he wouldn't have seen the headlines and read the story. He worked out every morning with people who lived and breathed such news. It would be the main topic of conversation in AWI's gym this morning. It would be the main topic for discussion in just about every office and household in Sydney that day. But not hers. She didn't dare bring the matter up.

Or did she? It wouldn't be normal not to mention it. Oh, she didn't know what to do for the best!

Justin was already in his office when she arrived, with his door firmly shut. She dumped the paper on top of her desk in full view, then set about making his usual mug of coffee, determined to act naturally. When it was ready she tapped briefly on the door then breezed right in, as was her habit these days.

Justin was sitting at his desk with his nose buried in the morning paper.

'So what do you think of Carl Toombs going broke like that?' she remarked casually as she put his coffee down. 'I was reading about it on the train on the way in. The papers are full of little else.'

When he glanced up at her, he didn't look too distressed. Just a bit distracted.

Rachel's agitation lessened slightly.

'Couldn't have happened to a nicer bloke,' came his caustic comment.

'I guess he's not really broke, though,' Rachel remarked. 'People like that never are.'

'Maybe not, but the media will hound him, wherever he goes. He won't have a happy life.'

'I pity the people who worked for him,' Rachel went on, and watched his eyes.

They definitely grew harder. And colder.

'People who work for men like Toombs are tarred with the same brush. If you lie down with dogs, don't complain when you get up with fleas.'

Rachel was shocked by the icy bitterness in his voice. Shocked and dismayed. He wasn't over Mandy at all. Not one little bit.

Her phone ringing gave her a good excuse to flee his office before she said something she would later regret. She was quite glad to close the door that separated them.

It was Alice, who'd seen the news about Toombs on a morning television programme.

'There was no mention of Mandy,' she said.

'No,' Rachel agreed.

'She always did keep a very low profile. How's Justin?'

'Hard to say.' Rachel didn't want to get into the habit of gossiping about Justin to his mother. 'Would you like me to put you through to him?'

'Lord, no. No, I was just wondering. I also wanted to say again how lovely you looked yesterday, Rachel.'

'Thank you, Alice. And let me say that was one fan-

tastic spread you put on. You're sure you weren't trying to fatten me up?' she joked just as the door from
the corridor opened and the most striking woman
Rachel had ever seen walked in. She looked like something you saw in the pages of the glossies. Long blonde
hair. Even longer legs. Enormous blue eyes. Pouting
mouth. A body straight out of an X-rated magazine.

'Er—Alice,' Rachel went on, trying not to sound as
sick as she was suddenly feeling. 'I...I have to go.
Someone's just come in...'

Not just *some*one, of course. *The* one. The cruel
bitch. The cruel but incredibly beautiful bitch.

'Can I help you?' Rachel asked frostily as hatred
warred with fear. It was no wonder Justin hadn't got
over her. Who could ever compare with this golden
goddess? She was the stuff men's dreams were made
of.

Admittedly, she was wearing a tad too much make-
up for day wear, especially around her eyes, and she
was dressed rather provocatively, if expensively. Her
camel suit had to be made of the finest leather—since
it didn't wrinkle—but it was skin-tight, with a short,
short skirt and a vest top with cut-in arm-holes and a
deep V-neckline. Her gold jewellery looked real,
though, again, there was a bit too much of it for
Rachel's taste. Several chain necklaces, one of which
was lost in her impressive cleavage. Dangling earrings.
A couple of bracelets on each wrist. Even an anklet,
which drew Rachel's gaze down to the matching
camel-coloured shoes, along with their five-inch heels.

She looked like a very expensive mistress. Or an
equally expensive call-girl.

'I was told this was Justin McCarthy's office,' she
said in a voice which would be an instant drawcard on

one of those sex phone lines. Low and husky and chock-full of erotic promise. 'Is that right?'

'Yes. And you are…?'

'I'm Mandy McCarthy, Justin's ex-wife,' she informed Rachel without a hint of hesitation. 'And you must be Justin's new PA,' she added with a strange little smile.

Rachel stiffened. 'That's right.'

'I see,' she said. 'Yes, I see. Is Justin in here?' she added, going straight over to Justin's door and winding her long bronze-tipped fingers around the knob.

Rachel was on her feet in a flash. 'You can't just walk in there.'

'You're wrong, sweetie,' the blonde countered, her smile turning wry. 'I can. And I'm going to. Please don't make a scene. I need to speak to Justin alone and I don't have much time.'

'If you say anything to hurt him,' Rachel ground out through clenched teeth, 'anything at all…I'll kill you.'

She laughed. 'You know, I do believe you would. Lucky Justin.' And then she turned the knob and went right in.

Rachel sank back down into her chair, ashen-faced and shaking.

Justin couldn't have been more shocked when the door opened and Mandy came in.

'What the—?' he muttered, automatically rising to his feet.

'Sorry to drop in like this, Justin,' she purred, shutting the door behind her. 'I don't think your girlfriend outside is too happy about it, but that can't be helped. You can tell her after I've gone that I'm no threat to your relationship.'

'Relationship?' Justin repeated, his head reeling.

'Don't bother denying it. Charlotte told me all about you two.'

It took Justin a couple of seconds to recall who Charlotte was.

'I have no intention of denying it,' he said coolly enough, pleased that he'd managed to find some composure.

'She looks very nice,' Mandy remarked and started to sashay across the room towards his desk. 'Much nicer than me.'

Justin couldn't take his eyes off her, the way she was walking, the way she looked. This wasn't the woman he remembered. Mandy had never dressed like this, or walked like that. Why, she looked like a tart! An expensive tart, admittedly. But still a tart.

'I won't take up too much of your time,' she went on in a voice he didn't recognise either. It was all raspy and breathy. 'I have to leave for the airport shortly. I'm joining Carl overseas. Don't ask me where and don't look so surprised. You must have read the paper this morning, and you must have guessed I'd go with him. Mind if I sit down? These high heels are hell. But Carl likes me to wear them. He says they're a turn-on.'

She pulled up a chair and sat down, her skirt so tight she had difficulty crossing her legs. When she did, he had a better view than a gynaecologist. Thankfully, she was wearing panties, though he didn't look long enough to check what type.

Justin sank back down into his chair, stunned. She was misinterpreting his surprise but it didn't matter now. What mattered was that he wasn't feeling what he always thought he'd feel if he crossed Mandy's path again. There was no pain. No hurt. Hell, he couldn't even dredge up any hate! When he looked at this...stranger...sitting across from him, she bore no resemblance to the woman he'd loved. She'd once been a truly beautiful person, both inside and out. Now she was exactly what she looked like: a woman for hire. Cheap, yet expensive. All he felt was confusion, and curiosity.

What did she see in Carl Toombs that she would do this to herself for him?

'Why, Mandy?' he asked. 'That's all I want to know. Why?'

'Why? I would have thought that was obvious, darling. I love the man. It's as simple as that.'

'I don't find that thought simple. One minute you were in love with me and then you were in love with him? What was it about Toombs that you fell in love with? From all accounts, he's an out-and-out bastard.'

She looked uncomfortable for a second. Then defiant. 'He's not all bad. You don't know him the way I do. Sure, he doesn't always play life by the rules, but he's the most exciting man I've ever known. I...I can't live without him, Justin. I'll go wherever he wants me to go; be whatever he wants me to be; do whatever he wants me to do.'

Justin was appalled. The woman was obsessed. But it wasn't a healthy obsession. It was dark, and dangerous, and self-destructive. The wonderful girl he'd loved, and married, was gone forever.

'What exactly are you doing here, Mandy?' he asked, feeling nothing but sadness for her. 'I don't understand...'

'I came here to apologise. In person. The things I said to you the day I left you. I didn't mean them. Any of them. I was just trying to make you hate me as much as I hated myself that day. You'd done nothing wrong and, despite everything, I still cared for you very much. But I...I just *had* to be with Carl.' Tears suddenly welled up in her eyes but she dashed them away. 'Silly me. Crying over spilt milk. What's the point? I am what I am now and nothing will change that.'

'And what are you now?' he asked, still having difficulty taking in the change in her.

Her eyes locked onto his and they were nothing like the eyes he remembered. These eyes had seen too much. Done too much.

Her laugh made his skin crawl. 'I'd show you if I had time, and if your lady friend out there wouldn't have to go to jail for murder.'

'What are you talking about?'

'When I came in just now she told me if I said anything to hurt you again she'd kill me.'

'Rachel said that?'

'That surprises you?'

'Did you tell her who you are?'

'Yes. But she already knew. I could see it in her face. I had the feeling she knew quite a lot about me. *You* didn't tell her?'

'No.'

'Well, she knows everything,' Mandy insisted. 'Trust me on this.'

His mother, he realised with a groan. Yesterday. Or possibly earlier. He shook his head in amazement. 'She never said a word.'

'Women in love will do anything not to upset their man.'

Justin stared at her. Was she right? Did Rachel love him? Dear God, he hoped so.

'Did I tell you how fantastic you're looking, Justin?

How handsome? How sexy? I'm a fool. I know I'm a
fool. But my fate is sealed, my darling. Just remember...I loved you once.' She uncrossed her legs and
stood up abruptly. 'Marry your Rachel, Justin. Marry
her and have children and be happy. I must go,' she
added when her eyes filled again. 'I have a plane to
catch.'

She was gone as quickly as she'd come, leaving
Justin sitting there, staring after an empty doorway.
When Rachel filled that doorway he blinked, then saw
how worried she was looking.

'It's all right,' he said reassuringly. 'She's gone. For
good.'

'But is she really gone for good, Justin?'

He rose, realising that was why Mandy had come.
To set him free; free to love again. She'd taken time
out from her not-so-good life to do a really good thing.

'Yes,' he said. 'Yes, she's really gone. For good.'

By the time he reached Rachel, she was crying. His
heart turned over as he realised she had loved him all
along. He drew her into his arms and held her close.

'We're going to get married, Rachel,' he whispered
against her hair. 'We're going to work together, buy a
home together and have children together. Oh, and one
more thing. I love you, Rachel. More than I have ever
loved before. Much, much more.'

Two months later, Carl Toombs' yacht was lost in a
hurricane near the Bahamas. All on board perished.

Ten months later Justin and Rachel were married, with
Rafe as best man and Isabel as matron of honour. Alice
minded Isabel's newborn daughter during the ceremony and the baby didn't make a peep. Alice was duly

voted by the wedding party as chief babysitter for all their future children and ordered never to sell her large home with its large back yard.

She didn't. And Alice's home was regularly filled with love and laughter for many years to come.

BEDDED BY
THE BOSS

MIRANDA LEE

CHAPTER ONE

'SO WHAT would *you* like in your Christmas stocking, Jessie? I'm going present shopping tomorrow. There's only just over two weeks till Christmas and I hate leaving things to the last moment.'

Jessie stopped applying her mascara for a second to smile wryly across the kitchen table at her elderly friend—and landlady.

'Do you know a shop which sells men?' she asked with a mischievous sparkle in her dark brown eyes.

Dora's own eyes widened. '*Men?* You told me just ten minutes ago that you thought most men were sleazebags and you were better off without one in your life.'

Jessie shrugged. 'That was ten minutes ago. Getting myself dolled up like this tonight reminded me of when I was young and carefree and didn't know the truth about the opposite sex. What I wouldn't give to be that girl again, just for one night, going out with some gorgeous guy on a hot date.'

'And if that fantasy came true,' Dora asked, still with a sceptical expression on her face, 'where would this gorgeous guy be taking you?'

'Oh, somewhere really swish for drinks and dinner, then on to a nightclub for some dirty dancing.' *After which he'd whip me back to his bachelor pad and...*

5

This last thought startled Jessie. In all honesty, ever since she'd had Emily, she hadn't missed men one bit. Hadn't felt like being with one at all.

Now, suddenly, the thought of having some gorgeous guy's arms around her again was quite pleasurable. *More* than pleasurable, actually. Almost a necessity.

Her female hormones, it seemed, had finally been jump-started again.

Her sigh carried a measure of frustration. And irritation. It was something she could do without. Men complicated things. They always did.

Useless creatures, all of them.

Except in that one department!

Now that her hormones were hopping again, she had to admit there was nothing to compare with the pleasure of being with a man who was a good lover.

Emily's father had been pretty good in bed. But he'd also been a feckless, reckless fool whose wildly adventurous spirit had finally been the death of him, snowboarding his stupid way off a mountain and into a crevasse even before Jessie had discovered she was having his baby.

Jessie had finally come to realise at the wise old age of twenty-eight that the members of the opposite sex who were good in bed were rarely good at commitment. Usually, they were charming scoundrels. She suspected that even if Lyall had lived, he would not have stuck by her and his baby.

No, she was better off without men in her life, in any capacity. For now, anyway. Emily was still only four and very impressionable. The last thing she needed was for her mummy to start dating guys who were only interested in one thing. There was no future in that. And no happiness.

Men could indulge in no-strings sex without suffering any lasting emotional damage. Women, not so easily.

Jessie had taken a long time to get over Lyall, both his death and the discovery she'd made afterwards that she hadn't been the only girl in his life.

'What I really want for Christmas more than anything,' she said firmly as she packed her make-up essentials into her black evening bag, 'is a decent job in an advertising agency.'

Jessie had worked as a graphic artist before she'd fallen pregnant, with an eye to eventually being promoted to the position of creative designer. She hadn't wanted to spend the rest of her life bringing other people's ideas to life; or having them take the credit when she improved on their designs. Jessie knew she had considerable creative talent and dreamt of heading her own advertising team one day; being up close and personal when the presentations were made; getting the accolades herself—plus the bonuses—when she secured a prestigious account for Jackson & Phelps.

That was the advertising agency she'd worked for back then. One of Sydney's biggest and best.

Having Emily, however, had rearranged her priorities in life. She *had* planned on going back to Jackson & Phelps after her maternity leave was up. But when the time came, she'd found she didn't want to put her baby daughter into day-care. She wanted to stay home and take care of Emily herself.

She'd thought she could work from home, free-lance. She had her own computer and all the right software. But a downturn in the economy had meant that advertising budgets were cut and lots of graphic artists were out of work. Freelance work became a pipedream.

Jessie had been forced to temporarily receive state benefits, and to move from the trendy little flat she'd been renting. Luckily, she found accommodation with Dora, a very nice lady with a very nice home in Roseville, a leafy northern Sydney suburb on the train line.

Dora had had a granny flat built on the back when her mother—now deceased—had come to live with her. It was only one-bedroomed, but it had its own bathroom and a spacious kitchen-cum-living room which opened out into the large and secure back yard. Just the thing for a single mum with an active toddler. Emily had turned one by then and was already walking.

The rent Dora charged Jessie was also very reasonable, in exchange for which Jessie helped Dora with the heavy housework and the garden.

But money was still tight. There was never much left over each fortnight. Treats were a rarity. Presents were always cheap little things, both on birthdays and at Christmas. Last Christmas hadn't been a big problem. Emily hadn't been old enough at three to understand that all her gifts had come from a bargain-basement store.

But Jessie had realised at the time that by this coming Christmas, Emily would be far more knowing.

As much as Jessie had enjoyed being a full-time mother at home, the necessities of life demanded that she get off welfare and go back to work. So last January, Jessie had enrolled Emily in a nearby daycare centre and started looking for a job.

Unfortunately, not with great success in her chosen field.

Despite her having her name down at several employment agencies and going for countless interviews, no one in advertising, it seemed, wanted to hire a graphic artist who was a single mum and who had been out of the workforce for over three years.

For a while, earlier this year, she'd done a simply awful—though lucrative—job, working for a private investigator. The ad in the paper had said it was for the position of receptionist. No experience required, just good presentation and a nice phone voice. When she'd got there, she was told the receptionist job had been taken, and she was offered investigative work instead.

Basically, she was sent out as a decoy to entrap men who were suspected by their partners of being unfaithful. She'd be given the time and place—always a pub or a bar—plus a short biography and photo of the target. Her job had required her to dress sexily, make contact, then flirt enough for the target to show his true colours. Once she'd gathered sufficient evidence via the sleek, hi-tech mobile phone which the PI supplied—its video recording was excellent—Jessie would use the excuse of going to the powder room, then disappear.

It had only taken Jessie half a dozen such encounters before she quit. Maybe if, just once, one target had resisted her charms and shown himself to be an honourable man, she might have continued. But no! Each time, the sleazebag—and brother, they were all sleazebags!—wasted no time in not only chatting her up but also propositioning her in no uncertain terms. Each time she'd dashed for the ladies', feeling decidedly dirty.

After that low-life experience, she'd happily taken a waitressing job at a local restaurant. Because of Emily, however, Jessie refused to work at night or at the weekends, when the tips might have been better, so her take-home pay wasn't great. On top of that, her expenses had gone up. Even with her government subsidy for being a single parent, having Emily in day-care five days a week was not cheap.

The only bonus was that Emily adored going to her pre-school. Jessie sometimes felt jealous over how much her daughter loved the teachers there, and the other kids. She'd grown up so much during this past year.

Too much.

She was now four, going on fourteen.

Last weekend, she'd begun asking questions about her father. And had not been impressed when her mother tried to skirt around the subject. A flustered Jessie had been pinned down and forced to tell Emily the truth. That her daddy had died in a tragic accident before she was born. And no, her mummy and her daddy had not been married at the time.

'So you and Daddy aren't divorced,' she'd stunned Jessie by saying. 'He's not ever coming back, like Joel's daddy came back.'

Joel was Emily's best friend at pre-school.

'No, Emily,' Jessie had told her daughter in what she'd hoped was the right sombre and sympathetic tone. 'Your daddy is never coming back. He's in heaven.'

'Oh,' Emily had said, and promptly went off, frowning.

Jessie had found her in a corner of the back yard, having a serious conversation with her life-sized baby doll—the one Dora had given her for her fourth birthday in August. Emily had fallen ominously silent when her mother approached. Jessie had been very relieved when her daughter had finally looked up, smiled brightly and asked her if they could go and see Santa at K-Mart that afternoon, because she had to tell him what she wanted for Christmas before it was too late.

Clearly, Emily was too young at four to be devastated by the discovery that the father she had never known was in heaven.

But Emily's reminder that Christmas was coming up fast—along with the fact that Jessie already knew the main present Emily wanted for Christmas—was what had brought Jessie to make the decision to do one more wretched job for Jack Keegan. The PI had said to give him a call if she ever needed some extra cash. Which she surely did, because a Felicity Fairy doll was the most expensive doll to hit the toy market in ages. Jessie would need all of the four-hundred-dollar fee she would earn tonight to buy the darned doll, along with all its accompaniments. There was a fairy palace, a magic horse and a sparkling wardrobe full of clothes.

Speaking of clothes…

Jessie stood up and smoothed down the short skirt of the black crêpe halter-necked dress she'd dragged out of her depleted wardrobe for tonight's job. It was the classiest, sexiest dress she owned, but it was six years old and Jessie feared it was beginning to look it.

'Are you sure this dress is OK?' she asked Dora in a fretful tone. 'It's getting awfully old.'

'It's fine,' Dora reassured. 'And not out of fashion at all. That style is timeless. You look gorgeous, Jessie. Very sexy. Like a model.'

'Who, me? Don't be ridiculous, Dora. I know I've got a good figure, but the rest of me is pretty ordinary. Without my make-up on, no man would give me a second glance. And my hair is an uncontrollable disaster if I don't drag it back or put it up.'

'You underestimate your attractiveness, Jessie.'

In every way, Dora thought to herself.

Jessie's figure wasn't just good, it was spectacular, the kind of body you often saw in underwear advertisements these days. Full breasts. Tiny waist. Slender hips and long legs. They looked even longer in the high, strappy shoes Jessie was wearing tonight.

It was true that her face wasn't traditionally pretty. Her mouth was too wide, her jaw too square and her nose slightly too long. But anchored on either side of that nose were widely set, exotically shaped dark brown eyes which flashed and smouldered with sensual promise, the kind of eyes that drew men like magnets.

As for her hair...Dora would have killed for hair like Jessie's when she'd been younger.

Blue-black, thick and naturally curly, when left down it cascaded around her face and shoulders in glorious disarray. Up, it defied restraint, with bits and pieces escaping, making her look even sexier, if that was possible.

Dora hadn't been surprised when that private detective had snapped Jessie up to do decoy work for him. She was the perfect weapon to entrap cheating husbands. And possibly non-cheating ones as well.

'Is this the guy?' Dora asked, picking up the photo that was resting in the middle of the table.

'Yep. That's him.'

'He's handsome.'

Jessie had thought so too. Far better looking than the other creeps she'd had to flirt with. And younger. In his thirties instead of forties or fifties. But she had no doubts about the type of man he was.

'Handsome is as handsome does, Dora. He's married with two little kids, yet he spends every Friday night at a bar in town, drinking till all hours of the night.'

'But lots of men drink on a Friday night.'

'I doubt he's just drinking. The particular city bar he frequents is a well-known pick-up joint,' Jessie pointed out drily.

'You could say that about any bar.'

'Look, the wife says this behaviour is out of character with her husband. She says he's changed towards her. She's convinced he's being unfaithful to her and wants to know the truth.'

'Doesn't sound like compelling evidence of adultery to me. She might wish she hadn't started this.'

'What do you mean?'

'You know, Jessie, I've never thought it was very fair on the men in question, sending a girl like you to flirt with them. This man might not have been unfaithful at all. Maybe he's just working very hard and having an extra drink or two at the end of the week to relax. Then you come along tonight and give him the eye, and he might do something he wouldn't normally do, something he might regret.'

Jessie had to laugh. Dora made her sound like some kind of siren. Irresistible she was not! Just ask all the male bosses who hadn't given her a job this past year.

No, poor Dora didn't know what she was talking about, especially regarding tonight's target. Still, Dora *was* sixty-six years old. In her day, maybe more men had more honour.

'Trust me, Dora. By the time wives go to see Jack Keegan and spend the kind of money he asks for, then there really isn't any doubt over their husbands' philandering. All they're looking for is proof to show the lawyers. Our Mr Curtis Marshall here,' she said, taking his photo out of Dora's hand and looking down into his baby-blue eyes, 'is not some poor, hard-working, misunderstood hubby. He's been playing out of his patch and he's about to get caught! Now I really must get going,' she said as she slid the photo in a zippered side-section of her bag. 'I'll just go check on Emily before I leave.'

Jessie tiptoed into the bedroom, where a sound-asleep Emily had kicked off her bedclothes. The evening was quite warm, so Jessie switched the over-head ceiling fan on to the slow setting, then pulled the top sheet up around Emily and tucked her in. Emily had not long given up her cot for a single bed and looked such a dot in the larger bed.

Pressing a kiss to her temple, Jessie straightened before just standing there and staring down at her daughter.

Her heart filled with love as it always did when she looked down upon her child.

That was what had surprised Jessie the most when she'd become a mother. The instant and totally un-conditional love which had consumed her from the moment she'd held her baby in her arms.

Had her own mother felt like that when she'd had her?

Jessie didn't think so. She suspected that any love her mother had had for her had been overshadowed by shame.

Jessie pushed this distressing thought aside and bent to stroke Emily's dark curls back from her fore-head before planting another gentle kiss on her daughter's cheek.

'Sleep tight, sweetie,' she whispered. 'Mummy won't be long.

'Thank you so much for staying here and minding

her, Dora,' Jessie said on returning to the combined kitchen and living room.

'My pleasure,' Dora said, already settled on the sofa in front of the television.

'You know where the tea and biscuits are.'

'I'll be fine. There's a good movie on tonight at eight-thirty. That's only ten minutes off. You'd better get going. And for Pete's sake, take a taxi home after you're finished. It's too dangerous on the train late at night, especially on a Friday night.'

'Hopefully, I won't be too late.'

Jessie didn't want to waste any of the travel expenses Jack had given her. She wanted to make as much profit out of this rotten evening as she could. Why waste thirty dollars on a cab?

'Jessie Denton,' Dora said sternly. 'You promise me you'll take a taxi home.'

Jessie gave her a narrow-eyed look from under her long lashes. 'I will if I need to, Dora.'

'You can be very stubborn, do you know that?'

Jessie grinned. 'Yep. But you love me just the same. Take care.' And, giving Dora a peck on the cheek, she swept up her bag and headed for the door.

CHAPTER TWO

KANE sat at the bar, nursing a double Scotch, and pondering the perversities of life.

He still could not believe what his brother had just told him: that he was miserable in his marriage and that he spent every Friday night drinking here at this bar instead of going home to his wife and children. Curtis even confessed to going into the office on the weekend sometimes to escape the tension and arguments at home.

Kane could not have been more shocked. There he'd been these past few years, envying Curtis for his choice of wife, his two gorgeous children and his seemingly perfect family!

The truth, it seemed, was a far cry from the fantasy world Kane had woven around his twin brother's home life. Apparently, Lisa was far from content with being a stay-at-home mum. She was bored and lonely for adult company during the day. On top of that, two-year-old Joshua had turned into a right terror this past year. Four-year-old Cathy threw tantrums all the time and wouldn't go to bed at night. Lisa could not cope and their sex life had been reduced to zero.

Curtis, who was never at his best at the art of communication, had started staying away from home more and more, and Lisa was now giving him the silent treatment.

He was terrified she was thinking of leaving him and taking the kids with her. Which had prompted his call of desperation to his brother tonight.

Kane, who'd been working late at the office, solving the problem of a defecting designer, had come running to the rescue—as he always did when his twin brother was hurt or threatened in any way. He'd been coming to Curtis's rescue since they were toddlers.

'I love my family and don't want to lose them,' Curtis had cried into his beer ten minutes earlier. 'Tell me what to do, Kane. You're the man with all the solutions. Tell me what to do!'

Kane had rolled his eyes at this. OK, he could understand why Curtis thought he could wave a magic wand and fix his problems with a few, well-chosen words. He *had* made a fortune teaching people how to be successful in getting what they wanted out of their working life. His motivational seminars drew huge crowds. His fee as an after-dinner speaker was outrageous. His best-selling book, *Winning At Work*, had been picked up in most countries overseas.

Earlier this year he'd gone on a whirlwind tour in the US to promote the book's release, and sales there had been stupendous.

His hectic schedule in America had drained him, however, both physically and emotionally, and since his return he'd cut back considerably on his speaking engagements. He'd been thinking of taking a long holiday when his friend Harry Wilde had asked him to look after his small but very successful advertising agency during December whilst he went on a cruise with his wife and kids.

Kane had jumped at the chance. A change was as good as a holiday. And he was really enjoying the challenge. It had been interesting to see if his theories could be applied to any management job. So far, so good.

Unfortunately, his strategies for success in the professional world didn't necessarily translate into success in one's personal life. His own, especially. With one failed marriage behind him and no new relationship in sight, he was possibly not the best man to give his brother marital advice.

But he knew one thing. You never solved any problem by sitting at a bar, downing one beer after another. You certainly never solved anything, running away from life.

Of course, that had always been Curtis's nature, to take the easiest course, to run away from trouble. He'd always been the shy twin. The less assertive twin. The one who needed protecting. Although just as intelligent, Curtis had never had Kane's confidence, or drive, or ambition. His choice to become an accountant had not surprised Kane.

Still, Kane understood that it could not have been easy being *his* twin brother. He knew he could be a hard act to follow, with his I-can-do-anything personality.

But it was high time Curtis stood up and faced life head-on, along with his responsibilities. He had a lovely wife and two great kids who were having a hard time for whatever reason and really needed him. Regardless of what a lot of those new relationship gurus touted, Kane believed a husband was supposed to be the head of his family. The rock. The person they could always count on.

Curtis was acting like a coward.

Not that Kane said that. Rule one in his advice to management executives was never to criticise or put down their staff or their colleagues. Praise and encouragement worked much better than pointing out an individual's shortcomings.

In light of that theory, Kane had delivered Curtis one of his best motivational lectures ever, telling his brother what a great bloke he was. A great brother, a great son, a great husband and a great father. He even threw in that Curtis was a great accountant. Didn't he do his brother's highly complicated tax return each year?

Kane reassured Curtis that his wife loved him and no way would she ever leave him.

Unless she thought he didn't love her back. Which Lisa *had* to be thinking, Kane reckoned.

At this point he sent his brother off home to tell his wife that he loved her to death and that he was sorry that he hadn't been there for her when she needed him. He was to vow passionately that he would be in future, and what could he do to help?

'And when Lisa falls, weeping, into your arms,' Kane had added, 'whip her into bed and make love to her as you obviously haven't made love to her in a long time!'

When Curtis still hesitated, Kane also promised to

drop over the next day to give his brother some moral support, and to provide some more proactive suggestions which would make his wife and kids a lot happier.

Hopefully, by then, he could think of some.

One divorce in their family was more than enough! Their parents would have a fit if Curtis and Lisa broke up as well.

Kane shook his head and swirled his drink, staring down into the pale amber depths and wondering just why he'd married Natalie in the first place. For a guy who was supposed to be smart, he'd been very dumb that time. Their marriage had been doomed from the start.

'Hi, honey.'

Kane's head whipped around to find a very good-looking blonde sliding seductively onto the bar stool next to him. Everything she had—and there was plenty of it—was on display. For a split-second, Kane felt his male hormones rumble a bit. Till he looked into her eyes.

They were pretty enough, but empty. Kane could never stay interested in women with empty eyes.

Natalie had had intelligent eyes.

Pity she hadn't wanted children.

'You look as if you could do with some company,' the blonde added before curling her finger at the barman and ordering herself a glass of champagne.

'Bad week?' she directed back at Kane.

'Nope. Good week. Not so great an evening,' he replied, still thinking of his brother's problems.

'Loneliness is lousy,' she said.

'I'm not lonely,' he refuted. 'Just alone.'

'Not any more.'

'Maybe I want to be alone.'

'No one *wants* to be alone, lover.'

The blonde's words struck home. She was right. No one did. Him included. But divorce—even an amicable one—made a man wary. It had been fifteen months since he'd separated from Natalie, three months since their divorce had become final. And he still hadn't found anyone new. He hadn't even succumbed to the many offers he'd had for one-night stands.

Women were always letting him know they were available for the night, or a weekend, or whatever. But he just wasn't interested in that kind of encounter any more. He'd been hoping to find what he thought Curtis had. A woman who wasn't wrapped up in her career. A woman who was happy to put her job aside for a few years at least to become a career wife, and mother.

Now he wasn't so sure if that creature existed. The sort of women he found attractive were invariably involved with their jobs. They were smart, sassy, sexy girls who worked hard and played hard. They didn't want to become housewives and mothers.

'Come on, lighten up a bit,' the blonde said. 'Get yourself another drink, for pity's sake. That one's history.'

Kane knew he probably shouldn't. He hadn't had anything to eat tonight and the whisky was going straight to his head. He wasn't interested in the blonde, but neither did he want to go home to an empty house. He'd have one more drink with her, then make his excuses and go find a place in town to eat.

CHAPTER THREE

THE bar Curtis Marshall frequented every Friday night was called the Cellar, so Jessie shouldn't have been surprised to find that it was downstairs from street level. Narrow, steep stairs. Stairs which made her walk oh, so carefully in her four-inch-high heels. The last thing she wanted was to fall flat on her face.

The music reached her ears only seconds before the smoke.

Jazz.

Not Jessie's favourite form of music. But what did it matter? She wasn't there to enjoy herself. She was there to do a job.

The bouncer standing by the open door gave her the once-over as she slowly negotiated the last few steps.

'Very nice,' he muttered as she walked past him.

She didn't answer. She straightened her shoulders and moved further into the smoke haze, her eyes slowly becoming accustomed to the dimmer lighting as they scanned the not-so-crowded room. Nine o'clock, she reasoned, was between times. Most of the Friday after-work drinkers had departed, and the serious weekend party animals had not yet arrived.

She'd never been to this particular bar before. She'd never heard of it. It was Jack who'd informed her that it had a reputation as a pick-up joint.

The décor was nineteen-twenties speak-easy style, with lots of wood and leather and brass. Booths lined the walls, with tables and chairs filling every other available space. The band occupied one corner, with a very small dance floor in front of it.

The bar itself was against the far wall, semicircular in shape, graced by a dozen or so wooden-based, leather-topped stools. A long mirror ran along the back behind the bottle shelves, which gave Jessie reflected glimpses of the faces of people sitting at the bar.

There were only half a dozen.

She recognised her target straight away. He was sitting in the middle, with a blonde sitting next to him on his left. There were several vacant stools to his right. As Jessie stood there, watching them, she saw the blonde lean over and say something to him. He motioned to the barman, who came over, temporarily blocking Jessie's view of the target's face in the mirror.

Had the blonde asked him to buy her a drink? Was he right at this moment doing exactly what his wife suspected him of?

Jessie realised with a rush of relief that maybe she wouldn't have to flirt with the creep after all. If she got over there right now, she could collect evidence of his chatting up some other woman without having to belittle herself.

Jessie's heart pounded as she headed for the bar, nerves cramping her stomach. She still hated doing this, even second-hand.

Think of the money, she told herself as she slid up

on the vacant stool two to the right of the target. *Think of Emily's beautiful, beaming face on Christmas morning when she finds that Santa has brought her exactly what she asked for.*

The self-lecture helped a little. Some composure returned by the time Jessie placed her bag down on the polished wooden bar-top. Very casually she extracted the mobile phone, pretended to check her text messages, turned on the video then put it down in a position which would catch what was going on to her left, both visually and verbally.

'Thanks,' the blonde purred when the barman put a glass of champagne in front of her. 'So what will we drink to, handsome?'

When the barman moved away, Jessie was able to watch the target's face again in the mirror behind the bar.

There was no doubt he *was* handsome, more handsome than in his photograph. More mature-looking, too. Maybe that photo in her bag was a couple of years old, because his hair was different as well. Not different in colour. It was still a mid-brown. But in place of the longer waves and lock flopping across his forehead was a short-back-and-sides look, with spikes on top.

The style brought his blue eyes more into focus.

That was another thing that looked different. His eyes. In the photo they'd seemed a baby-blue, with a dreamy expression. In reality, his eyes were an icy blue. And not soft at all.

They glittered as he smiled wryly and swirled the

remains of his drink. He hadn't noticed her arrival as yet.

'To marriage,' he said, and lifted his glass in a toast.

'*Marriage!*' the blonde scorned. 'That's one seriously out-of-date institution. I'd rather drink to divorce.'

'Divorce is a blight on our society,' he said sharply. 'I won't drink to divorce.'

'Sex, then. Let's drink to sex.' And she slid her glass against his in a very suggestive fashion.

Jessie, who'd stayed surreptitiously watching him in the mirror behind the bar, saw his head turn slowly towards the blonde, a drily amused expression on his face.

'Sweetheart, I think you've picked the wrong guy to share a drink with. I'm sorry if I've given you the wrong impression, but I'm not in the market for what you're looking for tonight.'

Jessie almost fell off her stool. What was this? A man with some honour? Had Dora been right about Mr Marshall after all?

'You sure?' the blonde persisted with a sultry smile playing on her red-painted mouth.

'Positive.'

'Your loss, lover,' she said and, taking her glass of champagne, slid off her stool and sashayed over to sit at a table close to the band. She wasn't by herself for more than ten seconds, before a guy who'd been sitting further down the bar had taken *his* beer with him to join her.

Jessie glanced back into the mirror to find that her

target had finally noticed her presence, and was staring at her. When their eyes connected in the glass
her heart reacted in a way which it hadn't in years.
It actually jumped, then fluttered, then flipped right
over.

Her eyes remained locked with his for longer than
was wise, her brain screaming at her to look away,
but her body took absolutely no notice.

Suddenly a man plonked himself down on the vacant stool that separated them, snapping her back to
reality.

'Haven't seen you in here before, gorgeous,' the
interloper said in slurred tones, his beery breath wafting over her. 'Can I buy you a drink?'

He was about forty, a very short, very drunk weasel of a man in a cheap, ill-fitting business suit that
bore no resemblance to the magnificently tailored
Italian number the target was wearing.

'No, thanks,' Jessie said stiffly. 'I like to buy my
own drinks.'

'One of them feminists, eh? That's all right by me.
Cheaper this way.'

'I also like to drink alone,' she added sharply.

The drunk laughed. 'A sexy piece like you
shouldn't be doing anything alone. What's the matter, honey? Last guy do you wrong? Or ain't I young
enough for you? Trust me. I've still got it where it
counts. Here, let me show you…'

He was actually fumbling with his fly when two
big hands grabbed him and literally lifted him off the
stool.

'Let *me* show *you* something, buster,' the target said. 'The door!'

Jessie watched, open-mouthed, as her unexpected knight in shining armour carried the drunk over to where the bouncer was frowning at them both. Words were exchanged after which the bouncer escorted the weasel up the stairs personally whilst Jessie's champion headed back for the bar.

She found herself admiring more than his handsome face this time.

There was the way his broad shoulders filled out his expensive suit. The way he'd just handled the situation. And the way he was smiling at her.

That smile was pure dynamite. As well as something else that wasn't at all pure.

Suddenly, Jessie was catapulted back to earlier that evening when she'd been thinking about how pleasurable it would be to be in some gorgeous man's arms.

She started thinking about how pleasurable it would be to be in *this* man's arms. He was definitely gorgeous.

But he was also married. And sitting back down, she realised breathlessly, *not* on his old stool but the one right next to hers, the one the drunk had occupied.

Dora's words came back to haunt her, the ones that she'd said about how it wasn't fair to send someone like her to flirt; that she might tempt her target tonight to do something he might regret.

But logic argued against this concern. That blonde

had been very attractive. If he was going to be tempted, then why hadn't *she* tempted him?

Maybe he doesn't go for blondes, came back another voice, just as logical. Maybe he likes leggy women with wild black hair. Maybe he likes women who aren't quite so obvious.

There were many reasons why men were attracted to one woman over another.

And he *was* attracted to her. She could see it in his eyes. And in that heart-stopping smile.

'Th...thank you,' she stammered.

'You can buy me another Scotch and soda in gratitude if you like,' he said, and downed what was left of his drink. 'Unless you really meant what you said about preferring to drink alone.' And he smiled at her again.

Jessie's heart ground to a shuddering halt.

Get out of here now, girl, her conscience warned. This guy is not just dynamite, he's downright dangerous!

'I was just trying to get rid of him,' she heard herself saying.

'I was hoping that might be the case. So what can I get you? After all, a gentleman doesn't really expect a lady to buy his drinks for him.'

Jessie swallowed. What are you doing, girl? Stop looking at him that way. Stop it right now!

I'm just doing my job, she tried telling herself. This is what I get paid for. Flirting with my target. Seeing what kind of man he is.

Yes, but you're not supposed to be enjoying it!

'Just a diet cola, thanks.'

His straight brows lifted in the middle. 'You come into a bar for a diet cola? Now, that's a strange thing to do. You can get one of those from a vending machine.'

'Maybe I came in looking for some company,' she said leadingly, and hoped like hell he'd put his foot in his mouth right away so she could get out of there.

'I can't imagine a girl like you would have to do that too often. You must have men asking you out all the time.'

Actually, she did. But no one she'd give the time of day to. The men who asked her out had her tagged as one of two types: waitressing slut or single-mother-and-desperate, depending on when and where they met her.

Either way, Jessie always knew exactly what they wanted from her, and it wasn't witty conversation.

She always said no to their invitations.

One-night stands held no appeal for her. Sex of any kind had held no appeal for her.

Till tonight…

'Give me another Scotch and soda,' the target directed to the barman. 'And get the lady a Bacardi and cola. *Diet* cola,' he added with a quick grin her way.

She swallowed. 'What if I don't like Bacardi and cola?'

'Come, now, you and I both know that the amount of Bacardi they put in drinks in places like this is barely detectable. All you'll taste is the cola.'

'True,' she agreed.

'So was that other chap right?' he went on whilst

the barman busied himself with their drinks. 'Did your last boyfriend do you wrong? Is that why you're all alone tonight?'

She shrugged. 'Something like that.'

'Aah. A woman of mystery and intrigue. I like that. It makes for a change.'

'A change from what?'

'From women who launch into their life story as soon as you meet them.'

'Does that happen to you often?'

'Too often.'

'Did the blonde over there do that?'

'Actually, no. But then, she had other things on her mind tonight. Looks as if she finally hit the jackpot.'

Jessie flicked a glance over at where the blonde was now leaving with the man who'd joined her earlier. It didn't take a genius to guess that they were going back to her place. Or his. Or maybe even a hotel. There were several within easy walking distance of this bar.

'Most men would have jumped at the chance,' she remarked.

'I'm not most men.'

'Yes. Yes, I can see that.'

Their drinks came, giving Jessie a breather from the tension that was gripping her chest. As cool as she was sounding on the outside, inside she was seriously rattled. She liked this man. *More* than liked. She found him fascinating. And sexy. Oh, so sexy.

'What about you?' she asked, deciding to deflect the conversation on to him, make him admit he was married. Anything to lessen her worry over where their conversation might lead.

'What about me?' he returned before taking a deep swallow of his drink.

'Did your last girlfriend do *you* wrong? Is that why *you're* alone here tonight?'

He drank some more whilst he gave her question some thought. Suspense built in Jessie till she wanted to scream at him to just confess the truth. That *he* was the one in the wrong here. Regardless of how stressed he might feel with life, he should be at home with his wife and kids. She'd heard him say that divorce was a blight on society. Did he want to find himself in the middle of one?

Finally, he looked up and slanted a smile over at her. 'You know what? I'm going to take a leaf out of your book. No talking about past relationships tonight. I think sometimes I talk way too much. Come on,' he pronounced and put his drink down. 'The music's changed to something decent. Let's dance.'

Jessie stiffened, then gulped down a huge mouthful of Bacardi and cola. 'Dance?' she choked out.

He was already off his stool, already holding out his hand towards her.

'Please don't say no,' he said softly. 'It's just a dance. Mind the lady's bag, will you?' he asked the barman. 'Better put your cellphone away as well. You don't want a natty little number like that to get swiped.'

She did hesitate, she was sure she did. But within moments she'd put the phone away and was placing

her hand in his and letting him lead her over to that
minute dance floor.

It *is* only dancing, she told herself as he pulled her
into his arms.

The trouble was, there was dancing...and dancing.

This was slow dancing. Sensual dancing. Sexy
dancing. Bodies pressed so close together that she
had no choice but to wind her arms up around his
neck. Her breasts lifted, rubbing against the well-
muscled wall of his chest. His hands moved rest-
lessly up and down her spine till one settled in the
small of her back, the other moving lower. The heat
in his palms burned through the thin material of her
dress, branding her. Her heartbeat quickened. The entire surface of her skin flushed with her own internal
heat. She felt light-headed. Excited. Aroused.

And she wasn't the only one. She could feel his
arousal as it rose between them.

When her fingertips tapped an agitated tattoo on
the nape of his neck, he stopped, pulled back slightly
and stared down into her eyes.

'Would you believe me if I told you that I haven't
done anything like this in a long, long time?' he murmured, his voice low and thick.

'Done what?' she replied shakily.

'Picked a girl up in a bar and within no time asked
her to go to a hotel with me?'

She stopped breathing. Stopped thinking. Her
world had tipped on its axis and she felt every ounce
of her self-control slipping. A voice was tempting her
to blindly say yes. Yes, to anything he wanted. She

had never in her life felt what she was feeling at this moment. Not even with Lyall.

This was something else, something far more powerful and infinitely more dangerous.

'Will you?' he said, and his smouldering gaze searched hers.

She didn't say a word. But her eyes must have told him something.

'No names,' he murmured. 'Not yet. Not till afterwards. I don't want to say anything that might spoil what we're sharing at this moment. Because I have never felt anything quite like it before. Tell me it's the same for you. Admit it. Say you want me as badly as I want you.'

She couldn't say it. But every fibre of her female body compelled her to cling to him, betraying her cravings with her body language.

'You do talk too much,' she whispered at last.

His lungs expelled a shuddering sigh. Of relief? Or was he trying to dispel some of the sexual tension that was gripping them both?

'Then you *will* come with me,' he said. 'Now. Straight away.'

They weren't questions, but orders.

He would be an incredible lover, she realised. Knowing. Dominating. Demanding. The kind she had used to fantasise about. And which she suddenly craved.

'I...I have to go to the ladies' first,' she blurted out, desperate to get away from him. Once some distance broke the spell he was casting over her, she would recover her sanity and escape.

'I suppose I could do with a visit to the gents' as well. I'll meet you back at the bar.'

She didn't meet him back at the bar. She spent less than twenty seconds in the ladies' before dashing back to the bar, collecting her bag from the barman and bolting for the exit. She ran all the way to Wynyard Station, where she jumped on the first train heading north.

It was only half an hour since she'd walked into that bar. But it felt like a lifetime.

CHAPTER FOUR

'THE phone's ringing, Mummy.' Emily tugged at Jessie's jeans. 'Mummy, are you listening to me? The phone's ringing.'

'What? Oh, yes. Thanks, sweetie.'

Jessie dropped the wet T-shirt she was holding back into the clothes basket and ran across the yard towards her back door.

Goodness knew who it would be. She'd already rung Jack first thing this morning to put in a verbal report about last night, petrified at the time that he'd know she was lying.

She'd made up her mind overnight to give Mr Marshall the benefit of the doubt and only tell Jack about the incident with the blonde, and not the conversation that had happened later. She'd already wiped that part off the video as well.

But no sooner had she told him that she'd witnessed the target turning down a proposition from an attractive blonde than Jack had stunned her by saying he wasn't surprised, that the wife herself had rung that morning in a panic to say that he could keep the money she'd already paid, but that she didn't want her husband followed any more. It had all been a mistake and a misunderstanding. He'd come home last night and explained everything and she was very happy.

At which point Jack had added smarmily that he could guess what had happened in the Marshall household last night.

'I can always tell,' he'd joked. 'The wives' voices have a certain sound about them. A combination of coyness and confidence. Our Mr Marshall really came good, I'd say. Like to have been a fly on their bedroom wall last night, I can tell you.'

That image had stayed with Jessie all morning— of her actually being a fly on that bedroom wall, watching whilst the man she'd danced with last night, the man who'd wanted her so desperately, was making love to his wife.

Jessie knew it was wicked of her to feel jealousy over a husband making love to his wife. Wicked to wish she'd been the one in his bed. Wicked, wicked, wicked!

But she couldn't seem to stop her thoughts, or her feelings. She'd hardly slept a wink all night.

Now, as she dashed inside to the strident sound of the phone, she could still see the desire in his eyes, hear the passion in his voice, feel the need of his body pressed up against hers.

Had he been telling the truth when he said this was a one-off experience? That he'd never done or felt anything like that before?

She was inclined to believe him. Possibly, he'd been more intoxicated than he looked. Or he'd been too long without sex. Silly to believe that there'd been something special between them, right from the first moment their eyes had connected.

That was the romantic in her talking. Men thought

differently to women, especially about sex. All she'd been to him was a potential one-night stand.

Maybe, after he discovered she'd done a flit, he'd been relieved. Maybe he'd rushed home in a fit of guilt and shame and genuinely made things up with his wife. Maybe he hadn't simply used the desire Jessie had engendered in him to make love to a woman he didn't feel excited by any more.

But why would he do that? For his children's sake?

Perhaps. Christmas was coming up soon. A family should be together at Christmas. He did hate divorce. She'd heard him say so. And he'd toasted marriage.

Clearly, his marriage mattered to him.

She had to stop thinking about him, Jessie decided as she snatched the receiver down off the kitchen wall. Whatever happened last night, it was over and done with. She would never see the man again. End of story. *Finis!*

'Yes,' she answered breathlessly into the phone.

'Jessie Denton?'

'Speaking.'

'It's Nicholas Hanks here, Jessie, from Adstaff.'

'Pardon? Who?' And then the penny dropped. 'Oh, yes, Adstaff. The employment agency. Sorry, it's been a while since I heard from you.'

'True, but, as I explained to you earlier this year, the market for graphic artists isn't very buoyant at the moment. Still, something came up yesterday and I thought of you immediately.'

'Really? Why me, especially?' Any initial jolt of excitement was tempered by her experiences in the past. Recruitment people were, by nature, optimists. You had to take what they said with a grain of salt sometimes.

'This particular advertising agency wants someone who can start straight away,' the recruiter rattled on. 'They don't want to interview anyone who's currently employed with another agency.'

Jessie's heart sank. There had to be dozens of unemployed graphic artists in Sydney. Once again, the odds of her securing this much-sought-after job was minimal.

'So which agency is it?' she asked, refusing to get her hopes up.

'Wild Ideas.'

'Oh!' Jessie groaned. 'I'd *love* to work for them.'

Her, and just about every other graphic artist in Sydney. Wild Ideas was only small compared to some advertising agencies. But it was innovative and very successful. Run by advertising pin-up boy Harry Wilde, it had a reputation for promoting any graphic artist with flair to the position of creative designer, rather than head-hunting them from other agencies.

'Yes, I thought you might,' came the drily amused reply. 'You have an interview there at ten o'clock Monday morning.'

'Gosh, that soon.' She'd have to ring the restaurant. Fortunately, Monday was their least busy day; if she rang early, they'd be able to call in one of the casuals, no trouble.

'Can you start straight away, if you have to?'

'Too right I can. But let's be honest…Nicholas, wasn't it…what are the odds of that happening?'

'Actually, you have an even-money chance. We sent over the CVs of several people on our books yesterday afternoon and they've already whittled them down to two. You're one of those two. Apparently, they're keen to fill this position, post-haste, and don't want to waste time interviewing all the would-bes if there are could-bes. I remember your portfolio very well, Jessie, so I know you have the talent required. And you interview very well. Frankly, I was very surprised you weren't snapped up for that art job I sent you along for earlier on in the year.'

Jessie sighed. 'I wasn't surprised. Regardless of what they say, some employers are dead against hiring a single mother. They don't say so straight out, but underneath they worry that you'll want time off when your kid's sick or something. I'm sure that's been part of my problem all along.'

'Jessie, your single-mother status is clearly stated on your résumé, which Wild Ideas has already seen. Yet they still specifically asked for you. Clearly, your being a single mum didn't deter them, did it? You do have your little girl in full-time care, don't you?'

'Yes. But…'

'But nothing. Your circumstances are no different from those of any other working mum, be they single or married. What will count with Wild Ideas is your creative talent, your professional attitude and your reliability. Impress them on those three levels and I feel confident that this job will be yours.'

Jessie had to struggle to control the stirrings of excitement. No way could she afford to get carried away with false optimism. She'd been there, done that, and at the end of the day was always bitterly disappointed.

'You talk as if I'm the only one going for this job,' she pointed out. 'There is another applicant, isn't there?'

'Er—yes,' came the rather reluctant reply.

'Well, presumably this person is just as well-qualified for this job as I am.'

'Mmm. Yes. And no.'

'Meaning what?'

'Look, it would be very unprofessional of me to say anything negative about the other applicant. She is a client of our agency as well.'

She. It was a woman.

'But let me give you a hint when it comes to what you wear for your interview. Nothing too bright or too way-out or too overtly sexy.'

Jessie was taken aback. 'But I never dress like that. You've met me. I'm a very conservative dresser.'

'Yes, but you might have thought that going for a job at Wild Ideas required you to present a certain...image. Trust me when I tell you that your chances of being employed there will be greatly enhanced if you dress very simply.'

'You mean, in a suit or something?'

'That might be overkill, under the circumstances. I would suggest something smart, but casual.'

'Would jeans be too casual? I have some really nice jeans. Not ones with frayed holes in them. They're dark blue and very smart. I could wear them with a white shirt and a jacket.'

'Sounds perfect.'

'And I'll put my hair up. Down, it can look a bit wild. What about make-up? Should I wear make-up?'

'Not too much.'

'Right.' Jessie speculated that the other applicant was possibly a flashy female, who tried to trade on her sex appeal. Not an uncommon event in the advertising world. Perhaps with Harry Wilde now being a married man instead of a playboy, he preferred to play it safe over who he hired these days. Maybe Nicholas was subtly advising her that the *femme fatale* type would not be looked upon favourably.

'Is there anything else I should know?' she asked.

'No. Just be your usual honest and open self and I'm sure everything will work out.'

'You've been very kind. Thank you.'

'My pleasure. I'm only sorry I haven't been able to find you a job sooner.'

'I haven't got *this* job yet.'

'You will.'

Jessie wished she could share his supreme confidence, but life had taught her not to count her chickens before they hatched.

'Have to go, Jessie. There's someone else on the line. Good luck on Monday.' And he hung up.

Jessie hung up as well, only then thinking of Emily still out in the back yard all by herself.

Her heart started thudding as a mother's heart always did when she realised she'd taken her eyes off her child for a few seconds too long.

Not that Emily was the sort of child who got herself into trouble. She was careful, and a thinker. Her pleasures were quiet ones. She wasn't a climber. Neither did she do silly things. She was absolutely *nothing* like her father. She was a hundred per cent smarter, for starters.

Still, when Jessie hurried back outside into the yard, she was very relieved to see Emily was where she spent most of her time, playing under the large fig tree in the corner. It was her cubby house, with the sections between the huge roots making perfect pretend rooms. Emily could happily play there for hours.

Her daughter had a wonderful imagination. Jessie had been the same as a child. Maybe it was an only-child thing. Or an inherited talent. Or a bit of both.

Whatever, the Denton girls loved being creative.

Jessie realised then that she wanted that job at Wild Ideas, not just for the money, but also for herself. Being a waitress had been a good stopgap, but she didn't want to do it for the rest of her life. She wanted to use her mind. She wanted the challenges—and the excitement—of the advertising world.

'Mummy, who rang our phone? Was it Dora?'

Jessie, who'd finished hanging out the washing, bent down and swept her daughter up into her arms. It was time for lunch.

'No, sweetie, not Dora. It was a man.'

Emily blinked. 'A nice man?'

'Very nice.'

'Is he going to be your boyfriend, Mummy?'

'What? Oh, no. Heavens, no! He's just a man who finds people jobs. It looks as if he might have found Mummy a job as a graphic artist. I have to go for an interview on Monday. If I get it, I'll earn a lot more money and I'll be able to buy you lots of pretty things.'

Emily didn't seem as impressed with this news as Jessie would have expected. She was frowning.

'Why don't you have a boyfriend, Mummy? You're very pretty.'

Jessie felt herself blushing. 'I...I just haven't met any man I liked enough to have as a boyfriend.'

Even as she said the words, a pair of ice-blue eyes popped into her mind, along with a charismatic smile. Her heart lurched at the memory of how close she'd come to making the same mistake her mother had made. Brother, she'd got out of that bar just in time.

'I have *you*, sweetie,' Jessie said, giving her daughter a squeeze. 'I don't need anyone or anything else.'

Which was the biggest lie Jessie had told her daughter since she'd said she liked being a waitress. Because last night's experience showed her she *did* need something else sometimes, didn't she? She needed to feel like a woman occasionally, not just a mother. She needed to have a man's arms around her once more. She needed some release from the frustration she could feel building up inside her.

Some day, she would have to find an outlet for those needs. A man, obviously. A boyfriend, as Emily suggested.

But who?

Those blue eyes jumped back into her mind.

Well, obviously not him. He was off limits. A married man.

If only she could get this job. That would bring a whole new circle of males into her world.

OK, so lots of guys in the advertising world were gay. But some weren't. Surely there had to be the right kind of boyfriend out there for her. Someone attractive and intelligent. Someone single—and a good lover.

Of course, attractive, intelligent *single* men who were good lovers were invariably full of themselves, and unwilling to commit. There would be no real future in such a relationship. She'd have to be careful not to fall for the guy. Or to start hoping for more than such a man could give.

Jessie sighed. Did she honestly need such complications in her life? Wouldn't it be better if she just went along the way she was, being a celibate single mum?

Men were trouble. Always had been. Always would be. She was much better off without one in her life. Emily was happy. *She* was happy. She'd be even happier if she got this job on Monday.

Feeling frustrated was just a temporary thing. She'd get over it. One day.

Jessie sighed again.

'Why are you always sighing today, Mummy?' Emily asked. 'Are you tired?'

'A little, sweetie.'

'Why don't you have a cup of coffee? You always do that when you're tired.'

Jessie looked into her daughter's beautiful

brown eyes and laughed. 'You know me very well, don't you?'

'Yes, Mummy,' she said in that strangely grown-up voice she used sometimes. 'I do. Oh, I can hear Dora's car! Let's go and tell her about your new job.'

'I haven't got it yet, Emily. It's only an interview.'

'You'll get it, Mummy,' she said with all the naïve confidence of a four-year-old. 'You will get the job.'

CHAPTER FIVE

THE offices of Wild Ideas were in north Sydney, on the third floor of an office block not far from North Sydney Station. A bonus for Jessie, who didn't own a car.

She arrived in the foyer of the building early, dressed in her best stone-washed jeans and a freshly starched white shirt, turned up at the collar. She carried a lightweight black jacket—in case the air-conditioning inside was brutal—as well as a black briefcase. Her shoes were sensible black pumps, well-worn but polished that morning till they shone.

Her hair was pulled back tightly and secured at the nape of her neck with a black and white printed scarf she'd borrowed from Dora. Her make-up was on the neutral side, especially around her eyes and on her mouth. The only jewelry she wore were small silver cross earrings. Plus her watch. She'd be lost without her watch.

She glanced at it now. Still only twenty-five minutes to ten. She wasn't going up to Wild Ideas yet. Only desperates arrived that early. Instead she headed for the powder room, where she spent a few minutes checking that she didn't look like a *femme fatale*.

Actually, her appearance would be considered *very* conservative in advertising circles. But she'd never

48

been a flashy dresser, even when she could afford to be.

Finally, she gave in to her pounding heart and rode the lift up to the third floor. It had been some months since she'd been for a job interview and she felt sick with nerves and tension. Not because she didn't think she could do the job. Jessie had never been lacking in confidence in her own abilities. But after being knocked back as often as she had, she'd begun to wonder if anyone would ever see what she had to offer.

Still, this chance was the best she'd had so far. *An even-money chance.*

As Jessie exited the lift on the third floor, she wondered if the other applicant was in there now, being interviewed, impressing the boss so much that he wouldn't even bother to see her. Maybe the receptionist would say 'Thank you very much but the job's already taken'.

Jessie took a deep breath and told herself not to be so silly. Or so negative. Harry Wilde had obviously liked her résumé. Surely, he'd have the decency to give her an interview.

The reception area of Wild Ideas fitted its image. Modern and colourful, with crisp, clean lines and furniture. Red-painted walls, covered in advertising posters. Black tiled floor. Very shiny. The sofas were in cream leather, the desk and coffee-tables made of blond wood.

The receptionist was blond as well, but not overly glamorous or overly beautiful. Possibly thirty, she

wore a neat black suit and a nice smile—not the sort
of smile used before delivering bad news.

'Hello,' she said brightly when Jessie walked in.
'You'll be Jessie Denton.'

'Yes, that's right,' Jessie replied, her palms still
distinctly sweaty. 'I'm a bit early.'

'Better than being late. Or not turning up at all,'
the blonde added ruefully. 'I'll just give Karen a ring
to let her know you've arrived. Karen's Mr Wilde's
PA,' she explained. 'Just take a seat over there for a
sec.' And she motioned towards one of the seats that
lined the waiting-room walls.

'Jessie Denton's here, Karen,' she heard the receptionist say quietly into the phone. 'OK... Yes, I'll
tell her.'

By the time she looked up, Jessie had sat down,
leant back and crossed her legs, doing her best to
appear cool and confident. Inside, she was a bundle
of nerves.

'Mr Marshall hasn't finished with the other applicant yet,' the receptionist informed her. 'But he
won't be long.'

'Mr *Marshall*?' Jessie choked out, her legs un-
crossing as she jerked forward on the seat.
'But...but...'

'Mr Wilde is overseas at the moment,' the receptionist cut into Jessie's stammering, and before she
could recover from her shock. 'Mr Marshall is in
charge while he's away.'

'Oh. I see. Right.' Jessie took a deep breath and
leant back again, exhaling slowly. Crazy to think that
this Mr Marshall was *her* Mr Marshall from Friday

night. Marshall wasn't such an unusual name. On top of that, *her* Mr Marshall was an accountant. What would an accountant be doing running an advertising agency, even temporarily?

'My name's Margaret, by the way,' the receptionist went on breezily. 'We might as well get to know each other. I probably shouldn't be saying this but I think you're more Mr Marshall's cup of tea than the girl who's in there now.'

'Why's that?' Jessie asked.

Somewhere on the floor a door banged.

'Judge for yourself,' Margaret murmured.

Just then this amazing creature swept down a corridor into the reception area.

The first thing that struck Jessie was her bright orange hair, which looked as if it had been cut with a chainsaw. A *rusty* chainsaw.

The second was the myriad gold studs and rings that adorned her starkly white face. Ears. Nose. Lips. Eyebrows. Chin.

Lord knew what other parts of her body had been pierced. Possibly a great many.

Thankfully, the girl was clothed from head to foot so Jessie could only speculate. Her style, however, was a combination of grunge and gothic and the garments she sported looked as if they'd been rescued from a charity bin. The kind they used for recycled rags.

'Tell Harry Wilde to contact me when he gets back, if he's still interested,' the escapee from the Addams Family tossed over her shoulder as she marched across the floor in her ex-army boots. 'I wouldn't work for him down there if he was the last man on earth. He knows absolutely nothing about the creative soul. Nothing!'

The moment she was gone Margaret looked over at a wide-eyed Jessie and grinned.

'See what I mean? I think you're a shoo-in.'

Jessie could not believe that fate had been so kind to her. 'I sure hope so. I really want this job.' She simply couldn't go the rest of her life being a waitress.

The reception phone buzzed and Margaret picked it up. 'Yes, Karen, I'll send her down straight away. And don't worry, he'll like *this* one. Your turn,' she said with an encouraging smile to Jessie as she hung up. 'Down to the end of that corridor. Go straight in.'

Jessie gulped, then stood up. 'Er—just one thing before I go. Do you happen to know Mr Marshall's first name?'

'Sure. It's Kane. Why?'

Jessie could not believe how relieved she felt. For a moment there…

She shrugged. 'I knew a guy named Marshall once and I was a bit worried this might be the same man. Thankfully, it isn't,' she muttered, and Margaret laughed.

'We all have one of those somewhere in our past.'

True. But the trouble was this one wasn't far enough in Jessie's past. He was only a couple of nights ago, and could still make her tremble at the thought of him.

Her nerves eased a lot with the surety that the Mr

Marshall about to interview her wasn't Curtis Marshall, married man and sexily irresistible hunk. She also couldn't deny she felt good that her competition had turned out so poorly. Clearly, Nicholas from Adstaff hadn't given carrot-top the same conservative-dressing advice he'd given her. Or if he had, she'd ignored him.

The door at the end of the corridor led into the PA's office. It wasn't quite as colourful as Reception, but still very nice and spacious and modern. Karen herself was nothing like Jessie had expected Harry Wilde's PA to be. She was forty-ish. A redhead. Pleasantly plump. And sweet.

'Oh, thank you, God!' she exclaimed on seeing Jessie. 'Did you see the other one?'

'Yes. Um. I did,' Jessie admitted. 'But to be honest, people like that are not unusual in the advertising world. She probably sees herself as an artiste with a certain avant-garde image to uphold.'

'We don't hire avant-garde artistes here,' Karen said wryly. 'We hire people with lots of innovative ideas who know how to work. And work hard. Now, did Margaret happen to mention that Mr Wilde's away right now?'

'Yes, she did.'

'Good. Then you'll understand why I'm doing part of your interview. Mr Marshall is an excellent manager and motivator, but he has no background in advertising. I've been with Mr Wilde a good few years and I know what he likes in an employee. I've already had a good look at your résumé, and I was impressed. Now that I can see you in person, I'm even more impressed. If you could just show me your portfolio, please?'

Jessie pulled out her portfolio and handed it over. She'd included samples of the best work she'd done over the years, plus mock-ups of ads she would like to do, if ever given the chance.

'Mmm. This is excellent. Michele is going to be pleased with you. Michele will be your boss. She's one of our top executives. Her assistant quit last week after they had an altercation over his lack of motivation. He's been having a lot of time off. A drug problem, we think. Anyway, she needs a good graphic artist to step into his shoes straight away. She has several things that need to be finished before the Christmas break. On top of that, she'll be going off on maternity leave in the middle of next year. She's having another baby. When that happens, we're hoping you'll be able to fill in for her. I gather from Adstaff that you do have ambitions to become a creative designer yourself, is that right?'

'It's my dearest wish. The sample ads at the back of my portfolio are my own original ideas. They're not actual campaigns I worked on.'

'Really. I hadn't quite got that far.' She flipped over some more pages of the portfolio, stopping to stare hard at one of the pages. 'Is this one of yours? This white-goods magazine ad,' Karen said, holding up a page.

'Yes, that's one I made up myself.'

The page had a vibrant blue background to highlight the white goods. In the middle was a dishwasher, washing machine and dryer, surrounded by other smaller kitchen appliances, all in stainless steel. Draped across the three taller items was a very glamorous Mae-West style blonde, her evening gown white with a very low neckline, her scarlet-tipped fingers caressing the appliances. Above her were the words, 'It's not the appliances in your life but the life in your appliances,' a parody of Mae West's famous comment, 'It's not the men in your life but the life in your men.'

'It's brilliant!' Karen exclaimed.

Jessie puffed up with pride. 'Thank you.'

'We have a new account for a kitchen-appliance company which this would be perfect for. I must show it to Peter. He's handling that account. I can see Michele and Peter fighting over you. Of course, Mr Marshall will have to hire you first,' she added with a grin. 'But I'm sure that's just a formality. Come on, let's get you in there. Hopefully, he's recovered from the last applicant by now. You should have seen his face when she walked in. My fault, of course. I was the one who picked her. Her résumé was impressive, but in reality she was not suitable at all.'

'Do you mind if I ask why not? Looks can be deceiving. She might have been very talented.'

'She was. A *very* talented graphic artist. But not suitable for promotion. Harry likes his front people to have a certain look, and style. After all, they have to deal with a wide range of clients, some of whom are very conservative. Harry believes first impressions are very important. Kane agrees with him. And

you, Jessie Denton, make a very good first impression.'

'But I'm only wearing jeans.'

'Yes, but they're clean and neat, and you wear
them with panache. And I simply love what you've
done with your hair. Very classy.'

Jessie could not have felt more confident as she
was ushered into Harry Wilde's office. Her self-
esteem was sky-high, her heart beating with pleasurable anticipation, not nervous tension.

Fate had been good to her, for once.

But then the man seated behind Harry Wilde's
desk looked up, and Jessie's heart literally stopped.

Oh, *no*, she groaned. How could this be? The receptionist had said his name was Kane, not Curtis!

But it *was* him. No doubt about it. She wasn't
about to forget what he looked like, especially when
he was even dressed the same, in a suit, shirt and tie.

His ice-blue eyes locked onto hers, his dark brows
lifting in surprise. Or was it shock?

'Yes, I know what you mean,' Karen said to him
with a small laugh. 'A definite improvement on Ms
Jaegers. This is Jessie Denton. Here's her portfolio.'
She walked forward and placed the folder on the
wide walnut desk. 'I've had a good look at it and it's
simply fabulous. Now, can I get either of you some
coffee? Or tea?'

'No, thanks,' Jessie croaked out.

'Not at the moment, Karen,' her boss said.

'OK, I'll leave you to it.'

'Re*lax*,' she mouthed to a shell-shocked Jessie as
she walked past her.

And then she was gone, shutting the door behind her.

Jessie just stood there in the middle of the large, plushly furnished office, her shock slowly draining away, anxiety rushing back. Anxiety and dismay.

Fate hadn't been kind to her at all. It had dangled the most wonderful opportunity in front of her nose like a carrot, only to snatch it away at the last moment. Because *this* Mr Marshall—regardless of what his first name turned out to be—wasn't about to hire her, no matter what she did, or said.

There was no way out.

If she told him the truth about why she'd been at that bar last Friday night, he would feel both humiliated and threatened. If she didn't tell him the truth, then she had to fall back on that other even more sordid reality. That she'd fancied him like mad and been tempted by him, despite knowing he was married.

No, that wasn't right, she suddenly realised. If she kept her decoy work a secret, then she would not have *known* he was married. He didn't wear a wedding ring. She'd noticed that the other night.

In that case, how could she explain her sudden disappearing act?

Saying simply that she'd changed her mind seemed rather lame. She would come across as a tease. She supposed she could say someone in the ladies' room had warned her he was a married man and that was why she'd done a flit.

That might salvage *her* pride and reputation, but it wouldn't do much for his.

The main problem here was that *he'd* known he was a married man all along, and he'd still asked her to go to a hotel room with him.

Recalling that highly charged moment brought back to Jessie the feelings she had shared with him that night. The mutual attraction. The rush of desire. The heat.

She stared at him as a new wave of heat flowed through her body, flooding her from her toes right up into her face.

There *was* no way out of this, except out the door.

'I guess I might as well leave right now,' she choked out. 'Just give me my portfolio back, please, and I'll get going.'

CHAPTER SIX

KANE rarely felt panic, but he felt it now. She was running out on him. *Again!*

He couldn't let that happen. Not now that he'd found her. The thought that he would never see her again had haunted him all weekend.

Of course, it would help to know why she'd run out on him in the first place. The only reason he could imagine was that he must have come on too hard and too fast for her.

Now he didn't know what to think.

All he knew was that nothing had changed for him since Friday night. One look from those incredible eyes of hers and he'd been right back there on that dance floor, his body consumed by the need to sweep her off into bed.

Bed? He almost laughed at that notion. A bed would not do. This all-consuming passion he was suffering from demanded a much faster, harder surface to pin her to. A wall. A floor. This desk, even.

Kane swallowed. He was really losing it!

And he'd lose her again, if she knew what was going on his head.

'Last Friday night has no relevance whatsoever to today,' he said with astonishing composure. Lust was a very powerful motivation. 'That was pleasure. This is business. But perhaps we should get the past out of the way first. Would you care to sit down and tell me why you left the way you did?'

She frowned, but stayed standing. He tried to stop his eyes from continually raking her from head to toe, but truly she was a magnificent-looking woman. And so sexy in those tight jeans, it was criminal.

'What's the point?' she said sharply, brown eyes flashing. 'I can't work for you. You must know that.'

He didn't, actually. Was she worried about sexual harassment in the workplace?

Perhaps she had just cause, given how much he craved her right now. But Kane could exercise control and patience when necessary. *And* when she wasn't touching him. The last thing he wanted to do was frighten her off. She was the first woman in a long time who had made him feel what he'd felt on Friday night. To be honest, he couldn't recall *ever* feeling quite what he'd felt on that dance floor.

Usually, he could stay in control. Usually, his brain was always there in the background, analysing the situation, making judgement calls, warning him when the momentary object of his desire was another waste of his time.

But it hadn't on that occasion.

Maybe that was why she'd obsessed about him all weekend. The way she'd made him forget everything but the moment. He hadn't known anything at all about her, except that she went into sleazy bars alone, dressed to thrill. Not a great recommendation.

Yet he'd still wanted her like crazy.

He still did.

No way was he going to let her escape from him

a second time. He wanted to experience the magic he'd felt in her arms once more. Too bad if it didn't go anywhere. He was sick and tired of thinking about the future and working his life to a plan. He'd got into a rather boring rut over the years. He'd forgotten how to be impulsive.

He wanted this woman, and he was going to have her, whether she was good for him or not.

'But you won't really be working for *me*,' he replied smoothly. 'You'll be working for Harry Wilde. I'm just the caretaker manager till Christmas, which is less than two weeks away now. After that, any boss-employee relationship between us is over.'

She still stared at him with wary eyes and he wondered why. Damn it all, she fancied him. He knew she did. She'd been with him all the way on Friday night, till she'd gone to the ladies'.

He'd been stunned when she hadn't showed up again.

'So what *did* happen on Friday night?' he asked, his teeth clenched firmly in his jaw. 'Did you just change your mind? Was that it?'

'I...I...'

Her fluster was telling. And quite enchanting. Maybe she wasn't the tease he'd been thinking she might be. Or a serial good-time girl, the kind who cruised bars at night looking for some cheap fun and excitement.

'It's not a crime to change your mind, Jessie,' he said gently. Though it had felt like it at the time. He'd been furious.

'I didn't change my mind,' she said, which totally confused him.

'What, then?'

Jessie felt she had to come up with some explanation, or look a right fool.

'A girl in the ladies' told me you were married,' she blurted out. 'I...I don't sleep with married men.'

There was no doubt her excuse startled him. His head jerked back and he blinked a couple of times. But then he did the strangest thing.

He smiled.

'Married,' he said with a low chuckle. 'How come I didn't think of that? *Married!*' And he laughed again.

'I don't think it's funny,' she snapped. She knew a lot of modern people didn't take marital vows seriously. But she did.

'Aah, but it is funny. Because I'm *not* married,' came his astonishing announcement. 'My brother is, however. My twin brother. My *identical* twin brother. He's been frequenting that particular bar every Friday night for a while, so it's understandable that someone made a mistake, thinking I was him.'

Jessie opened her mouth, then closed it again. The man she'd flirted with, and wanted so badly on Friday night, hadn't been her target at all. It had been this man, Kane Marshall, Curtis Marshall's twin brother!

As amazing as this revelation was, it did explain the small differences between the target's photograph and the man in front of her. His hairstyle. The colour of his eyes. And his whole personality. The man in the photograph had seemed softer.

There was nothing soft about Kane Marshall.

A second realisation hit Jessie with even more force. Kane Marshall was single. And available. There was absolutely no reason why she couldn't say yes if he ever asked her out.

Which he would. She could see it in his eyes.

A thrill—or was it a chill?—rippled down her spine. So much for her decision not to have a man in her life.

Of course, she hadn't anticipated at the time that she could possibly have *this* man. He was a whole different ballgame.

'You're *definitely* not married?' she asked.

'Definitely not. My divorce came through a few months ago.'

This added news didn't thrill her. She wasn't sure why. Perhaps because most of the recently divorced guys she'd met were always on the make. It was as though after casting aside their wives, sex was the *only* thing on their minds. They were always on the hunt for new prey. She'd met quite a few newly divorced men at the restaurant and they usually gave her the creeps, the way they looked at her, and the way they assumed she'd be easy meat.

Was that what Kane Marshall had thought of her on Friday night, that she was easy meat? She'd gone into that bar alone, after all. Why would a girl go into a bar alone on a Friday night, if not to pick up some guy? The only excuse she'd given him for not going to a hotel room with him was that someone had told her he was married.

Now that he knew she knew he wasn't, he had to be assuming she'd fall into bed with him next time without a qualm.

As much as the *idea* of falling into bed with him was incredibly exciting, Jessie knew that the reality might not be wise.

'No wife,' he stated firmly. 'No children. And no current girlfriend. Just so we don't have any more misunderstandings.'

Jessie blinked. That was sure laying his cards on the table. Next thing he'd be telling her if he had any communicable diseases!

'So are you quite happy to work here now?' he went on.

'Are you offering me the job?'

'Absolutely.'

'But you haven't even looked at my portfolio!'

'No need. I trust Karen's judgement regarding your creative talents. She has much more experience in this field than I do. I just wanted to see you in the flesh, to make sure you had the presence and style that Harry requires in his executives.'

Jessie frowned over his words, 'in the flesh'. Maybe his offering her this job had nothing to do with her talents and everything to do with his wanting to see *more* of her in the flesh, so to speak.

Still, if she was strictly honest with herself, she wanted the same thing. Whenever his eyes were upon her—which was all the time—she could think of nothing but being in his arms once more.

Hadn't she come to the conclusion at one stage over the weekend that she needed a man in her life? A boyfriend? A lover? Why not Kane Marshall? He wasn't married. Clearly, he fancied her as much as she fancied him. Crazy to fight an attraction as strong as this was. She would only lose.

'Even if I wasn't comparing you to the last applicant,' he went on suavely, 'I would be suitably impressed, and very happy to offer you the job. If *you're* still interested, that is.'

Jessie suspected he was asking her if she was still interested in him, as well as the job.

'Yes, of course I am,' she said, deciding it would be hypocritical to say anything else.

'Good,' he said, then delivered another of those dazzling smiles of his.

He was smooth! And incredibly confident.

He both excited and rattled her. A strange combination. She'd always been attracted to physically strong men, but Kane Marshall represented more than just physical strength. His persona carried exceptional charisma. A magnetism which perturbed her. His steely gaze had the capacity to sap her willpower. But it was his sexy smile that could do the most damage. She suspected that if they became lovers, he could make her *do* things. Wild things. Wicked things.

Her thoughts sent an erotically charged quiver rippling down her spine. Suddenly, her knees felt like jelly.

'I...I think I'd better sit down,' she said, reefing her eyes away from his and pulling up one of the upright wooden chairs adjacent to the desk. She sank down onto its solid surface, grateful not to have to look at him for a while. But eventually, she had to face him once more. When she did, her shoulders were rammed back against the chair-back, her back was as stiff as a board and her legs were tightly crossed.

Her rigid body language was wasted, however. He wasn't looking at her. His handsome face was down, and he was going through what looked like her résumé.

'I see here that you're a single mother,' he remarked before finally glancing back up at her.

Jessie's chin lifted defiantly. 'Is that a problem?'

'Absolutely not. I admire unmarried women who keep their babies,' he added with warmth in his voice and another of those winning smiles.

'I meant, is that a problem with my job?' she bit out, irritated with herself for going to mush inside again.

'I don't see why it should be. You have your little girl in day-care, it says here.'

'Yes, but there will be times when she gets sick. Or I might have to attend a school concert. Or some emergency.'

'Work conditions here at Wild Ideas are very flexible. You can work your own hours, or at home if you want. All that is required is that the work is done, meetings are attended and deadlines met. Your immediate boss is the mother of a little girl herself, with another baby on the way, so I'm sure she will be very understanding about such matters. Speaking of Michele, I think perhaps I should take you along to meet her shortly. She rang earlier with instructions to have someone sitting at the computer by her side before lunchtime. Or else.'

'You mean you want me to start straight away, *today*?' Jessie gasped.

He raised a single eyebrow at her. 'I thought you understood that. Is there any reason you *have* to leave?'

'No...no, I guess not. But I will have to ring the day-care centre and tell them I'll be a bit later than usual picking Emily up.'

'Will that worry your little girl?'

'No. But it might worry me. I'm not sure how often the trains run and how long it will take me to get there. I have to pick Emily up before six. They close at six.'

'You don't have a car?'

'No,' she admitted. 'I haven't been able to afford to run one.'

'You should be able to now. Your pay is sixty-five thousand dollars a year, with bonuses.'

All the breath was punched from Jessie's lungs. 'You're joking! Sixty-five thousand?' Before she'd had Emily, she'd only been on forty thousand.

'That's right. Your basic salary will be reviewed every six months, with rises given on performance.'

'That's incredible.'

'Don't worry. You'll have to deliver.'

'I'll deliver. Don't you worry about that.'

Their eyes met once more, with Jessie wondering if their conversation still carried a double meaning.

She hoped not. She'd hate to think that underneath his impressive surface, Kane Marshall was just another divorced creep.

'You should consider leasing a car,' he went on. 'Curtis always tells me that leasing is a much more sensible option in business. My brother is an accountant,' he added.

Unnecessarily. Jessie already knew that. But she could hardly say so. Still, it sent her wondering exactly where Kane Marshall usually worked. Karen had said he was an excellent manager and motivator. But for what company?

'If you like,' he was saying, 'I could get Karen to organise the leasing for you. All you have to do is tell me what kind of car you'd like.'

'I...I don't really know. I'll have to think about it.'

'If you tell me the make and model in the morning, it can be ready for you by the time you finish up tomorrow. Meanwhile, I'm quite happy to drive you home after work tonight. I wouldn't want you to worry about your little girl.'

Jessie stared at him. He certainly wasn't wasting any time in making his move.

'You don't have to do that,' she said. 'I do have a friend I could ring to pick Emily up if I think I can't make it.'

'A man friend?'

The question sounded casual, but Jessie could see more than curiosity in his eyes. Insane to imagine he was jealous. But it felt as if he was.

'No,' she said, and was sure he looked relieved.

'An elderly lady. My landlady, in fact. I rent a granny flat from her. But she's also a good friend.'

'It's no trouble for me to drive you home, Jessie,' he said. 'You don't live that far away. Besides, I'd like the opportunity to talk to you some more. Out of the office.'

'All right, then,' she agreed, if a bit stiffly. She wished she could get the thought out of her head that she was being weak. 'Thank you.'

'It's my pleasure.' And he smiled at her again.

Jessie suppressed a moan. Oh, he was just so gorgeous. How could she possibly say no?

Yet she hated for him to think she was easy.

Jessie was well used to the way most men thought about single mothers. They were considered desperates. Desperate for sex. Desperate for company. Desperate for some man—*any* man—to give them the emotional and financial support they obviously weren't getting from whoever had fathered their child.

In truth, there were quite a lot of single mothers who did act that way.

But Jessie wasn't normally like most single mothers. She'd always prided herself on her self-sufficiency. After Lyall, she'd never wanted to rely on any man for anything. Not even for sex.

Not till she'd met Kane Marshall.

Now he was all she could think about. Already, she was looking forward to his driving her home. Her skin actually broke into goose-pimples at the thought.

Yet she should have been concentrating on the job she'd just been given.

Jessie jumped to her feet. 'Now that that's all settled, I'd better get started, don't you think?'

He was much slower in rising, buttoning up his jacket as he did so.

His action drew her eyes to his suit. It wasn't the same pale grey number he'd worn on Friday night. This one was a darker grey. But it was just as expensive-looking and stylish. Not a wrinkle marred the line of its sleeves, or where the collar sat neatly around his solid neck.

He was a big man, she noticed once more. Not overweight. Just tall, and strong, with the broadest shoulders.

He would look good, naked. *Feel* good, too.

Oh, dear, Jessie groaned to herself. I'm in trouble here. Big, big trouble.

'This way,' he said as he walked around and gestured towards the door.

Thankfully he didn't touch her. His eyes were bad enough. The way they kept running over her.

He wasn't all that different from those other divorced creeps who'd pursued her, Jessie realised as she bolted through the door ahead of him.

The difference lay in her. Those other men hadn't made her tremble with a look. They hadn't made her forget every wise word of warning her mother had ever given her about men.

No, that wasn't true. She hadn't forgotten any of her mother's warnings. She knew what Kane Marshall was, and what he wanted.

The difference this time was that she wanted exactly the same thing he did.

CHAPTER SEVEN

JESSIE could not believe how quickly the day went, and how nice everyone was at Wild Ideas, especially her immediate boss.

In her early thirties, Michele was an attractive brunette, married, with one little girl and another baby on the way. She was warm and welcoming to Jessie, but at the same time efficient and precise. *Very* precise with her directions. She knew what she wanted—art-wise—and expected things to be done exactly as she wanted.

But Jessie was used to that. Jackson & Phelps had been a demanding company to work for. They had high standards and had trained her well.

But she much preferred working for Wild Ideas. Such a friendly atmosphere. The staff was relatively small—about twenty—and pretty well everyone had popped their heads into Michele's office at some time during the day.

Actually, calling it an office was misleading. It was more of a work station. The behind-the-scenes office layout at Wild Ideas was open plan, cut up into cubicles, some larger than others. Michele's area was quite large, but not fancy in any way. Plain pine furniture. No carpet. No doors. One window that looked out on to the main road.

Still, everything in it was clean and functional,

with state-of-the-art computer equipment, along with every piece of software imaginable. Jessie got very excited to work on the very latest G5 Macintosh, which was so much faster than her old Imac.

Just as well, because her predecessor had left things in a right mess. There was so much to sort through that when lunchtime came she ate a sandwich at her desk. Margaret from Reception dropped by and brought her some coffee, which was sweet of her. Jessie could see that they were going to become friends.

The only breaks she had were to go to the ladies' room and to make three phone calls. The first was to the restaurant to say that she was quitting. Since she was only a casual anyway, they didn't much care. They'd fill her spot within hours. The second was to the day-care centre. True to form, Emily didn't give a hoot that she would be late picking her up. Traitorous child! The third was to Dora, who was thrilled Jessie had got the job.

Unfortunately, Jessie couldn't explain about the fiasco with the Marshall brothers, not with Michele sitting right next to her.

Actually, Jessie liked it that she worked right beside Michele and wasn't off in another section on the floor, either in a corner by herself or with a whole bunch of other graphic artists. It seemed that at Wild Ideas, each creative designer had their own personal graphic artist. Sort of like their own private assistant. Jessie could see that this was a very successful way of doing things. New team leaders were being trained all the time. No wonder Harry Wilde never had to head-hunt executives from other agencies. He didn't need to.

'Time to wrap it up for today, girls. It's almost five.'

Jessie whipped her head round at Kane's voice to find him leaning against the open door frame, watching her. He looked as if he'd been there a while.

Actually, she'd surprised herself, the way she'd been able to put the man out of her mind for most of the day. But the moment their eyes met once more, all the feelings he evoked in her rushed back.

Not just heart-pounding desire. That was a given. But accompanying jabs of panic, and worry.

Her life since Emily had been born had been so simple. And straightforward. Maybe a little boring. And yes, lonely at times. But not too stressful.

If she became involved with Kane Marshall—even on just a casual basis—he would begin to make demands on her time and her space. As a single mother who now had a full-time job, Jessie knew she wouldn't have much spare time for leisure and pleasure.

'So how did our new girl work out, Michele?' Kane asked.

'Excellent,' Michele replied crisply. 'She's very good at what she does. And I suspect she'll be very good at what I do. Eventually,' she added with a cheeky wink.

Jessie didn't know what to say in reply to such fulsome praise, so she said nothing.

'We'd better get going, Jessie,' Kane asked. 'The traffic will be heavy. I'm driving Jessie home today,' he explained to Michele. 'She has to pick her daughter up by six and she's not sure about the train timetable.'

'Yes, I know. Jessie told me all about your knight-to-the-rescue act,' Michele said drily, a slightly knowing smile playing on her mouth. 'Off you go, love. And thanks for all your hard work. See you tomorrow at eight-thirty.'

'Eight-thirty?' Kane echoed. 'I thought the hours here were nine to five.'

'Jessie and I had a talk and we decided eight-thirty till four-thirty would suit us better. We're both up early with our children anyway. Might as well get them to day-care and get to work. Then we'll have more time to spend with them in the evening.'

'Whatever.' Kane shrugged his broad shoulders, his nonchalance reminding Jessie that men like Kane didn't have to worry about making time for children. All they had to think about was themselves.

Men did that very well, she reminded herself. So don't go thinking he's driving you home because he's genuinely kind. He's driving you home because he wants to get into your pants.

Jessie was appalled when this thought didn't repulse her, as it normally would. Maybe she shouldn't have stayed celibate this long. Suppressing a sigh, she turned off her computer, picked up her bag and stood up.

'Bye, Michele. Thanks for being so nice. See you in the morning.'

'She *is* a nice woman, isn't she?' Kane said as they

rode the lift down to the basement car park. He sounded surprised.

'Very,' Jessie agreed. 'Good at her job, too,' she added, determined not to let her secret thoughts and desires make her go all stiff and awkward with him again.

'Harry doesn't hire any other kind,' Kane commented.

'I hope he won't be disappointed with me when he gets back.'

'I'm sure he won't be, Jessie. This way,' he directed when the lift doors opened.

She was glad when he didn't get all handy once they were alone in the car park. She wasn't keen on guys who used any opportunity to grab at a girl.

'Here we are,' he said, stopping beside a sleek silver sedan. Inside, she noticed, it had grey leather seats and that lovely new smell. Jessie didn't know what the make was and she didn't ask. She knew next to nothing about cars. Which reminded her...

'By the way, I won't be leasing a car just yet,' she advised him as he drove expertly round the circular ramp that led to the street.

'Why not?'

'I don't like to rush into things. I like to think about them first before taking the plunge.'

'Is that a learned habit, a statement of fact, or a warning for me?'

'Do you need a warning?'

The car emerged into the late-afternoon sunshine, and very heavy traffic. Kane's very masculine mouth

remained shut till they stopped at the first set of
lights.

'Jessie, let's not play games with each other,' he
said firmly. 'You came into that bar the other night
looking for male company. If you hadn't been told I
was a married man, we'd already be lovers.'

Jessie decided then and there that the time had
come for the truth. Her pride demanded she not let
him think she made a habit of cruising bars at night,
picking up perfect strangers and agreeing to go to
hotel rooms with them.

'No one in the ladies' told me you were a married
man, Kane,' she confessed, her chin lifting as she
turned her head his way. 'I made that up.'

'You *what*? But why? I mean… Oh, go to hell!'
he muttered into the rear-vision mirror. The lights
had gone green and the driver behind was honking
his horn.

'Look, just drive and listen!' she told him in that
tone she used on Emily when she wouldn't go to bed
at night.

Once he got over his shock at her giving him orders like that, he actually obeyed. The silence gave
her the opportunity to tell him the truth, starting with
her working as a decoy earlier this year when she
hadn't had any money. She explained how she hated
it and had quit, but agreed to do it one last time so
that she could buy Emily the expensive fairy doll for
Christmas.

He *did* throw her a startled look when she said
she'd only gone into that bar last Friday night to do
a decoy job. When she revealed who her target was,

his car almost careered into the wrong lane. She had to tell him to keep his eyes on the road again, after which she was able to finish her story. She even mentioned that she hadn't labelled his brother a potentially unfaithful husband because Kane had knocked back the blonde.

'Of course, I didn't know at the time,' she added, 'that it was *you* knocking back the blonde and not your brother, Curtis.'

Kane was speechless at first. Then a bit stroppy.

'Well, thank you very much for not ruining my brother's marriage! Why didn't you? Guilt?'

'*Guilt?* Why should I feel guilty?'

'Come on, doll, let's face it. If I had been some poor, unhappily married bloke, and you'd swanned into that bar making eyes at me whilst I was sloshed, I'd have had a hard job resisting you, too.'

'Don't exaggerate,' she said. 'I'm not that sexy.'

'Trust me, sweetheart, you are. You're one hell of an actress, too. I could have sworn you were genuinely turned on last Friday night, that you really wanted me to make love to you.'

This was her out, if she wanted to take it.

Jessie decided on a middle course.

'I *did* find you rather attractive,' she admitted with considerable understatement. 'But I would never have gone to a hotel room with you. Not within minutes of meeting you.'

That was her story and she was going to stick to it.

'I didn't know your name, either,' he muttered. 'But I couldn't have given a damn.'

'Yes, well, you're a man. You're a different spe-
cies entirely. Women are, on the whole, a little more
careful.'

'Not all women,' he ground out.

Possibly, he was remembering the blonde.

'I do realise that. I also realise that single mothers
have a certain reputation for being…shall we
say…easy marks? I wouldn't like you to make that
mistake if you're thinking of asking me out. Which
I presume you are. Because why else would you be
here, driving me home?'

Another set of lights brought the car to a halt. His
head turned till his eyes met hers once more. He
smiled wryly.

'You seem to have me taped perfectly. What can
I say? Yes, I want to ask you out. And yes, up till
now, my intentions have not been entirely honourable.'

'And now?'

'I still want to take you to bed. But I also want to
spend time with you out of bed. You're a very intriguing woman, Jessie Denton.'

Jessie felt herself blushing. She turned her head
away to stare out at the halted traffic, which was
thicker than when they'd left north Sydney. She
glanced at her watch. It was almost half-past five and
they were only at Chatswood. Still, once they got
through this bottleneck it should be plainer sailing to
Roseville. They should arrive before six. But it
would be much quicker on the train.

'So will you go out with me?' he persisted.

Jessie turned back to face the road ahead. She

could feel him looking at her but refused to look his way again. Those eyes of his made her melt almost as much as his smile.

'Maybe,' she said, pleased with her cool tone.

'When?'

'Don't rush me, Kane.'

Kane. She'd called him Kane. She couldn't remember calling him that before.

'How about this Friday night?' he jumped in immediately. 'You must have had someone mind your daughter last Friday night. You could do the same this Friday night. We could go out to dinner, then on to a club, or whatever you like to do. The movies. A show. Anything.'

Going to bed with him would be nice, she thought, shocking herself again. Truly, she was in a bad way. But her pride was still greater than her need.

'I'm not sure about this Friday,' she said. 'I still don't know all that much about you. I mean, you've at least read my résumé. I don't even know what you usually do for a living, when you're not minding the store for Harry Wilde.'

'You'll find the answer to that question on your desk in the morning. Easier than trying to explain what I do. It would take all night.'

Jessie blinked over at him. He called her intriguing. He was the intriguing one.

'OK, but I still don't know much about you personally. I mean, you said you were divorced. How long were you married and why did your wife divorce you?'

'We were married for three years and *I* was the one who asked for a divorce.'

'Good heavens. Why? Was she unfaithful?' The idea seemed ludicrous to Jessie. If Kane were her husband she would never look at another man.

'Not that I know of.' The lights went green and the car crawled on through the busy intersection. 'My wife and I had a difference of opinion about the matter of having children,' he explained. 'We should have discussed it before we got married, I suppose, but... Did you see that bloke cut me off?'

She did and it was a near miss. Still, they weren't going fast enough to have a serious prang.

'Driving a four-wheel-drive, of course,' Kane ground out angrily. 'Worse than truck drivers, they are. Why any sane person would need a mini-tank to get around the city I have no idea. They should all be banned. Now, where was I? Oh, yes, my divorce. Look, when I realised that I couldn't change my wife's mind about having kids, I decided to call it quits. It was quite an amicable parting. We're still very good friends.'

Jessie couldn't help feeling disappointed that Kane was one of those selfish modern men who didn't want children. Truly, he should never have got married in the first place. That poor woman, wasting three years of her life on a man who would never give her what she wanted.

Which was a good warning for herself.

'I see,' she said, nodding.

'And what about you, Jessie?' he counter-questioned whilst she was still pondering if it was worth the risk of falling in love with Kane Marshall, just to have the pleasure of going to bed with him. 'Why aren't you still with the father of your child?'

She could have told him the long version. But she decided he probably wouldn't be interested.

'He died,' she said. 'In a snowboarding accident. Before Emily was born.'

'God, how awful!' He seemed genuinely shocked and sympathetic. 'That's tragic, Jessie. Truly, I'm very sorry. I hope his family has been supportive.'

'I never told them about the baby. Lyall was estranged from his folks, and frankly, I didn't like the sound of them. Anyway, they live over in New Zealand. I could hardly afford to fly over all the time. I thought it best to raise Emily by myself.'

'But what about your own folks?'

Jessie winced. 'Not a pretty picture there either, I'm afraid. Mum was a single mother herself. My father was a married man. She was Irish and Catholic, so getting rid of me was out of the question. Anyway, she emigrated to Australia when I was a baby, by which time she was all bitter and twisted about men. A few years ago she went back home. She wasn't at all pleased about my becoming a single mother. Said I was a fool. But I'm a very different single mother from my mum, I can tell you.'

'I don't doubt it. You're one very strong character, Jessie Denton. Very brave.'

'Brave?' Jessie gave that notion some thought. 'Not really. I was scared stiff at the time. Not to mention seriously depressed. I didn't have post-natal depression. I had pre-natal depression. But I couldn't have done anything else. Emily was my baby. And really, other than having a few money worries, it's been an incredible experience. I wouldn't change a day of it. And now that I've got a decent job, I won't even have any money worries,' she added, not wanting him to think she needed money from any man. Or that she might look at him as a possible meal ticket.

'I read on your résumé that you've been working as a waitress,' he said. 'Did you like doing that?'

Jessie shrugged. 'Not overly. But it was the only job I could get other than decoy work. And I couldn't bear doing that on a regular basis. I only did it this one last time for the money. Do you have any idea how much a Felicity Fairy doll costs?'

'Actually, yes, I do. I've been instructed to buy one for my niece for Christmas. She's about the same age as your Emily. Maybe we could go Christmas shopping together.'

She slanted him a wry smile. 'You planning on seducing me amongst the soft-toy section of Sydney's biggest department store? Save yourself the price of a dinner?'

He laughed. 'I can't see any man seducing you on the cheap, Jessie.'

'One did. *Once,*' she added tartly. 'And I ended up with Emily.'

'So I'm being punished for some other man's misdeeds, am I?'

'Let's just say I look before I leap these days. But you're out of luck. Dora bought Emily's doll for me last Saturday. So you'll have to go Felicity Fairy shopping by yourself. A word of advice, however. Do it soon or there won't be any left to buy.'

'I'll do that. We're getting close to Roseville. I might need some directions soon.'

Jessie glanced at her watch again. 'We'll only just make it in time.'

'What happens if you're late?'

'There are penalty rates for every quarter of an hour you keep them waiting after six o'clock.'

'That's rough. What if there was an accident and the traffic was backed up for miles?'

'Indeed,' she said drily. 'That's why I'll be catching the train in future. But it gives you a little inkling of the stresses and strains of being a working mother. Not much time left over for extra-curricular activities, either. Take the next corner on the left. The day-care centre is four blocks down, on the left. It's cement-rendered, painted pale blue. You can't miss it.'

'Would you go to work if you didn't have to?' he asked as he swung round the corner.

'I don't *have* to work. I could stay at home on welfare. But I don't think that's much of an example to Emily as she grows up. I think if you can work, you should. On top of that, it's nice to have some extra money. Welfare sucks, I can tell you.'

'What if you were married, and your husband earned a good income? Would you work then?'

Jessie laughed. 'I don't indulge in futile fantasies, Kane.'

'I was thinking of my brother's wife, Lisa. She's been a stay-at-home mum for over four years. I thought she was happy but she's not. I advised her this weekend to get a baby-sitter in a bit more often and join a gym. But I have a feeling that's just a temporary solution. I think she needs more.'

'She should find a good day-care centre and go back to work, even if it's only part-time. Or do some voluntary work, if she doesn't need the money. She needs adult company occasionally. And challenges outside of motherhood and wifery.'

'Yes,' Kane said. 'That's good advice. Thanks, Jessie. You might just have saved my brother's marriage for a second time. Aah, there's the place. And it's still only two minutes to six. We've made it!'

'Only just,' Jessie said, scrambling out of the car as soon as Kane slid into the kerb. 'Thanks a lot, Kane. Please don't wait. You've been very kind but you can go home now. It's only a ten-minute walk for me and Emily from here. We'll be fine. Bye. See you tomorrow.'

She didn't wait for him to argue with her, just slammed the passenger door and dashed inside.

Kane stared after her, then broke into a wry grin.

'You don't get rid of me as easy as that, honey,' he muttered.

Switching off the car engine, he climbed out from behind the wheel and walked around to the pavement, where he leant against the passenger door, folded his arms and waited patiently for Jessie to return.

CHAPTER EIGHT

SHE emerged after only two minutes, leading a little clone of herself by the hand. Black curly hair. Pale skin. Square jaw.

Jessie's expression, when she saw him waiting for her by his car, was a mixture of surprise and irritation. Her daughter's big brown eyes carried curiosity and delight.

Introductions were made rather reluctantly, with Jessie calling him Mr Marshall.

Emily gave him an odd look. Some of the delight had gone out of her eyes. 'Are you my mummy's new boss?' she asked. 'The one who made her late?'

'I am,' Kane confessed. 'But I'm going to make it up to you both by driving you home, then ordering a couple of pizzas to eat for dinner so that Mummy doesn't have to cook tonight.'

He'd opened both passenger doors invitingly whilst delivering this plan for the evening to a frowning Emily. When he glanced up at Jessie to find out her reaction, a rather strange smile was playing on her generous mouth.

'Is there a problem with that idea?' he asked, looking from mother to daughter.

'Mummy won't let me go in any car that hasn't got a proper car seat,' Emily announced primly whilst Mummy just kept on smiling. 'And Mummy won't let me eat pizzas. She says they're rubbish.'

'Aah. Headed off at the pass,' Kane muttered. 'Calls for right-flank action. OK, how about I walk home with you and Mummy? That way I'll know where you live for future reference. Then I can come back and get the car whilst you find out from your mummy what I *can* buy you both for dinner.'

'We always eat with Dora on a Monday,' the little powerhouse of information countered. 'Today is a Monday. Isn't that right, Mummy?'

'Yes, sweetie,' her mother said. With great satisfaction in her voice, Kane noted ruefully.

'Checkmate, I think,' Jessie added with a wicked gleam in her eyes.

Kane's teeth clenched hard in his jaw. He'd see those eyes glitter for a different reason one day. Or he wasn't the guy voted most likely to succeed!

'Is that the correct metaphor?' he asked, his soft voice belying his hard resolve. 'Besides, chess is just a game. This is war. I will reconsider my tactics on the way to your house.'

Slamming the car doors, he zapped the lock, slipped the keys in his trouser pocket, then faced the enemy with one of his how-to-win-friends-and-influence-people smiles.

'May I carry your bag for you, little lady?' he offered, reaching for the small backpack which Emily had been dragging along the pavement.

'I can carry my own bag, thank you very much,' she informed him pertly. Although she needed her mother's help to put it on.

Kane slanted Jessie a droll look. 'A new feminist in training?'

'No. An independent spirit. Everyone needs to be one of those these days to survive.'

'You could be right. OK, how about *you* carry the bag, Emily, but I'll carry *you*?'

Without waiting for her next objection, Kane hoicked Emily up to sit on his shoulders, one leg on each side of his head. She really was very light, even with a bag on her back.

'You wrap your arms around my neck and I'll hold your feet,' he told her. But when he grabbed her sandal-clad feet, a shower of sand sprayed down the front of his designer suit.

'What the...?'

'Emily spends a good deal of each afternoon in the sandpit,' Jessie explained without any apologies.

'Right,' Kane said through gritted teeth.

'It'll brush off easily enough,' Jessie told him blithely. 'Here... Look...'

He stiffened when she started brushing him down.

'I think the sand's all gone now,' he said curtly after a minute's torture.

She kept on doing it. 'I don't want you blaming me for ruining your lovely suit. Italian, is it?'

'Yes.' He named its designer.

She rolled her eyes at him. 'I should have guessed.'

At last, she took her hands off him.

'OK, you've been returned to your usual sartorial splendour. Let's walk.'

Kane was very relieved to walk. Still, his reaction

to her merely brushing his hands down over his chest gave him an inkling of how incredible it would be to have her touch him without clothes on.

'It's fun!' Emily's excited voice brought Kane back to the moment in hand. He'd loved riding on his father's shoulders as a child.

'It's a bit like horse-riding,' he said. 'Have you ever been horse-riding, Emily?'

'Yeah, I take her every weekend,' Jessie muttered under her breath beside him. 'When I can fit it in between the ballet and the violin lessons.'

Fortunately, Emily didn't hear her mother's sarcasm.

'No, I haven't,' she said politely. 'Mummy, can I go horse-riding?' she asked in all innocence.

'There aren't any horses in the city, sweetie,' Jessie replied. 'We'd have to drive out into the country and we'd need a car for that. We don't have a car.'

'I'll take you,' Kane said, and was rewarded with the most savage glare from Jessie.

'You don't have to do that,' she bit out.

'But I want to,' he said. 'I'd enjoy it.'

And it was true. He would enjoy it.

'When?' Emily chimed in. 'When?'

'Soon,' Kane promised.

'Not till after Christmas,' Jessie intervened abruptly. 'We're all too busy before Christmas. On top of that, Mr Marshall would have to get a proper child seat before we could go anywhere in his car. Such things take time.'

Her slightly smug smile suggested to Kane that she

thought that getting a car seat would be just too much trouble.

'Kane,' he said firmly. 'You are to call me Kane. *Not* Mr Marshall.'

'Very well. This way...*Kane*.'

She led him round a corner that brought them into a tree-lined street that was much quieter than the road the day-care centre was on. Emily had fun picking leaves off the trees, her happy chatter distracting the two adults from their verbal foreplay.

Because that was what it was. Kane knew it, even if Jessie didn't. She wanted him as much as he wanted her. She was just too cynical about men to give in to her desire and just go with the flow. She thought if she delayed the inevitable, Christmas would come, he'd leave Wild Ideas and that would be that. Out of the office and out of her life.

Kane refused to be deterred. The more difficult she was, the more he was determined to have her, not just in his bed, but in his life. His feelings might not be true love as yet, but they were more than lust. Oh, yes, much more.

Five minutes later, she stopped to open the front gate of a delightful old Federation house. It had a lovely rose garden on either side of a paved front path that led up to an enclosed front porch and a front door with stained-glass panels on either side.

Dear Dora, it seemed, was not exactly poor. Homes like this in Roseville were not cheap. Kane wondered if she rented out her granny flat to Jessie and Emily more for the company than the money.

'I'll have to put you down now, Emily,' he said

as he approached the front steps. 'Otherwise you'll hit your head on the porch roof.'

Jessie's heart turned over as she watched Kane lift Emily off his shoulders and set her gently down. The look of adoration that her child gave him made her want to hit the bastard.

Because that was what he was being. A right bastard. Using Emily to get to her.

Well, it wasn't going to work. She wasn't going to bed with him now, no matter how much she'd wanted to when she'd been brushing him down a few minutes back. The man was built, all right. Clearly, he worked out a lot.

Dora must have heard them arrive because she whisked open the front door before anyone rang the bell.

Jessie had to laugh at the look on her face when she saw Kane.

'This is Mr Marshall,' Emily piped up. 'Mummy's new boss. But he likes to be called Kane. He wanted to drive us home but he didn't have a car seat for me, so Mummy said no. But his car is lovely,' she rattled on. 'It's very shiny and silver. He's going to take me in it to go horse-riding after Christmas. He's going to have a car seat by then. He wanted to buy us pizza tonight but Mummy said no. Can he come to dinner, Dora? You always cook too much food. Mummy said so last Monday night.'

Jessie was besieged by a mixture of pride that her four-year-old daughter could talk so well, and embarrassment at the ingenuous content of her chatter.

Dora just laughed. She was used to Emily. Kane looked genuinely enchanted, which confused Jessie to no end. Was he that good an actor, or did he really like Emily?

She would have thought a man who didn't want his own children would be more impatient and less kind.

He must really want to go to bed with me an awful lot, Jessie decided, not sure if she felt flattered or infuriated.

'I'll have to pop a few extra potatoes in,' Dora said. 'It's roast lamb tonight. Do you like roast lamb, Mr Marshall?'

'Love it. And it's Kane, remember?'

'Kane,' Dora repeated. 'But I thought...' And she threw Jessie a frowning glance.

'Would you believe Kane has a twin brother named Curtis?' Jessie replied. 'An *identical* twin brother? He's married, whereas Kane is divorced.'

'Really?' Dora said, enlightenment in her eyes. 'Fancy that!'

'Yes,' Jessie agreed drily. 'Fancy that.'

'I haven't got any brothers or sisters,' Emily said with a sigh. 'That's because my daddy died.'

'Yes, your mummy told me about that, Emily,' Kane said, squatting down to her height. 'That was very sad. But you're sure to get a new daddy one day. Your mummy's a very pretty lady. Would you like a new daddy?'

Before Emily had a chance to reply, Jessie hurried over and swept her up into her arms. 'Enough idle chit-chat. We have to get Emily bathed and changed before dinner. Why don't you stay and talk with Dora, Kane, while I do that? Dora, ply our guest here with some of your cream sherry. That should keep him out of mischief.'

'I don't ever drink and drive,' Kane replied, an amused lift to the corner of his mouth. 'But I'm sure Dora and I can find plenty of subjects to talk about whilst I watch her cook.' And he gave Jessie a look which implied that by the time she returned for Dora's roast-lamb dinner, he'd know everything there was to know about her.

She and Dora had had many deep and meaningful discussions over the last year or so, and women, unlike men, usually told the truth about themselves. A clever questioner could find out anything he wanted to know.

Jessie suspected she'd just made a tactical error.

But it was too late now.

She comforted herself with the knowledge that no matter what Kane discovered, she still had her own mind, and her own will-power. He couldn't force her to do anything she didn't want to do.

The trouble was that deep down, in that hidden woman's place which she'd been ignoring for over four years, the craving to be made love to was growing.

Sexual temptation was a wicked thing. Dark and powerful and primitive. It was not swayed by reason, or pride. It was fed by need, and fanned by desire. She wanted Kane's body inside her much more than Dora's roast dinner.

She wanted him in ways that she'd never wanted Lyall.

So what are you going to do about it, Jessie? she asked herself bluntly as she went through the motions of giving her daughter a bath.

'Mummy,' Emily said as Jessie massaged the no-tears shampoo through her thick curls.

'Mmm?' Jessie murmured a bit blankly. Her mind was elsewhere, after all.

'I like Kane. He's nice.'

'Yes, yes, he is.'

'Do you like him, Mummy?'

'I…well…I…'

'He likes you.'

Jessie sighed. No point in trying to pull the wool over Emily's eyes. Or in lying. Not if she eventually gave in and went out with Kane on Friday night.

'Yes,' she said simply. 'I think perhaps he does.'

Jessie waited for the next question. But none came. Emily just sat there in silence.

Jessie bent down to see the expression on her daughter's face. But it carried that brilliantly blank look which her daughter could adopt when she wanted to hide her feelings from her mother.

'Emily Denton, what are you thinking?' Jessie demanded to know.

'Nothing.'

'Don't lie to me. Tell.'

'I was thinking about Christmas, Mummy. Does Santa *always* give you what you ask for?'

Jessie was glad of this change of subject. 'He does, if you're a good girl.'

'*I'm* a good girl.'

Jessie smiled and gave her daughter a kiss and a cuddle. 'You surely are. You have nothing to worry about, sweetie. Come Christmas Day, you're going to get absolutely *everything* you asked for.'

CHAPTER NINE

JESSIE should have predicted that Kane would charm both Dora and Emily to the degree he did. The man was a charmer through and through. By the time she and Emily returned to the main part of the house for dinner, he had Dora eating out of his hand.

As for Emily...Santa Claus himself couldn't have caused more excitement in the child. She insisted on sitting next to Kane, who treated her as no one had ever treated her before. As if she was a special little princess whose every word was precious and every wish immediately catered to.

Any worry Jessie harboured over her daughter growing too attached to a man who would only be a temporary part of her life was momentarily pushed aside when she saw how happy Emily was. When it was time for her to go to bed—way past her usual time—Emily begged Kane to read her a bedtime story. Which he duly did, and very well too.

Naturally, when the first story was finished, Emily begged for more. A family trait, Jessie decided bitterly, always wanting more.

Kane read her another story, then another, till Emily's yawns finally stopped and she fell asleep.

'She's dropped off,' Jessie said from where she'd been standing in the bedroom doorway with her arms

95

crossed, watching Kane's performance with swiftly returning cynicism. 'You can stop reading now.'

He looked up from the book. 'But I need to find out if Willie Wombat finds his long-lost father,' he protested with a mischievous gleam in his eyes and the most charming smile.

Jessie steeled her heart and rolled her eyes. 'Fine. You take Willie Wombat out into the living room and finish the story whilst I tuck Emily in. I'll be with you shortly to see you out.'

'What, no nightcap?'

'No. It's late and I have to go to work tomorrow. You do too.'

'I'm the boss. I can come in late.'

'Well, I can't. I'm on probation for three months.'

'Who says?'

'Michele. Apparently, that's Harry Wilde's hiring rule. If a new employee can't cut the mustard in three months, he or she gets their walking papers.'

'Harry never told me that. There again, I don't think he expected me to have to do any hiring during the month he was away. Does the idea of probation worry you, Jessie?'

'No. I can cut the mustard. No problem.'

'I'll just bet you can.'

He stood up from where he'd been sitting on the side of Emily's bed, glancing over at the other bed as he made his way towards the door.

Jessie was eminently grateful that she shared a room with her daughter. Also that her own bed, like Emily's, was nicely single. It eliminated temptation.

Jessie stepped aside to let him through the doorway.

'Don't make yourself too comfortable,' she warned drily. 'I won't be long.'

He didn't answer, just gave her a searching look as he moved past.

Jessie wished she'd shut her mouth. Saying too much was almost as bad as saying too little.

She hadn't done much talking during the roast-lamb dinner. Dora and Emily had done enough. And Kane, of course. Brother, could that man talk.

The trouble was he was so darned interesting. And entertaining. Yet, in retrospect, he hadn't actually talked about himself, an unusual trait for a man. His concentration had mostly been on Emily and Dora.

Dora must have told him her whole life story during the course of the meal, from her childhood to her childless marriage to her husband's death, then her recent years of looking after her increasingly fragile widowed mother. She had even revealed how much she resented her younger brother's not having helped with their mother, something she hadn't even told Jessie.

Kane had made all the right noises at the appropriate places. He had a knack with sympathetic murmurs, that was for sure.

Emily had tried to outdo Dora, giving Kane a minute-by-minute description of everything she did every day, pausing for words of praise at intervals, which she duly got.

Jessie smiled wryly down at her daughter as she tucked the sheet around her. Cheeky little devil. A right little flirt too, fluttering her long eyelashes up at Kane all the time.

Jessie had steadfastly not fluttered or flattered or flirted with the man in any way all evening. But despite her keeping a safe distance, he'd still got to her. A quiet look here. A smile there.

Oh, yes, he'd got to her. Made her want things she hated herself for wanting. Not just sex. But more. Too much more.

He was the devil in disguise, tempting her, tormenting her. She knew she should resist him, but feared she was fighting a losing battle. All she could salvage was a bit of pride by not making her surrender too easy. Jessie suspected that Kane Marshall had always found winning much too easy. It would do him good to work for her conquest, such as it would be. Nothing special to him. Just another bit of skirt. Another notch on his gun.

Jessie wondered how many women there'd been since he'd split with his wife. She resolved to never let him know he was the first man she'd even looked at since Lyall, let alone wanted this badly.

'All finished,' she said brusquely as she marched from the bedroom into the living room. 'Let's go.'

He was sitting on the sofa, the one that ran along the wall opposite the television. It was a very roomy sofa. His suit jacket, she noted, had been removed and was draped over one of the kitchen chairs. His tie was there as well, and the top button of his business shirt was undone.

Clearly, he had seduction on his mind, not leaving.

A tremor raced through Jessie.

'You have a very intelligent little girl,' he said as he snapped shut the book he'd been flicking through, placed it on the side-table next to the sofa and stood up. 'Very sweet, too,' he added.

'Unlike her mother,' Jessie snapped, once again folding her arms across her chest.

'Oh, I suspect the mother could be even sweeter than the daughter,' he said as he walked slowly towards her, bypassing the chair with the jacket and tie. 'In the right circumstances.'

'Don't you dare touch me,' she warned when he was less than an arm-length away.

She was standing in the middle of the kitchenette, with her back not far from the kitchen sink.

He stopped and frowned at her. 'You do realise you are being ridiculous,' he said softly.

Was she?

Possibly. But she wasn't about to back down.

'I will not have sex with you with my daughter sleeping in the next room.'

His eyebrows lifted. 'Sex was not what I had in mind for now, Jessie. Just a kiss. Or two.'

'Huh! Men like you don't stop at a kiss or two.'

He frowned. 'Men like me,' he murmured. 'Now, I wonder what you mean by that? Presumably nothing very complimentary. I suspect you've already lumped me in with the type of divorced guy who wants to sow his wild oats, with no strings attached. Or perhaps the sleazebags you told me about who target single mothers because they think they're desperates. Am I right?'

'Something like that.'

'You're wrong. I'm nothing like that at all.'

'I only have your word for that.'

'I haven't been with a woman since my divorce,' he shocked her by saying. 'Natalie was the last woman I slept with.'

Jessie blinked. It was over a year since he'd left his wife! It didn't seem possible. A man like him, so handsome and virile-looking. Women would have been throwing themselves at him all the time.

'But why? Are you seriously undersexed or something?'

He laughed. 'You wish.'

'But…but…'

'Look, I guess after the failure of my marriage I became a bit wary, and very selective. Casual sex held little appeal. I wanted a real relationship with an intelligent woman who wanted the same things I wanted.'

A career woman, she interpreted that to mean. One who'd give him company and sex, but not expect him to fulfill the traditional roles as husband and father of her children.

Jessie couldn't see a single mother with a demanding four-year-old filling those requirements. Not on a permanent basis.

'Then last Friday night,' he went on, 'I was hit by a thunderbolt. You. Suddenly, I didn't care what you were or who you were. I just had to have you. Be with you. Make mad, passionate love to you.'

She looked away from his eyes, lest he see the same crazy compulsion in hers. He reached out to turn her face back to the front again, his fingers both gentle and possessive. Her arms—suddenly heavy—slipped out of their crossed mode to hang loosely by her sides.

'You want that too, Jessie,' he whispered. 'Don't deny it. I've seen the desire in your eyes. And the fear. You think I'll hurt you. You and Emily. But I won't. I promise. I'd cut out my heart before I did anything to hurt either of you. I can see how special you are together. More special than any mother and daughter I have ever known. I want only good things for you both. Trust me. I'm one of the good guys. Now kiss me, Jessie Denton.'

She didn't kiss him. Because he kissed her first, cupping her face and taking her mouth with his, not waiting long before prying her lips open and sending his tongue to meet hers. The contact was electric, firing a heat that raced through her veins and skin, spreading like a bushfire raging out of control. Her arms rose of their own accord to slide around his body, her palms cementing themselves to his back as she pulled him closer. Then closer still.

He moaned deep in his throat, the sound an echo of what was going through her own head. The yearning for even closer contact was acute, but they couldn't be any closer if they tried. They were already glued together, mouth to mouth, chest to chest, stomach to stomach, thigh to thigh.

The anticipation of how he would feel, filling her to the utmost, took Jessie's breath away. If only she wasn't wearing jeans. A skirt could have been lifted, panties thrust aside. They could have done it right there and then, standing up. She'd never done it like that, standing up. She'd never even thought about it before.

She thought about it now and literally went weak at the knees. Did he feel her falling? Was that why he pushed her back up against the sink, to stop her from falling to the floor?

Jessie instinctively shifted her legs apart, giving him better access. His hips moved against her, the friction exquisite. Soon, she was moaning with abject need and total surrender.

'Mummy!'

Emily's high wail cut through Jessie's near-orgasmic state, bringing her back to earth with a crash.

'Oh, God,' she moaned, wrenching her mouth away from his. 'Emily.'

The mother in her, she swiftly realised, was still stronger than the woman, even the wanton woman Kane had so swiftly reduced her to. In another second or two, she would have been practically screaming. Disgusted with herself, she squeezed out from behind Kane's heaving chest, leaving him to sag against the sink whilst she dashed into the bedroom.

'What is it, Emily?' she asked in a voice that mocked what was still going on inside her. So calm-sounding.

'I had a bad dream,' Emily whimpered. 'There was a bear. A big one. I was scared.'

Bears often figured in Emily's nightmares. Jessie sometimes wished there weren't so many children's stories with bears in them.

'There are no bears living in Australia,' Jessie explained gently for the umpteenth time. 'Except in the zoo. You don't have to be scared about bears.'

'Is Kane still here?' Emily asked fretfully.

'Yes. Why?'

'He won't let the bear get me. He'll chase it away.'

Jessie rolled her eyes. 'Fine. You don't have to worry about any bears then, do you? So go back to sleep now,' she crooned, gently stroking her daughter's head. 'OK?'

Emily yawned. 'OK.' She closed her eyes and was back fast asleep in no time.

Jessie envied her child that ability. Sometimes, Emily would fall asleep as soon as her head hit the pillow. Jessie had never been a good sleeper, finding it difficult to shut her mind down at night. She knew she would do more than her fair share of tossing and turning tonight.

But it was clear that to continue fighting her feelings for Kane was futile. And rather ridiculous. He was right when he'd said that. They were adults. They wanted each other. OK, so she probably wanted more from Kane than he wanted from her but that was always going to be the case. She was a woman and he was a man.

Jessie had always been a reasonably decisive person, unlike her mother, who'd muddled through most of the events that had shaped her and Jessie's lives. When she was growing up, taking charge of her own life had been one of Jessie's main goals. Mostly, she'd been successful. In hindsight, Lyall had been a big error in judgement, but the consequences of her mistake had led to great joy.

Getting involved with Kane was possibly unwise. But at the same time she was only human, not a saint.

Having tucked Emily in once more, she returned to the living room, determined not to muddle through.

She was surprised to find Kane putting on his jacket.

He turned with a troubled expression on his face. 'I'm sorry, Jessie,' he said, stuffing his tie into one of the pockets. 'I didn't mean for things to go that far. I really didn't. But you do have an unfortunate effect on me.'

Jessie frowned. 'Unfortunate?'

Kane smiled a wry smile. 'I'm not used to losing control. I pride myself on being a planner. I rarely go off at half-cock.'

She couldn't help laughing, although she smothered it so as not to risk waking Emily.

'Yes, well, if I had actually *gone* off at half-cock,' he muttered, 'I might be able to laugh too.'

'Oh,' she said, taken aback by this revelation. 'I thought…'

'No,' he growled. 'I didn't.'

'It must have been a darned close call.'

'Agonisingly so.'

'Could you wait till Friday night, do you think?'

His eyes flared wide. 'Do you mean what I think you mean?'

'I would imagine so.'

His face actually lit up. 'Wow. That's a turn-up for the books.'

'I decided you were right. I was being ridiculous.

But I want you to understand that this can't really go anywhere. I'm not the woman you're looking for, Kane. I have Emily for starters. And a full-time job now. At best, I could be your friend and part-time lover.' There! She'd taken charge and it felt good.

He didn't say a single word for a few seconds, just let his eyes search her face. She could not tell what he hoped to find.

'I can handle that,' he said at last.

Jessie wished she knew what he was thinking. And planning. He'd just told her he was a planner. Something in his voice and his face suggested his agenda wasn't quite the same as hers.

But what?

She hoped he wasn't underestimating her. Or thinking she was a push-over after all.

Time for some more taking charge.

'By the way, on Friday,' she said firmly, 'I won't be staying anywhere with you all night, so don't go thinking I will. You have from seven till midnight. I can't expect Dora to mind Emily later than that. She's an old lady.'

'I could pay for a baby-sitter,' he suggested.

'Someone I don't know? No way, José. It's Dora, or nobody.'

'Fine. I won't argue. But I think you're in danger of becoming an over-protective mother.'

'Think what you like. It won't change my attitude towards my daughter.'

'I never thought it would. But that's OK. I admire a woman who knows her own mind.'

'And I admire a man who respects a woman's wishes.'

'I'll remember that.'

Yes, but for how long? Jessie wondered.

Till Friday night, naturally. That was the aim of this game after all. Get the girl into bed. But after that, Kane might not be quite so accommodating.

Still, she would cross that bridge when she came to it.

Till then, she was going to have a hard job thinking about anything but Friday night.

CHAPTER TEN

A COPY of a book called *Winning at Work* was sitting on Jessie's desk when she got in the next morning.

'Is this from you?' she asked Michele, who was already there at her desk, beavering away.

'Nope. It was there when I got in. I imagine Kane dropped it off for you to have a look at.'

Jessie recalled he'd said something about a book.

She picked it up and turned it over, blinking at the sight of Kane's photo on the back.

'Good lord!' she exclaimed. 'He's the author!'

Michele glanced up with a surprised look on her attractive face. 'You mean you didn't know the man who drove you home yesterday was *the* Kane Marshall, management guru and motivator extraordinaire?'

'No! I've never heard of *the* Kane Marshall.' Other than his being the twin brother of Curtis Marshall, possible philanderer.

'Something tells me that's about to change,' Michele muttered under her breath.

'He actually *wrote* this?' Jessie said, still stunned.

'Sure did. I gather it's been a runaway best-seller in the USA. It hasn't come out here yet. We Aussies aren't into self-help books as much as the Americans. But we're getting there.'

'Have you read it?'

'Nope.'

Jessie stared at the bio inside the front cover. Kane had a list of professional credits a mile long. Degrees in business and marketing. *And* a degree in psychology. This was his first book, but he was apparently well-known in the business world for his weekend seminars called 'Solving Work Problems'. He was described as a gifted after-dinner speaker, with his services being highly sought after by companies as a consultant and an educator.

Jessie sighed. Any secret hope she'd been harbouring that Kane Marshall might change his mind about what kind of woman he was looking to have that real relationship with just went out the window. He was a workaholic!

'You sound tired,' Michele said. 'Late night?'

'No. Just not enough sleep.'

'Aah. Man trouble.'

'What?'

'When a mother can't sleep it has to be man trouble. And it doesn't take much to guess which man. Although I'm not sure what the problem is. Do you already have a boyfriend? Is that it?'

'Goodness, no, I haven't had a boyfriend since Emily's father.' She and Michele had chatted a bit about their backgrounds over coffee yesterday, so Michele knew about Lyall.

'Aah…' Michele nodded. 'The once-bitten, twice-shy syndrome.'

'Can you blame me? After Lyall died, I found out he wasn't just two-timing me. He was triple-timing me.'

'Not nice,' Michele agreed. 'But that was Lyall, not Kane.'

'Maybe, but in some ways they're alike. Both tall, dark and handsome, with great smiles and the gift of the gab. Those sort of guys are hard to trust.'

'So you didn't say yes when he asked you out?' Michele ventured.

Jessie sighed. 'Yes. I did. We're on for Friday night,' she confessed.

'Playing hard to get, I see. Smart girl.'

'You call that playing hard to get?' Jessie put Kane's book down on her part of the work station and pulled out her chair.

'Sure. That's five whole days since you met him.'

Jessie sank down into her chair. 'Actually, it will be a week since I met him.'

Michele's eyes widened. 'Really? You'd met him before the interview on Monday?'

'Yes. In a bar in town last Friday night. But we didn't exchange names. I—er—drank with him and danced with him, but I did a flit when he wanted more than dancing. He was as shocked as I was when I showed up here yesterday.'

'Shocked, but still pleased. He's obviously very taken with you, Jessie.'

'You think so? It's hard to tell with men. It could just be sex, you know.'

'Nothing wrong with that. Lots of relationships start with sex. Don't fall into the trap of being too cynical about men, Jessie. There are some genuinely good ones out there. I don't know Kane all that well, but what I know I like. Everyone here thinks he's

great. So give him a chance. Oh, and don't forget to
go thank him for the book. He'll be dying to know
what you think, I'll bet. Lunch-time would be a good
time, when Karen's out. She and Margaret have
lunch together at a café up the road every day at one.
Kane has his lunch delivered, Margaret tells me. He's
an obsessive reader and usually stays at his desk.
You could pop along any time after one and he'd be
all alone.'

'Are you sure that's a good idea?'

'Why not? What do you think he's going to do?
Ravish you on his desk?'

Jessie didn't like to admit that that was exactly
what she thought he might do. Worse was the reality
that she wouldn't mind one bit.

She'd already come into work wearing a skirt, instead of jeans. And no stockings.

The clear blue sky this morning had promised a
hot summer's day, so her selection of a pink and
white floral wrap-around skirt, a simple pink T-shirt
and slip-on white sandals was really quite an appropriate outfit for work. No one could have guessed by
just looking at her that whilst she'd dressed she'd
secretly thrilled to the thought of how accessible she
was, if by some chance Kane found the time and the
place to seduce her at work.

Stupid fantasy, really. But darned exciting to think
about.

By lunch-time, every nerve-ending in Jessie's
body was tap-dancing. She was grateful when
Michele left to do some shopping. A trip to the
ladies' room assured her that her make-up was still

in place. She wouldn't have been surprised if it had melted all over her face. But she looked OK. Her hair was up, secured by a long pink clip. She toyed with taking it down, then decided that would be on the obvious side. The last thing she wanted was to be obvious.

Thankfully she had a good excuse for going to his office. She didn't want to show up looking like a desperate. Even if she was fast becoming one.

Another attack of nerves sent her bolting into a toilet cubicle. Five minutes later, she was back at her desk, where she skip-read a few chapters of the book to get the gist of it whilst she stuffed down one of the two sandwiches she'd brought from home. That done, she made her way to Kane's office. It was one-twenty.

Karen's desk was blessedly empty. Fate hadn't made her stay back for some reason. Jessie's heart sank, however, when she saw the door to the inner office was half open and a woman's voice was emerging.

Don't tell me Karen is in there with him, she thought.

Jessie took a couple of steps towards the door, grinding to a halt when the woman—who didn't sound like Karen—said something about being pregnant.

'Pregnant!' Kane exclaimed in a shocked voice. 'Good God, Natalie.'

Jessie sucked in sharply. Natalie. That was his ex-wife's name.

'Don't worry, darling,' the woman said in a droll

tone. 'It's not yours. I'm only a month gone and it's at least a couple of months since we were together. Besides, if I recall rightly, you used a condom.'

Jessie's heart squeezed tight. A couple of months ago Kane had still been sleeping with his ex. Yet he'd made her think he'd been celibate since they split up over a year ago. She'd thought at the time that was unlikely. What other women had he lied to her about?

'Who's the father?' she heard Kane ask.

'Some guy I met at a party. A lawyer. I didn't even find out his last name, would you believe? But I could find it out if I want to.'

'What are you going to do about the baby?'

'I know you'll think I'm mad, but I'm going to have it.'

'You're joking!'

'No. No, Kane, I'm not.'

Jessie couldn't bear to stand there, listening to any more of this conversation. She turned and fled back down the corridor as quietly as her pounding heart would permit. Tears threatened, but she made it back to the toilet cubicle, dry-eyed. Even then, strangely, she didn't cry. She wanted to, but something inside her was damming back the tears, a big, cold, angry lump.

One part of her wanted to go back and confront him, throw his lies in his face. But another part of her argued that to do that was to finish it between them.

Could she bear that? To walk away without going to bed with him, at least once?

Jessie supposed she could. She could do just about anything once she put her mind to it.

But it would be hard, especially with his being here at work every day. She would keep running into him. And wanting him.

So, no, she wouldn't be confronting him, Jessie decided as she made her way back to her desk. Or accusing him. She would use him as he was using her. For sex.

At least this added knowledge of his character would stop her from falling in love with him. The man was a lying scumbag, like most men. An empty charmer. Just because he'd made a raging success of his professional life didn't make him a good guy, as he claimed to be.

When she thought about his choice of career it suited him very well. What was he, really, but a glorified salesman? A con artist. A seller of dreams. Such seminars as he conducted preyed on people's weaknesses, making them think they could be winners too, if only they listened to him. He'd spin her a whole world of dreams too, if she let him.

But she wasn't going to let him. Or listen to him. He could talk all the bulldust he liked. None of it was going to get to her any more.

'What are you muttering to yourself about?'

His voice behind her came out of the blue, startling her.

Jessie swallowed, then spun slowly round on her office chair, a cool smile at the ready.

'Just thinking of all the things I have to do before

Christmas,' she said, her eyes running over the man himself for the first time that day.

Yes, he *was* gorgeous. Utterly. With that air of masculine confidence which she found almost irresistible.

But she was ready for him now, ready and armed with the knowledge of his true self.

'I did offer to take you shopping,' he said with one of his winning smiles.

'So you did. And I might have to take you up on that by this time next week.'

'What about this Saturday? Emily could come with us. I promise I'll have a proper car seat by then.'

Jessie found her own smile. A slow smile. A saucy smile. 'Do you think you'll be capable of getting out of bed after Friday night?'

His blue eyes registered shock. But then he smiled back. 'Is that a challenge of some sort?'

'Let's just say it's been a while for me. I might take some satisfying.'

A flicker of a frown skittered across his face. 'Boy, when you decide to do something you do it full throttle, don't you?'

'I have a take-no-prisoners attitude to life sometimes.'

'That's what I like about you. You're so damned honest and upfront. Except when you're cruising bars looking for straying hubbies, that is,' he added ruefully.

Jessie shrugged. 'That's all in the past now that I have a decent job. And it's not as though most of those guys didn't deserve to get caught. So tell me, Kane, were you ever unfaithful to your wife?'

'What a question!'

'One you don't want to answer, I see.'

'No, I don't mind answering it. I was never unfaithful. I sowed my wild oats plenty in my younger years. Once I got married, however, I put all that behind me.'

'One of the good guys,' she said just a fraction tartly.

He frowned. 'I take it you're still not convinced.'

'Does it matter?'

'It matters to me.'

Jessie decided this conversation was running off the rails. 'By the way, thank you for your book. I was suitably impressed. And a little surprised. I didn't realise you were famous.'

'I'm not so famous,' he said modestly.

'But you will be. Your book is fabulous.' Jessie knew you could never flatter a man enough. Flattery, she could handle. And flirting. Just no falling in love.

He looked so ridiculously pleased, she felt guilty. 'But you can't possibly have read it yet.'

'Well, not properly. But I will. Before Friday night.'

'Stop talking about Friday night!' he suddenly bit out in an agitated fashion. 'I know it's only three days away, but after last night it seems like an eternity. I don't think I slept a wink.'

He did look tired, now that she came to think of it. There were dark circles under his eyes.

'I didn't sleep very well myself,' she confessed.

'Jessie, this is ridiculous. Why should we torture ourselves? Be with me tonight. Get Dora to mind Emily. She told me last night that she'd be quite happy to mind Emily any night we wanted to go out. I asked her. I even offered to pay her but she refused. She said she'd be happy to do it any time.'

Jessie felt both flustered and furious. 'You had no right to go behind my back like that.'

'No right to do what?' he countered. 'Try to organise things so that I can spend some time with a woman I'm crazy about?'

Jessie flushed at the passion in his voice. 'I told you. I don't like to be rushed.'

His sigh was ragged. 'OK. Yes, I am rushing you. I'm sorry. It's just that life is so short and when you see something that you really want, you have to reach out and grab it before something happens and it gets away from you.'

'Is that what you tell people in your book?'

'Not that I recall. This is something which has come upon me just lately. It's possibly worse today.'

'Why is it worse today?'

'Would you believe my ex-wife has just been in to see me? And guess what? She's pregnant, by some guy she doesn't even know the name of. *And* she's going to keep the baby.' Kane shook his head in utter bewilderment.

'What's wrong with that?' Jessie challenged. For pity's sake, did he expect her to have an abortion? He'd divorced her because she wanted children. The man just didn't understand how strong the maternal impulse could be. She could never have terminated *her* baby, and she hadn't even been craving one at the time.

'You don't know Natalie,' he muttered. 'She's not the single-mother type.'

'Is there a single-mother type?'

'No. I guess not. It was just so unexpected, not to mention quick. Our divorce papers only came through three months ago. You can imagine how I felt when she announced she was pregnant.'

Actually, Jessie didn't have to imagine anything. She'd been there and heard his reaction. He'd been worried sick that it was *his*.

'It's not as though you're still in love with her,' Jessie said impatiently. '*Are* you?'

'No, of course not!'

'Then her having another man's baby is irrelevant. Leave her to her life and you get on with yours.'

He stared at her for a second before his mouth broke into a wry grin. 'Yes, Dr Denton. I'll do just that. Which brings me back to tonight. What do you say, Jessie? Would you let me take you out to dinner? Just dinner.'

That was about as believable as 'the cheque's in the post'!

Jessie scooped in a deep breath whilst every pore in her screamed at her to agree. But to say yes would be the kiss of death. She'd show her weakness and then he'd have her right where he wanted her.

'I'm sorry, Kane,' she said, quite truthfully. 'I make it a policy never to go out during the week. You'll just have to wait. You can always have a lot of cold showers,' she suggested with more than a hint of malice.

Their eyes met, and held.

'I don't think there's enough cold water in the world to fix my problem,' he bit out. 'Still, I guess I'll survive. But I would suggest that if you're going to come into work each day looking good enough to eat, then for pity's sake, keep well out of my way!'

CHAPTER ELEVEN

'Mummy's got a boyfriend! Mummy's got a boyfriend! Mummy's got a...'

'Yes, all right, Emily,' Jessie interrupted sharply. 'I've heard you. And do stop jumping up and down on your bed. It's not a trampoline. Look, go and put a video on. I'll never be ready in time if you keep distracting me.'

Emily was off the bed and out of the room in a flash. If there was one thing that would successfully shut Emily up, it was watching one of her favourite videos.

Being left alone, however, didn't help Jessie as much as she had hoped. Her hands kept shaking for starters, and her usually decisive mind could not seem to settle on what she should wear tonight.

Kane had told her in an email yesterday—one of several he'd sent her during the last three days—that she didn't need to be dressed up. Something casual would be fine.

Jessie had been relieved at the time. Her wardrobe was ninety-five per cent casual. But most were on the cheap side.

The evening promised to be warm, so a skirt was probably a good choice. She pulled out a black and white one similar to the pink floral she'd worn to

119

work the other day, the one which Kane had said made her look good enough to eat.

Oh, dear. She shouldn't have thought about that. Her nipples tightened and a little tremor ran down the back of her legs.

A glance at her watch brought instant panic. She only had a quarter of an hour before Kane was due to pick her up at seven. She'd already showered and done her make-up since arriving home, but she was still naked under her robe, her hair was a mess and Dora would be arriving any moment with Emily's dinner.

The darling woman had promised to feed the child, as well as look after her for the night. She seemed just as excited at Jessie having a so-called boyfriend as Emily was. Jessie hadn't liked to disillusion them over Kane's true intentions—they both thought he was the ant's pants—so she let them think what they liked.

Meanwhile, Jessie just kept telling herself that to-night was nothing serious. Just fun and games.

'Fun and games,' she repeated as she opened her underwear drawer and pulled out a black satin bra and matching G-string from underneath her more sensible sets. They had been outrageously expensive when she'd bought them pre-Emily, and had rarely been worn. Motherhood had made her breasts larger, so when she put the bra on, her cups really did run-neth over.

But oh, my, she did look seriously sexy, with a cleavage deeper than the Grand Canyon. The G-string looked OK from the front. But she didn't even risk a peek at a rear view. What she didn't know couldn't depress her.

A knock on the granny-flat door was followed by Dora's voice as she opened the door and came in. 'It's just me, Jessie, with Em's dinner.'

'I'm still not ready, Dora. Can you organise things out there for a few minutes?'

'No worries. We'll be fine, won't we, Emily?'

No reply from Emily.

'Emily,' her mother shouted whilst she manoeuvred on the stretchy black cross-over top she'd bought to go with the skirt. 'Sit up at the table for Dora. I've set a place for her, Dora. And her apple juice is in her special cup in the fridge.'

'Yes, yes, stop fussing. I can manage. You get on with getting ready. Kane will be here soon, you know.'

'I know,' Jessie muttered, hurriedly wrapping the skirt around her hips and tying the sash tightly at the back. One thing motherhood hadn't improved on her figure was her waistline. It was slightly thicker now. Still, her bigger bust and hips balanced that, so the overall look was still hourglass.

Reasonably satisfied with the result—the amount of flesh she had on display in the deep V-neckline gave her a few butterflies—Jessie turned to doing something with her hair, which was a bit of a frizz, due to the humidity in the air. The only thing for it was up, of course. So up it went, brushed back from her face quite brutally and anchored to her crown with a black scrunchie.

Naturally, quite a few strands and curls escaped

but guys had always told her they liked that. They said it looked sexy. And sexy was definitely the look she was aiming for tonight.

Her jewelry she kept to a minimum. A silver chain locket necklace and silver loop earrings. Her perfume was an expensive one, a present from Dora for her birthday back in June. It was called True Love.

True irony, Jessie thought wryly as she slipped her feet into the same strappy black high heels she'd worn the previous Friday. Her only regret about her appearance was that she hadn't invested in some fake tan. No sleeves and no stockings meant that a lot of her pale flesh was on display. But she hadn't been paid yet and could have only afforded the cheap variety. Better to have no tan than to have orange streaks and oddly coloured elbows and ankles.

'Kane's here,' Dora chimed out a few seconds before he knocked on the door. She must have heard his footsteps on the concrete path which led around to the granny flat.

'Coming,' Jessie replied, amazed at how nauseous she was suddenly feeling. What had happened to the carefree girl she'd used to be?

Well, that girl was gone, Jessie realised, replaced by a nervous wreck who was scared stiff that she'd be so hopeless that Kane wouldn't want to see her again after tonight. Which might be for the best. But somehow, at this precise moment, wisdom wasn't Jessie's long suit.

Thinking about the girl she had used to be, however, reminded her that she didn't have any condoms. Still, she was sure Kane would be well prepared. A man who didn't want children would *always* be prepared.

'Kane! Kane!' Emily's excited voice reached Jessie.

Jessie hoped her daughter didn't start chanting to him about his being her mummy's boyfriend.

'Won't be a sec,' she called out from the bedroom as she hurriedly put her make-up, brush and wallet into her black patent evening bag and headed for the bedroom door.

Kane hadn't actually come inside. He'd stayed standing on the back doorstep under the light that shone down from above.

'Oh,' she said on seeing him. 'We're colour co-ordinated.'

He was wearing a black suit—casually tailored—with a white T-shirt underneath. No doubt a very expensive designer white T-shirt. Not that it mattered. On him, anything looked good.

By the look in his eyes what she was wearing was meeting with *his* approval as well. It was good that men rarely knew what a woman's clothes cost. She wouldn't mind betting that his T-shirt had cost more than her whole outfit. Minus the lingerie and the shoes, of course. They *had* been expensive.

'Doesn't Mummy look pretty?' Emily said from where Dora, by some miracle, had kept her sitting at the table, eating her dinner. Admittedly, it was spaghetti bolognaise, Emily's favourite. But Jessie had pictured her daughter hurling herself into Kane's arms the moment he arrived.

'Yes, indeed,' Kane agreed with gleaming eyes.

'Are you going to ask Mummy to marry you?'

It was just the sort of question Jessie had feared.

She groaned her embarrassment whilst Dora laughed.

Kane, the suave devil, took it in his stride. 'Would you like me to?' he said.

'Oh, yes,' Emily replied.

'Your wish is my command, princess. The trouble is I don't think your mummy's quite ready to marry *me* yet.'

'Why not?' Emily demanded to know, scowling up at her mother.

'Kane and I have only known each other a week,' Jessie said with more patience than she was feeling. 'You don't marry someone until you've known them much longer than that.'

'Two weeks?' Emily suggested, and both Dora and Kane laughed.

Jessie rolled her eyes. 'At *least* two weeks. Now, you be good for Dora tonight and go to bed when she tells you to. Thanks a bunch, Dora.'

'My pleasure, love. Just you and Kane have a good time. And don't go thinking you have to rush home. Stay out as long as you like. I'll go to sleep on your sofa.'

'I shouldn't be too late,' Jessie said firmly. More for Kane's ears than Dora's. 'Bye, sweetie.' She gave Emily a kiss. 'Love you. See you in the morning.'

'At least two weeks, eh?' Kane said as they walked together along the side-path. 'In that case, we should be engaged by Christmas.'

'Very funny,' Jessie said.

'Who says I'm joking?'

'Kane, *stop* it.'

'Stop what?'

Jessie ground to a halt beside Dora's prized hydrangeas, which were in full bloom. 'Stop being ridiculous. You and I both know you would never marry me.'

'Why not?'

'For one thing I have Emily.'

'I think Emily's fantastic. Cutest kid I've ever met.'

Jessie shook her head in exasperation. 'This is a stupid conversation and I don't want to continue it.'

'Good, because I'm sick of talking, anyway.' Before she could read his intention, he pulled her into his arms and kissed her, right there and then.

Jessie's first instinct was to struggle. What if Dora came out and around the side of the house and saw them? She even opened her mouth to protest.

Silly move.

His tongue darted inside and she didn't think about anything much after that for a full five minutes. By the time he let her come up for air, her head was swimming and her body was on the countdown to lift-off. She actually moaned in dismay when his mouth lifted. Her fingers tightened on what she thought was his back, but was actually her evening bag, resting against his back.

'Now I know what to do with you,' he said thickly as he stroked an erotic finger over her puffy lips. 'Every time you start to get stroppy tonight, I'm going to kiss you. So be warned and try to behave yourself in the restaurant. Unless, of course, you'd rather we didn't go out to eat. We could drive straight to my place if you prefer. I do have food there in my freezer and a perfectly good microwave. Wine too, and fresh fruit. I'm actually quite domesticated. I only turn into a wild beast around you.'

'I like the wild beast,' she heard herself saying in a low, husky voice. But that finger on her lips felt incredible. Before she could think better of it, her tongue-tip came out to meet it. He stared down at her mouth and then slowly, ever so slowly, inserted his finger inside.

Her stomach somersaulted.

'Suck it,' he commanded. And she did, thinking all the while that she would do anything he told her to do tonight.

The thought blew her away. This was dangerous territory she'd just entered. But more exciting than anything she'd ever experienced before. Lyall was kindergarten playtime compared to this man.

His blue eyes narrowed as he watched her blindly obey him.

His tortured groan shocked her, as did the way he reefed his finger out, as if she were a cobra, not a woman on the verge of becoming his sex slave.

'Enough,' he growled. 'You are one contrary woman, Jessie Denton,' he added. 'You run hot and cold all the time. So what is it to be tonight? You decide. The restaurant, or my place?'

Jessie was way beyond hypocrisy. She was as turned on as she knew he was. Any further delay would brand her a tease and she'd never been that.

'Your place,' she said, dropping her arms back to her sides as she took a step back from him.

He didn't reply, just grabbed her free hand and dragged her out to his car as if the hounds of hell were after them.

'Belt up,' he ordered as he fired the engine. 'And no chit-chat. It's not that far to my place at Balmoral but the traffic's heavy going into the city. I need to concentrate.'

Balmoral, she thought, her earlier dazed state slowly receding. An exclusive inner north-shore sub-urb with an equally exclusive beach. She'd been there once to a restaurant on its foreshores. Very up-market. Very pricy. After the recent housing boom, even the simplest apartment there would cost the earth.

She couldn't see Kane having a simple apartment. It would be a sleek bachelor pad with a view and jacuzzi. Or a penthouse, with a pool, leather furniture and a king-size animal-print-covered bed.

She was wrong on both counts. First it was a house, not an apartment. Secondly, it wasn't modern or overtly masculine. It was old—probably built in the thirties—with lots of art deco features and loads of antique furniture. The only thing she was right about was the water-view, which was magnificent from its site up on the side of a hill.

'Did you live here with your wife?' were Jessie's first words after he had led her into the cosy front sitting room. Through the windows she could see the sea down below. And the lights of the restaurant she'd once visited.

'No,' he replied. 'We had an apartment in town. I bought this when we separated. My parents live a couple of streets away. And my brother lives in the next suburb.'

Jessie thought it was nice that he'd chosen to live so close to his family.

'This is not what I expected,' she said.

He smiled. 'I know. That's one reason why I wanted to bring you here. Seeing for yourself is worth a thousand words. I keep telling you I'm not what you think, Jessie. Now, put that infernal bag down and come here...'

Jessie sucked in sharply. She should have known he'd get right down to it, once they were alone. It was what she wanted too. Inside.

But her earlier decision to come here and jump straight into bed with him had been easy when she was still in his arms, with his kisses still hot in her memory and his finger in her mouth. Not quite so easy standing here in his living room with the lights on and nothing but the sound of the sea in the background.

He frowned at her when she didn't move. 'Don't tell me you're nervous. Or that you've changed your mind,' he added darkly.

'No. No, I haven't changed my mind. But yes, I am nervous,' she confessed shakily. 'It's been so long and I...'

'How long?' he broke in.

Jessie was shocked when tears pricked at her eyes. Goodness, what was there to be crying about? 'I...I haven't been with a man since Lyall.'

She was thankful that he didn't act all surprised, or suspicious, over this statement of fact.

'I see,' he said simply, then smiled. A soft, almost loving smile. 'That's wonderful.'

She was the one who was shocked. 'Wonderful? What's wonderful about it? I've probably forgotten how to do it!'

He laughed. 'You haven't forgotten, sweetheart. You're a natural. But if you have,' he said as he walked forward and put her bag down for her, 'you have me to show you how all over again. But *my* way. Not Lyall's way, or any other man's way.'

'And what's your way?' she choked out as he took her hand and started leading her from the room.

The look he threw over his shoulder sent shivers rippling down her spine. 'The way which gives you the most pleasure, of course. I have a plan, as usual. But if at first I don't succeed, then I'll try, try again. You might be amazed at how many times I can make love in five hours.'

'It...it's already half past seven,' Jessie blurted out, trying to stop herself from totally losing it. But dear heaven, he meant to make love to her for the whole five hours?

'So I'll be a little late getting you home,' he said as he drew her through a doorway, switching on a light as he went. 'I'm sure Dora will forgive me.'

The room was, naturally, a bedroom. A huge bedroom with polished wooden floorboards, high ceilings, antique furniture and a wide brass bed covered in a silvery grey satin quilt with matching pillows. The lamps each side of the bed had brass bases with

white shades and long fringes. The chandelier over-
head was crystal and brass. Lace curtains covered the
long windows on the wall adjacent to the bed. In the
opposite wall was another door, which was open and
led into an *en suite* bathroom. The light shone in just
far enough for Jessie to see it was more modern than
the rest of the house, being all white. Possibly a recent renovation.

It was a beautiful bedroom, only the colour of the
bedding betraying that a man slept here, and not a
woman.

Although, of course, women could have slept here.
With Kane. His ex-wife perhaps. And others Kane
had forgotten to mention.

Jessie didn't like that thought.

'What's wrong?' Kane said immediately.

'Nothing,' she lied.

'Come, now, Jessie, don't lie to me. You looked
at that bed and something not very nice came into
your mind. What was it?'

'I guess I didn't like to think of you having been
in there with other women.'

'But I told you. There have been no other women
since Natalie.'

'What about Natalie?'

'What about her?'

'You slept with her recently. I know you did. I
overheard both of you in the office the other day. I
went to thank you for the book at lunch-time that
day and you were discussing her pregnancy and she
said you weren't to worry, because it wasn't yours.'

Kane stared at her. 'Why didn't you say anything before this?'

'I...I didn't want to.'

'You just kept it to yourself and held it against me. Hell, Jessie, I wish you'd said something.'

'Would it have changed anything? You did sleep with her, didn't you?'

His grimace showed true anguish. 'Look, it was three months ago and only the once. We'd met up in her flat the night our divorce papers came through. She'd offered to cook me dinner as a kind of celebration, to show there were no hard feelings. We had too many glasses of wine over dinner and she said how about it, for old times' sake? If I hadn't been drunk and lonely it would never have happened. I can't tell you how much I regretted it afterwards. So did she, I think. It wasn't even good sex. We were both plastered. I didn't mention it because I didn't want you to think I was one of those guys who get rid of their wives and then keep sleeping with them when they feel like a bit, as a lot do. I'm sorry, Jessie. I wasn't trying to deceive you. I just wanted you to believe me when I said on that first Friday night that I wasn't in the habit of picking up women. You were a one-off, believe me. You still are. I want you, Jessie, more than any woman I've ever known. And I know you want me. Please don't keep finding excuses to push me away.'

Jessie knew he was a good talker. A clever persuader. But there was a sincerity in his voice and his eyes that touched her. Surely, he *had* to be telling the truth.

'You really haven't been with anyone else?' she asked.

'Cross my heart and hope to die.'

'I wouldn't want you to die, Kane,' she murmured, stepping forward and snaking her arms up around his neck. 'I want you very much alive.'

He groaned, his mouth crashing down to take hers in a kiss of mind-blowing hunger. Their tongues met, danced, demanded. Their bodies pressed closer, and closer. Their hips jammed together, then ground against each other.

'No, no, not that again,' he gasped as his mouth burst free from hers. 'I haven't waited the last three days for that.'

Her head was spinning but she concurred whole-heartedly. That was not what she wanted, either. She wanted him naked, and inside her. She wanted it all.

She reached round behind her back to untie the bow.

'No,' he said swiftly. 'Let me…'

Kane started undressing her as no man had ever done in her life. So slowly and sensually, his eyes smouldering with desire, his hands not quite steady. First to be disposed of was her skirt, leaving her standing there before him with nothing below her hips but that skimpy G-string.

'Arms up,' he ordered, then he took her top by its hem and began to peel it upwards over her head.

The action covered her eyes for a second or two, Jessie quivering in her momentary darkness, turned on by the thought of how she must look with her arms up, her face masked, but her body being more

and more exposed to his gaze. She'd never thrilled
to a sex-slave fantasy before but she did so now,
imagining herself having been bought by him, being
a helpless prisoner to his passion, with no other purpose than to be an instrument of pleasure.

Not her own.

Suddenly, her own pleasure seemed irrelevant.
This was all for him. Her lord and master. Her soon-
to-be lover.

Even when her top was thrown away, she kept her
eyes shut, enjoying the sensation of being outside
herself, looking in on what was happening with her
mind. She heard him gasp. In admiration, she hoped.

And then his hands were on her again, still soft,
but just as knowing. He took her G-string off first,
which surprised her. She wobbled a bit when he
picked up first one foot and then the other. She stiffened expectantly when he straightened, sucking in
sharply when one of his hands stroked over her belly.
Her eyes squeezed even more tightly together when
it drifted lower, a startled gasp torn from her throat
when both his hands slid between her thighs. But he
didn't touch her there, just eased her legs apart.

'Yes, like that,' she heard him say.

And then his hands were gone, only to be felt
again on her bra clasp. When it gave way and her
breasts were finally naked before his eyes, she felt
no embarrassment, only the most all-consuming
craving to have them touched.

But he didn't touch them.

'Open your eyes,' he told her forcefully.

Of course she obeyed. How could she not? It was the voice of the master.

Opening her eyes, however, brought a wave of dizziness.

'Watch it,' he said, and grabbed her shoulders to steady her swaying body.

Once she was still, his hands moved up to dispose of the scrunchie, letting her hair tumble in wild disarray around her shoulders.

She had never been so turned on, or so compliant.

'I want you to just stand there like that,' he murmured, 'whilst I get undressed.'

Of course, she thought. What else would I do?

He stripped off his own clothes much faster than he had hers. And he took off everything, displaying the kind of body she'd imagined him to have. Muscly and hard, with not too much body hair, a broad chest and a six-pack stomach.

Jessie tried not to stare when he collected a condom from the bedside chest and drew it on.

But she did lick her very dry bottom lip.

'No, not that either,' he snapped, misinterpreting her action. 'Not yet. Later.'

Whatever you want, she almost said. Whenever you want it.

He walked around her a couple of times, just looking at her, standing there in nothing but her high heels. Only when she was at screaming point did he touch her, coming up close from behind, pushing her hair away from one shoulder and bending his head to kiss her neck, softly at first, then more hungrily.

The wild beast swiftly emerged again, and soon

he was sucking on her throat whilst his hands ran roughly up and down her arms. Her back automatically arched against him, the action lifting her breasts in wanton invitation. This time he obliged, cupping them in his hands and squeezing them together whilst his thumbpads rubbed rather cruelly over the already stiffened nipples.

Sensations shot through her like a series of lightning bolts, sizzling with electricity, leaving her burning with a fire which she knew could only be erased one way.

His mouth covered her ear, hot and heavy with his breathing.

'Don't close your legs,' he commanded on a raw whisper.

And then he took her hands in his and stretched them out in front of her, bending her forward till her fingers reached the nearest brass bedpost.

'Hold on to that,' he advised.

Very good advice. Because she might have fallen otherwise. Or fainted.

No man had ever made love to her like this before, in this position. Jessie's head whirled. But there was little time to think before he was inside her, holding her hips captive whilst he ground into her body.

She had never experienced anything so decadent before. But it felt so delicious this way. Wild and wicked and wonderfully wanton. Her mind swiftly joined her body in quest of nothing but more of the pleasure which was rippling through her entire body. She started rocking back and forth against him, tightening her insides in response to each of his forward thrusts.

'Oh, God,' he groaned. 'Yes, yes, that's it, sweetheart. That's the way.'

He let go of her hips and took hold of each of her nipples with his thumbs and forefingers, squeezing them and pulling them downwards. The combination of sensations was way beyond pleasure. It reached the outer stratosphere.

Jessie cried out, then splintered apart with the most intense orgasm she had ever had. By the time Kane followed her several seconds later, she felt as if she'd fallen into quicksand. She clung on to that bedpost for dear life, knowing that if she let go she would surely sink to the floor.

And then she *was* sinking, but somehow she didn't hit the floor. Instead, Kane scooped her up in his arms. How could he do that? her befuddled mind tried to grasp. He was behind her, deep inside her still throbbing flesh. She could still feel him there. But, no, it seemed he wasn't there any longer. She *was* being carried, and being lain down on top of his bed, his very soft, very comfortable bed. He started stroking her hair and her back and her legs, and that wave of exhaustion which had been hovering at the edges of her mind floated softly down over her. She mumbled something. It might have been 'thank you'. She yawned.

Then everything went black.

CHAPTER TWELVE

KANE returned from his trip to the bathroom to gaze down at Jessie asleep on top of his bed, smiling when he saw that she still had those sexy shoes on her feet. Carefully, slowly, he picked up each foot and removed them. She didn't stir.

He'd read her right. She liked men who took charge in the bedroom, who treated her to a bit of caveman style. Yet Kane had never acted quite like that with a female before. Natalie had been of the ilk who, ultimately, liked to be on top. To begin with, he'd liked the fact he didn't have to work hard for his sex. Time and familiarity, however, had eventually dulled his desire for her. Lack of love too, Kane realised. Resentment had built up over her unwillingness to have his children and by the end he hadn't been interested in pleasing her.

He wanted to please Jessie Denton more than any woman he'd ever met. Of course, that was because he'd fallen in love with her. Deeply. Truly. It wasn't just lust. Or fool's love, as he called it. He'd been there, done that, and he knew the difference. He wanted her, not just as his lover but also as his wife and the mother of his children. He might have only known her a week, but he was surer of that than he had been of anything in his life.

He suspected she felt pretty strongly about him,

too. But she was wary after her experience with that scumbag, Lyall. Cynicism was stopping her from seeing he was sincere.

Pity about her overhearing him with Natalie like that. She must have thought him a callous liar. But despite that she'd agreed to come out with him, something she hadn't done in years. His male ego had been very flattered when she'd told him he was the first man she'd been with since Emily's father. His love for her had grown at the news she didn't sleep around. As had his respect. She had character, did Jessie Denton. A tremor ran down Kane's spine as he recalled the force of her orgasm.

He couldn't wait for her to wake up. He was already hard again.

Why *should* you wait? spoke up the caveman still lurking inside him. She wouldn't want to sleep the evening through. If you want her, wake her, take her. Go to it, tiger!

Kane didn't hesitate. He hurried over to the top drawer of the bedside chest, where he'd dropped a newly opened box of condoms earlier that day. Twenty seconds later, he stretched himself out beside her still unconscious form and began trailing his fingers up and down her spine.

Jessie surfaced to consciousness with a shiver of pleasure. Yet it took quite a few seconds for awareness of where she was and what had happened earlier on to strike.

Oh, dear, she thought, grimacing into the pillow. Thankfully she was lying face down. It gave her some extra moments to compose herself before she had to admit she was awake.

Though maybe she wouldn't. Maybe she'd just lie there and pretend she wasn't really awake, just stirring in her sleep. But then that hand, which was sending shivers up and down her spine, moved into territory that jackknifed her over.

'Don't do that!' she gasped.

He smiled, then slid that devilish hand back between her legs. 'Glad to see you've rejoined the living,' he said as he teased her with a fingertip.

She flushed, then gasped when he lightly grazed over her exquisitely swollen peak. 'You're not a good guy at all,' she said breathlessly. 'You're wicked.'

His smile broadened. 'I'll take that as a compliment. Do you want to be on top this time?'

Her mouth fell open as she stared up at him. She had never been with a man who was so forthright, or so...so...

'No? That's OK. Next time, perhaps.' And he bent his head to her nearest nipple. At the same time that tantalising finger stopped what it was doing to delve further into her.

Jessie's mind was torn between two sources of pleasure. His mouth on her breast, licking, sucking, nibbling. But it was what was happening inside her which had her breathing really hard. Her belly began to tighten and she thought she would warn him.

'I...I'm going to come,' she blurted out.

He lifted his head and smiled. 'That's good. Now, are you sure you don't want to be on top?'

It must have been a rhetorical question because before she knew it, he'd hauled her up to be straddling him.

'Now take me in your hands and just ease me inside you as you sink down,' he instructed, sensing perhaps that she'd never done it like this before either. Jessie realised that she'd had a rather boring sex life up till now. Lyall had been forceful in bed but selfish, she realised. Her other boyfriends had just been ignorant. Only her natural love of being kissed and caressed and, yes, penetrated had made those sexual encounters pleasurable.

She took Kane in her hands. Just the thought of putting him inside her body with her own hands was so exciting.

Suddenly, shyness wasn't an option.

'Hey,' he said when her fingers enclosed tight around him. 'Gently does it.'

She didn't even blush. She was too focused on feeling his beautiful hardness, then inserting him deep into her eagerly accepting flesh. And ooh…it felt as good as she had known it would. No further instructions were needed, though he did take hold of her hips when she began to ride him. Probably to slow her down. The urge to go faster and faster was almost unbearable. Her need for release was intense.

'Yes!' she cried out when the first spasm hit.

He must have come, too. She vaguely recalled his own raw groan of release whilst she was moaning and groaning. When she finally collapsed across him, his arms enclosed her, very tenderly, she thought.

This time, she didn't fall asleep. She didn't feel tired at all. Just blissfully at peace. And incredibly happy.

When he eventually rolled her over and eased himself out of her body, she actually whimpered in protest. It had felt lovely with him still inside her. As he moved off the bed and away from her, the feeling of abandonment was acute. And worrisome.

How could she ever live without this again? How could she ever live without *him*?

The prospect appalled her.

He'd gone to the bathroom. She could hear him in there, whistling. The shower taps were turned on and she was imagining him in there washing himself all over when suddenly he was standing in the doorway, stark naked and dripping wet.

'OK, get yourself in here, woman,' he said. 'Refresh time.'

Jessie wanted to. Desperately. But didn't that make her a desperate? She had to stay cool, and strong.

'You and I know what will happen if I get in the shower with you,' she pointed out with what she hoped was sufficient sophistication. 'And I couldn't possibly do it again. Not this soon. Besides, I'm getting hungry. I'll need something to eat soon.'

'Funny you should say that,' he quipped, a wicked gleam in his eyes.

Jessie's mouth opened, then closed again. He meant it. He actually meant it. Worse, the idea excited her. She was getting to be as wicked as he was.

'Do you want me to come over there and carry

you?' he challenged. 'I will if you don't get that delicious butt of yours off that bed in five seconds flat.'

The thought of his carrying her naked body in his
arms was almost as thrilling as her going down on
him in the shower.

She stayed right where she was, and six seconds
later he swept her up into his masterful and muscular
arms.

'Just before I forget to tell you,' he said as he
carried her into the bathroom, 'I think you are the
most beautiful, sexiest, loveliest woman I have ever
met.'

His words startled her. But she tried not to let them
turn her head—or her heart—too much. Men like
Kane were always good with words.

'Knowing you, you're sure to be thinking I'm only
interested in you for sex,' he went on. 'And I have
to confess,' he added as he placed her down under
the hot jets of water, 'that right at this moment, sex
is pretty much my main focus.'

His hands reached up to smooth her hair back from
her face whilst the water soaked it through.

Jessie had often seen movies where water was
used as a symbol of eroticism. Now she knew why.
There was something primal about standing naked
with your lover under water. The way it ran down
over your body, making you aware of every exposed
curve and hidden orifice. It splashed inside her
mouth, beat on her nipples, pooled in her navel and
ran down between her buttocks, soaking her secret
places before trickling down her inner thighs.

'But it's the same for you tonight, isn't it?' he

murmured as he cradled her face with his hands and looked deep into her dilated eyes. 'We need this, you and I. Need to do everything to each other. We have to get this out of the way first or we won't be able to think of anything else. I've dreamt about you like this all week. Naked and willing in my bed, and in my shower, and in every room of my house. I won't let you wear any clothes tonight, Jessie, not even when we're eating. You're going to stay naked for me. You're going to let me touch you whenever I want to, *take* you whenever I want to. Give me permission, beautiful Jessie. Tell me that you want that, too.'

'Yes,' she heard herself say from some darkly erotic far-off place. 'Yes...'

CHAPTER THIRTEEN

'WELL? How was it last night?' Dora asked when they finally caught up with each other over mid-morning coffee. 'I was too sleepy to ask you when you got home. Sorry. I hope you didn't think I was rude to leave like that.'

Jessie had actually been grateful. She'd staggered home around one, having declined Kane's offer to walk her to the door, using the excuse that it was late enough. But she must have looked a right mess with her hair all over the place and not a scrap of make-up remaining on her face. Anyone other than a half-asleep old lady would have known on sight that she'd been having sex all night.

Jessie swallowed at the memory. Not just sex. Hot sex. Incredible sex. Sex such as she'd never known before.

'I had a very enjoyable time,' she said with an amazingly straight face. 'The food at the restaurant was fabulous. You know that place down on the beach at Balmoral?'

Dora didn't, thankfully. She said she'd never been to Balmoral, either the suburb or the beach.

Jessie invented a menu from scraps of memory of the last time she was there, all the while trying not to think of the incredible meal she *had* had last night. The food hadn't been incredible. It was just a couple of frozen dinners, washed down with white wine and finished off with a selection of melons. Incredible was the fact that they'd been naked whilst eating, and sharing one of the kitchen chairs, with her being forbidden to feed herself.

In hindsight, their various sexual encounters the previous night seemed decadent. But at the time, they'd simply been exciting.

'Where did you go afterwards?' Dora asked.

'Just back to his place for a while,' Jessie said nonchalantly.

'And?'

'He has a very nice house. Not unlike yours.'

'And?'

'It has a glorious view of the ocean and it's chock-full of antiques. Kane must be worth a fortune.'

'And?'

'And what?'

'Jessie Denton, did you or did you not go to bed with the man?'

Jessie blushed at this unexpectedly forthright question. 'Don't ask questions like that, Dora. Emily might hear.'

'Not at this distance, she won't,' Dora replied.

They were sitting at the small plastic table setting outside their communal laundry, which was a good way from where Emily was happily playing in her fig-tree cubby house.

Jessie sighed. 'Yes, I did,' she confessed.

'Good,' Dora pronounced. 'He's a really nice man.'

Jessie clenched her teeth hard in her jaw lest she

open her mouth and say something to disillusion Dora.

'And he really likes Emily,' Dora added.

'He divorced his wife because he didn't want children,' Jessie couldn't resist throwing into the conversation.

'What? Are you sure about that?'

'Positive. He told me so himself.'

'Strange. He doesn't act like a man who doesn't like children. He's very patient, for starters. And kind.'

'Maybe he just doesn't like babies. Emily is not a baby.'

'True. But that's a shame. I thought he might have been the one.'

'Which one is that?'

'The one who'll marry you and be a father to Emily. She's very keen on that idea, you know.'

No, Jessie didn't know. 'You mean, on having a father? She's never spoken about it to me. Emily hasn't missed out on anything, not having a father,' she argued defensively.

'How do you know? She's a deep little thinker, your Emily. She sees other fathers coming to pick up their children at the day-care centre. She might have been wanting a father for ages, but didn't want to say anything to upset you. She loves her mummy a great deal but I think she'd love to have a daddy, too. That's why Kane's been such a big hit with her. And why she asked if you two were going to get married last night.'

Jessie's heart turned over. It was already happening, what she'd feared all along. If she kept seeing Kane, Emily was going to get more and more attached to him and one day, poof, he'd be gone and her little girl would be broken-hearted. Her own broken heart she could cope with. She was a grown-up. But how could you explain to a four-year-old that adult relationships didn't always end in marriage? They usually just ended.

'He wants to take me and Emily out this Sunday,' Jessie said with a worried frown on her face. 'I'm going to have to call him and tell him no.' She should never have said yes in the first place. She was weak, weak, weak!

'But why, for pity's sake?'

'Because it's not fair on Emily, letting her think he really likes her. It's not Emily he wants, Dora. It's just me.'

'You don't know that. Ask him.'

'No. He'll only lie to me.'

Dora looked at her with shocked eyes. 'I knew you were cynical, Jessie. I didn't realise you were *that* cynical. For what it's worth, I think you're making a big mistake. He's a nice man and deserves a chance. Not only that, *you* deserve a chance. And Emily, too. Don't make hasty decisions. Give your relationship with Kane a bit of time. OK, so it might not work out, but if you don't try you'll never know. Life can be cruel but it can also be wonderful. You have to believe that or life isn't worth living. I was very lonely and depressed till you and Emily came along. In fact, I was in danger of being a miserable old witch of a woman, I was so full of regrets and resentments. But you brought some light into my life. You and Emily. You're a lovely girl, Jessie Denton, but where men are concerned you're way too hard. And way too distrustful. I've seen a lot of life and I'd put my money on Kane being a decent man. He might even change his mind about having children now that he's become involved with you and Emily. People can change, you know.'

Jessie didn't think that a man who divorced his wife over that single issue was likely to change. At the same time, she supposed she was being a bit hard on him. He'd really been wonderfully warm and considerate last night. He had the capacity to be a sensitive new-age guy as well; he was very capable in the kitchen. And he could give a massage like a professional. He made a great boyfriend and lover, even if not a husband and father.

She'd be out of her mind to voluntarily give him up. Just the thought of never experiencing again what she'd experienced last night made her feel sick. At the same time, she had to make some firm ground rules between them. No pretend family outings. No coming over till Emily was asleep at night. And no expecting her to stay at his place all night on the occasions they did go out.

There! That was reasonable.

Kane didn't think so when she rang him during Emily's after-lunch nap.

'You're being ridiculous again,' he growled. 'About everything. Jessie, I really like you. No, that's a lie. I love you, damn it.'

Jessie gasped into the phone.

'Yes, yes, I'm sure you don't believe me. But it's true.'

'It's you who's being ridiculous,' Jessie countered once she got over her shock. 'I know what you love, Kane Marshall, and it isn't the real me. It's the silly, weak woman I became last night. I don't know what got into me to let you do all those things. My only excuse is that I hadn't been with a man in such a long time. *And*, of course, you seemed to know just what to do to tap into my dark side.'

'Your *dark* side? I wasn't trying to tap into your dark side, sweetheart. Just your feminine side. That side you put on hold most of the time whilst you're being one tough mamma who thinks all men are lying scumbags who couldn't possibly love you or want you for anything other than sex. For pity's sake, I know you've been hurt by other men in the past. Your less than admirable father and that creep, Lyall. But that doesn't mean *all* men are bad. You don't like other people misjudging *you*, or jumping to conclusions over *your* morals, but you're only too ready to jump to conclusions over mine.'

Jessie winced. He was right. She knew he was right.

'You're a wonderful girl, Jessie,' he said more gently. 'But you really need to get that chip off your shoulder. I want you in my life. You *and* Emily. But you have to believe in me, and trust me. I don't know what else I can say to convince you that I'm sincere. Look, if you don't think you could ever love me back, then I suppose I'm just wasting my time. If last night was just you exorcising your sexual frustrations then I guess that's that, then. Just let me say that last night was the most incredible night of my life. You are everything I want in a woman and a lover, Jessie Denton.'

Jessie felt totally chastened by his speech. And moved. 'I...I thought last night was pretty incredible, too. I'm sorry I said what I said, Kane. And I'm sorry I'm such a bitch.'

He laughed. 'In a way, I like that about you. But I like the woman you were last night, too. They're both you, Jessie. And I love them both.'

'I wish you wouldn't keep saying that you love me.'

'Why?'

'Because I'm afraid of it.'

'Yes, I know that, sweetheart. But you're going to have to get used to it. I love you and I'm not going to go away.'

She was beginning to see that, his reassurance flooding through her heart like a giant wave, washing away some of those old fears, the ones where she did think no man would ever truly love and want her, not now that she had Emily. Her mother had drummed into her that no man really wanted another man's child.

But was he talking marriage here? She didn't like to ask. It was premature. And what about the matter of children? Dora could be right there. Maybe he would want children with her, if he loved her enough. If not, at least she already had Emily. And he seemed to genuinely like Emily.

'It might be nice if you told me what you feel for

me,' Kane inserted softly. 'I need some encouragement here.'

'I doubt you ever need encouragement when you want something, Kane Marshall.'

'I've never wanted something quite so unattainable before.'

'How can you say that after the way I acted last night? You said "jump" and I said "how high?"'

'That's just during sex. On a day-to-day basis, you're extremely difficult to handle. Now, am I allowed to come over today?'

'No.'

'How come I knew you were going to say that? What about tomorrow? Can I take you and Emily out, as I was going to?'

'Yes, but no sex.' This edict was more for her benefit than his. She was so tender down there, it wasn't funny.

'I wasn't expecting any. Besides, I'm knackered.'

'That's today. You'll be recovered by tomorrow.'

'You could be right. I'll be even more recovered by Monday.'

'Monday is a work day.'

'Yes, but there's always our lunch-hour. Karen always goes out and I have that lovely office—complete with that huge Chesterfield—all to myself.'

Jessie's cheeks burned at the thought. Just as well he couldn't see her. 'You don't honestly expect me to do that, do you?' she said, trying to sound shocked and not excited.

'A man can always hope.'

'Friday night is our date night,' she said primly.
'You'll have to wait till then.'

'Friday night is a definite, then? No excuses?'

'No excuses.'

'Next Friday night is the office Christmas party,'
he told her in an amused tone. 'As the acting boss,
I'm obliged to attend. As a new employee, I will
expect you to be there too, in a sexy party dress.'

'You devil! You tricked me.'

'You should have remembered.'

'I'm not having you make love to me in your office.'

'You gave me your word. You told me you were
a woman of your word.'

'That's emotional blackmail.'

'No one will notice if we slip away from time to
time,' he said softly. 'My office is out of the way.
And it has a lock on its door.'

'But I wouldn't be able to relax,' she protested.
'I'd be worried what people might be thinking.'

'Who cares what they think? After Christmas, I
won't be the boss there any longer and no one will
think a thing.'

'They'll always think you hired me because you
fancied me.'

'Mmm. Could be true.'

'But it isn't! You know it isn't!'

'Yes, I know. I was only teasing. We'll be very
discreet. Tell me you love me, Jessie Denton.'

'No.'

'But you know you do.'

'All I know is that you're a very arrogant man.

And far, far too sure of himself. You need pulling down a peg or two.'

'And you, missie, need a lot more loving.'

'Is that what they're calling it these days?'

'Would you rather I used a cruder term?'

'No.'

'Good, because I'm not just talking about sex. I'm talking loving in the wider context. You need everything a man who loves you can provide. You need caring for. And protection. And support. And security. You need someone there to help you when things go wrong, someone you can turn to and rely upon.'

Oh, how wonderful that would be, she thought with a deep sigh. But was it just a dream, a mad promise from a lust-crazed fool, or the offer of a man genuinely in love?

Jessie had been cynical too long to accept what Kane was offering without any wariness whatsoever.

'What you need,' Kane finished, 'is me.'

'Yes, I certainly do,' she agreed. 'You've revitalised my libido with a vengeance. But we'll both have to wait till Friday to tackle it.'

He swore. The first time he'd sworn in front of her.

'What you need, madam,' he ground out, 'is being put across my knee and having your bottom soundly smacked.'

'Ooh,' she said mockingly. 'Is that a promise or a threat?'

'You're full of bulldust, do you know that? You're scared stiff of me, that's the truth. You're scared stiff of what I can make you feel and what I can make you do. Come Friday night, you *will* tell me you love me. Right there, in that office. Even if I have to smack your bare bottom to get you to say it. And that's a promise!'

Jessie was speechless, her heart pounding at the images he evoked. And the feelings. This couldn't be love, she told herself. This was just lust. He'd totally corrupted her last night.

'That's not love,' she whispered shakily.

'What is it, then?'

'It's torture.'

'Aye, it's that too, till you surrender to it. I've surrendered to my feelings for you. So when are you going to do the same? No, don't answer that. I can be patient. Just remember I'm never going to let you go, Jessie Denton. You are mine. So get used to it.'

CHAPTER FOURTEEN

TEN o'clock Monday morning saw Kane sitting at Harry's desk, feeling quite satisfied with the way his relationship with Jessie was going. Yesterday, he'd proved to her that they didn't have to be making mad, passionate love to enjoy each other's company. He'd also showed her—at least he hoped he had—that he had the makings of a good father for Emily.

On the Saturday, he'd bought a child car seat so there'd be no objections to his driving them out to the rural outskirts of Sydney on the Sunday. After an hour's investigation on the internet, he'd found a horse-riding establishment that catered for children, and had other entertainment as well. Bouncy castles and the like.

Emily had enjoyed herself enormously, although by the time they arrived back home around six o'clock, she'd been very tired and a little out of sorts. She hadn't eaten much of the take-away pizzas Jessie had allowed him to buy this time, which Jessie said wasn't like her at all.

Kane had insisted on taking Emily's temperature— he'd heard horror stories of children coming down with meningitis lately—but her temperature proved to be normal. Jessie had said she was probably over-tired. They'd done a lot that day. After a bath, Kane had read Emily a story till she dropped off.

Afterwards, even though Jessie had let him stay, Kane had made no attempt to make love to her. He'd watched the Sunday-night movie with her—a Harrison Ford action thriller which could bear reviewing—and chatted about various topics during the ads. Books. Movies. Music. Kane had discovered she had a wide taste and knowledge of all three, which didn't really surprise him. She was a smart cookie. He'd known that from the first moment he looked into her eyes. She had intelligent eyes.

Although he'd been dying to make love to her, Kane had contented himself with a goodnight kiss. He suspected Jessie wouldn't have objected too much if he *had* seduced her, but he hadn't wanted to take the chance. She always seemed so quick to believe the worst of him.

By Friday, however, he wouldn't be capable of being so noble. He wouldn't be waiting till the party finished, either. Hell, no. Kane shuddered over the thought of how long this week would prove to be.

When the phone rang, he reached forward and snatched it up.

'Kane Marshall.'

'Kane, I have a problem.'

Kane snapped forward in his chair. It was Jessie, sounding worried.

'What is it? I thought you were here, at work.'

'I am. The day-care centre has just rung me. Emily has come down with conjunctivitis. Apparently, one of the other children had it on Friday. Anyway, because it's so contagious, they want me to go and pick her up.'

'That's fine, Jessie. You go. No problem. I'll square it with Michele.'

'That's just it. Michele's not here. She had an appointment with her obstetrician this morning, and she's relying on me to do this magazine layout by the time she gets back. I would really hate to let her down, Kane. I've tried to ring Dora but she's out, too. Lord knows where. She's usually home on a Monday. I *can* leave Emily at the centre but they'll put her in a room on her own. It's a kind of quarantine rule they have. They did this to her once before when I was working at the restaurant and she got very upset. She thought she was being punished. I...'

'I'll go get her, Jessie,' Kane immediately offered. 'Just ring them and let them know who I am and that you're giving me permission to pick Emily up. I'll take her to the doctor, too. Get her some drops for her eyes.'

'Would you, Kane? Would you really?'

Kane was amazed at the surprise in her voice. 'Yes, of course. It would be my pleasure. Poor Emily. There's nothing worse than having sore eyes. Does she have a regular doctor you take her to?'

'Not exactly. I always go to a nearby twenty-four-hour clinic. They bulk bill, but you have to be seen by whatever doctors are on call that day.'

Privately Kane resolved that little arrangement would change, once *he* was responsible for Jessie and Emily. And he aimed to be, one day. Still, that clinic would do for today.

'Right. I'll come and get her medicare card from you. Jot down the address of the clinic and I'll be on my way.'

Kane jumped to his feet and reached for his suit jacket straight away. It could only have been thirty seconds before he'd made it to Jessie's desk, where he was stunned to find her with tears running down her face.

'Jessie. Darling. What's up?' he said as he hunched down beside her chair. 'Why are you crying?'

She could not seem to speak, just buried her face in her hands.

'Jessie, talk to me. Tell me what's wrong.' He took her hands in his and lifted them to his lips.

She stared at him through soggy lashes. 'I've never known anyone like you,' she choked out. 'You can't be real.'

Relief zoomed through Kane, as well as the most ego-boosting pleasure. She wasn't unhappy. She was actually complimenting him with her tears.

But how sad that she would feel disbelief that a man would do something nice for her and her daughter.

'I'm real, all right,' he said with a soft smile. 'Just ask my mum. Now, stop being a silly billy, give me what I came for, then get back to work. You don't want everyone saying I hired a nincompoop just because I fancied her, do you?'

He liked it when a smile broke through her tears. God, but she was beautiful when she smiled. Her eyes glittered and her whole face came alive.

'We couldn't have that, could we?' she said, dashing the tears away with her fingers.

'Absolutely not.'

'OK. Here's the medicare card and the clinic's address. Now, what are you going to do with Emily after you've been to the doctor? They didn't say she was actually sick, but perhaps she should go home. I could give you the keys to the granny flat if you wouldn't mind staying with her. There's plenty of food in the fridge and the cupboards. She usually has a sleep after lunch. If she gets bored or stroppy, she likes to watch videos. She has a whole pile of them in the cabinet under the TV.'

'Sounds good to me. I'll give you a call when I get there, and I'll wait with her till you come home.'

'I don't know what to say, Kane,' she said as she drew her keys out of her handbag. 'Are you sure you can manage? I mean…you haven't much experience looking after kids on your own.'

'I happen to be an extremely devoted uncle, so you're wrong there. What do you think I did on Saturday night when you wouldn't let me come over? I minded the two terrors so that their parents could go out and relax together. Actually, I don't know what their mother complains about. They were as good as gold. Of course, I plied them with junk food and lollies till they fell asleep on the sofa in front of the TV. Then I carried them up to bed. Works every time,' he said with a quick grin.

'Now, don't you worry,' he added. 'I'm more than capable of looking after Emily. And I won't feed her junk food, or lollies. To be honest, it'll be a pleasant change from sitting at that damned desk, pretending to work. Things wind down leading up to Christmas. My entire workload this week is choosing what grog to buy for the Christmas party. *Very* challenging.'

He stood up, pocketing her keys and picking up the medicare card and piece of paper with the address. 'I'll call, OK? And don't worry.'

'I won't,' she said, looking much more composed. 'I can't tell you how grateful I am.'

Kane threw her one last smile and whirled on his heels.

Nothing made a man feel better, he decided as he strode manfully away, than being able to help the woman he loved.

Jessie worked hard and fast for the next few hours, not leaving her desk till the magazine layout looked perfect. To her, anyway.

Michele returned shortly after she'd finished, and only minutes after Kane had rung saying he was at the flat with Emily and that her conjunctivitis wasn't too bad. He'd already put one lot of drops in, they'd shared Vegemite toast and a glass of milk, followed by a banana each. Now they were settling down to watch *The Lion King*.

With her worries about her daughter waylaid, Jessie could focus on Michele's reaction to her work. When Michele started frowning, Jessie's alarm grew. Maybe the layout wasn't as good as she thought it was.

'I would never have imagined doing it this way at all,' Michele said at last, tipping her head from side to side as she studied the computer screen. 'But yes, I like it! You are very creative, Jessie. Kane's found a real gem in you. Harry's going to be delighted at your joining his staff.'

Jessie sighed her relief. 'Thank you. But…would you mind if I left now?' she asked hurriedly. 'I know it's only two o'clock, but my little girl has conjunctivitis. The day-care centre rang and wanted me to go get her straight away, but I didn't feel I could without finishing the layout first.'

'That was very professional of you, Jessie. But honestly, I would have understood. That kind of thing happens to me all the time. And yes, of course you can go. I hope your little girl is OK.'

Jessie didn't want to tell her about Kane coming to the rescue. That was her own personal business.

'I'm sure she will be,' Jessie said, standing up hurriedly and getting her things together. 'Thanks, Michele. I did work through my lunch-hour. And I'm happy to do some extra work at home to make up for the extra hour and a half.'

'Are you kidding me? You've achieved more here in less than a day than your predecessor would have done in a week!'

Jessie laughed and left.

The day outside wasn't overly hot, but it was humid, Jessie's blouse sticking to her back as she hurried to the train station. Sydney in December could be very sticky.

The train she caught was quite crowded, Jessie

lucky to get a seat. But she was still pressed up against other people, and the air-conditioning didn't seem to be working too well. Everywhere seemed crowded at the moment, even outside of peak hours. Lots of people doing Christmas shopping, she supposed.

Jessie was glad she'd finished hers. She had Emily's Felicity Fairy doll and accessories all wrapped up and hidden on a high shelf in one of Dora's wardrobes, along with a few little cheaper gifts she'd bought during the year. She'd long sent her mother's card and gift to Ireland. A lovely set of linen serviettes and holders that her mother would probably put away and never use. Truly, she was a difficult woman to buy anything for.

For Dora, she'd bought some place mats and matching coasters in a blue and white willow pattern. She hadn't spent as much money on her as her mother, but she knew Dora would appreciate the gift more, and actually use it. Dora loved that willow pattern. She had a tea set in it, a vase and a large serving plate.

It came to Jessie during the train ride home that she hadn't bought Kane anything. In truth, his rather sudden intrusion into her life had driven Christmas from her mind, which was ironic given what she'd said to Dora that night before she'd gone to the bar. Hadn't she wanted a man for Christmas, some gorgeous guy who'd give her a good time?

Kane had certainly done just that, and more. Much more.

Jessie still found it incredible that he loved her.

But he said he did and she had no real reason to doubt him. Frankly, she didn't *want* to doubt him any more. She was tired of her cynicism, tired of trying to stop herself from falling in love with him. Dora was right. Life could be cruel but it could be wonderful.

Kane was a wonderful man, despite his not wanting children of his own. Why he didn't she had no idea, but she would certainly ask him. Soon.

And if he still insists he doesn't, Jessie, where can this relationship go? You would want children with the man you loved. And you do love him, don't you? That was one of the reasons you were crying earlier. Because you knew you couldn't stop yourself loving him any longer.

You love him and you'd make any compromise just to be with him.

But maybe you're jumping the gun here, Jessie Denton.

Maybe he just wants to continue being your boyfriend and your lover. Maybe he doesn't want to live with you, or marry you. Maybe the way it is now is all he'll ever want.

Dismay clutched at Jessie's heart. It wasn't enough. Just seeing him on a Friday night. And occasionally at the weekend. Not enough at all.

But it would have to be enough. She couldn't force him to want marriage, let alone children. She couldn't force him to do anything.

Unless...

No, no, that wasn't right. She would not try to trap him with a baby. It wouldn't work, anyway. The man who'd written *Winning at Work* would never succumb to that kind of emotional blackmail. He was strong on his beliefs, be they right or wrong.

The train pulling into Roseville brought a swift end to her mental toing and froing. During her hurried walk home Jessie told herself she should stop questioning everything and just live one day at a time for a while. Things were good in her life at the moment. Kane was good for her. And he was good for Emily. Why risk what they had by wanting more? She was a fool.

'Sssh,' Kane said when she burst in through the back door. 'Emily's asleep. She nodded off during the video and I carried her into bed. But that was only ten minutes ago. Gosh, you look hot.'

'I am hot. It's terribly sticky outside.' The granny flat was nicely cool, with double insulation in the roof and fans in the high ceilings. Kane looked very cool, sitting on the sofa with his arms running along the back of the sofa and his long legs stretched out before him, crossed at the ankles. Very cool and very sexy.

Suddenly, Jessie felt even hotter.

'I'll have to have a shower and change,' she said hurriedly. 'Once Emily's asleep, usually nothing wakes her up, so we don't have to creep about. I won't be long,' she said, and fled into the bedroom.

Emily stayed blessedly asleep whilst her mother stripped off, showered then pulled on a simple cotton sundress in pink and white checks, which looked sexier on her than she realised.

*   *   *

Kane gritted his teeth when she emerged, thinking to himself that he'd better make himself scarce, or all his resolutions about not touching her till Friday were about to fly out the window. But when he rose and reached for his jacket, which was draped over a kitchen chair, her face betrayed that his leaving was the last thing she wanted.

They stared at each other for a long moment. And then she said something that floored him. His mouth literally dropped open.

'Say that again,' he blurted out, not daring to believe what he thought he'd heard.

'I love you,' she repeated, her face flushed, her eyes glistening.

Kane knew that in years to come, he would always remember that moment. A dozen different emotions warred for supremacy. Disbelief? Shock? Joy? Delight? Satisfaction? Desire?

Desire won in the end. Or was it just his own love for her? How could you not take a woman into your arms who'd just told you she loved you with such moving simplicity?

She went without any hesitation this time, not a trace of doubt in her face any more.

But he didn't kiss her straight away. He looked down into those beautiful eyes and savoured the sincerity he saw in their depths.

'When did you decide this?' he said softly.

'On the way home on the train.'

'A very good place to make decisions.'

'Much better than when I'm like this,' she told him

with a small smile. 'I can't think straight when I'm in your arms.'

'That's good to know as well.'

Her arms slid even tighter around his neck, pulling their bodies hard against each other. 'Aren't you going to kiss me?' she asked breathlessly.

'Soon.'

'You have a sadistic side to you, Kane Marshall.'

'I never claimed to be a saint.'

Neither was he a masochist. His mouth was within a millimetre of contacting hers when there was a knock on the door.

His head lifted, and they groaned together.

It was Dora, all a-flutter.

'I saw Kane's car out the front,' she said. 'Is anything wrong?'

Jessie gave her a quick run-down on the little drama with Emily. Dora looked relieved.

'I'm so glad it's nothing serious. And that Kane could help. Sorry I wasn't here, dear. But you'll never guess what's happened.'

Kane and Jessie exchanged a look that carried both amusement and exasperation.

'Why don't I make us all some coffee,' Jessie said, 'and you can tell us what's happened?'

Kane suppressed a sigh and pulled out a kitchen chair for Dora, sitting down himself once the old lady was settled.

Apparently she'd received an unexpected call from her brother that morning, the one who hadn't been much support to her during their mother's last years. Dora hadn't spoken to him for a good two years.

'If it hadn't been Christmas I wouldn't have spoken to him today, either,' she said defiantly. 'But I'm so glad I did.'

Apparently, her brother explained how he'd been inundated with business and family problems when their mum had been ill, but admitted that he knew he hadn't done enough. He'd recently had a health scare himself and had been thinking that he wanted to make it up to Dora. The upshot was he'd come and taken Dora out to lunch, over which he'd asked her to go to his place for Christmas, and for the week afterwards, right up to New Year. It seemed his business was doing very well now; he owned a couple of cafés down around the Wollongong area on the south coast. He had a huge holiday house down there, and every one of their relatives was coming.

Kane saw Jessie's face fall at this news, and guessed that she and Emily always spent Christmas with Dora. After all, she had no one else. It was just the opportunity he'd been waiting for.

'That's great, Dora,' he piped up. 'And it sure takes a load off Jessie's mind. You see, I asked her and Emily to come spend Christmas with me and my family. But she was worried sick about you, thinking you'd be all alone. Of course, you'd have been welcome to come too, but this solves everything much better.'

Dora seemed relieved and pleased at this announcement, whilst Jessie went a little quiet. After Dora bustled off to go do some more Christmas shopping, Kane was left to face a slightly cool Jessie.

'What a smooth liar you are,' she said.

Kane could feel the doubts rising in her again.

'There's nothing wrong with little white lies, Jessie,' he pointed out. 'Especially when they're partially true. I was going to ask you to spend Christmas with me.'

'*And* with your family?'

'Yes.'

'And what were you going to introduce me as?'

'What would you like me to introduce you as?'

'I don't know. You tell me.'

'How about fiancée?'

She stared at him and he sighed. 'I guess that is rushing you somewhat. How about my new girlfriend, then?'

Jessie just kept shaking her head, her expression bewildered. 'Were you seriously asking me to marry you? You weren't joking?'

'I wouldn't joke about something like that.'

'But we've only known each other ten days!'

'I know I love you and I know you love me.'

'But we don't really *know* each other.'

'I beg to differ. I know you very well. Much better than I knew Natalie when I married her, and we'd been dating for months. The problem is you don't think you know me. But you had the wrong picture of me from the start. I rather hoped I'd managed to get rid of that poor image by now, but it seems I haven't.'

'That's not true. I...I think you're wonderful. You must know that. But *marriage*? That's a very big step, Kane. For one thing, we don't agree on one very important issue. The same issue you didn't agree on with your first wife.'

'*What?* You mean *you* don't want children, either? Hell, Jessie, I thought…' A great black pit yawned open in Kane's stomach. He could not believe it. Jessie didn't want his children. The woman he loved. The woman he adored. How cruel was that?

Jessie blinked. Had she heard that right? His *ex* hadn't wanted children? But that couldn't be right. She'd said she was pregnant that day in Kane's office and that she was keeping the baby. Of course, lots of women who didn't think they wanted children changed their minds once they actually got pregnant. But if that was the case…

'Hold it there,' she said. 'Why, exactly, did you divorce Natalie?'

'Mainly because she refused to have children. But I think I also realised I didn't really love her.'

'Oh!' Jessie exclaimed with a gasp. 'I thought it was *you* who didn't want children!'

'*Me?* I love children. How on earth did you get that ridiculous idea? I thought I explained the reasons behind my divorce quite clearly.'

'You told me you disagreed with your wife over the matter of having children and I just assumed it had to be you who didn't want kids.' Jessie felt truly chastened. But secretly elated. 'I'm so sorry, Kane. My old prejudice against men again.'

He nodded, unable to feel unhappy, now that he knew Jessie wanted more children. 'An understandable mistake.'

'So you really do want children?'

'A whole tribe of them, if possible. The more the merrier.'

Jessie beamed. 'Me, too.'

'What about your career?'

'My career would never come before my kids. But hopefully I could juggle both.'

Kane's delight was as great as his despair had been. 'In that case, come here, woman, and make it up to me for thinking such dreadful things.'

She ran into his arms. This time, he actually got to kiss her for five seconds before they were interrupted.

'Mummy...'

They pulled apart to find Emily standing in the bedroom doorway, rubbing her eyes.

'Hello, sweetie,' her mother said. 'You feeling better now?'

'I'm thirsty. And my eyes are sore.'

Jessie gave a small sigh. 'I'll get you a drink of water. Kane, where are those eye drops?'

'Over here on the coffee-table. I'll get them.'

Their eyes clashed momentarily, Kane seeing that Jessie was watching him for signs of impatience.

Instead, he smiled, then hurried over to sweep Emily up into his arms. 'Did you have a good sleep, princess?'

She tipped her head on one side. 'Were you kissing Mummy just then?'

Jessie stopped breathing.

'I sure was,' Kane said. 'It was very nice, too. Do you mind my kissing Mummy?'

'No. Will you kiss me, too?'

He laughed and planted a peck on her forehead. 'There. Now let me get those eye drops into you.'

'Do you *have* to?' she wailed.

'Yes. I *have* to,' Kane returned firmly.

Jessie heaved a great sigh of happiness. Even more wonderful than everything which had happened today was having someone else put Emily's eye drops in.

CHAPTER FIFTEEN

WORK the following Friday came to a halt by lunch-time, at which point the males on the staff pitched in to transform the main office floor into party land. Several of the central cubicles were dismantled to provide a more than adequate dance floor. Desks were cleared and decorations and disco lights went up.

Peter—who apparently loved playing DJ each year—set about filling his area with his latest hi-fi gear, whistling *Jingle Bells* as he worked. Kane and Karen took charge of stocking up the temporary bar, whilst Margaret roped Jessie and Michele into helping her with the food, which they spread out, buffet-style, on several desks pushed together. A local catering company had supplied a wide selection of cold meats, seafood and salads, with some delicious cream-topped cakes for the sweet tooths, plus loads of snacks.

Jessie thought that there was way too much to eat and drink for their small staff, but when she remarked on this to Michele, she was informed that their office party was so popular that loads of other people in the building came, along with clients, past and present.

'And everyone's other halves usually drop in as well,' Michele added. 'Tyler's sure to be late, work-

172

aholic that he is, but he'll make an appearance at some stage, even if only to see me safely home.'

Tyler, Jessie knew by now, was Michele's husband.

'And speaking of other halves,' Michele said after a glance over at Kane, 'yours is looking very bright-eyed and bushy-tailed tonight. What *have* you been doing to him, girl?'

Absolutely nothing of what Michele was implying. There'd been no actual lovemaking, despite their spending every evening this week together. Kane didn't seem to mind stopping at a goodnight kiss. He'd even promised he wouldn't press her for more in any shape or form here at the party tonight.

'He does look yummy in black, doesn't he?' Jessie said with that swirl in her stomach that always occurred whenever she looked at the man she loved. It had been difficult controlling her own desires these past few days, but it had been more important to her to know that Kane's love was not just sexually based than to indulge in some passing pleasure.

'You haven't told anyone else here about our being engaged, have you?' she added swiftly. She didn't mind Michele knowing. They were fast becoming firm friends and she just couldn't keep her good news totally secret.

Still, it was good that Kane hadn't bought her a ring yet. That way he couldn't be annoyed with her for not wearing it at work. Jessie was still worried over what the other people at Wild Ideas might think.

'No. I haven't told anyone else,' Michele said with a sigh. 'But if you keep looking at each other the way you do, people will begin to suspect something is going on.'

Kane turned his head at that moment, and their eyes connected. His smile carried so much obvious love that Jessie could see what Michele meant.

'OK, everyone!' Kane announced to the room. 'Everything's ready for the party. Time for the girls to go and put their glad rags on. The guys too, if you've brought something more colourful to change into.' He glanced at his watch. 'At three o'clock, the doors will be thrown open and it'll be all systems go. Though speaking of systems, please make sure that your computers are safely turned off, passwords hidden and all important files discreetly locked away. I don't want Harry coming home and finding that all your wonderfully wild ideas have been stolen, or sabotaged. OK?'

'OK, boss!' they all chorused, Jessie included.

How proud of him she felt, this wonderful, gorgeous, sensible-thinking man who loved her.

Twenty minutes later, she was nervously viewing herself in the full-length mirror that hung on the back of the ladies' room door. Her cocktail dress was brand new, and very sexy. Black silk with turquoise swirls on it, it had a halter neckline, a wide, extremely tight waistband and a swishy skirt.

Her shoes were new, too. Turquoise, in the currently fashionable slip-on style, which showed off her pretty ankles and scarlet-painted toenails. This time she'd been able to afford fake tan, so her bare legs and arms glowed a nice honey colour. Her hair was down for once, and not too bushy, courtesy of the more expensive hair products she could also now buy and which tamed the frizz somewhat. She was wearing more make-up than she would usually wear in the office as well, and considerably less underwear. No bra for starters and just the briefest thong underneath.

'Wow!' Margaret said when she saw her.

'Yes, wow!' Karen agreed.

Michele just raised her eyebrows in a knowing fashion.

Kane's reaction when he saw her was not quite as enthusiastic. He wasn't too pleased, either, when Jessie was subjected to instant male attention. The men flocked around her, getting her drinks, constantly asking her to dance and pretending to be devastated when she refused.

Jessie suspected Kane was jealous, but if so, why did he keep his distance? Why didn't *he* come and ask her to dance? She wouldn't have said no to him.

Finally, after the party had been raging for over two hours, he walked over to her, his expression tight.

'Could I have a private word, Jessie?'

'Of course,' she replied, and threw her circle of admirers a bright smile. 'Won't be long.'

Kane's grip on her elbow was firm as he steered her away from the party and along the corridor towards his office. Jessie quivered inside at his forcefulness, but it was a quiver of excitement, not nerves. A few glasses of champagne had dispensed with her earlier worries, replacing them with a deliciously carefree attitude.

'I said I wasn't going to do this, remember?' she remarked blithely, all the while quite happy with the prospect of being ravished on Kane's desk.

'I haven't brought you here for sex,' Kane snapped as he banged the door shut behind them.

'Oh…'

'Look, I know you're worried about the rest of the staff thinking you weren't hired on your merits. And I've tried damned hard tonight not to embarrass you by staking my claim on you publicly. But you *are* my woman, Jessie,' he pronounced firmly. '*Mine*. And it's time everyone out there knew that.'

'Oh…'

'I've asked you to marry me and you've said yes. You should be wearing my ring.'

'But…'

'No buts. I'm tired of your buts.' With that he drew a blue velvet box out of his jacket pocket and flipped it open. 'I hope you like it.'

Jessie stared down at the solitaire diamond engagement ring, then swallowed. Oh, God, she was going to cry. 'It…it's beautiful,' she stammered.

'*You're* beautiful,' he said thickly, and taking the ring out of the box, he put the box back in his pocket, then came forward and picked up her left hand.

'I love you, Jessie Denton,' he said as he slipped it on her trembling ring finger.

Her eyes flooded, then tears spilled over, running down her cheeks. 'And I love you,' she choked out.

He wiped the tears away with his spare hand, then bent to kiss each wet cheek. 'That's nothing to cry about,' he said with a soft smile in his voice. 'At least, I hope not.'

'Oh, no,' she denied hotly. 'Never!'

With a rush of sweet emotion, Jessie wound her arms up around his neck and pulled him close. 'You mean the world to me!' she proclaimed.

His hesitation was only slight before he kissed her. Soon, there was no hesitation, only passion. His kisses were fierce, his clasp so tight around her back that her breasts were totally flattened against his chest.

His sudden wrenching away came as a shock.

'Sorry,' he ground out. 'I promised I wouldn't do that.'

She loved it that he cared enough about her to stop. But the time for testing him further was long over.

'It's all right, Kane. I *want* you to make love to me.'

'What? You mean...*here*?'

'Yes, here. Now.'

He watched, gaze smouldering as she kicked off her shoes then reached up under her skirt to peel her panties off. That done, she untied the bow at the back of her neck, letting the straps fall so that her bare breasts were exposed.

When Kane sucked in sharply, her stomach quivered and her already erect nipples tightened further.

'I'd better lock the door,' he rasped.

He did so, then took her hand and led her over to the nearby Chesterfield. There, he drew her down onto his lap, kissing her and playing with her breasts till she was breathless and shaking. Only then did he slide one hand up under her skirt.

'No,' she protested. 'No, I don't want that, Kane. I want you. With nothing between us.'

'But…'

'No buts. It's all right. It's a safe time in my cycle. And if I'm wrong, what does it matter? I love you. You love me. We're getting married. A baby would be just fine.'

Kane could not believe the impact of her words. She must really love him and trust him, if she didn't mind conceiving his baby before they were married. He could not ask for more.

How he wanted her! His lovely Jessie. His woman.

He groaned at the first contact of their naked bodies, then moaned when his flesh began to enter hers. The look on her face as she sank all the way downwards told him she felt very much what he was feeling. When her hands cradled his face and she looked deep into his eyes, it took all of his will-power not to weep.

'I love you,' she whispered, and began to rise and fall upon him in a voluptuously sensual rhythm. 'I love you,' she repeated, pressing tiny kisses all over his face at the same time.

Kane closed his eyes in defence of the emotion that ripped through him. Never in his life had he felt anything like what this woman could make him feel. He could not wait to marry her, to promise to love and cherish her till death did them part. Because nothing short of death would destroy their union.

They were as one, not just in their bodies but also in their minds. She was going to be his soul mate. His best friend. The mother of his children.

When he took her hands from around his face and held them to his lips, she stopped moving to stare at him with glazed eyes.

'I...I never thought it could be like this,' she said in a voice that betrayed some lingering bewilderment over their relationship.

'I don't think it is very often,' he returned. 'We're very lucky.'

'Yes,' she agreed. 'Very.'

'We're going to go back to the party afterwards and announce our engagement,' he commanded, taking full advantage of the moment.

Jessie nodded. 'Yes. All right. But Kane...about tomorrow night...'

Kane frowned. 'What about tomorrow night?' She and Emily were supposed to be coming to sleep over at his house. It was Christmas Eve. He'd already bought a Christmas tree. A real one. And loads of decorations, which he planned on putting up with Emily. Not to mention more presents than was wise.

But how often did a man fall in love and get an instant family, one that probably hadn't been spoiled as he intended to spoil them, if he was allowed to?

'Don't tell me you've changed your mind about coming!'

She laughed a wicked little laugh. 'I'll be coming all right. Tonight. But Kane...about tomorrow night. I know it's probably old-fashioned of me, but I won't sleep in your bed with Emily in the same house. Not until we're married.'

Kane wasn't going to argue with her. Not at this precise moment. 'Fine,' he said. 'But I give you the right to change your mind again.'

'I won't change my mind this time.'

'We'll see,' he said, taking hold of her hips and urging her to start moving again.

When she cried out in naked ecstasy, Kane suspected he was in there with a pretty good chance.

CHAPTER SIXTEEN

'LOOK, Mummy, it's a Felicity Fairy doll!' Emily squealed as she ripped off the rest of the wrapping paper. 'And her horse! And her castle!'

'What a lucky girl you are,' Jessie replied from where she was curled up in the corner of Kane's sofa, dressed in the red silk nightie and robe Kane had given her on the stroke of midnight last night. They'd been up late talking and wrapping presents for Emily.

Of course, he'd insisted on seeing Jessie in his gift, one thing had led to another and, well…at least she hadn't actually slept in his bed. This room, however, had been witness to some torrid but tender lovemaking between even more provocative present-giving: perfume, body lotion and chocolates, which he'd fed her one by one as rewards for various services rendered.

Around one o'clock, a sated Jessie had given Kane the gifts she'd bought him. A book about the teachings of the Dalai Lama, a Robbie Williams CD and a DVD of the *Lord of the Rings* trilogy. She'd gleaned his taste from their many talks. He'd been so overcome that he had to listen to the CD and watch some of the DVD before making love to her again as a thank-you.

Shortly before three, a totally spent Jessie had stumbled into the second guest room, climbed into the bed and fallen into a deep sleep, where she had remained, not moving an inch, till Emily started tugging on her hair around six, saying Santa had been and Mummy just had to get up.

After Jessie had opened a single bleary eye, Emily had rushed off, saying she would wake Kane up, too.

That had been about fifteen minutes ago.

Jessie yawned just as Kane came into the living room with two mugs of freshly brewed coffee. He was actually wearing clothes. Shorts and a T-shirt. He needed a shave but he looked good like that. Very sexy.

'I really need this,' she said as she took one of the mugs and cradled it in her hands. 'It's just as well you took me to meet your family the other night when I looked all right. I look like something the cat dragged in today.'

'You look beautiful,' he said, and bent to give her a peck on the forehead before settling next to her. 'Glowing, in fact. Being in love suits you.'

Jessie glanced down at her engagement ring then up at the man who'd given it to her. 'Being in love with *you* suits me,' she said. 'You are the most incredible man.'

'But of course!' He grinned. 'Didn't I tell you that from the start?'

She laughed. 'You're also very arrogant.'

'Not true. I just know what I want when I see it.'

'Mummy, look at this!' Emily said, holding up the prettiest pink dress. 'Isn't it beautiful? I'm going to wear it when we visit Kane's mummy and daddy. I'll look like a princess, won't I, Kane?'

'Indeed.'

Jessie's heart turned over at how happy her daughter was. Kane had brought joy to both their lives, as well as the promise of a secure future.

'So, did Santa bring you everything you asked him for?' Jessie asked her daughter.

'Oh, yes,' Emily said, surveying all her new toys and clothes and games. 'He didn't forget a thing.'

'What do you like most?' Jessie asked, knowing exactly what her daughter would say: the Felicity Fairy doll.

'I like my new daddy the most,' came her unexpected reply. 'Can I call you Daddy now, Kane?' she added, crinkling her forehead up into a frown.

'I'd like nothing better, princess. Now, come over here,' he said as he put his coffee down on a side-table, 'and give your new daddy a hug.'

Emily smiled as only a child could smile, then ran into Kane's waiting arms.

Jessie frowned.

'Emily,' she said once her daughter was comfortable on Kane's lap, her arms tightly wound around his neck, 'did you ask Santa for a new daddy that day at the shops?'

'Yes,' came the reply. 'You said if I was a good girl he would get me anything I asked for. And he did.'

Jessie blinked at Kane, who shrugged. 'The ways of the lord are very mysterious.'

She stared at him. 'I didn't know you were religious.'

'I'm not overly. But I think we might pop into a church later today, just to say thank you.'

'Can I go to church with you, Daddy?'

'But of course, princess. That's what daddies are for. To do whatever our little girls want us to do. And our big girls, too,' he added with a sexy wink Jessie's way.

'Next year,' Emily said excitedly, 'I'm going to ask Santa for a baby brother.'

'What a good idea,' Kane replied whilst Jessie tried not to choke on her coffee. 'I'm sure Santa won't have any trouble with that order. Though you have to remember that even Santa can't order the sex of a baby. That's up to God.'

'Then I'll ask God.'

'Go straight to the top. Excellent thinking. What do you think, Mummy?'

'I think we should clear away all that paper over there, then have a shower and get dressed.'

Emily pulled a face when her mother got up and went over to start picking up the mounds of Christmas paper.

'Mummies aren't as much fun as daddies,' she pronounced.

Kane smiled. 'Oh, I don't know, Emily. Your mummy has her moments. And she is a very good mummy, isn't she?'

'Oh, yes,' Emily said, and smiled over at her mother.

Jessie thought her heart would burst with happiness. She didn't know what she had done to deserve such happiness but she resolved never to take it for granted, to work hard, to always be a good wife to Kane, and an even better mother to Emily and whatever other children she might be blessed with.

Her mother was going to be surprised when she rang her later today and told her that some man did want to marry her, even with some other man's baby.

But of course Kane wasn't some man. He was a very special man.

'Daddy,' Emily whispered to Kane, 'why is Mummy crying?'

'She's crying because she's happy, princess,' he told Emily, a lump in his own throat. 'Grown-ups cry sometimes when they're happy.'

'When I cry, Mummy kisses me better.'

Kane nodded. 'What a good idea. Let's go kiss her better.'

EPILOGUE

ROBERT WILLIAM MARSHALL arrived just after midnight on Christmas Eve the following year, much to the delight of his big sister, Emily, who immediately started planning her next year's wish list, which included a pony, a boyfriend for Dora and a visit from her Nanna in Ireland, who'd been writing to her a lot since she'd become something called a Buddhist.

Within a few hours of her beautiful boy's arrival, Jessie decided work could go hang for a while. As much as she had enjoyed her time at Wild Ideas—and she'd worked till she was eight months pregnant—she felt the time had come for an extended maternity leave.

No doubt she would go back to work at some stage. Maybe she'd even start up her own boutique advertising company, run from home. When she mentioned this to Kane he was all for it, as long as he could become her partner.

When a fluttery and flushed Dora visited later that day with her new lodger on her arm—an aspiring writer in his sixties who'd never been married—Jessie and Kane exchanged knowing looks whilst Emily wondered if Santa and God had read her mind and simply got in early.

Jessie was allowed to bring the baby home on Boxing Day, which they spent at her in-laws' place.

She felt remarkably well, but it was still lovely to be waited on, and fussed over. Kane's mother could not stop picking up the baby and goo-gooing over him.

'Happy, darling?' Kane asked her when they finally went home that night and both their babies were asleep.

'Couldn't be happier,' Jessie replied.

'Care for a dance with your husband?' he said, and put on a suitable CD.

As Jessie went into her husband's arms, she remembered the first night they'd met, and danced.

Was it destiny that had brought them together?

It would be romantic to think so.

But it wouldn't be destiny that kept them together.

It would be love.

THE MAN EVERY WOMAN WANTS

MIRANDA LEE

CHAPTER ONE

RYAN Armstrong never mixed business with pleasure.

His was very much a case of once bitten, a zillion times shy. Not that the word 'shy' fitted Ryan's confident and outgoing personality. So cross out 'shy' and put 'wary' instead.

Ryan was wary of the complications and consequences which came from mixing business and pleasure. *Very* wary.

When he'd been younger and not involved in the business world there'd been no need to resist temptation when it had come to the fairer sex. If he'd been attracted to a girl, he'd never stopped to think before his male hormones had sent him off in pursuit. He was usually successful in that pursuit, Mother Nature having endowed him with the sort of tall, broad-shouldered and extremely athletic body which women lusted after and which had seen him rise to become one of the world's most successful and well-paid goalkeepers. From the ages of twenty-three to twenty-nine, during which he'd played international soccer for several European clubs, he'd had more girlfriends than he'd saved goals.

When injury had forced early retirement at the age of thirty, and he had set up his own sports-management company back in Sydney, Ryan unfortunately had not developed the good habit of either controlling or ignoring his sexual urges. So when one of his first female clients—who was very attractive as well as a great athlete—started flirting with Ryan, it was inevitable that they would end up in bed together. Given she was nearly thirty and totally dedicated to her sports career, Ryan never imagined that she would want anything more from him than a casual fling.

By the end of their second date, however, Ryan had seen that he'd made a huge mistake. The girl had constantly sent him text messages raving about his love-making abilities, then saying how much she was going to enjoy being his wife. When he'd tried to finish things—very tactfully, he'd thought—she had gone all out to destroy his business. She'd released confidential information to the papers, plus had tried to drag his name through the mud in every possible way.

Unfortunately, by then he'd deleted all those revealing messages and it had been a case of her word against his. He'd come out the winner in the end, but it had been a close call. Ryan shuddered whenever he thought how close he'd come to losing everything he'd worked for. His business had still suffered for a while, hence his rule about mixing business with pleasure.

These days, he only dated mature, sensible women who had absolutely nothing to do with the Win-Win Sports Management Agency. He steered well clear of female clients and employees. He even trod carefully when it came to any kind of close business-colleague. His current girlfriend was a public-relations executive from a firm whose services he never used. Erica was blonde, thirty-five years old, divorced, childless and ruthlessly ambitious.

Thankfully, she was no more interested in marriage than he was. Or falling in love, for that matter. She'd been there, done that and it hadn't worked out. She suited Ryan's needs admirably, being attractive, intelligent and sexy. Ryan had discovered over the last few years that driven career-girls were usually hot between the sheets—and not given to huge tantrums when he wanted to move on.

Ryan moved on every few months. Occasionally, a relationship would last a little longer, but usually not. Often they ended earlier, once or twice after only a few weeks. Ryan always opted out very quickly if he thought he was becoming involved with a potential problem. He'd reached an age—he would turn thirty-eight next birthday—by which most guys had given up their bachelor days in favour of marriage and a family. He'd seen it happen time and time again. All his male friends were now married, even the ones whom he'd thought would never succumb to the urge to settle down and have children.

Ryan could well understand why members of the opposite sex saw him as a suitable target for marriage. Because he never talked about his past, what they didn't know was that he'd decided a long time ago that he would never become a husband and father. And he hadn't changed his mind about that.

A sharp tap-tap on the office door interrupted his thoughts and sent his eyes to the clock on his desk. Exactly three p.m.; right on time as usual, Ryan thought with illogical irritation. He actually admired punctuality. He hated wasting time waiting for people, especially when he'd made an appointment. So why didn't he admire it at three p.m. every Friday afternoon?

'Come in, Laura,' he called out through clenched teeth.

She came in, looking exactly the same as she always looked: severely tailored black suit with black hair up in an equally severe French pleat. No make-up. No jewellery. No perfume.

As she crossed the room towards the chair she always occupied during their weekly meeting, Ryan looked her up and down and wondered why she did that to herself. Did she imagine that this was how a female lawyer should look—tough, hard, and totally sexless?

Anyone could see that she could be a very attractive woman if she tried. She had a good figure and an interesting face with high cheekbones and exotically shaped grey eyes. Admittedly, those eyes were usually as cold as an arctic sky, especially when they looked at him.

So Ryan was startled when their eyes met and he glimpsed not chilly indifference for once but a type of pained regret. She even stopped walking for a second to stare at him.

'What?' he said straight away.

'Nothing,' she replied, and shook her head. 'Sorry. Let's get straight down to business, shall we?' She sat down, crossed her legs with her usual crisp modesty then leant forward to pick up the first of the contracts which were sitting on the edge of his desk waiting for her perusal.

It was a lucrative endorsement deal he'd personally negotiated for an up-and-coming young male tennis-player whom Win-Win had been lucky enough to sign up the previous month. A lot of Ryan's work involved negotiating contracts of one sort or another, all of which he always had checked over by one of the best legal brains in the whole of Sydney—which Laura had.

She wasn't an employee of Win-Win; Ryan didn't need a lawyer to work for him full-time. His company was more of the boutique variety. She worked for Harvey, Michaels and Associates, an American-owned legal firm with a Sydney branch which was conveniently located in the same building as Ryan's business and which boasted a stable of brilliant criminal and corporate lawyers.

When Ryan had become one of their clients several years ago, they had originally sent him a young male lawyer at Ryan's request—a smart guy, but a very bad driver who'd wrapped his car around a tree two years back. When the firm had suggested a female replacement, Ryan had been hesitant at first, especially when he had found out she was only thirty and single. But as soon as he had met Laura Ryan had realised there was no chance of his becoming involved with her. Or vice versa.

She still wasn't a problem in that regard. But she could be irritating all the same. Ryan wasn't used to being treated with such patent indifference by members of the opposite sex. It irked his male ego, which was considerable. Sometimes her disinterest seemed to border on outright dislike. It crossed his mind occasionally that she might not be interested in men, but he had no real evidence of this. It seemed more likely that past experiences had turned her into a man-hater—either that or she'd never met a man capable of melting her frozen exterior.

Once, a couple of weeks ago when she'd been particularly frosty with him, he'd been taken by the sudden urge to pull her into his arms and kiss her silly, just to see if he could get a reaction out of her.

He hadn't given in to that urge, of course. Ryan knew if he did any such thing he'd have a world of trouble on his hands faster than a world-class striker could score a goal—amazingly fast.

Besides, he had a lot more control over his testosterone these days. On the surface, that was. His mind, however, had given way to fantasies about the infernal woman all that afternoon.

A wry smile curved his lips as he recalled what he'd done to her in his head, and how avidly she'd responded.

In your dreams, Ryan!

'What's so funny?'

Ryan's head snapped clear at her caustic question, his amusement replaced by surprise. It wasn't like Laura to notice anything when she was reading through a contract. She almost never glanced up until she was finished, which she obviously wasn't. By the look of things, she'd only reached the second page of the five-page document.

'Nothing to do with you, Laura,' he lied. 'Just looking forward to the weekend. I'm going sailing with some friends tomorrow.' Which he was. Erica was away this weekend in Melbourne, attending a conference.

Laura's sigh also surprised him. It sounded…envious.

'Lucky you.'

'Want to come?' The invitation was out of his mouth before he could snatch it back.

She blinked with shock before dropping her eyes back to the contract. 'Sorry,' she said brusquely. 'I'm busy this weekend.'

Wow, he thought. That was a narrow escape. Whatever had possessed him to invite her? Still, his ego was slightly stroked by her not having said no outright. Maybe she wasn't as indifferent to his charms as she always seemed.

Ryan knew most women were attracted to him, as they were to most tall, good-looking, successful men.

No false modesty about Ryan.

He didn't interrupt her as she finished reading the contract but his mind remained extremely active. So did his eyes.

She really did have great legs. He liked women with shapely calves and slender ankles, and feet which weren't too big. Laura's feet were quite daintily small for a girl of her height. Pity about those awful shoes she was wearing!

Her hair was great too: dark, thick, glossy and obviously long. It would look fabulous spread out against a pillow...

Whoops. He was doing it again: having sexual fantasies about her. He really had to stop this.

Swinging his chair round to the huge window behind him, Ryan stared out at the view of the harbour which he always found pleasurably diverting and was one of the reasons he'd rented this particular suite of rooms in this building. The other reason was that it was less than two blocks from where he lived in an apartment building which also had a wonderful view of the harbour.

When Ryan had first retired from soccer, he'd missed spending most of his life outdoors. He hated the feeling of being closed in. He liked space around him, liked to see the sky—and water, he'd discovered to his surprise. He hadn't grown up with a love of water, mostly because it hadn't been a part of his life; he had never even been taken to the beach as a child. He hadn't learned to swim till he was twenty, and that had only happened because he'd been forced to train in a pool for a few weeks whilst he recovered from injury.

After his return to live in Sydney, however, he had found himself very drawn to the water, hence his buying an apartment and leasing an office that both came with harbour views. Recently, he'd developed a real love of sailing, and was considering buying a boat.

There were plenty of boats out on the harbour that afternoon, winter having finally given way to spring. The rain which had plagued Sydney for the past two months was thankfully gone; the sky was clear and blue and the water inviting.

His eyes zeroed in on one of the boats which was just moving past Bennelong Point, heading out to sea. It was a large white cruiser, an expensive toy for someone with plenty of money.

Maybe I'll buy one of those, Ryan thought idly.

He could well afford it; Win-Win wasn't Ryan's only source of income. Back during his goalkeeping days, he'd had the sense to invest most of the huge salary he'd earned each year into property. By the time he had retired, he was the owner of a dozen or so units, all located in Sydney's inner-city suburbs where the rental returns were excellent and the apartments never empty for long.

His extensive property portfolio was another thing Ryan didn't talk about, however, knowing it wasn't wise to broadcast one's wealth. He'd found it didn't do to court envy. He had a small group of friends who were successful men in their own right, though not multi-millionaires like him. He enjoyed their company and was loath to do anything to spoil their friendship. Of course, now that they'd all tied the knot, he didn't have quite as much to do with them as he used to. But they still got together occasionally to go to the football or the races.

None of them owned a boat. The 'friends' Ryan was going sailing with tomorrow were not real friends. They were professional yachtsmen whom he'd met through his job and who'd been teaching him the ropes about sailing.

'I can't seem to find anything wrong with it,' Laura said at last, in a troubled tone which suggested she should have been able to.

Ryan swung his chair back round to face her.

'You're quite sure?' he asked. It wasn't like Laura not to want him to change something. She often spotted potential legal loopholes which weren't to his client's advantage.

'Maybe I should read through it again.'

Ryan was as surprised by her suggesting this as he'd been by the odd look she'd given him earlier. Really, she wasn't herself today. Now that he'd stopped filling his mind with distracting images, he could see that *she* was the one who was distracted.

What was it that had upset her so much that her mind wasn't on her work? It had to be something serious.

A curious Ryan decided to see if he could find out.

'No need to do that,' he said. 'I'm sure it's fine. Why don't you have a quick whizz through the other two contracts? They're just renewals. Then we'll call it a day and I'll take you down to the Opera Bar for a drink.' If he could get her to relax, she might open up to him a bit.

She surprised him again by not saying no straight away.

Curiouser and curiouser.

But she didn't say yes, either.

'Look,' he said firmly. 'I'm not asking you out on a date. Just for a drink. Lots of work colleagues go for drinks on a Friday afternoon.'

'I do know that,' she said stiffly.

'Then what's your problem?'

Again, she hesitated.

'Look,' he went on determinedly, 'I do realise that you don't like me much. No no, Laura, don't bother to deny it; you've made your feelings quite obvious over the past two years. I have to confess that I haven't exactly warmed to you, either. But even the most indifferent and insensitive male would notice that you're not yourself today. As unlikely as it might seem, I find myself quite worried about you. Hence my invitation to take you for a drink. I thought you might relax over a glass of wine and tell me what's up.'

And why you gave me that odd look when you first came in, he added privately to himself.

'Even if I tell you,' she replied, her eyes unhappy, 'There's nothing *you* can do about it.'

'Let me be the judge of that.'

She laughed, but it was not a happy sound. 'You'll probably be annoyed with me.'

'That's a very intriguing thing to say. Now, I simply won't take no for an answer. You are going to come for a drink with me—right now. And you're going to tell me what this is all about!'

CHAPTER TWO

LAURA knew it was silly of her to feel flattered by his concern—and even sillier to agree to have a drink with him at the Opera Bar, of all places.

The Opera Bar was *the* place to go for an after-work drink in Sydney's CBD, conveniently located near the quay and with one of the best views in town—the Opera House on the right, Circular Quay on the left, the Harbour Bridge straight ahead, not to mention the harbour itself. Half the staff at Harvey, Michaels and Associates gathered there every Friday evening. Even non-social Laura occasionally went with them. She knew that it would cause a stir if she was seen drinking there in the company of Ryan Armstrong.

Why, then, had she agreed?

This was the question which tormented her during the short walk down to the quay.

By the time they arrived at the bar—early enough not to be spotted by any of her work colleagues yet, thank heavens—Laura was no nearer a logical answer.

Alison would have said that she was secretly attracted to him. There again, dear Alison was a hopeless romantic, addicted to those movies where the heroine hates the hero on sight but somehow falls madly in love with him before the credits go up at the end.

Laura could never buy into that plot. When she didn't like

someone, she didn't like them—end of story. She'd never liked Ryan Armstrong and certainly wasn't secretly attracted to him.

Okay, so he was good-looking, smart and, yes, highly successful. Ten years ago, she might have found him fascinating. These days, however, she was immune to handsome charmers who used women for their sexual satisfaction—sometimes for other rotten reasons—and gave them nothing in return but the dubious pleasure of their company. They shared nothing of themselves, either emotionally or financially. They were greedy selfish men who wanted their cake and wanted to eat it too. Laura had been involved with two such men in her life and had developed a sixth sense whenever she met a man of their ilk.

Ryan Armstrong had set off warning bells in her head from the first moment they had met, which was why she made an extra effort every Friday to down-play her looks even more than had become her habit during the last few years.

Not that she needed to worry about his making a play for her. It had been obvious from the start that he didn't like her any more than she liked him. That was why she'd been surprised today by his suddenly being nice to her. He'd got under her guard a couple of times already and now here she was, about to have drinks with him.

It was all very perverse.

'Let's sit outside,' Ryan said, and steered her out to the alfresco area where the sun was still shining, providing enough warmth to counter the freshness of the harbour breeze.

'What would you like to drink?' Ryan asked as he pulled out a chair for her at an empty table right by the water's edge.

'Bourbon and coke,' she replied, which made him raise his eyebrows. But he made no verbal comment before turning away and returning to the bar inside to order the drinks.

Being left alone gave Laura even more time to think and to worry. Not about her virtue—no way could she ever be seduced by the likes of Ryan Armstrong—but about the confession which Ryan was seemingly intent on getting out of her.

She still could not believe she'd been stupid enough to do what she'd done. And now it had backfired on her, big time. Not that she could have foretold that the doctors would be proved wrong and that her grandmother would come out of her coma and remember every single word that her granddaughter had said as she had sat by her bedside. Laura's intentions at the time had all been good, but what did that matter now?

A weary sigh escaped her lips. What was that old saying? 'The road to hell was paved with good intentions.'

The sight of Ryan walking towards their table with the drinks in his hands reminded her of why she'd chosen *him* to lie about to her grandmother. He really was the epitome of what her grandmother would think the perfect partner for her favourite granddaughter. First there was the matter of his looks. Gran had always said that she liked a man to look like a man, advising Laura to steer clear of pretty boys whom, she'd said, invariably had no backbone and, more importantly, no muscles to speak of.

'And they usually go bald early,' Gran had claimed with a perfectly straight face.

Laura had never been overly impressed by her grandmother's tendency to make superficial judgements when it came to the opposite sex. Though perhaps she should have listened, since the two men who'd broken her heart had both been pretty boys.

Ryan certainly wasn't a pretty boy. All his facial features were large and masculine. He had a broad forehead, an aquiline nose and a strong, square jaw which wasn't softened at all by the dimple in the middle of his chin. His hair was dark brown and would have been thick, if he ever grew it past his military-style crew cut. He certainly wasn't in danger of going prematurely bald, with no sign of a receding hairline.

Gran also liked men with blue eyes, for some reason.

Ryan's eyes were blue, though they were so deep-set under his thick dark brows that they sometimes looked black from a distance. Up close, however, their blue was the colour of a bright summer sky—but not nearly as warm. His eyes carried a hardness which no doubt served him well when he was negotiating a deal.

His body would have gained Gran's tick of approval as well, being tall and broad-shouldered, with muscles in all the right places. Admittedly, Laura had never seen him dressed in anything but a business suit—the kind he was wearing today— but she had seen him jacket-less with his sleeves rolled up and there was no hiding the fact that the man was very fit, with a flat stomach and no flab anywhere.

It was no wonder that she'd chosen him as her imaginary Mr Right, she realised as she watched Ryan walk towards her. He fitted the bill perfectly. Not only did he look like a man physically, but he was financially secure, charming when he wanted to be and, yes, old enough to be experienced in life.

Gran always said that a girl should never marry a man around her own age.

'Boys mature much later than girls, Laura,' she'd advised her granddaughter on more than one occasion. 'They need to experience life before they're ready to settle down.'

Of course, when she'd been waxing lyrical about Ryan by her Gran's hospital bed, she hadn't mentioned just how 'experienced' he was, Laura thought caustically. She didn't think her rather old-fashioned grandmother would approve of a man who'd had more women than underpants. And who changed them just as often.

Frankly, it always amazed Laura why women kept getting sucked into having a relationship with Ryan Armstrong. If you could call what he had with women 'relationships'. They were just ships passing in the night from what she'd heard. And she'd heard plenty over the past two years.

He smiled as he placed the drinks down on the table, a wickedly sexy smile which gave her a glimpse of how dangerously attractive he could be. If one was susceptible to that kind of thing.

'I decided to have what you're having,' he said as he sat down and swept up his own bourbon and coke. 'Cheers!'

She picked up her drink, clinked it against his, then took a deep swallow. Their eyes met over the rims of their glasses. His glittered with wry amusement whilst she kept hers as cool as always. But, underneath the silk lining of her black jacket, Laura was startled to feel her heart beating a little faster.

Maybe she wasn't as immune to the man's charms as she imagined. But it was not enough to worry about.

Nevertheless, she glanced away at the harbour. It really was a spectacular setting for a city, especially on a warm spring afternoon. Lots of boats were out on the sparkling water, creating a visual feast for all the tourists who'd flocked to the quayside area to take holiday snaps of the bridge and the Opera House.

'Sydney's a truly beautiful city, isn't it?' Laura said with pride in her voice.

'It surely is,' he agreed. 'You only have to live in other cities in other countries to know how lucky we are.'

She looked back at him. 'You sound like you've lived in lots of other countries.'

Ryan shrugged. 'Quite a few. But no more prevaricating, now,' he said as he put down his glass. 'Tell me what's going on in your life which has sent you into such a spin today.'

'I'm not in a spin,' she said defensively.

'Laura, you're sitting here having a drink with me. That's evidence enough that something has thrown you for a loop. So stop denying it. Given you're not the sort of girl to make a professional mistake, it has to be a personal problem. And I'm involved in some weird way. Am I right about that?'

'Yes,' she said, seeing no point in lying. It was obvious Ryan wasn't going to let up until he knew every depressing detail, so she took a deep breath then launched into her tale of woe.

'It's a bit of a long story, so please be patient with me.'

Patience, she knew, was not one of Ryan's strong points. But he didn't say a word, the expression on his face showing genuine interest. He might feel differently when he learned the part he'd played in her disaster, albeit unknowingly.

'Two weeks ago, my grandmother had a bad fall down some steps and ended up in a coma in hospital. Not in a Sydney hospital— In John Hunter Hospital in Newcastle. Gran lives up in the Hunter Valley. Anyway, the family was told she wasn't likely to pull through. In fact, the doctors didn't even expect her to last the night. So I sat with her all that night and, because I didn't want to go to sleep and not be with her if and when she did pass away, I kept talking to her. And, because I thought it wouldn't matter, I told her all the things that I knew she'd always wanted to hear: that I'd finally found Mr Right and I was very, very happy.

'Of course, it didn't take very long to make that simple announcement, so I was forced to elaborate somewhat to fill in time. Unfortunately, I've never had a great imagination; creativity is not a talent of mine. So I thought of all the men I knew and worked with and came up with the one who fitted the bill of Mr Right from my grandmother's viewpoint. Superficially, that is,' she added with a rueful glance Ryan's way.

'Good God,' he said, sitting up straight. 'You're talking about me, aren't you?'

'Unfortunately, yes,' she admitted dryly.

He laughed, then laughed again. 'Damn it, but that is funny, Laura. In an ironic way,' he added. 'I don't think what happened to your poor grandmother is funny. I have a soft spot for grandmothers.'

Indeed, his eyes did soften with his words.

'I must be missing something here,' he went on, his forehead crinkling into a frown. 'What harm did it do for you to invent a fictitious Mr Right on your grandmother's deathbed? Frankly, I think it was rather sweet of you to do what you did.'

Laura sighed. 'Sweet, but stupid. I should have known that Gran would pull through. She's always been a fighter. Not only did she pull through, but somehow she remembered every single word I said when she was supposed to be unconscious.

Well, perhaps that's a slight exaggeration. But she did remember my saying that I'd finally met Mr Right and his name was Ryan Armstrong. Now she's out of hospital and wants me to bring you home to meet her this very weekend.'

'Naturally,' Ryan said, then laughed again.

'Don't laugh—it really isn't funny, because she's still not at all well. The doctors found out that she'd had a small stroke, and that was probably why she fell. The family's been warned that she could have another stroke at any time. Or even a heart attack. They did lots of tests whilst she was in hospital and things are not good, artery-wise; there are a few serious blockages. But she refuses to have a bypass or any kind of invasive treatment. Says she's had a good life and is quite happy to go.'

'Oh dear,' Ryan said with some genuine sympathy in his voice. 'You really have landed yourself in a right pickle, haven't you?'

'I really have. But it's not your problem. I only told you because you insisted.'

'So what are you going to do?'

'I guess I'll delay things for as long as I can. I'll make up some excuse for why you can't come to meet her this weekend—a business trip, or an illness. But I can hardly keep on saying that. In the end, I'll have to tell her the truth—though I don't want to say that I lied about our relationship. She'd be so disappointed with me. I'll have to say that things just didn't work out between us after all.'

'You can say that I didn't want to marry you. Which is true, after all,' he added, smiling.

'Very funny.'

'It is, rather, if you stop to think about it. I can't imagine two more unlikely lovers.'

'Well Gran doesn't know that, does she?' Laura snapped, piqued by his remark.

'No, she doesn't. Of course, there is one other solution to your problem.'

'I can't imagine what.'

'Of course you can't. You don't have an imagination.'

Laura rolled her eyes at him. 'Then enlighten me, oh brilliant one.'

'I could go with you to your grandmother's place this weekend and pretend to be your Mr Right.'

Laura almost spilled the rest of her drink, but she soon gathered her usual poise and gave Ryan the drollest look. 'And why, pray tell, would you do something as sweetly generous, but as patently ridiculous, as that?'

CHAPTER THREE

WHY indeed? Ryan wondered as he quaffed back a good portion of his drink.

He suspected it was because the idea amused the hell out of him. He rather fancied the prospect of Laura having to act the part of his doting girlfriend.

But of course he could hardly say that. And there *was* another reason, one which might convince the surprisingly sentimental Laura into going along with his suggestion.

'As I mentioned before,' he said, 'I have a soft spot for grandmothers. Mine was marvellous to me. I don't know what I would have done without her.' He certainly wouldn't have gone on to be a success in life. She was the one who had first taken him to soccer—even though he was a little old at thirteen to take up the sport, which was why he ended up a goalkeeper. And she was the one who had made him believe that he could put the past behind him and become anything he wanted to be.

'I've always regretted that she died before I could give her all the good things she deserved in life,' he added. More than regret—remorse was more like it. He hadn't realised until she was gone just how much she'd done for him, and how much she meant to him. He'd cried buckets when he found out she'd died, though not in front of any of his teammates. He'd been a very selfish twenty-two at the time and had just been signed to his first contract with a premier league English team. He hadn't returned to Australia for his grandmother's funeral, another deep regret.

He'd been touched by Laura sitting with her grandmother all night, not wanting to leave her to die alone. Clearly, the old lady meant a lot to her.

'It's obvious that you're very close to your grandmother,' he said.

'I am,' Laura said, her voice sounding a little choked up. 'She raised me after my parents were killed in a plane crash.'

'I see...' And he did see. His grandmother had raised him after his own mother had died.

Damn it all, but he didn't want to think about *that*!

'So what do you say to my suggestion?' he asked, not feeling quite so amused any more. But it was too late to retract his offer.

Laura's expressive eyes showed considerable reserve. 'I have to confess that I'm tempted. But I'm not sure we could bring it off—pretending to be lovers, that is. I mean, we don't even like each other.'

'True,' he said bluntly.

'You don't have to agree with me so readily,' she snapped. 'What is it, exactly, that you don't like about me?'

He smiled. 'You don't really want me to tell you that, do you?'

'I certainly do.'

'Okay, you asked for it. First there's your appearance.'

'There's nothing wrong with my appearance!'

Ryan raised an eyebrow sardonically and infuriatingly she felt herself blush. He continued, 'Then there's your manner.'

'What's wrong with my manner?'

'Well, "ice queen" would be an understatement. Of course,' he went on, unbowed in the face of her outrage, 'If I could persuade you to let your hair down in more ways than one, then it'd be a breeze. Do you think you could do that?'

'I'm not going to tart myself up for the likes of you, Ryan Armstrong,' Laura pronounced huffily.

'And there we have the main reason that I don't like you: because *you* don't like *me*.'

'No,' she bit out. 'I don't.'

'Why not?'

'You don't really want me to tell you that, do you?'

He chuckled. She might not have an imagination but she did have a sharp wit. 'Actually, I'm not so sure that I don't like you,' he said. 'You are very amusing company.'

She made no comment, just gave him another of her dry looks.

'Do you have a boyfriend, Laura?' he asked abruptly.

'Don't be ridiculous,' she retorted. 'If I had a boyfriend do you think I would be in this damned awful predicament?'

'Having a boyfriend does not equate with your finding Mr Right. But let me rephrase that—are you sleeping with anyone at the moment?'

Her eyes grew even colder, if that were possible.

'I'm between boyfriends at the moment,' she said tartly.

'Ah.'

'And what does that mean?' she demanded to know.

'Ah just means ah.'

'I very much doubt that. You think I'm not capable of getting a boyfriend, don't you? You think I'm too cold.'

Wow, he thought, how right you are. But rather fascinatingly frosty. What he wouldn't give to have the chance to melt some of that ice. Unfortunately, a man could get frostbite trying.

He'd have to watch himself with her this weekend.

'What I think,' he said after careful consideration, 'Is that you've been hurt by some man in your past which has given you a jaundiced view of the male sex.'

The slight widening of her eyes showed him he was on the right track with his analysis of her character.

'Lots of attractive women who've been badly treated by men subconsciously do things to make themselves less attractive so that they won't be hit on. Some change their appearance by putting on weight. Some dress in a manner which hides their femininity. Which I think—'

The sound of his phone ringing interrupted his spiel.

'Excuse me,' he said to Laura as he fished the phone out of his jacket pocket and glanced at the identity of the caller.

Damn. It was Erica.

CHAPTER FOUR

LAURA welcomed the interruption. Ryan's interpretation of her character was too close to the bone for her liking. Because of course he was right. Subconsciously, she knew why she dressed the way she did and acted the way she did. But no man had said as much to her out loud before.

She didn't like it. It made her feel vulnerable and weak. A coward, even. Yet she wasn't a coward—*was* she?

The thought tormented her. Alison was always saying that she should give the male sex another chance. But then what would Alison know? She was married to a great guy who was loving and loyal and would never hurt her. She'd never known what it felt like to have one's heart ripped out, not just by one man, but two. Laura knew she couldn't afford to open herself to hurt of that kind ever again because if she did, and disaster struck a third time, she suspected she would not survive.

Admittedly, sometimes she was very lonely. Sometimes, she wished her life had been different; if only she'd found some-one decent when she'd been younger and still full of hope. Life's experiences, however, had finally turned her into a hard-hearted cynic, but quite a good judge of character. Nowadays, when she met an attractive man, she quickly saw through his looks to the man beneath.

She knew exactly what sort of man Ryan Armstrong was: the sort who would break a girl's heart and never lose a mo-ment's sleep over it.

But he was not totally bad, she accepted as she glanced over the rim of her glass at him. Clearly he was capable of kindness.

'Hi,' he said into his phone. 'How's things going?'

He'd turned his body away from the table to answer the phone but Laura could still hear him clearly enough. The bar was beginning to fill up but the noise wasn't too bad, and the music hadn't yet started.

'That boring, huh?' he went on. 'No, I'm down at the Opera Bar having a drink with a friend from work.'

Laura frowned, knowing instantly that Ryan was being evasive to whomever he was talking to on the phone. His girlfriend, perhaps? He was sure to have one. He always had some girl on tap from what she'd heard. She'd forgotten about that when he'd offered to pretend to be her Mr Right this weekend.

What on earth did he plan to tell the girlfriend if she agreed to his suggestion? Laura couldn't imagine any female enjoying their boyfriend pretending to be another woman's boyfriend, no matter how innocent it really was.

'I'll ring you later tonight, sweetheart,' she heard him saying, confirming her suspicion that he was talking to his current girlfriend. 'Bye for now.'

He hung up and swung back to face her. 'Now, where was I?' he said as he put his phone away.

Laura decided to put a spanner in his works with some much-needed honesty.

'Your girlfriend wouldn't like you pretending to be my Mr Right,' she said with chilly disdain in her voice. 'Or were you thinking about not telling her?'

His eyes grew even colder than her own, if that were possible. 'Erica does not own me, Laura. Besides, she's in Melbourne this weekend for a conference.'

'You mean what she doesn't know doesn't hurt her?'

'Actually, I have every intention of telling Erica when I ring her back later tonight.'

'Really.' Laura could not keep the sarcasm out of her voice.

In her experience, lying to their girlfriends was second nature to men like Ryan.

'Yes, really. But I can see you don't believe me.'

'Does it matter what I believe? It's all irrelevant anyway, because I've decided not to accept your kind offer.'

'And why's that?'

'Because it can only lead to further complications. Gran's eightieth birthday is coming up soon. If her health improves, the family is sure to throw her a party and she'll expect me to attend, along with my newly found Mr Right. I can't honestly expect you to go along to that as well. By then, we'll be asked eternal questions about when we're getting engaged and when the wedding's going to be. Everything will snowball and you'll wish you hadn't started it in the first place. Much better I go home this weekend and say we've already broken up.'

Ryan shrugged. 'If that's what you want to do. But it wouldn't worry Erica.'

'If you think that, Ryan, then you don't know women very well. I think I should go now,' she added, becoming nervous that people from her work would start arriving any minute now. 'Thank you for the drink, and for your offer. It really was very nice of you. But not a good idea.'

She finished her drink and stood up. 'I'll see you next Friday at three,' she said.

'I tell you what,' Ryan said before she could escape. 'I'll give you my private mobile-number just in case you change your mind. Do you have a biro in that bag of yours? I'll bet you do,' he added with a quick smile.

'Yes, but…'

'Just write it down, Laura,' he said with a hint of exasperation. 'You never know.'

'Oh, very well,' she said, and did what he asked, writing the number he gave her down on the back of one of her business cards.

Then she bolted for the exit, thankfully not spotting anyone she knew on the way out. Laura was out of breath by the time she made it to the quay and onto the Manly ferry for the ride home, glad to subside into a seat in a private corner, glad to be alone with her still-whirling thoughts.

But, once her head settled and her heart stopped beating like a rock-band drummer, Laura knew she'd made the right decision, knocking back Ryan's offer. It was ridiculous to keep such a deception going, no matter how tempted she'd been.

What was that other saying, now? 'Oh what a tangled web we weave when first we practise to deceive'?

As she'd spelled out to Ryan, it would have been extremely difficult to carry off such a pretence without their dislike for each other shining through somehow. No, she'd done the right thing. The only thing. But she still winced at the thought of telling the family that she'd lied about finding Mr Right. She did have her pride.

No, she'd do what she originally said she'd do: make some excuse why Ryan couldn't join them this weekend. Then later on, if Gran continued to recover, she could say that they'd broken up because Ryan refused to get married. That would save her pride too. If Gran didn't recover—Laura's heart contracted fiercely at this thought—then it wouldn't matter. Gran would at least have died happy.

CHAPTER FIVE

BY THE time the ferry docked at the Manly wharf and Laura started off up the hill for the walk home, she'd become reconciled to her decision, except for one small regret. It would have been seriously satisfying to go home with a man like Ryan on her arm, she thought with a rather wistful sigh, just to see the looks on the faces of her aunt and uncle, both of whom never let an opportunity go by to point out what a loser she was in the dating department.

Of course the truth was that they didn't like her. Uncle Bill had resented her from the moment she'd been brought home to her grandparents' place to live and it had became obvious that his mother preferred her estranged daughter's daughter to the son he and Cynthia had produced.

Laura didn't think this should have been a surprise, since all the men in the Stone family were odious. Her grandfather especially. Jim Stone had been a male chauvinistic pig of the first order. His son and his grandson had taken after him, believing they were superior beings and that women were only put on this earth to pander to their needs. After actually living in her grandfather's house, Laura understood fully why her mother had run away from home as soon as she was old enough and why she'd married a man like her father who, though a strong man, had been compassionate and gentle in his dealings with people, especially women. He'd been a lawyer also; Laura had adored him.

She'd disliked her grandfather intensely and hadn't been at all sad when he had died. But even in death Jim Stone had been able to make her angry, leaving the family property to his son rather than his long-suffering wife. She'd tried to get her gran to contest the will but she wouldn't, saying that it didn't matter, that Bill promised to look after her until she died.

But that wasn't good enough, in Laura's opinion. The home which Gran had lovingly tended for over fifty years should have been hers until she died. Instead, she'd been relegated to the role of a poor relative, reliant on her son for charity. All her gran had been left was a miserable twenty-thousand dollars a year, not much more than the old-age pension. That was until Laura had had a little chat with her uncle and insisted that he bump the amount up to forty thousand at least, warning him that if he didn't then she would use every bit of her power and influence to get his mother to contest the will.

Naturally, her firm stance hadn't gone down too well, but he'd done what she had asked. Of course, he'd made it sound like it was all his idea. When Laura had seen how touched her grandmother had been—she probably wasn't used to the men in her life treating her nicely—she hadn't said a word. Several times, during the five years since her grandfather had died, Laura had tried to persuade her grandmother to come to Sydney to live with her, but to no avail. Her gran said she was a country girl and wouldn't be happy living in the city.

Yet I have a very nice home, Laura thought as she pushed open the gate which led up the path to the three-bedroomed cottage which had belonged to her parents and which had come to her when they were so tragically killed. Her grandfather had tried to sell it after she'd gone to live with him, but her darling grandmother—who had been sole executor of her daughter's will—had refused to give permission for the sale. So the contents had been stored and the house had been rented out until Laura had left school and moved back to Sydney to attend university, at which point she'd taken possession of it again.

She'd lived there ever since, mostly happily. Only once had the house been instrumental in bringing her unhappiness. But that hadn't really been the house's fault.

Laura inserted the key in the front door, knowing that as soon as she turned the lock and opened the door Rambo would come bolting down the hallway, meowing for food.

And there he was, right on cue. Putting her bag down on the hall table, she scooped him up into her arms and stroked his sleek brown fur. It was better to pick him up, she'd found, than to leave him down on the floor to trip her up.

'How was your day, sweetie?' she said as she made her way down to the kitchen.

His answer was some very contented purring.

Once in the kitchen she plopped Rambo down on the tiled floor and set about getting him his favourite 'fussy cat' food, steak mixed with chicken. She'd just filled his dish with the meat and shoved the plastic container in the garbage bin when her phone rang—not her mobile, her land line. Which meant it wasn't Alison or any of her work colleagues. The only people who used her land line were telemarketers and family.

Laura steeled herself as she swept up the receiver from where it was attached to the kitchen wall.

'Hello,' she said somewhat abruptly.

'I finally got you,' Aunt Cynthia replied with an air of frustration. 'I tried ringing earlier but you weren't home.'

Laura glanced up at the kitchen clock. It was only five-thirty. She was rarely home on a Friday night before six.

'You can always get me on my mobile,' Laura told her. 'I did give you the number.'

'Bill said I wasn't to ring people on their mobiles. He said it cost a fortune.'

Laura sighed. 'Not these days it doesn't, Aunt Cynthia. Anyway, what did you want me for? There's nothing wrong with Gran, is there?' she added with a sudden jab of worry.

'No, no, your grandmother's doing quite well, considering. I'm ringing because Shane asked me to.'

Shane was her vile only-son and heir who was a chip off the old Stone block. He'd tormented Laura from the day she'd gone to live with her grandparents. His family had lived nearby in a smaller house on the same property. Thankfully, when she had finished primary school, Gran had sent Laura to boarding school in Sydney, a move which she'd appreciated. Her grandfather had objected at first on the grounds of the cost but her gran had stood firm again, saying the fees could easily be covered by Laura's inheritance. Both Laura's parents had had excellent insurance policies which had paid out double because they'd died in an accident.

Laura had quite enjoyed her school days—not her holidays so much, which her wretched cousin had made a right misery. Admittedly, he'd improved slightly with age, mainly because he'd married a modern girl who refused to put up with his boorish behaviour. In truth, the last time they'd met, Shane had surprised Laura by being reasonably civil to her. But Laura couldn't imagine why he would ask their mother to ring her.

'What does he want?' she asked warily.

'To find out if your new boyfriend is the same Ryan Armstrong who was a famous goalkeeper a few years back. His father told him that it was highly unlikely, given he was dating you, but I promised to ask you just the same. Because Shane said, if he was, he wants to meet him.'

'And if he wasn't?' Laura asked archly.

'What?'

Laura gritted her teeth. They really were a most annoying family!

'Yes,' she bit out. 'Ryan is, or was, a famous goalkeeper.' She only knew that because she'd been told of Ryan's international success by a sport-loving colleague of hers who'd been quite jealous about her securing Ryan as a client.

'Heavens to Betsy!' her aunt exclaimed. 'I can't believe it. Shane's going to be *so* excited. You know how much he loves watching the soccer.'

Actually no, Laura didn't know any such thing. She'd had as little to do with Shane as possible over the years.

'I must say I'm somewhat surprised,' her aunt rattled on, 'That you've got yourself a boyfriend at all, let alone a famous one.

'I was saying to Bill just the other week that it looked like you were going to end up an old maid. You're not a bad-looking girl, but you do have an unfortunate way about you. You state your opinions much too strongly. Men don't like that, you know. And the way you dress is…well, not very feminine. Still, I guess there's someone for everyone in this world. So how old is your Mr Armstrong? I dare say he's not all that young.'

Laura couldn't say a word for a moment, having been rendered speechless by her aunt's tactless commentary.

But, as she struggled to find her tongue, Laura knew that there was no way now that she was going up to that house tomorrow alone. No darned way!

'To tell you the truth, Aunt,' she said at last, 'I'm not sure exactly how old Ryan is. Middle to late thirties is my best guess.'

'You'd think you'd know your boyfriend's age,' her aunt said snippily. 'How long did you say you'd been going out with him?'

'We've been business acquaintances for two years. But we've only started dating recently.'

'Oh, I see. So he's not that serious about you yet.'

'He's *very* serious about me,' she heard herself saying. 'You don't think he'd agree to come home with me and meet Gran if he wasn't serious, do you?'

'What? Oh no, no, I suppose not. So what time do you think you might arrive?'

Laura closed her eyes and prayed that Ryan would not change his mind and retract his offer when she rang him.

'Around noon?' she suggested.

'Could you make it later than that?' her aunt said. 'Say, around three? That way I won't have to do lunch tomorrow as well as dinner that night and lunch again the next day. That's a lot of work, you know.'

'But we weren't going to stay the night,' Laura protested.

'Don't be silly, of course you are. I've already bought the food and the wine. On top of that your grandmother is expecting you to stay for the weekend, not just for a few short hours. You wouldn't want to disappoint her, would you?'

'No, of course not,' Laura said, but her head was spinning. How on earth was she going to keep up such a ridiculous charade for that long? And what if Ryan refused to go with her? Giving her his phone number was no guarantee he would say yes a second time.

'We'll see you tomorrow around three, then?'

'All right,' Laura agreed somewhat weakly.

'And Laura…?'

'Yes?'

'Bring a dress to wear for dinner tomorrow night, will you? I don't want to see you at the table wearing those ghastly jeans you seem to live in.'

Laura sucked in a deep breath through wildly flaring nostrils. She was about to launch into a counter-attack when she realised the line had already gone dead. She glared down at the receiver for several furious seconds before slamming it back on the hook.

If there was anyone who could get under her skin even more than her uncle, it was her aunt—stupid, self-important, insensitive woman! Laura felt sorry for her grandmother, having to live with two such impossible people. She deserved better after putting up with that wretched husband of hers for fifty-five years.

Thinking about her grandmother's feelings put some perspective back into Laura's growing frustrations over the weekend ahead. Okay, so she'd backed herself into a right royal corner now. Too bad. Gran was worth putting up with pretending to be Ryan Armstrong's girlfriend for longer than a few hours. And worth having to put her pride aside to ring him back and tell him that she'd changed her mind and wanted to accept his offer. If he prevaricated, she would beg him to come with her, if she had to. Hell, she'd even bribe him if she had to. Though what with, she had no idea.

The thought of offering him sex popped into her head out of the blue. It was such a crazy idea that she threw back her head and laughed out loud. As if the prospect of sex with her would persuade a man like Ryan to do anything! It would more likely make him run in the other direction.

Shaking her head, she marched back down the hallway to where she'd left her handbag, rifling through it to retrieve the business card she'd written his number down on.

Her stomach tightened into a knot as she picked up her mobile phone and punched in the numbers. For what *would* she do if he refused? What *could* she do? Laura felt sick just thinking about it. She hit the call button and started praying.

CHAPTER SIX

'RYAN Armstrong,' he answered quite promptly in his very male voice.

Laura straightened her spine and squared her shoulders at the same time. 'Ryan, it's Laura. Laura Ferrugia.'

'Laura!'

No doubting the surprise in his voice.

She could hear noise in the background, people laughing and talking, and live music playing. If she wasn't mistaken he was still at the Opera Bar.

Laura decided not to waffle; she wasn't a waffly person at the best of times. 'Is your offer still open?' she asked abruptly.

'Absolutely.'

'Thank God,' she couldn't help saying.

'That sounds somewhat ominous. What's happened to make you change your mind?'

'My aunt happened, that's what,' she said sharply.

'Sorry. Have I missed something?'

'I'll fill you in tomorrow during the drive up there.'

'Up where?'

'Didn't I tell you? Gran lives in the Hunter Valley. So does the rest of my family. I'm sure I told you.'

'You probably did. I remember you mentioning the John Hunter hospital.'

'Yes, well, the John Hunter hospital is not really near the

Hunter Valley. I take it you're not familiar with the Newcastle area?'

'No. Never been up that way at all.'

'It's a relatively easy drive. You just take the freeway north and turn off at the signs to the vineyards. I usually make it in just over two hours. If I leave home out of peak hour, that is.'

'And where's home?'

'Manly. Do you have a nice car?'

'That's an odd question. Ah, yes, I get the drift. You want to impress.'

'You have no idea,' she said with so much feeling that he laughed.

'In that case, you'll be pleased to know I have a very nice car. A navy-blue BMW convertible. Will that do?'

'Wonderful. And Ryan, I hate to tell you this, but my aunt assumed that we'd be staying the night and I simply couldn't get out of it. Though you don't have to worry that we'd have to share a bedroom. Gran would never tolerate that in her home.'

But it wasn't her gran's home any more, came the sudden thought.

Surely her aunt wouldn't put them in the same bedroom?

Surely not?

But she just might…

Best not say anything, or Ryan might back out of the deal.

It was a worry all the same.

'So, what's your address?' he asked. 'And when do you want me to pick you up tomorrow?'

'What?'

'Laura, get with the programme.'

'Sorry,' she muttered and gave him the details he requested.

'What clothes should I take with me?' he asked. 'I'm getting the feeling that your family has money. Am I right?'

'They're well off but not seriously rich. Still, my aunt fancies herself a social hostess, so she'll pull out all the stops for dinner tomorrow night. But you won't need a dinner suit or anything like that.'

'What kind of place is it?'

'Years ago it used to be a large stud-farm for thorough-bred horses, with hundreds of acres of prime pastureland. But when there was a downturn in the horse-racing industry my grandfather sold off all the horses and went into cattle. Then when he died a few years back and my uncle took over he sold off most of the land to a property developer and invested the money, though he did keep a few cows. Nowadays, the property's just a small farm, really.'

'I've never been to a farm.'

'You haven't missed much.'

'I take it you're not a country girl at heart.'

'You take it correctly. There's something else I should tell you.'

'Shoot.'

'I have a male cousin named Shane who's apparently a mad soccer-fan and is sure to be at the family dinner tomorrow night. He twigged that you were once a famous goalkeeper and is dying to meet you. Are you all right with that?'

'Won't bother me a bit.'

'I didn't think it would but I thought you should know all the same.'

'That's very thoughtful of you, Laura.'

'You're the one who's being thoughtful. I'll be forever grateful for you doing this.'

'It's my pleasure. If you must know, I'm quite looking forward to it.'

'I don't know why. I'm terrified.'

'Yes, I can hear the tension in your voice. Look, don't make me wait till tomorrow to find out what your aunt said to force you to change your mind. You have to tell me now or I won't be able to sleep for imagining all sorts of crazy scenarios. It wasn't just because she found out about my goalkeeping past, was it?'

'No, nothing like that. It was what she said about me.'

'What did she say about you?'

Laura told him—every insulting detail of her conversation with her aunt, even the bit where she implied Ryan must have been ancient to be interested in her. She could feel her temper rising as she gave vent to her feelings of hurt and humiliation.

'Do you know she had the hide to tell me to wear a dress to dinner tomorrow night?'

'Shocking.'

'Are you making fun of me?'

'Not at all,' he denied. 'I think your aunt was very rude.' He paused, somehow managing to sound completely unconvincing, and Laura remembered his comment about her appearance.

She bristled. 'I'll have you know that I own several dresses. And quite a bit of make-up. I just don't choose to wear either to work. Or at weekends in the country.'

'But you will *this* weekend, if you're serious about impressing your family. It's not just me who'll be on show, sweetheart, but us as a couple.'

'You're not going to call me that, are you?'

'Call you what?'

'Sweetheart,' she bit out.

'Not if you don't like it.'

'I don't like it.'

'What would you like me to call you, then?'

'Laura.'

'Laura it is, then. And Laura…?'

'Yes?'

'Try to relax a bit before tomorrow, will you? You're way too uptight.'

'Sorry. I can't help it. I hate having to do this.'

'What? Pretend that you're in love with me?'

Laura winced. Did he have to be so baldly honest?

'I guess,' she said.

'You've been madly in love before, haven't you?'

'Yes,' she confessed reluctantly. Twice. First with Brad, and then with Mario. Finding out Brad was a selfish, greedy, amoral rat had been devastating enough. But it had been the super-charming Mario who had nearly destroyed her. Because she should have known better by then. Should have seen through his lies.

But she hadn't.

'Act with me the way you acted with him, then,' Ryan suggested.

'I could never act that way again,' she said coldly. 'It was pathetic.'

'That bad, huh? Okay, just don't freeze up if I put my arm around you or give you a little kiss occasionally. Strictly no tongues.'

'I should hope not!'

He laughed. 'I can see that tomorrow might be a stretch, but what the hell? We're doing this for your gran, right?'

Laura blinked. She'd almost forgotten about her. Ever since that horrid phone call from her aunt she'd been thinking more about herself and her pride.

'Yes,' she said, feeling ashamed of herself. 'Yes, of course.' There wasn't anything she wouldn't do for her gran. 'Ryan...?'

'Mmm?'

'You can call me sweetheart if you want to.'

He laughed. 'That's more like it. Now you just need to find a dress. Red would look good on you.'

'But I don't own a red dress.'

'Then go buy one! You have all tomorrow morning. And some sexy shoes as well. Have to go now, Laura, someone's trying to ring me. I'll see you at your place tomorrow at one o'clock sharp.'

Laura opened her mouth to protest, but he'd already hung up.

Dear God, what have I done?

But he was right, she supposed. Any girlfriend of Ryan's would dress sexily.

Laura hadn't dressed sexily since she'd split with Mario,

which was quite a few years ago now. Frankly, she wouldn't even know where to start to find a sexy red dress.

But Alison would. Alison was right into fashion.

Laura pulled a face. If she asked Alison for help that would mean telling her what she was doing this weekend—and with whom. This would also mean confessing what she'd said to her gran when she'd been in the coma.

Alison would be hurt that she hadn't confided in her earlier. The two girls pretty well told each other everything, had done ever since their boarding-school days together. Confessing that she'd kept a secret from her would be hard but it had to be done.

Hopefully, she wouldn't judge her too harshly. Biting her bottom lip, she punched in Alison's number and walked slowly into her bedroom. There she sank down on the side of the bed and waited for her best friend to answer.

Please don't let her have gone out tonight, she prayed as the phone rang and rang.

A split second before it would have gone to her message bank, Alison's harried voice came down the line. 'This had better be important, Laura. You know how dreadful the children can be at this time of night.'

In truth, Laura could hear the sounds of arguing in the background. Alison had a boy of eight and a girl of six who didn't always get along, especially when they were tired. Clearly it wasn't the time for true confessions right at this moment.

'Sorry,' Laura said. 'But I am desperate. Could you get Peter to mind the children tomorrow morning whilst you come shopping with me?'

'Shopping for what?'

'A dress. A sexy red dress.'

'Bloody hell, Laura, I almost dropped the phone just then. Did I hear you correctly? Did you say you wanted to buy a sexy red dress?'

'Yes,' Laura admitted, knowing that she'd just opened the

floodgates to Alison's curiosity, which was second to none. 'Could I possibly explain tomorrow?'

'You can explain later tonight, madam, when I have time to call you back and listen to what I'm sure will be a fascinating story.'

'All right,' Laura said with a resigned sigh. 'Just be gentle with me. I'm feeling a bit fragile.'

'Rubbish! You don't do fragile. You kids, if you don't stop fighting I'm going to get off this phone and strangle you. Laura, I have to go kill the kids. I'll ring you back later.'

'Fine,' Laura said wearily and hung up.

CHAPTER SEVEN

'MY MIND'S still boggled by all this,' Alison said as she put down her coffee cup.

They were sitting in a café in Centre Point Tower, having spent a good two hours since the shops opened finding the right sexy red dress, not to mention a pair of equally sexy shoes.

'I mean, why Ryan Armstrong of all people?' she went on disbelievingly.

'You know why, Alison,' Laura replied patiently. 'He's exactly the type of man Gran would think was a good catch.'

'But you can't stand him.'

'I don't dislike him as much as I thought I did,' Laura admitted. How could she when he was doing this for her?

'Ah-*ha*!' Alison pounced. 'I get it. You've been secretly attracted to him all along. And he to you.'

'Please don't start that romantic rubbish, Alison.'

'But why else would he agree to this… This…?'

'Charade,' Laura finished for her. 'I told you—he's doing it because he has a soft spot for grandmothers.'

Alison rolled her eyes. 'Oh, phooey! He's probably just doing it to get into your pants. Now that I've had time to think about it, I can see it's not romance he wants but sex. I keep forgetting not all men are sincere like my Peter. We both know what kind of guy Ryan Armstrong is, Laura. He's a player, with an obsession about winning. If what you've told me is true, you've been giving him the cold shoulder ever since you got him as a client. Am I right?'

'Yes.'

'Men like that don't expect women to give them the cold shoulder. They're used to being flattered and flirted with. You've become a challenge, Laura. You yourself said you were surprised at his asking you out for a drink.'

And to go sailing with him, Laura suddenly recalled.

'That was move number one,' Alison said wryly.

'But he has a girlfriend!' Laura protested.

'Who's away in Melbourne for the weekend. My my, how convenient.'

'It isn't like you to be so cynical, Alison. That's usually my bag.'

'Yes, well, I can see that you're in danger of being taken in by this creep. I mean, the guy asks you to buy a sexy red dress and you actually go and buy one. The Laura I know would never have done that.'

Laura sighed. 'I'm not being taken in by him. I just don't want to look like an old maid this weekend.'

'Well, you sure as hell won't look like an old maid in that red dress. And those beck-and-call-girl shoes you bought.'

'You told me to buy them.'

'That was before I worked out what the guy was really up to.'

'I hate to mention this, Alison, but it takes two to tango. And I have no intention of sleeping with Ryan Armstrong, even if he wanted me to.'

Which he didn't. But Laura could see where Alison was coming from. Her friend's view of Ryan's character had been tainted by what Laura had said about him in the past. If she met him, Alison would see that he wasn't some kind of sleazebag who couldn't go a weekend without sex. As much as it pained Laura to admit it, he'd shown her another side yesterday, one which had both surprised and impressed her.

'He's just being kind,' Laura stated firmly. 'Now, I have to get going. Ryan's picking me up at one. Thanks a bunch for coming with me, Alison. I would never have found that dress without you.'

'Don't thank me yet,' Alison said dryly. 'That is not any old dress. Even if he doesn't fancy you yet, he will when he sees you in it.'

Laura worried about Alison's last words all the way home on the ferry. It *was* a sexy dress. But not over-the-top sexy, she decided once she had the opportunity to have a second look at it in the privacy of her bedroom.

Of course the scarlet colour was a bit in your face. As was the wide, black patent-leather belt which was decorated with rows of silver studs. Still, the fashion world seemed to have become addicted to glamour and glitz during the last few years so it was hard to buy a cocktail dress which wasn't shiny or didn't have some bling on it. The same applied to shoes. The black patent high-heels Alison had talked her into buying had the same silver studs decorating the straps which ran up the front of her foot to the wide ankle strap.

Laura winced when she looked at the shoes again. Perhaps it would be wise to wear another pair of shoes, one which was less provocative, and decidedly less dominatrix-inspired. But when she rummaged through her wardrobe in search of something else Laura soon saw that there was absolutely nothing there that wouldn't look positively dreary. After her break-up with Mario, she'd thrown away all the sexy clothes and shoes that she'd happily worn for him, replacing them with a wardrobe which wouldn't have stirred a single hormone in any man.

Whilst Laura didn't actually want to stir Ryan Armstrong's hormones this weekend, she did want her family to think she was capable of doing so. If a by-product of this was that Ryan might look at her temporarily with different eyes, then so be it. She couldn't imagine that he would actually make a pass. Why would he when he already had a girlfriend who was no doubt providing him with plenty of sex? Whilst Ryan had a reputation for trading in his girlfriends with monotonous regularity, he did not have a reputation for two-timing. As perverse as it might seem, he was well thought of around Sydney as a man of integrity.

Up until yesterday, Laura had taken that opinion of her esteemed client with a grain of salt. But, now that she'd had more to do with him, she was beginning to feel that he could be trusted, which was a very odd thing for her to think about any man, let alone a swinging-bachelor type like Ryan.

Whatever, she didn't have time to worry about such matters right at that moment. It was getting on for twelve-thirty, leaving her only half an hour to finish getting ready then have a bite to eat before Ryan arrived. At least she was already dressed in decent clothes, even if they were just jeans and a simple white shirt. Overnight, she'd considered buying herself something else to wear for the drive up there—a skirt and sweater, perhaps. But it had taken all her time this morning to find the red dress. And, really, jeans were sensible for wearing on a country weekend.

Neither was she going to leave her hair down. She hated having it hang around her face all day; It was bad enough that she had to wear it down for dinner tonight. But she would compromise by putting it up into a ponytail which was a little more feminine than her usual style. Plus she would wear lipstick. Not red lipstick, however; the red-lipstick-wearing could wait until tonight.

Tonight…

Laura shuddered at the thought of *tonight*.

Then don't think about it, Laura, she lectured herself. *Thinking about it won't help. It will only make you more nervous. The deed is done now and there's no backing out.*

Think of Gran if you have to think of anything. Think of making her happy. Think of all those good intentions you had when you first told her that Ryan Armstrong was your Mr Right.

Laura couldn't help it, she burst out laughing. Ryan was so spot on. It really was rather funny, his being cast as her Mr

Right, because if anyone was the perfect Mr Wrong for her it was him.

But her gran wouldn't know that, Laura conceded as she began to pack. She would only see what she wanted to see, a handsome, successful, charming, mature man.

What she didn't know wouldn't hurt her.

Hopefully.

Laura groaned. Somehow she couldn't get past the niggly feeling that this weekend wasn't going to go exactly as planned—that before this day was out, it was going to be a colossal disaster!

CHAPTER EIGHT

RYAN glanced at the digital clock on the dash as he neared the street where Laura lived. Only a quarter to one; he was a little early. Not a good idea to be too early; he pulled over to the kerb to let a few minutes pass before proceeding.

Time ticked slowly by, during which his thoughts inevitably returned to what had happened when he'd rung Erica last night and told her his revised plans for this weekend.

Ryan shook his head at the memory of her reaction. Laura had been so right; maybe he didn't know women as well as he thought he did. Because Erica had not been happy. Not only that, she'd been decidedly jealous!

Being on the end of jealousy was something which brought out the worst in Ryan. When Erica started accusing him of also having fancied Laura and that this was just a ploy to sleep with her, Ryan had told her in no uncertain terms that if that was what she thought then it was time they went their separate ways. After which he had hung up.

The fact that Erica subsequently sent him several grovelling—then abusive—text messages over the next hour had only confirmed his opinion that he'd done the right thing in breaking up with her. But the episode had bothered him all the same. He'd turned his phone off in the end, but he suspected that more messages would be there if and when he turned it back on again. Though what she had left to say he had no idea.

He'd already been called every derogatory name in the diction-ary from a filthy louse to a 'something' libertine.

He hadn't been quite sure what a libertine was, so he'd looked it up and discovered that a libertine was a licentious and lascivious man who did as he pleased—which he thought was a bit harsh, though not entirely inaccurate. He did do as he pleased in the main. And it pleased him not to continue a relationship with a female who was hypocritical as well as foul-mouthed. It also pleased him to pretend to be Laura's Mr Right this weekend and make an old lady's last days happy.

The clock on the dash showed it was now twelve-fifty-three. Time to arrive.

The house at the address Laura had given him came as a surprise. Not because it was grand, or large—it had possibly only three bedrooms. Federation cottages in good condition, however, were still worth a mint, especially when positioned high on a hill overlooking Manly Beach. He wondered if she owned it or was just renting.

It seemed an odd choice for a rental, he decided as he climbed out from behind the wheel and made his way through the front gate and up the flagged front path. The garden on ei-ther side was well tended, he noted, and the green paintwork around the front windows looked freshly done.

Not a rental, he concluded by the time he stepped up onto the ivy-covered front patio and rang the polished brass door-bell. Laura owned this lovely little house. He was sure of it.

Ryan was about to ring the bell again when the front door was swept open and Laura stood there, looking a darned sight better than she usually did. Gone was the funereal black suit; in its place were nicely fitted dark-blue jeans, black ankle-boots and a crisp white shirt with rolled-up sleeves and a turned-up collar. Her hair was swept back up into a ponytail and she'd put on some pink lipstick. All in all she looked five years younger than she had yesterday, and a good deal more fanciable.

Not that he fancied her. Not really; Erica was quite wrong about that. He would never have put himself in this position with a woman he seriously fancied. He was not that much of a fool.

'You're early,' she said, almost accusingly.

Some things, Ryan realised, could not be changed as easily as appearances. She should have been grateful, not irritated. He always liked it when people were on time.

Except at three on a Friday afternoon...

Now why did he have to think of that?

Ryan shrugged in an effort to rid himself of the annoying thought that something was eluding him here. 'Only five minutes. You're looking good,' he complimented her.

'Thank you. So do you,' she returned, if a little grudgingly.

'We aim to please,' he said with a smile.

She didn't smile back, though something flickered in her eyes. He wasn't sure what—more irritation, probably. Man, but he had his work cut out for him this weekend. It wasn't going to be easy pretending to be in love with Miss Prickly.

'I won't be long,' she said, whirling and walking quickly back down the hallway. 'The bathroom's in there,' she said over her shoulder, indicating a door halfway up the hall on the right. 'That's if you want to go before we leave.'

'I'm fine,' he called back.

She was as quick as she said she would be, dragging a small black travel-case in one hand and carrying a plastic suit-cover in the other. Ryan stepped forward to take the bag, leaving her with the coat hanger.

'I presume that's a dress you've got in there,' he said as they made their way out onto the front porch.

'Yes,' came her brusque reply. 'Here. Hold it while I lock up.'

He was standing there, both hands full, when a cat suddenly curled around his right ankle, a sleek brown-coated feline who had 'show cat' written all over him. Until it peered up at Ryan.

'Good God!' he exclaimed in shock. 'Is this your cat?'

'What? Oh yes.'

'He's only got one eye!'

'Hmm, yes,' Laura agreed dryly. 'I had noticed that, Ryan.'

'What happened to him? Was he in a fight?'

'No. He had a run-in with a car about a year ago. Didn't you, sweetie?' she said, her voice turning soft as she scooped the cat up into her arms. 'Cost me a small fortune at the vet. Over three-thousand dollars.'

Ryan just stared at her. Over three-thousand dollars on a cat?

'Yes, I know,' she said, back to her droll tone. 'Not what you might have expected from hard-hearted Laura.'

'You're certainly proving to be more sentimental than I imagined.'

'Sorry to disappoint you.'

'I'm not at all disappointed. You should never apologise for having a softer side, Laura. It's what makes a woman a woman.'

'It's what makes fools of them,' she retorted sharply. 'Especially where men are concerned.'

'I can't see any man making a fool of you.'

'As I said last night, Ryan, you don't know women as well as you think you do. Which reminds me, what did your girl-friend say about your pretending to be my boyfriend for this weekend? Or didn't you tell her?'

Ryan realised straight away that the truth would complicate things unnecessarily. Far better Laura not know how badly Erica had reacted, or that they were no longer a couple.

'Of course I told her,' he lied. 'And she was fine with it.'

Laura shook her head. 'Amazing.' She bent down to drop the cat gently at her feet. 'Be a good boy, Rambo, and don't go on the road whilst I'm away.'

'He'll be fine being home alone?' Ryan asked as they made their way out to the car.

'It's only for one night. He has plenty of food and water and his own cat slap. I've asked one of the neighbours to keep an eye on him as well.'

'What breed is he?' Ryan asked as he laid the suit-cover down on the back seat then placed the bag alongside his in the boot.

'Abyssinian.'

'Ah. I thought he was a pedigree cat. Have you had him long?'

She shot him one of her impatient looks. 'What is this, twenty questions?'

Ryan decided to ignore her stroppiness. 'I'm just collecting some basic facts about you. After all, a genuine boyfriend would know about your cat, wouldn't he?'

Laura sighed. 'I suppose so. In that case, his name is Rambo and he's almost five. I bought him after I...' She broke off abruptly, her mouth tightening.

'After you what?'

'After I broke up with Mario,' she went on at last, her voice as bleak as her face.

'I see,' he said, wondering what exactly dear old Mario had done to turn Laura into such a man-hater. Had she caught him with another woman? Or was it the classic deceit of his having been a married man? His behaviour must have been pretty bad to devastate Laura the way it obviously had. Most women would have moved on by now. Five years ago, she'd said. Wow. Did that mean she'd gone without sex for the last five years? Ryan couldn't imagine a life without regular sex. It was as necessary to him as eating and drinking. Still, he supposed women were different to men in that regard. At least, some obviously were.

'Enough of the third degree for now,' he went on, deciding to forget the awkward questions for a while. 'So, what do you think of my car? Impressive enough for you?'

CHAPTER NINE

LAURA looked at the car and wished that she didn't find being in Ryan's company such a struggle. But from the moment she'd opened the door to him, she'd been thrown off-kilter.

She'd thought she was used to his good looks. After all, she'd seen him every Friday for two years and had never been rendered weak at the knees. But that was exactly how she'd felt a few minutes ago.

Perhaps it was the way he was dressed—all in black. Black jeans, black T-shirt and a black leather jacket. It was not the kind bikers wore but a softer, sleeker kind of jacket. It still gave him a distinctly macho edge. In it, he looked not just handsome but drop-dead gorgeous.

It had taken all of her composure not to stare. But she'd been rattled all the same, even more rattled when he had smiled and said how good *she* looked.

Thankfully, she hadn't done anything humiliating like blush. Unfortunately, however, she'd become defensive and uptight and, yes, downright bitchy. Which was the last thing she wanted to be with him today. If she was going to convince Gran and the rest of the family that Ryan was her real boyfriend, she'd have to stop being her usual sarcastic self and start being nice. Seriously nice.

To compliment his car would be a good idea, but she refused to gush. Gushing was going way too far.

'It's very nice,' she said. 'I like the dark-blue colour.'

'Get in,' he said, coming round to open the passenger door for her.

She did so, sighing with undeniable pleasure as she sank into the soft, cream leather seats.

'Comfy?' he asked.

'Very,' she said, and glanced up at him.

Bad idea. He was smiling at her again. God, but he was just so gorgeous when he smiled like that!

'You can't beat leather, can you?' he said, still smiling.

When her stomach actually fluttered, she gritted her teeth, put on her seat belt then turned her eyes straight ahead.

Unfortunately after he closed the door he strode round the front of the car, right past her line of vision.

Even the way he walked was sexy, she realised, his legs moving with long, jaunty strides and his broad shoulders rocking slightly from side to side. It was a confident walk. Confident and cocky.

Laura sighed with relief when he moved out of view. But her relief only lasted until he opened the driver's door and slid in behind the wheel.

'I think under the circumstances,' he said as he gunned the engine, 'That we should put the top down.'

Instant panic sent her eyes jerking in his direction. She wanted to tell him not to do that, but already the roof was retracting and, really, what could she say? It wasn't as though it was a cold day. There was absolutely no wind and there wasn't a cloud in the clear, blue sky. There was no logical reason why she should be alarmed. But she was.

'You'll enjoy it,' he added, his eyes meeting hers. 'Trust me.'

Laura gave him a tight little smile. It wasn't him she didn't trust, she realised with a jab of dismay. It was herself.

Where had this sudden mad attraction come from?

Admittedly, Ryan was a very attractive man in a physical sense; as cynical as she was about the male sex, Laura wasn't blind. Okay, so he wasn't her usual type. Unlike her gran, she'd always gone for elegantly built males of average height who didn't tower over her. Big, broad-shouldered, macho men had always made her feel uncomfortable.

Ryan was certainly making her feel uncomfortable right at this moment, but in a disturbingly delicious and insidiously corrupting way. It was as well that he didn't fancy her, Laura realised. A blessing, too, that he had a girlfriend, otherwise she just might have been tempted to make a fool of herself this weekend.

Her stomach churned at the development of this highly unexpected situation. There she'd been, thinking she'd have trouble pretending to be Ryan's girlfriend. Now she was faced with having to control the urge to seduce the man!

Not that she would know how to seduce a man. She'd only had two lovers in her life, both of whom had done the seducing. She had absolutely no confidence in bedroom matters, and not a lot of interest these days, either.

Until this moment…

Perhaps her years of celibacy had finally caught up with her. It was the only reason Laura could find for the way she was feeling, so horribly aware of the man sitting next to her. Her sudden vulnerability to him brought a peculiar tension to her body which she could not remember experiencing before. Her shoulders stiffened, then pressed back hard against the seat, her hands twisting together in her lap.

'Relax, Laura,' he commanded as the car accelerated away from the kerb and hurtled off down the street. 'Everything's going to be fine.'

She wasn't so sure about that. Even if she got through this weekend with her pride intact she'd have to give Ryan up as a client. She could not bear the thought of going to his office every Friday afternoon with the same kind of feelings running through her that were running through her now.

It wasn't long, however, before she forgot about her pride and succumbed to the exhilarating and highly seductive experience of riding along in a convertible. Lord, but it was fun, whizzing through the city streets with the sun beating down on her face and the wind in her hair. It was impossible to remain uptight. Soon she relaxed back into the seat, thoroughly enjoying the envious looks on people's faces as they passed them by. Perhaps it was silly of her to feel pleasure at the misconception that Ryan was her boyfriend, but she couldn't seem to help it.

'See?' Ryan said after a few minutes. 'I told you you'd enjoy it. Want me to put some music on?'

'If you like,' she replied, having to work very hard to keep her voice cool and in no way flirtatious.

'Tell me what *you* like,' he countered. 'Music wise. I should know your taste in music, don't you think? And vice versa.'

Laura shrugged. 'I like just about anything which has a melody, a good beat and interesting words. I'm not into hard metal, or rap. I don't have a favourite artist or a band. I never was the sort of teenager who went ape over some singer. Unlike Alison who was—and is—simply crazy about Robbie Williams.'

'Who's Alison?'

'My best friend. We went to boarding-school together.'

'Ah. Perhaps we should leave the music off for now whilst you give me a quick update on your life so far. You don't have to tell me everything. Just the things you think I should know.'

'I'm certainly *not* going to tell you everything,' she retorted, thinking of Brad and Mario.

And she certainly didn't mention those two humiliating relationships. But she did tell Ryan about her mother running away from home to Sydney and eventually marrying her father, who'd been a runaway of another kind. Carmelo Ferrugia had been a lawyer, a refugee from Columbia whose first wife and children had been murdered by some very bad people. Carmelo had been twenty years older than her mother, a kind, compassionate man who'd spent the rest of his life helping people in difficulty.

She also told him about their tragic death in a small-plane crash when she'd been only eleven, about her years living up

in the Hunter Valley with her grandparents and her time at a
Sydney boarding-school.

'I always knew that I would stay in Sydney as soon as I finished school,' she added. 'And that I would become a lawyer,
like my dad. I actually worked for legal aid for a while, like
he did. But I didn't like it all that much. I found it a bit… boring.'

'So you moved on to Harvey, Michaels and Associates.'

'No, I joined another legal firm first, one which specialised
in criminal defence.'

'You couldn't have found *that* boring.'

'No, I loved it. But I…um…'

'You what?'

Too late Laura realised where this conversation was heading.

She winced. She hated talking about Mario. Brad had hurt
her, but Mario had cut very deep.

'I had a relationship with a client that ended badly,' she finally admitted.

'I see.'

'I doubt it.'

'No, I *do* see. I had a relationship with a client once. That
ended badly too. It almost destroyed my business.'

Laura was shocked. 'What happened?'

'In a nutshell I had a brief fling with a client. When I broke
up with her she did her very libellous best to bring my company—and me—to our knees. It was a close call, I can tell
you. Makes you damned careful in future. I've never dated a
client since. I dare say you feel the same way.'

'You could say that.'

'Just as well this isn't a real date, then. Still, I don't think
I have to worry about your ever getting obsessed with me,
Laura.'

Oh, the irony of that remark, she thought as she turned droll
eyes his way. 'I think you're reasonably safe.' *Provided you
don't do anything stupid like make a pass at me.*

His laugh carried real amusement. 'You know, it's quite refreshing being in the company of a woman whom you can entirely trust.'

'Meaning?' she said a bit more tartly that she meant to.

'Meaning I would never have offered to pretend to be your boyfriend if I thought you liked me at all. Because let's face it, Laura, if that was the case this weekend could have complicated our working relationship.'

'I don't see how. Even if I liked you, you don't like me.'

'Not true, sweetheart. How could I possibly continue to dislike a woman who spent three-thousand dollars saving the life of her poor little puddy-tat?'

'Oh,' she said, and then did the unthinkable.

She blushed.

CHAPTER TEN

RYAN could not believe it when Laura's cheeks flushed a bright red. For a second or two, he was troubled by her reaction. But then he saw it for what it was: a natural response to the unexpected occurence of a man saying something genuinely nice about her.

Ryan suspected that Laura had been short of male compliments over the past few years, particularly with the way she dressed and acted. Clearly, she'd shut down after that disastrous affair she'd had with her client. He would have liked to know a few more details about that affair but knew better than to ask right now.

'I hope I haven't said anything out of order,' he said instead. 'There's no reason why I can't like you, is there?'

To give her credit, she regathered her composure with astonishing speed. 'Of course not,' she said with her usual brusqueness. 'You just took me by surprise, that's all. And, for what it's worth, I find I can't continue to totally dislike a man who would give up his weekend to make my gran happy.'

He had to smile. 'Careful. We don't want to get too carried away with the mutual compliments, do we?'

'You don't want me to start lying to you, do you?' she countered tartly.

'Not till we get to our destination, at which point I think some judicious lying will be necessary, along with some judicious flattery and flirting.'

'Flirting!'

He almost chuckled at the horror on her face.

'Absolutely,' he said with a brilliant poker face. 'You do know how to flirt, don't you, Laura?'

'I've never been a flirter. *Or* a flatterer.'

No, he thought ruefully. You wouldn't have been.

'In that case, it's time you learned. Or are you planning on spending the rest of your life as an old maid?'

She shot him a mutinous look. 'How I spend the rest of my life is none of your business.'

'For pity's sake,' he snapped, feeling angry with her now. 'What is it with you? Okay, so some bastard hurt you way back when, obviously very badly. But he's only one man, not the whole male race. We're not all rotters. You have to move on, woman. Get back on the horse, so to speak.'

'Thank you very much!' she ground out sarcastically.

'You will, if you do what I say. Look, this weekend is a perfect opportunity for you to learn how to flirt. You can practise on me to your heart's content without having to put up with any awkward consequences.'

'No kidding.'

'You can cut the sarcasm for starters.'

Her sigh sounded…what—weary? Frustrated?

Suddenly he saw that he was being way too forceful. It was a bad habit of his, trying to fix things and to control things. A result maybe of his childhood where everything had been out of his control.

'Sorry,' he said. 'I'm being obnoxious, aren't I?'

'Very,' she said.

'You can tell me to shut up, if you like.'

'Shut up, Ryan.'

He laughed. 'I promise not be so bossy when we get to your family's place.'

'Don't change too much,' she advised him dryly. 'Gran likes forceful men.'

'But you don't, Laura. I'm playing *your* Mr Right, not your gran's.'

'And you think you know what my Mr Right would be like?' she scoffed.

'I could hazard a guess.'

'Do tell.'

'He'd be a true gentleman, for starters. Slightly old-fashioned in a way. But there'd be no chauvinism in him. He'd treat you wonderfully, like a princess. He'd be passionate, but gentle at the same time. Gentle and protective.'

When he slanted a quick glance her way, he could see that he was right on the mark.

'What are you?' she asked with surprise in her voice. 'A mind reader?'

'No, but I'm a pretty good listener. I heard the way you described your father and I realised he was your ideal man. I dare say the man who hurt you so badly *seemed* like your ideal man, but it was only a façade. Underneath, he was anything but.'

Laura's grim silence touched an empathetic chord inside him. Ryan understood full well that talking about some things did not help. All it did was dredge up old memories which were better left unvisited.

'Sounds like he was a right bastard,' he continued. 'One best forgotten.'

Still, she didn't say a word.

'Time for some relaxing distraction, I think,' he said, and put on the radio.

'Now put your seat back a little and let some of that tension flow out of your body,' he ordered. 'And, before you tell me to shut up again, I think you should know that there's a small part of every woman who wants a man to be forceful with her when the time is right—which is now. So swallow that sarcastic remark which I'm sure your tongue is itching to deliver and just do what I'm telling you. Okay?'

He was pleased when she didn't object. In fact, she did exactly as he suggested—put her seat back, closed her eyes and let out a very long sigh. He wasn't quite sure what was going on inside her head, but soon she began to look a lot more relaxed. In fact, if he wasn't mistaken, she actually drifted off to sleep. It occurred to him that she might not have slept much the night before, worrying over the weekend ahead.

Still, it was as well that he knew the way north as far as the Hawkesbury river. Otherwise, he might have had to rouse her for directions. If he remembered rightly, the Hawkesbury was about a half-hour drive from where they were at the moment. That would give Laura enough time for a cat nap before he'd be forced to disturb her.

Five minutes later, he turned right onto the motorway where he accelerated up to a more enjoyable speed. The traffic thinned appreciably with the triple lanes and the powerful car ate up the miles. The suburban landscape quickly gave way to thick bushland on either side of the road which had been cut through the rocky hills. In considerably less than the half-hour he'd estimated, Ryan began the long incline which he recalled led down to the river and the small hamlet of Brooklyn.

He'd rented a houseboat there once, on a recommendation from a mate who said it was just the place for a romantic weekend getaway.

Ryan frowned as he struggled to remember the name of the girl he'd brought with him. Strange; that had only been about three years ago. Maybe not even that long. Yet he could not remember her name, or even her face. All that came to mind was his pleasure at being out in the open on the water. And the fact that he'd caught a fish.

He glanced over at Laura for a moment. This weekend would hardly qualify as a real romantic getaway. But Ryan rather suspected that he would never forget it, just as he would never forget Laura Ferrugia.

Ryan smiled wryly at this last thought. Impossible to forget the most irritating female he'd ever met!

CHAPTER ELEVEN

LAURA woke with a start, shocked to find that she'd been asleep for almost an hour and a half.

'Why didn't you wake me?' she demanded to know when she realised the time.

Ryan's shrug was nonchalant. 'I figured you needed the rest.'

'Where are we?' she said, suddenly aware that they'd left the motorway and were on a single-lane road. Panic set in until she realised they were on the right road, heading for Cessnock. 'I thought you said you didn't know the way!'

'I figured there would have to be signs. When I saw an exit which led to the vineyards, I took it.'

'You should still have woken me.'

'Will you stop fussing?' he said, his voice showing some impatience. 'We're not lost.'

'But we could have been,' she muttered.

'And if we had been? It wouldn't have been the end of the world, Laura. We both have mobile phones. We could have called and explained that we would be a little late.'

'Maybe, but I don't want to give Aunt Cynthia any reason to criticise me.'

'She won't criticise you with me by your side. She'll be putty in my hands in no time flat.'

Laura rolled her eyes. The arrogance of the man!

'Believe it or not,' he went on with a wry smile curling one

corner of his mouth, 'I have a good track record with the opposite sex. Most women—especially the older ones—find me
totally charming.'

Laura didn't doubt it. But no way could she let him get
away with such self-praise without putting a small dent in his
insufferable male ego, as well as reminding herself to be on
her guard against him at the same time.

'Which is exactly why I chose you as my Mr Right, Ryan,'
she said in droll tones. 'Because you have all those superficial
qualities which pulls the wool over the eyes of most women.
It's only the once-bitten, eyes-wide-open females like myself
who recognise that charm like yours is just so much hogwash.'

He laughed a very dry laugh. 'And there I was, thinking
you were starting to truly warm to me.'

'In your dreams, Ryan. Now concentrate on the road, please.
We're coming into Cessnock. I'll direct you from here. It's a bit
tricky getting through the town and out onto the right road.'

He took her directions without a hitch, and they were soon
through the old mining town and turning onto the road which
would take them to their destination.

'Not too fast along here,' she warned him as he whizzed
along what probably looked to him a very straight, very good
road. 'After all the rain we've had lately, there'll be a lot of
potholes.'

Ryan slowed appreciably, which allowed him to take his
eyes off the road occasionally to study the countryside.

'This is a very pretty area, Laura.'

It *was* pretty, she conceded, with lots of rolling hills and
trees and well-looked-after properties, not all of which were
vineyards. Tourism had spawned quite a few plush resorts to
cater for holiday makers who enjoyed wine-tasting tours, plus
five-star food and accommodation. It was also a popular place
to retire to, with several new villages for the over-fifties who
wanted to enjoy country living without the hassle of having
to do too much work.

'I guess my view is jaundiced by my not being happy living here.'

'Just as your view of men is jaundiced by your not having been happy with one.'

Laura's teeth clenched down hard in her jaw.

'We all have jaundiced memories, Ryan,' she countered coolly. 'I dare say you have some of your own.'

How right you are, sweetheart, Ryan thought with a mixture of annoyance and admiration. She gave as good as she got. But shooting back poisoned darts must get exhausting. He couldn't wait until they got to her place and she would be forced to behave herself. Maybe even be sweet to him. The mind boggled at how she would handle it when he put his arms around her. Maybe even kissed her. Just for appearance's sake, of course. Even so, his heartbeat quickened at the thought.

'How far to go now?' he asked.

'Less than a kilometre. Take the next road on your right.'

It was a wider road, recently tarred and with no rough edges or potholes, which he commented on.

'There's been a lot of development along this road,' Laura explained. 'Several new wineries and a brand-new golf resort built on the land Uncle Bill sold them. We're just coming to that now on your right.'

'Wow!' Ryan exclaimed. 'That's some golf course.'

'It's not just a golf course, it's an estate as well. If you buy a house there you get automatic membership to the golf club. But it'll cost you at least a million. Crafty old Uncle Bill made sure a life membership to the club came with the land deal. He's crazy about golf. I suppose you are, too. Most sporty men are.'

'I wouldn't say I'm crazy about the game, but I like it well enough. To be honest, you have to be able to play golf when you're in the sport-management business. You've no idea how many deals I've negotiated on a golf course, especially at the nineteenth hole.'

Laura frowned over at him. 'I thought there were only eighteen holes?'

Ryan smiled. 'I see *you* don't play golf. The nineteenth hole is the golf club.'

'Oh, silly me. Slow down a bit; our driveway's coming up. There…' Laura pointed a finger to a spot just ahead. 'Between those two gum trees. You won't have to stop, the gates are always left open.'

'I can't see any house,' Ryan said, glancing around as he turned into the driveway.

'That's because you're not looking in the right place. That's it on top of that hill over there.'

His eyes followed the direction of her finger to what was a large two-storey homestead sitting majestically on the crest of a very distant hill. It was rectangular and colonial in style, with a high-pitched roof, and verandahs all the way around, top and bottom. Several chimneys more evidence of real fireplaces, no doubt with elegant hearths to go with the elegant architecture of the building.

'I thought you said your family wasn't seriously rich,' came his rueful remark.

'They're not,' Laura replied.

'Possibly you and I differ on what 'seriously rich' is.'

Unless this property was mortgaged to the hilt, then the owner, in Ryan's opinion, was seriously rich. The fences around the paddocks were in excellent condition and the cattle grazing on the pastures were fat and healthy looking. Despite his knowledge of country living being confined to watching the occasional programme on TV, Ryan could already see he was looking at money.

'I presume all the land leading up to the house belongs to your grandmother?' he asked as they crunched over the gravelly surface.

'No. The whole property actually belongs to Uncle Bill. My grandfather—dear, sweet man that he was—left everything to his son rather than his wife.'

Ryan frowned. 'Why would he do that?'

When he glanced over at her, he saw Laura's face crinkle up in disgust.

'Because he was of the old school,' she said sourly. 'The one which believes that men should rule the world and own all the land.'

Mmm. Perhaps Laura's man-hating ways started long before that client she slept with. Still, Ryan could understand that a girl of Laura's intelligence would find it hard to accept her grandfather's chauvinistic—and decidedly unloving—ways.

'Was your grandmother very hurt at the time?' he asked.

'She was disappointed,' Laura said. 'But she didn't make a fuss, though she should have. I certainly did when Uncle Bill gave her a pitiful allowance out of all the money he'd inherited.'

'What did you do?'

'Threatened the bastard that I'd persuade Gran to contest the will if he didn't give her a decent amount each year. Which he did do, grudgingly.'

'I'll bet you weren't too popular for a while.'

'I've never been popular with the men on this side of my family,' she replied.

Ryan laughed. 'I wonder why?'

'Why should I suck up to the opposite sex?' she asserted with her usual stroppiness. 'I'm as good as they are.'

'Yes, well, just remember that for the next couple of days you're playing the part of a woman in love.'

The expression on her face when he said this was worth all the money in China.

'I knew this was a terrible idea,' she muttered. 'I don't know what possessed me to do it.'

'Pride possessed you.'

'Yes, you're right,' she said with a deeply weary sigh. 'Good old pride—one of the seven deadly sins.'

She looked so dispirited all of a sudden that Ryan felt genuinely sorry for her.

'Not just pride, Laura,' he said gently. 'Kindness too. Let's not forget that. We're here to make your gran happy. What does it matter if you're forced out of your comfort zone for a couple of days? It's not like it will last for ever. Let me do most of the talking. You just smile and agree to everything I say. Which I know will be extremely difficult for you,' he added before she could say a single word. 'But it's all in a good cause.'

She was quiet for a long moment, but then she nodded. 'I'll do my best.'

'Good.'

Good!

Laura felt anything but good every time she looked at the man. She wanted to hit him for making her find him so darned attractive all of a sudden.

It wasn't pride that was possessing her at this moment. It was another of the seven deadly sins, one that terrified the life out of her.

Laura was not intimately acquainted with lust, had never been held in its thrall before. Both Brad and Mario had seduced her into their beds, and she'd gone out of the need to be loved, not the need to have sex with them.

But she wanted to have sex with Ryan. It was a most disturbing thought. Her sigh carried regret that she'd ever thought of this charade in the first place. Regret too that she'd given in to Ryan's suggestion and bought that sexy red dress.

Alison had spelled it out for her. That dress was the sort which would get an octogenarian's hormones up and going. And Ryan was a lot younger and hornier than that. It worried her, what might happen if he did make a pass at her tonight?

'Come now, Laura,' Ryan said with a touch of exasperation in his voice. 'Anyone would think you were going to your execution.'

An execution would be preferable to ending up in bed with you, Laura thought, keeping her eyes firmly off his corrupting body and on the road ahead. She tried thinking of what he'd just said, about this all being in a good cause, but nothing could unwind the knots of tension in her stomach. The niggling fear she'd had that this weekend would end in disaster became steadily magnified as they drew closer to the house. The sight of her Aunt Cynthia standing on the verandah waiting for them reminded her of that other fear she'd had earlier today—the fear that they'd be put in the same bedroom for the night!

CHAPTER TWELVE

ONE look at Aunt Cynthia gave Ryan a clue as to why Laura was so tense.

The woman was formidable looking to say the least, tall and solidly built, with a manner of the sergeant major about her as she stood there at the top of the front steps with her arms folded over her battleship bosom and her thick-ankled legs slightly apart. The skirt and top she was wearing was battleship grey as well. Possibly in her late fifties, she had very short, tightly curled blonde hair—probably permed and dyed—large facial features and the hint of a moustache above her thinly pressed lips. Her eyes were small and closely set, widening slightly as Ryan braked the convertible to a halt at the bottom on the front steps.

'Don't you dare get out of this car,' Ryan muttered under his breath as Laura automatically reached for the door handle.

When her eyes jerked round to his he bestowed a one-thousand-kilowatt smile upon her, then bent over to graze her right cheek with his lips.

'Just do as I say,' he whispered at the same time. 'And smile, for pity's sake.'

She didn't smile, he noted. But she did as he said, staying put while he exited the car and strode round to open the door for her like a gentleman of the old school. Ryan deliberately didn't look up at Aunt Cynthia until Laura was standing up, her hand safely enclosed in his.

By then he was gratified to see true surprise on the woman's face, along with an almost welcoming smile. She'd even unfolded her arms by the time he dragged Laura up onto the verandah with him. Thankfully, the woman was staring at him and not at her rather robotic niece.

'You must be Aunt Cynthia,' he said, beaming broadly. 'What a lovely place you have here!'

When she stepped forward to extend her hand, her beady eyes, which turned out to be a faded blue, actually sparkled at him.

'We think so. It's so nice to meet you at last, Mr Armstrong.'

Ryan shook her hand with his right hand, at the same time keeping his left tightly clasped around Laura's lest she bolt for it. Which she just might do, judging by the tension in her fingers.

'Call me Ryan, please,' he insisted warmly. 'And perhaps you'd allow me to call you Cynthia? After all, you're way too young to be *my* aunt.'

'Oh, go on with you,' she simpered in return, her cheeks going pink with pleasure as her free hand fluttered up to touch her hair.

Laura could not believe it—Aunt Cynthia, actually blushing. The man was a menace all right. But this was why she'd brought him with her today, wasn't it? To see this kind of reaction from her family, and Aunt Cynthia most of all. It was worth taking the risk of making a fool of herself with him in private to experience this moment of public satisfaction.

When her aunt turned stunned eyes towards her, Laura found a slightly smug smile along with a surge of confidence.

'He is gorgeous, isn't he?' she said.

Ryan was momentarily thrown, not only by Laura's compliment but by the smoky voice she used.

Wow, he thought. A guy could get used to her talking to him like that. Of course, he knew it was just an act, but a very convincing one. It looked like he didn't have to worry about her making a hash of their charade.

'Thank you, darling,' he said, giving her hand a little squeeze. 'You're so sweet.'

Laura almost laughed out loud at the look on her aunt's face. Dear, but it was priceless! Like she had something stuck in her throat.

'How's Gran doing?' Laura asked whilst her aunt was still floundering.

Cynthia blinked. 'What? Oh... Er, not too badly.'

'Can we go and see her straight away?'

'Perhaps we should take our things in first,' Ryan suggested. 'I'd like to freshen up as well.'

'Yes, yes, of course,' Cynthia said, quickly recovering her composure to play the perfect hostess, gushing over the car whilst Ryan collected their luggage. He carried Laura's bag as well as his own, though he left Laura with the coat-hangered dress to carry, along with his dinner suit, which was also underneath a plastic cover. Ryan was glad now that he'd brought a suit with him, rather than more casual clothes. It wasn't a tux, just a dark grey, single-breasted number which looked good on him and fitted in with any occasion.

The house was as grand inside as out, Ryan noted, with a wide foyer covered in black-and-white tiles an elaborately carved hall-stand which had to be an antique, and an impressive curved staircase made of a rich red wood.

'It's cedar,' Cynthia informed Ryan proudly when he asked about it. 'There's quite a lot of cedar in this house,' she continued as she led the way upstairs. 'The house was built back in the thirties before the war almost ruined everyone, the racing industry as well. Did Laura tell you this was once one of the most successful racehorse studs in Australia? No, of course she didn't,' the woman rattled on before Ryan could reply. 'Laura's not all that interested in this place or its traditions.

'Now I didn't put you in your usual room, Laura,' she threw over her shoulder towards her niece who was trailing a little behind. 'It's way too small for two people. Shane and Lisa aren't staying the night, so I made up the main guestroom for you,' she said, opening a brass-handled door on their right with a flourish.

Ryan heard Laura make a small choking sound which, thank heavens, her aunt didn't seem to notice, perhaps because she was busy bragging about the people who'd once slept in the very large four-poster bed which dominated the room. She mentioned a past prime minister, as well as a governor general, a couple of English aristocrats and a Hollywood star along with her very wealthy lover.

'This house has a lot of history,' she finished up by saying.

'It's a very beautiful house,' Ryan complimented, having dropped both their bags by the door to wander across the room to the French doors which led out onto the verandah. 'And a very beautiful room.'

He turned to see a pale-faced Laura still standing in the doorway, staring over at the bed. 'But Gran won't like us staying in the same bedroom,' she suddenly blurted out.

Cynthia made a dismissive gesture with her hand. 'Jane doesn't need to know,' she said airily. 'She's not allowed to walk up the stairs any more.'

'So where's she sleeping?' Laura asked as she entered the room and draped the coathangers over the back of a chair.

'We've refurbished the old servants' quarters for her.'

'The servants' quarters!' Laura exclaimed, her face flushing.

'Before you blow a gasket, missy,' her aunt said sharply, 'Jane is very happy with the arrangements. So don't you go making a fuss and making her unhappy.'

'Laura would never do or say anything to make her gran unhappy,' Ryan defended her, moving over to put a protective arm around Laura, warning her with a sharp squeeze not to lose her temper.

'Yes, I do appreciate that, Ryan,' Cynthia said through slightly pursed lips. 'But Laura has the bad habit of opening her mouth before her brain is in gear.'

'She *can* be a bit impulsive,' he said, tightening his arm

again around her shoulders. 'But she always has people's best interests at heart. Especially her gran's.'

'I suppose so. But, as I said, Jane won't find out unless you tell her. Of course, if you'd *prefer* to have separate rooms, then…'

'Absolutely not!' Ryan broke in forcefully. 'I've been dying to get Laura away for a romantic weekend together. And, let's face it, that bed has romance written all over it.'

Laura might have enjoyed the flash of envy on her aunt's face if she hadn't been in a state of complete panic. Her worst fear had come about, that of having to share a bed with Ryan. It was bad enough having to stand where she was with his arm wrapped tightly around her shoulders, but at least they were dressed, and there was someone else in the room. How would she be able to cope lying side by side whilst wearing next to nothing with no one else in the room to stop… *To stop what, exactly?*

Laura knew full well that Ryan would never force himself on her. So what was she afraid of?

Herself again, of course. That self which even now was trembling inside at his touch.

'Now, my dears, I really must go downstairs and tell Jane you've arrived,' her aunt said brightly. 'I thought since it's such a nice day we could have afternoon tea together out on the back verandah. Could you join us there in, say, fifteen minutes?'

'No trouble,' Ryan said when Laura remained silent. 'See you shortly.'

The moment Cynthia closed the door after her, Laura twisted out of his hold. 'That woman is just so impossible!' she exclaimed heatedly. 'Fancy just presuming we'd want to share a room.'

'It's perfectly logical that we would,' Ryan said. 'It's not as though we're teenagers, Laura. We're an adult couple, having an adult relationship. Of course we'd be sleeping together.'

'But we aren't, damn it! And now we'll have to—actually

sleep together, that is. I mean, just look around you. There's nowhere else to sleep in here except on the floor.'

'Well you can count me out on that one,' Ryan said, marching over to lift his bag up and carry it over to the bed, where he dumped it down on top of the richly embroidered red-velvet quilt. 'I'm not sleeping on any wooden floor. Look, this is a very big bed. You can put some pillows down the middle if you like. That should stop me from accidentally brushing up against your very desirable female body and ravaging you on the spot. Which is exactly what you're thinking, isn't it? That I might not be able to control myself.'

Laura just stared at him for a long moment, before dropping her eyes and shaking her head irritably. 'That's not what I was thinking at all.'

'Really? What *were* you thinking, then? And don't say nothing. You are never thinking nothing, Laura.'

She turned and walked over to collect her own bag, wheeling it across the room before hoisting it up onto the bed on the opposite side to where he was.

Her eyes, when they finally lifted to meet his, were decidedly mutinous. 'I don't have to tell you what I'm thinking. And I don't have to sleep in the same bed as you. *I'll* sleep on the damned floor if I have to.'

Ryan scowled at her. She was one seriously irritating woman! 'Be my guest,' he said. 'Just try to do it quietly. I don't want to be kept awake with your moaning and groaning.'

'I don't ever moan and groan,' she snapped.

Ryan gave her a droll look. 'Now *that* I can believe.'

'Very funny,' she bit out.

'Actually, I'm not finding any of this at all funny,' he shot back. 'To be perfectly honest, I wish to God I'd never made this ridiculous offer in the first place. I must have had rocks in my head if I thought I could bring off pretending to be your Mr Right.'

The moment the words were out of his mouth, Ryan regretted them. Not that she didn't deserve some criticism—she wasn't making his job easy—but he hated seeing the crestfallen expression on her face. Hated having hurt her like that.

'I'm sorry,' he said straight away. 'That was uncalled for.'

'No no,' she said, shaking her head unhappily. 'You had every right to say what you did. The way I'm acting... It's silly and, well, it's just plain silly.'

'Then you won't be sleeping on the floor?'

'No,' she said, her chin lifting in an oddly defiant gesture as though it was a big deal, agreeing to share the bed with him.

'Good. Now I have a very important question to ask you before we go downstairs for afternoon tea.'

'What?' she replied, looking worried again.

'Where's the bathroom?'

CHAPTER THIRTEEN

LAURA showed him the door which led into an absolutely huge bathroom, the like of which would never have been seen in a modern house. There was a claw-footed bath sitting against the far wall of the black-and-white-tiled room, a brass-framed shower stall in a corner to its right, a toilet behind the door and a large marble-topped vanity table which had an equally large mirror on the wall above it.

'Wow!' Ryan said. 'I don't think I've seen a bathroom quite like this one before.'

'It is rather old-fashioned,' Laura said.

'Maybe, but I like it.'

'That other door there—' Laura pointed out before she left '—opens out onto the main hallway, so don't forget to throw the lock or you might have an unwanted visitor.' Though she couldn't imagine who. Uncle Bill and Aunt Cynthia would be the only others sleeping upstairs tonight, and the master bedroom was at the other end of the hallway, complete with its own private bathroom.

'Fine,' Ryan said and Laura left him to it, relieved when he closed the door and left her alone in the bedroom. It would be good to be away from his disturbing presence, even for a short while, give her the chance to calm the butterflies in her stomach and to find some much-needed composure.

Unpacking her bag, however, didn't help much, especially when confronted by the pink satin nightie she'd brought with her. Whilst not overly provocative, it was still rather low-cut, with spaghetti-thin straps. At least she'd had the foresight to pack the matching robe, though she could hardly wear that to bed, could she?

Her stomach contracted at the thought of how she would feel, sleeping next to Ryan tonight. She wouldn't be getting much sleep, that was for sure.

He emerged from the bathroom and she took the opportunity to escape.

'I won't be long,' she said, snatching up her toilet bag and dashing past him.

Ryan shook his head at her body language. He wondered what he could say or do to calm her down. It wasn't afternoon tea that she needed, he decided as he hung up his suit and unpacked the rest of his things, but a good, stiff drink. Either that or...

Ryan chuckled with dry amusement. It would be a bit difficult to relax Laura with some sex if just the thought of sharing a bed platonically with him horrified the life out of her. Which it obviously did.

The idea that she might not trust him to keep his hands off irked Ryan a little. What had he ever done to her? Okay, so he probably had a reputation around Sydney as a bit of a womaniser. But he wasn't a sleazebag, or a cheat.

Not that making a pass at Laura would make him a cheat, given he and Erica had now split up. But that was beside the point. Even if he fancied Laura—which he didn't, not *really*— no way would he want to start something this weekend that could only cause him trouble in the future. Laura was a valued work colleague. She was also of a much more vulnerable nature than Ryan had realised.

To contemplate seducing her, even out of a perverse sort of compassion, went totally against his rules. Not that Laura would *let* him seduce her, he conceded ruefully. She would have to be attracted to him a little to do that, which she obviously wasn't, so why was he even having this stupid conversation with himself?

The bathroom door opened and she came out, looking a little less harried. Which was just as well, since he was beginning to run out of patience with her.

'Don't forget what I said about smiling,' Ryan advised brusquely as they made their way down the curving staircase ten minutes later. When she didn't say anything in reply, he stopped at the foot of the stairs to throw her a firm look.

'Come on, show me some of those nice white teeth you have.'

When Laura attempted a smile, Ryan scowled. 'Good God, is that the best you can do, woman?'

Laura winced. 'Sorry. I guess I'm nervous.'

'Lord knows why, with me by your side.'

'Are you always this incorrigibly egotistical?' she demanded to know.

Ryan shrugged. 'I suppose so. It comes with the territory of having been a successful goalkeeper. You have to have total confidence in your abilities or you're dead in the water, because you're alone out there. You can't let a single negative thought creep in or you're done and dusted. But you're not alone today, Laura. You have me to help you. Though you still do need to help yourself. So, smile and make it convincing.'

She smiled, but she still didn't look like a woman in love.

'Only marginally better,' he said, feeling totally exasperated with her and with himself for being so affected by her. 'Here, give me your hand.'

When she hesitated, he suddenly grabbed both her hands then yanked her hard against him.

'The trouble with you, madam,' he ground out as he glared down into her shocked eyes, 'Is that you've been way too long between men. *And* kisses.'

He didn't mean to do it. Hell, he didn't mean to manhandle her in any way, shape or form. But all of a sudden his much-valued control slipped and his mouth came crashing down on hers.

For a split second, Laura froze. This was what she'd feared after all, Ryan making a pass at her at some stage. Not that you could call what he was doing a pass. It was more of an onslaught. He even dragged her hands behind her back and pressed them into the small of her back, forcing her breasts against the hard wall of his chest.

Laura knew at the back of her whirling mind that she could still escape his captive embrace if she chose to. All she had to do was lift her knee into his groin and he'd let her go, quick smart. But she didn't lift her knee or do anything else. Instead, she just stood there and let him do what he was doing. She didn't fight him. She didn't even make a sound.

But the moment he pried her lips apart and sent his tongue deep into her mouth she definitely did make a sound.

It was a moan, soft and throaty and full of sensual surrender.

Ryan moaned too, though not quite so softly. For a few more mad moments, the impassioned ravaging of her mouth continued before he abruptly wrenched his lips off hers, stepping back to stare down at her with shocked eyes. His prominent cheekbones had spots of red slashed across them, and his chest was rising and falling in a ragged rhythm.

Laura hated to think what *she* looked like, standing there with eyes wide and the back of a trembling hand lifting to hide her still-burning lips. 'Stunned' did not begin to describe her own feelings. How could she possibly have liked what he had done? Yet she had—more than liked, actually. She'd thrilled to his forcefulness. Even now the heat he'd evoked was still charging through her veins. She tried to feel ashamed of what she'd just allowed and enjoyed. Tried to feel angry with him. But she couldn't, and didn't. How utterly and perversely amazing!

Suddenly he smiled, a warm, tender smile which confused her even more.

'I don't think you dislike me as much as you think you do,' he said as he stepped forward to take her still-flushed face within the cradle of his large palms.

Before Laura could say a single word in her own defence, he was kissing her again, a much gentler kiss this time but still deep, his soft lips and less-savage tongue seducing her just as easily as the first time. Somehow her arms found themselves clamped around his waist as she rose up onto her toes, pressing herself harder against him.

'Oh!' a female voice exclaimed from somewhere near them.

'Don't move,' Ryan muttered into her startled mouth before she could spring back from him.

With considerable *savoir faire* he casually dropped his hands to her hips and turned her round. Laura tried to match his nonchalant attitude at being caught kissing, but she could still feel her face flaming. Fortunately, however, Aunt Cynthia seemed to be worrying about her own embarrassment, not her niece's.

'I'm so sorry,' she blurted out. 'I just came to see what was keeping you. I didn't mean to, er, um…'

'It's perfectly all right, Cynthia,' Ryan said smoothly. 'We're the ones who should be saying sorry for keeping you waiting.' And he gave Laura's right hip an affectionate little squeeze.

Laura didn't say a word; her throat was as dry as parchment and her thoughts in total disarray.

'I fully understand,' Cynthia said, gushing at him again. 'But Jane is very anxious to meet you, as you can imagine.'

'And I to meet her,' Ryan returned. 'Do please lead the way, and we'll be hot on your heels.'

During the short walk from the front entrance hall to the back verandah of the house—during which Ryan took her hand firmly in his—Laura struggled to get her composure back.

It was difficult; her head was all over the shop.

Seeing her gran, however, sitting there on the back verandah in a wheelchair, was enough to push aside any worry over what had just happened. Laura's heart contracted at how fragile she looked. Fragile and old.

'Hello, Gran,' she said softly, extracting her hand from Ryan's as she bent to kiss her grandmother on the cheek. 'How are you feeling?'

'Fine, love, just fine. Now that you're both safely here,' she added, glancing up at Ryan. 'So this is the young man you've been telling me about.'

Laura could not help feeling proud of Ryan as her grandmother's still-sharp grey eyes raked over him, no doubt taking in everything from his face, to his clothes, to his impressively built body.

'You've done well this time, granddaughter,' she said, smiling with obvious approval. 'How do you do, Mr Armstrong?' she added, and held out one very thin, wrinkly hand towards him.

He cupped it gently within both of his. 'I will do very well, ma'am, provided you call me Ryan and not Mr Armstrong.'

'Of course...Ryan,' she agreed, her smile turning a little coy. 'But only if you promise to call me Jane. Now, sit down here next to me and tell me all about yourself.'

Ryan laughed, but he sat as ordered. 'You must be planning on a long afternoon tea, Jane.'

'I'm planning on finding out if your character matches your good looks,' she shot back without missing a beat.

'Gran!' Laura exclaimed, slightly horrified at her grandmother's directness.

'It's all right, darling,' Ryan reassured her with a warm smile. 'I have nothing to hide. Besides, if I know you, you've already told your gran everything about me.'

'Well, yes, I suppose I have.'

'Then there's nothing to worry about, is there?'

Nothing except that you just kissed me twice and reduced me to mush both times!

Don't think about that, Laura, she lectured herself. *Think*

*of the reason you did this in the first place. Think of making
Gran happy, even if only for this weekend.*

It actually turned out to be rather interesting, listening to
Ryan's answers to her grandmother's many questions. Laura
soon realised that, whilst she knew about Ryan's sporting and
business successes, she knew very little about his family background, except that at some stage he'd been brought up by his
grandmother. It turned out he was the only child of a single
mother, born and bred in the Western suburbs of Sydney. His
father had done a bunk before he was born and his mother had
died of breast cancer when she'd been only thirty-four, leaving him to be raised by his maternal grandmother who'd been
a widow and lived on a pension.

'She had very little but what she had she gave to me,' he said
with a slight catch in his voice. 'She was a wonderful woman.
I loved her to death.'

'I presume she's passed on now?' her gran asked quietly.

'Many years ago, actually. Before I began to earn big money.
She never saw me play for any of the famous European teams,
though she did see my local team win a few grand finals when
I was a teenager. Not that she actually *saw* them,' he said with
a wry chuckle. 'She used to get so nervous that she would walk
around the fields watching other games rather than mine. Then,
whenever a loud cheer went up, she'd race back to see if it was
my team scoring or the other one.'

'I used to get nervous watching Shane play soccer,' Cynthia
piped up as she offered Ryan a plate of lamingtons. 'Shane's
my son. Did Laura tell you that he's coming to dinner tonight
just to see you? You're one of his soccer heroes.'

Ryan smiled as he took one of the cakes. 'She did mention
it.'

'I hope you don't mind.'

'Not at all.'

And that was how the afternoon tea continued, with Ryan
being charming in the extreme and Laura sitting there in the
late-afternoon sunshine, basking in her grandmother's ap-

proval. She could not help looking at him all the time and thinking how incredibly handsome he was. Handsome and sexy.

Before long she started playing some crazy 'if only's in her head.

If only Ryan was her real Mr Right and not a pretend one.

If only his kisses from a while ago actually meant something to him.

If only he wasn't the kind of two-timing womaniser who was obviously not beyond taking advantage of the situation to try to get into her pants.

Alison had been right about that, Laura conceded with a twist in her heart.

But, even as this brutal truth hit home, she had difficulty ignoring the fact that she'd not only enjoyed his kisses, she wanted more. More kisses. More of everything a man like Ryan had to offer.

He would be a good lover; she could see that by his kisses. Wildly passionate, but tender and gentle as well. Brad had been an ignorant and selfish lover, uncaring of her pleasure. Mario hadn't been all that much better. Neither of them had ever kissed her the way Ryan had just kissed her, like he was a man dying of thirst in the desert and she was a sweet spring which would bring him back to life. At the same time, she had responded in a way *she* never had before—boldly. Brazenly. Blindly.

Laura knew that if they shared a bed tonight and he tried to seduce her she would be his for the taking. In every way.

This last thought truly shocked Laura. He already had a girlfriend, hadn't he?

But it didn't change a thing. This was why lust was one of the seven deadly sins, she realised—one of the strongest. One which called to the dark side which lurked in every person, which banished conscience in the selfish search for carnal pleasures.

Now, as she looked over at him, she started stripping him

in her mind, seeing him naked and looming over her in bed tonight. He would be big down there, she fantasised. Big, powerful and forceful. She would cry out when he entered her, and moan when he began to move. Already she could feel him there, inside her, filling her totally, taking her to places that she'd never been before.

Laura had never had an orgasm during actual intercourse before. But she would with Ryan; she just knew she would.

Such thinking took her breath away. What was happening to her here?

Thank God she didn't love him. Because, if she did, she would have been doomed.

Suddenly, she realised that her grandmother was talking to her.

'What was that, Gran?' she said as she lifted the tea cup to her lips and drained the rest of the stone-cold tea.

'I suggested you take Ryan for a walk around the property before it gets too late. It's lovely down by the creek at sunset and there should be a good one today.'

'All right,' Laura agreed. How could she possibly do anything else?

'Come and see me when you return,' her gran continued. 'I'd like to talk to you. Alone, if you don't mind, Ryan.'

'Not at all.'

'Bill will be home soon,' Cynthia said. 'He plays golf on the course next door every Saturday afternoon but he promised to come straight home after the game. Should be here by four-thirty—five at the latest, he said. You and he could have a game of billiards before dinner, Ryan. That is, if you play billiards?'

'I certainly do.'

Jane chuckled. 'I dare say you're good at it too.'

Ryan smiled. 'I'm good at most sports and games.'

Was sex a sport to him? Laura wondered ruefully. Or a game?

'Come on then, darling,' he went on as he stood up. 'Let's get going before the sun goes down.'

Suddenly, Laura didn't want to be alone with him. Certainly not down at the creek which was a very private spot, totally out of sight of everyone. She had little option, however, but to stand up and do exactly what had been suggested. To refuse would have seemed odd.

He took her hand, as she knew he would, and she didn't object, as she knew she wouldn't. No doubt they looked like lovers, strolling down the hill together, hand in hand. But love had nothing to do with the feelings which were zooming through Laura. She tried to say something, anything at all. But she remained silent. Ryan didn't say anything, either. When they reached the shelter of the trees which lined the creek, he let go of her hand and turned to face her.

'Tell me what you're thinking.'

She dragged in a deep breath which she exhaled slowly as she assembled her thoughts. No way could she tell him what she was *really* thinking. But she had to make some comment to excuse the way she'd responded to his kisses.

'I'm thinking you were right about my being too long between men. *And* kisses.'

He frowned. 'So you're saying that that's why you enjoyed my kissing you as much as you obviously did? Because you're sexually frustrated?'

She kept her eyes cool. 'It seems a logical explanation, don't you think?'

'True. But I can hardly make the same claim. I certainly haven't been five years without a woman. But I sure as hell enjoyed kissing you, Laura. Maybe Erica was right after all. And so were you.'

'About what?'

'You said I didn't know women as much as I thought I did. Erica actually went off her brain when I told her what I was doing this weekend. Accused me of fancying you.'

'Really?'

'Yep. I got so mad at her that I broke up with her on the spot.'

'You *did*?' Lord, but she shouldn't have been quite so happy about that. But she was. Oh yes, she definitely was. How stupid could she get?

'Sure did,' he confirmed. 'I didn't want to say so earlier on because I thought it might cause you some worry. But she was right, wasn't she? I do fancy you.'

'*Really?*' Now she was even happier! Until she remembered that Ryan fancying a woman meant next to nothing. He'd obviously fancied Erica and look what happened to her.

'Yes, *really*. But my fancying you is not a good idea, Laura.'

'Why?' Oh Laura, Laura, did you have to sound so disappointed when you said that?

His eyes showed that she'd betrayed herself to a degree.

'You are a work colleague and I do not date work colleagues,' he stated.

'I see,' she said, not quite so happy now.

'You wouldn't want to date a man like me anyway,' he ground out. 'I'm not what you want. Or what you need.'

Laura shook her head from side to side. 'I'm not sure what I want or need any more.'

'Then let me remind you: you want a man who'll love you, marry you and give you children. That man will never be me, Laura. Because that's not what *I* want.'

Laura frowned at this last statement. What had happened to Ryan in the past that he never dared to risk getting emotionally involved with anyone? Something must have happened, because it wasn't natural to shun love. Everyone wanted to love and be loved.

'And why is that?' she couldn't resist asking. 'What have you got against love and marriage and children?'

'Absolutely nothing,' he bit out. 'It's just not for me. Look, it's as well that we've had this little talk. I would hate to think that I would do something tonight which we would both regret. Under the circumstances, I think you should ask Cynthia to put me in a separate bedroom when we get back.'

Laura sucked in air sharply. 'But I can't do that!'

'Why not?'

'Because I just can't!'

His eyes narrowed on her, with a glint of wicked humour. 'Is this your pride speaking, or something else? Don't tell me you've been secretly attracted to me all this time?'

'Don't be ridiculous!' she snapped. 'No one was more surprised than I when I reacted the way I did when you kissed me.'

'I wouldn't say that,' Ryan said dryly. 'I was pretty surprised myself. Okay, so it's a matter of pride. In that case I won't ask for a separate room, but I think I will sleep on the floor. I don't trust myself to keep my hands off you if we share a bed. Hell on earth, woman, stop looking at me like that!'

'How am I looking at you?' she asked, trying to sound innocent but feeling anything but. She didn't want him to sleep on the floor. And she certainly didn't want him to keep his hands to himself.

'Don't try to play games with me, Laura. I'm way out of your league in the games department. Erica called me a libertine.'

'I don't believe you're a libertine at all,' she said, feeling angry with Erica for saying such a nasty thing. 'A libertine doesn't care about people's feelings. You obviously care about mine to warn me off you. A libertine would just take what he wanted without a second thought.'

'Would he now?'

For a split second, his eyes grew so cold that a shiver ran down Laura's spine. But then he whirled away from her and strode over to the edge of the creek. She stared after him, not knowing what to say or do. So she just stood there and waited. Eventually, the sun dipped down behind the hills and the air turned suddenly cool, at which point he turned and walked back towards her.

'Let's get back,' he said, and grabbed her hand once more. But there was nothing warm or affectionate in his grip. She could feel anger in his fingers, but wasn't sure who he was more angry with, her or himself.

'I promise I won't look at you like that any more,' she said during their hurried walk up the hill.

'Good,' he snapped. 'And I promise I won't bloody well kiss you any more!'

CHAPTER FOURTEEN

'HE's absolutely gorgeous, Laura,' was the first thing Gran said. 'I can't tell you how pleased I am for you.'

They were in the old servants' quarters, Jane propped up in bed and Laura sitting in an armchair not far from her. Cynthia had certainly done the room up nicely, Laura conceded privately, with everything Jane could wish for. The walls had been painted a rich cream colour. There was a brand-new flat-screen television sitting on a high chest-of-drawers opposite the foot of the bed and the old wooden floorboards had been freshly polished and varnished.

'He's a very special person,' Laura said, trying to ignore her disappointment over Ryan's decision not to take advantage of her obvious desire for him. It was perverse of her, she knew, but she almost wished that he *would*. She could not believe how much she wanted him to make love to her for real. It was cruel, the intensity of her yearning for him.

'I hope you don't think I'm being rude asking you this,' her gran said. 'But have you been to bed with him yet?'

Laura's hands tightened over the ends of the armrests.

For a moment, she wasn't sure what to say. But then decided to go with the truth.

'No, Gran,' she said. 'I haven't.'

'Wise girl,' her grandmother said. 'Playing hard to get is the way to land a man of the world like your Ryan. Though I doubt he's as tough as he looks.'

'What do you mean by that?'

'I suspect that underneath his macho façade your Ryan is quite a sensitive fellow. Reading between the lines, I wouldn't think his childhood was a bed of roses. It must have been hard on him, not having a father, then having his mother die when he was still just a child. Damaged children can sometimes find it hard to trust, and to expect happiness. In that regard you two have something in common.'

'I'm not damaged, Gran,' she said defensively.

'Aren't you, dear? I would have thought that any girl as attractive as you who reaches your age still single has to be somewhat damaged, for one reason or another.'

'Gran, that's old-fashioned thinking! Girls don't have to get married today to be happy.'

'That's tommy rot. Every girl wants commitment. And children. You do want children, don't you, Laura?'

'Of course I do, in due time. Now, Gran, please don't start dropping hints about marriage and children at dinner tonight. Men like Ryan like to run their own race. He'll get round to proposing when he's good and ready.'

'He's nearly forty, Laura. What's he been waiting for all these years?'

'For the right girl to come along, I suppose,' Laura said, but not very convincingly.

'He won't get a better girl than you.'

Laura's heart turned over at the compliment. Her gran had always loved her, no matter how she'd acted. Laura knew she'd been a difficult teenager after the shock and grief of her parents' tragic deaths. Not to mention having to live in a house where she wasn't exactly wanted. Without her gran's love she would have been even more wretched than she was. How on earth was she going to survive without her? Yet she would have to. And soon. There was a grey pallor to her grandmother's skin which frightened Laura.

A weary sigh escaped her grandmother's lips. 'I would dearly love to see you married before I go to meet my maker.'

'You will, Gran,' Laura said, blinking back tears. 'You will.'

'You'll have to be quick, my darling girl. I don't have much longer on this earth.'

'Nonsense. You'll live till you're a hundred!'

Her grandmother smiled a wry, knowing smile. 'I'll be content with eighty. Which gives you just over a month to get Mr Perfect to propose. Now, I think I should have a little nap before dinner, dear. I get very tired these days. You go make yourself beautiful for that man of yours—not that you don't already look beautiful. Being in love agrees with you.'

Laura tried not to look guilty. She longed to tell her gran that it wasn't love making her cheeks flush and her eyes sparkle but good old lust. Not that there was anything good about it. Or old, for that matter. This was an entirely new experience for Laura, which perhaps was why she didn't know how to handle it. If she'd been one of those girls who'd had loads of lovers she might not be so confused, or so lacking in confidence where sex was concerned. A more experienced woman would use sharing a bedroom tonight to seduce Ryan herself. She would not be letting him go all noble on her and sleep on the floor. She would vamp him into bed and enjoy his absolutely gorgeous male body all night long.

Would she dare do that? *Could* she?

Probably not. She wouldn't even know where to start.

Laura suppressed a sigh as she rose from the armchair and gave her grandmother a kiss on her papery-thin cheek. 'See you at dinner, Gran.'

'I hope you've got something pretty to wear,' Jane said.

It was then that Laura remembered the sexy red dress she'd bought. And the very sexy shoes.

Her heartbeat quickened at the thought that maybe she wouldn't have to do a single thing. Her outfit might do the seducing for her!

She beamed down at her grandmother. 'I have a smashing red dress,' she told her. 'Alison helped me pick it out this morning.'

'Ah... Dear Alison. She's been a wonderful friend to you over the years, hasn't she?'

'She certainly has.'

'She's a good girl. You're a good girl, too.'

Am I? Laura wondered as she closed the door. Would a good girl want what she wanted? What had happened to her long-held belief that she would need to be in love before she could enjoy sex with a man? Why did she suddenly want nothing more from Ryan than his body?

Shaking her head, she began to make her way back along the hallway which would carry her to the front of the house, and the stairs.

The sound of muffled male laughter met her ears as she passed the door of the billiard room. Clearly, Uncle Bill was back and Ryan had followed Cynthia's suggestion that they have a game of billiards. They sounded like they were enjoying themselves. Laura could see that Ryan would get along well with Uncle Bill, who was a man's man. No doubt Ryan would know exactly how to act in her uncle's company. He was clever that way, she could see. He had more social skills than herself, no doubt a product of running his sports-management company. She often put her foot in her mouth, whereas Ryan seemed to know exactly what to say to please everyone.

Except her, she thought with sudden mutiny. He hadn't said what she wanted to hear down at the creek. Hadn't done what she'd wanted him to do, either. How dared he kiss her like that and then reject her?

Okay, so he probably thought he was being cruel to be kind, not sharing her bed tonight. Clearly, he thought she was way too vulnerable a female to cope with an affair with the likes of him. Added to that was his own wariness at sleeping with people he worked with. Both reasons did show Ryan as a man of surprising character but, damn it all, couldn't he see that he'd already gone too far? Nothing was ever going to be the same again anyway. She could not possibly show up at his office every Friday, feeling like this. So she might as well do her best to seduce him tonight and be damned with the consequences!

CHAPTER FIFTEEN

'LAURA! For God's sake!' Ryan exclaimed as he rapped sharply on the bathroom door. 'What's taking you so long in there?'

He'd returned to the bedroom around six-thirty to find Laura sitting cross-legged in the middle of the four-poster bed in the corner, talking to someone on the phone. Given she was giggling, he assumed it was her girlfriend, Alison something-or-other. Nothing annoyed Ryan more than the furtiveness of females when they talked to each other on the phone. If only women could be as straightforward as men, then the world would be an easier place to live in and life wouldn't get so damned complicated.

Laura did interrupt her conversation briefly to tell him to use the bathroom first to get ready for the dinner, so he had, all the while perversely peeved by her lack of attention to him. He should have been pleased that she'd stopped looking at him like he was her favourite dessert. And he should have been proud of himself for resisting the temptation to take advantage of the sexual frustration that she claimed she'd *have* to be suffering from to fancy him all of a sudden.

Instead, he'd gone about showering and shaving in quite a foul mood, even nicking himself once with his razor, which he hadn't done for years. He'd also forgotten to take his clothes in with him, forcing him to come out of the bathroom with nothing on but a towel wrapped around his hips. Now, Ryan knew he had a good body, but what had Laura done? Nothing; not a single stare in his direction. Instead, she'd nonchalantly gathered up her clothes and sashayed past him into the bathroom without giving his bare chest a second glance.

Ryan's considerable male ego had been severely dented, so much so that he almost decided then and there to abandon his resolve to keep his hands—and his mouth—well away from her. He spent ten gratifying minutes fantasising about what he was going to do when she emerged. First he would kiss her until she started moaning again. Then, when she had totally melted against him he would lift her up and carry her onto that incredibly sexy bed where he would show her that, even if she didn't truly fancy him yet, she sure would soon.

Unfortunately the passage of time had a way of ruining perfectly good fantasies, and at the same time of increasing one's level of frustration. Which was why, after Laura had been in that infernal bathroom for forty minutes, an extremely irritated Ryan started banging on the bathroom door.

'Cynthia said to be down in the front lounge at seven-thirty for pre-dinner drinks,' he said through gritted teeth.

'I'm having a bit of trouble with my hair,' she replied airily. 'Why don't you go down and make my apologies? I'll join you as soon as I can.'

'Fine,' Ryan bit out, thinking that maybe a drink or two would soothe his ill temper.

Laura sighed with relief when she heard the bedroom door open, then close. She wasn't really having trouble with her hair, or her make-up. She'd surprised herself by doing both very well indeed. The fact was she'd been ready for some minutes but just hadn't been able to find the courage to leave the bathroom and face Ryan, looking the way she did in her new dress and shoes.

Which was crazy. It was what she wanted, wasn't it—to see his eyes darken with desire for her? To drive him mad with how sexy she looked?

And she did. Oh yes, she very definitely did!

Alison had given her strict instructions over the phone as

to how to present herself if she wanted to get laid that night: hair down and curled lightly around her face. Lots of dark eye-liner and mascara. The reddest of red lipsticks. And she wasn't even to consider putting some silly pin into the neck-line of the dress to hide her cleavage.

Laura had gone along with everything she had suggested and the result was wicked! She could hardly believe it was her staring back. She could also hardly believe that Alison had been so eager to have her succeed in going to bed with a man like Ryan.

When Laura had first told her what had happened so far, Alison had been genuinely shocked—not by Ryan making a pass but by his backing off.

'I don't understand it!' Alison had exclaimed. 'Not if he's already got rid of the girlfriend. It just doesn't make sense.'

Laura explained that he had this life rule about not dating anyone he worked with. She didn't tell Alison about his near-disastrous fling with a client, as she felt that had been a con-fidential confession.

'But you don't want him to *date* you,' Alison had shot back, exasperation in her voice. 'You just want him to bonk you silly all night. Isn't that right?'

'Er…yes,' Laura had admitted, her throat drying at the thought.

'In that case, this is what you must do…' At which point Alison had relayed a long list of instructions as to how Laura was to look. And to act—especially after they returned to the bedroom at the end of the evening.

Laura had been laughing over her outrageous suggestion in that regard when Ryan had walked back into the room. Suddenly, she had realised it was one thing to talk about se-duction techniques over the phone and quite another to go through with them; just having him in the same room made her hyperventilate with nerves. But she knew she would only have this one chance. So she'd hurriedly shunted him off into the bathroom, putting some calming distance between herself and the object of this insanely powerful desire. Then later, when he'd emerged—wearing no more than a towel, for pity's sake!—she'd kept her eyes rigidly averted from his breathtakingly beautiful male body and followed Alison's advice to act cool and indifferent to his charms.

'Your gran was right,' Alison had said earlier. 'Playing hard to get is the way to go. If I'm any judge at all of the male sex, then once he sees you in that dress and shoes you won't have to do much later on. But if he's still resistant you might have to go to plan B.'

'Plan B' was performing a none-too-subtle striptease.

Laura swallowed as she tried to imagine following that last piece of advice from her friend. She wasn't sure if she could be that bold. Hopefully, it wouldn't come to *that*.

Right now, she didn't even feel bold enough to go downstairs. Everyone was going to be shocked when they saw her, not just Ryan. They weren't used to seeing her dressed like this. She wasn't used to seeing *herself* dressed like this. It had been years since she'd shown her cleavage in public. Years since she'd spent the night in a man's arms. Years since she'd trembled at the thought.

Laura frowned as she accepted that she'd never felt quite like the way she felt at this moment. She might have become concerned if her brain had still fully been connected with her body. But logical thinking had become difficult since Ryan had kissed her earlier this afternoon. Her mind had shrunk to one focus and one focus only: to get him to make love to her tonight.

Now she frowned some more. For she didn't want him to 'make love' to her, did she? That would suggest an emotional involvement with the man. Only a fool would fall for Ryan Armstrong, and she was no fool.

So, rephrase that, Laura Ferrugia. You want to have sex with him. That's all. Then, once this weekend is over, you don't want to see him ever again!

CHAPTER SIXTEEN

'Go AND see what's keeping that girl, Ryan,' Bill said when ten to eight came round and Laura still hadn't made an appearance downstairs.

Ryan had spent a sociable twenty minutes in the elegantly furnished living room, talking to Laura's cousin and his pretty blonde wife and sampling some of Bill's top-quality scotch. Laura's grandmother hadn't joined them for drinks but she would be at dinner, he'd been told. His earlier irritation had dissipated somewhat with Laura's absence. But it seemed his respite was at an end.

'She's probably still having trouble with her hair,' he said, repeating the excuse he'd made for her not accompanying him downstairs at seven thirty.

'Yes, well, Cynthia said dinner would be served precisely at eight,' Bill said ruefully. 'And when Cynthia says eight, she means eight.'

Ryan knew Laura wouldn't want to offend her aunt or anyone else in the family. This weekend was supposedly about impressing them.

'I'll go get her,' he said, and headed for the double doors which led out into the main hallway. He was just approaching the bottom of the staircase when Laura appeared at the top.

He couldn't help it—he stared. And then he swore, a crude four-letter word which echoed what he would have liked to do to her in no uncertain terms. Fortunately, he hadn't said it loud enough for her to hear.

'You'd better get yourself down here,' he managed between gritted teeth. 'The natives are getting restless.'

And so am I, by God, he thought agitatedly as he watched her sashay down the stairs.

No one would have recognised her as the drearily dressed creature that showed up at his office every Friday. He'd thought she looked pretty good today when he'd picked her up. But this was something else.

She was shockingly gorgeous in that low-cut red dress and those incredible shoes. He didn't know where to look at first, his eyes raking over her impressive cleavage before dropping to her shapely legs which were on show as she moved slowly down the stairs. He'd always thought her legs were good. But in those shoes, they looked unbelievable. Not wanting to ogle her like some lecher, he lifted his eyes back up to her face. No peace there, however. Made up, and with her expertly waved hair moving slinkily around her bare neck, she looked like one of the sultry screen-sirens of the forties and fifties. Ava Gardner, with a bit of Lauren Bacall thrown in.

There had been times in Ryan's life when he'd regretted things he'd done. He supposed everyone had regrets. But right at this moment he really regretted telling Laura that he'd sleep on the floor tonight.

'I think I made a mistake telling you to buy a red dress,' he bit out when she finally made it to the bottom of the stairs.

She seemed taken aback. 'You don't like it?'

He laughed a dry laugh. 'You know damned well that I like it. You look absolutely stunning.'

'Thank you,' Laura said, thrilling to his compliment. 'You look pretty good yourself.'

'In this old thing?' he returned, smiling a crooked smile.

It wasn't the first time Laura had seen him in a suit and tie. But usually his suit was business black, the shirt white and his tie a conventional grey or blue. Tonight he was wearing a single-breasted one-button charcoal-grey suit combined with a silk shirt in a burgundy colour and a striped tie in burgundy and silver. He looked every inch an irresistible man of the world.

She wondered momentarily just how many lovers he'd had. Hundreds, no doubt. Whereas she'd had the grand sum of two.

But she was going to crank up that number to three tonight, or die trying. Not of humiliation, she hoped.

Surely he would not reject her? She'd seen the hunger in his eyes just now. All she had to do was convince him that she wasn't the fragile emotional flower that he thought she was.

'Ryan,' she said abruptly when he stopped at the lounge and reached for the knob.

'What?' he returned a tad impatiently.

Laura cleared the lump which had suddenly filled her throat. 'I…er…don't want you to sleep on the floor tonight,' she blurted out, trying not to blush but failing miserably.

Ryan's eyes narrowed as they ran over her once more. 'I see,' he said, and she wondered what it was that he saw.

'So it was just an act up in the room just now?' he went on.

Laura winced. 'Yes,' she admitted, and blushed some more.

'There's no need to feel embarrassed. I'm flattered that you want me enough to bother playing games, since that's clearly not your style. Frankly, however, I'd much rather you were straightforward with me. I despise deception and hypocrisy and holier-than-thou attitudes towards sex. There's absolutely nothing wrong with wanting to get laid, Laura. As long as you don't make a big deal out of it.' He looked at her, banked heat in his eyes. 'Are you sure this is definitely something you want to do? Think about it over dinner and we'll speak later on. Okay?'

Clearly, he didn't expect an answer. Opening the door, he cupped her elbow and ushered her into the lounge.

Dinner was a triumph and a trial. Everyone thought she looked fantastic, and said so, even Aunt Cynthia. The food was surprisingly good, the wine superb and the conversation lively. If Laura didn't say all that much, no one seemed to notice. Once everyone had stopped complimenting her on her appearance, the attention had naturally swung to Ryan who was a much more interesting subject. Shane bombarded him with questions about his soccer career. So did Bill. Jane seemed content to just sit and smile at the happy couple across the table.

Laura could not have felt less content. Or less hungry—for food, that was.

She could not stop thinking about what Ryan had said. What if, because of her so-called sensitivity, he ultimately rejected her again? What if he did indeed sleep on the floor and leave her to lie in that big bed all alone, all night long? How could she bear it? She could hardly bear sitting here at this table, listening to everyone talking absolute rubbish and making each course last much longer than it should. Didn't they know that she wanted the meal over and done with in record time? She had to know one way or another what was going to happen. Not knowing was killing her.

By ten, dessert had finally been cleared away and they all moved back into the front lounge, where Cynthia served up coffee in ridiculously small gilt-rimmed cups that she no doubt thought elegant. Laura supposed they were. She didn't want coffee at first, until she remembered that coffee kept you awake. After that, she had her cup refilled three times from the large silver coffee-pot which they were told had once belonged to a French Count and which Cynthia had bought online. When Gran declared she was tired and wanted to go to bed, she asked Laura to take her. Naturally, she couldn't refuse. As she rose from the sofa, Bill also stood up, suggesting the men retire to the billiard room whilst the women cleared up. In the past, Laura would have made some cutting remark over this chauvinistic attitude, but decided to bite her tongue this time. She did, however, glance at Ryan, who smiled in wry approval at her silence.

'Thank you, darling,' Jane said when she was safely tucked

up in bed. 'Now, don't let Ryan forget to take me for that ride in his car before you go tomorrow.'

Laura just stared at her grandmother. 'What ride?'

Her gran smiled a soft smile. 'You *were* away with the pixies at dinner tonight, weren't you, dear?'

'A little bit.'

'Thinking about that man you love, I dare say?'

'Yes,' Laura agreed. It was only a half-lie. Her mind had been full of Ryan but not with thoughts of love.

Jane sighed. 'I don't think you should wait for him to propose, dear.'

'What?'

'Before you go to bed with him.'

'Oh. Oh yes. I think you could be right about that.' If she waited for him to propose then she'd never go to bed with him!

'I am right. Now, off you go. It's time I went to sleep.' And she yawned.

Laura gave her grandmother a kiss and left the room, closing the door quietly behind her.

The old servants' quarters were just across the back hallway from the kitchen where she found Cynthia and Lisa busily washing up a huge stack of dishes. It still annoyed Laura that her uncle and his son felt that housework was entirely a woman's domain, but Cynthia didn't seem to mind. If truth be told, her aunt liked having total control in the house. Possibly, Lisa was of a similar ilk. Although younger, she must have been a bit like Cynthia for Shane to marry her.

'You know, Aunt Cynthia,' Laura said as she picked up a tea towel to help Lisa wipe up. 'You really should have a dishwasher installed.' It wasn't as though they couldn't afford it.

'What on earth for?' Cynthia retorted waspishly. 'They don't save you any time at all. You still have to scrape all the food off the plates, then rinse them down before you even load the infernal thing. Then you have to unload all the plates afterwards and put them away.'

'I suppose you're right,' Laura said, determined not to fight with the woman tonight. 'By the way, Aunt, that was a lovely meal tonight. Thank you for all the trouble you went to.'

Her aunt turned a surprised face her way. 'You know, Laura, meeting that marvellous man has done wonders for your attitude. Not only are you looking so much better, you've finally found some manners.'

Laura shook her head whilst Lisa grimaced behind her mother-in-law's back.

Laura was itching to say something seriously catty in return when Ryan suddenly came into the room.

'How's it going with you lovely ladies here?' he said brightly as he made his way across the floor of the truly large kitchen to where they were grouped by the sink. 'Need any help?'

'Heavens no,' Cynthia trilled, lifting her gloved hands from the sink as she turned towards her guest. 'This is women's work. Anyway, we're just about done here.'

'In that case, would you mind if I stole Laura away?' he asked as he slid a warm arm around Laura's waist. 'Driving always makes me tired and I didn't want to go to bed alone.'

Laura was glad that she wasn't required to say anything. Talking might have been difficult at that moment.

'You go right ahead,' Cynthia said obligingly. 'We can finish up here. As I said, it's almost done anyway, isn't it, Lisa?'

'Absolutely,' Lisa concurred. 'It was lovely to meet you, Ryan. Shane and I have something else on tomorrow so we won't see you again this visit. But I'm sure we'll see you again soon,' she added with a knowing little look Laura's way.

'I'm sure you will,' Ryan said. '*Au revoir* for now, then. See you in the morning, Cynthia.' And he swept Laura away before Cynthia could land them with a specific time for breakfast—which she was likely to do. Cynthia liked to run the house like an army sergeant, with a time for everything.

But Cynthia's rigid schedules were the least of Laura's worries as she was steered with considerable speed along the hallway towards the staircase. Ryan's fingertips were digging into her right hip and his body language reeked of anger.

'What's wrong?' she blurted out when they reached the bottom of the staircase.

'Everything's wrong,' he bit out, and started pushing her up the stairs.

'But... But...' she stammered, totally confused by his suddenly aggressive attitude. He'd seemed so agreeable in the kitchen just now.

'No buts,' he broke in savagely. 'And no talking. I've had enough talking for one day. And enough thinking. I already know this is a bad idea. I know that neither of us might be happy about it in the morning. But I'm sure as hell going to be happy about it tonight. And so, by God, are you! Or you will, if you just shut up and let me do what I'm good at. Which sounds arrogant, I know, but there's no virtue in false modesty. I was a damned good goalkeeper and I'm a damned good lover.'

Relief that his bad mood didn't mean he still intended to sleep on the floor swept through Laura. At that moment, she didn't care if he was unbelievably arrogant—which he was. Though maybe he had good reason to be. She'd never doubted for one second that he'd be good at sex. And now she was about to find out.

A shiver ran down her spine, then right down to her toes, making her shudder all over.

Ryan immediately stopped at the top of the stairs and pulled her close. 'Don't go pretending that you're cold, madam. You're hot for me.'

He was right.

'I thought you said no talking,' she said huskily, and pressed herself against him.

Ryan laughed, but then he fell silent, his eyes turning to a midnight blue just before his mouth crushed down on hers.

It was a kiss which told a story, if either kisser or kissed could read between the lines. The story was one of total frustration, both sexual and intellectual. Neither could understand the attraction they felt for each other this weekend. It was a mystery to them both. But they'd reached the point of no return, where logic had no power and all that existed for them was desire.

When voices in the hallway below threatened to disturb the marvellous madness of the moment, Ryan scooped Laura up in his arms and carried her into the bedroom, kicking the door shut behind him. He didn't miss a beat as he charged across the room and fell with her into the middle of the four-poster bed. They kissed on and on, their limbs tangled, neither of them coming up for air.

Ryan was the first to lift his head and draw a decent breath.

'We're acting like horny teenagers,' he said with a ragged sigh. 'All speed and absolutely no finesse.'

With almost shocking abruptness, he rolled off her and right off the bed.

Laura could not help the groan of dismay which escaped her lips. Immediately, he sat back down on the bed, leaning over to cup her face with gentle hands.

'I didn't want to stop either,' he reassured her softly. 'But allow me to know what's best in this situation. I could be wrong, but I have the impression that sex for you hasn't exactly been of the bell-ringing variety in the past. If it were, you wouldn't have gone five years without it.'

Laura blinked, both at his intuitive conclusion and his rather amazing ability to take control of the wild passion which had been raging between them less than a few seconds earlier. She could not possibly have stopped, yet he had. Laura guessed that was what made him a man of the world and her a...what? A naïve fool? No, not a fool. Just much less experienced in sexual matters.

Perhaps not so inexperienced after tonight, she conceded with a rush of excitement.

'What do you want me to do?' she asked him breathlessly.

His smile carried a wicked edge. 'Now, that's a very leading question. Ask me again later. For now, I don't want you to do anything except just lie there and relax.'

'Relax?' He might as well have asked her to climb Mount Everest.

His smile turned a little wry. 'You're right, I don't really want you to relax. But I have something to attend to before proceeding.' And he stood up.

'What?'

'I'm going to light the fire. It's become quite cool in here.'

'I didn't notice.'

'You will, once you get naked.'

Naked...

Laura could not help shivering at the thought.

'After I'm done lighting this,' he said, moving over to hunch down in front of the fireplace, 'I want to undress you.' He glanced over his shoulder at her.

Laura swallowed. Her throat was horribly dry all of a sudden.

'Now, don't start thinking,' he growled before returning his attention to the fire. 'It's too late for second thoughts. Or for worrying. You want me to make love to you and I want that too. We may regret it in the morning, but who knows? Maybe we won't. Maybe we'll look back on tonight and think of it as an incredible experience which neither of us would have missed for the world.

CHAPTER SEVENTEEN

WANTING a moment to recover herself, Laura got off the bed and went into the bathroom where she was momentarily startled by her reflection in the large mirror. She'd forgotten how different she looked tonight. For a split second it bothered her that Ryan's intense desire for her was nothing more than a superficial reaction to her suddenly sexier appearance. But then she shrugged the thought aside. Of course that was why he desired her. That was the nature of the male sex; their hormones were easily turned on by physical beauty. She had to confess that even the female sex could fall victim to such shallow attractions. If Ryan hadn't been so handsome, with a drop-dead-gorgeous body, she would hardly want to sleep with him tonight, would she?

By the time she emerged a couple of minutes later, the fire was crackling, with flames leaping high up the chimney. Ryan was back on his feet, leaning on the mantelpiece and staring down at the flames. His jacket and tie had been removed, and the top two buttons of his shirt undone. He looked pensive, and so sexy Laura could hardly breathe.

He turned and stared at her, his expression unreadable as his gaze moved slowly down and up her body. Gone was the overt hunger from his eyes, but they still called to the woman in her.

'Have I told you how incredibly beautiful you are tonight?' he said thickly. 'No, don't answer. And don't come any closer.

I've changed my mind about undressing you. I want you to do it for me.'

Her eyes widened.

'Don't be shy. You must know you've nothing to be shy about. No, not the shoes; leave the shoes on. The belt first. Then the dress—but not over your head. Undo the zip then slide it off your shoulders.'

She did as he asked, her hands shaking, her heart thudding so fast and so loudly behind her ribs she thought it must surely go into cardiac arrest. By the time she reached to push the dress off her shoulders, her whole body was trembling. The thought of standing there before him in nothing but a black satin thong and a pair of high heels was both daunting and horribly exciting. As her fingers curled over the edge of the neckline, her nipples tightened further, as did her belly.

And then it was done, the red silk dress pooling at her feet with a soft whooshing sound. Her spine and shoulders straightened as he stared at her, and for a long moment neither of them moved or spoke.

But then he sighed. 'I'm not sure one night is going to be enough,' he muttered in gravelly tones.

She should not have been thrilled by his words, but she was.

'Come here,' he commanded.

Where did she find the courage to walk almost naked towards him?

Possibly courage wasn't an issue when she was so turned on that nothing mattered any more except that his eyes stay fixed on her bared breasts.

Which they did.

'Stop,' he commanded again when she was within arm's reach of him.

She stopped, her heartbeat momentarily suspended as she waited for him to reach out and touch her. When he did— brushing the back of one hand across her stunningly erect nipples—a lightning rod of electricity zapped through her body, making her gasp.

'Turn around,' was his next surprising order.

She teetered a little on her high heels as she did so.

'Steady,' he directed, taking a firm hold of her shoulders from behind. 'Now, move your legs apart a little.'

Such a small, insignificant movement but, oh, what incredible feelings it evoked. She'd never felt so wicked. Or so wanton.

Her head literally spun. Was this the kind of thing he did with all his women? Stripped them, not just of their clothes but their conscience and their pride? No, no, that last bit wasn't right; her pride wasn't at risk here. She didn't feel in any way humiliated by the things he'd asked her to do. She'd seen the admiration flare in his eyes when he'd looked over her near-naked body. Laura had felt perversely proud of herself at that moment, perhaps because she knew he'd looked upon more beautiful bodies than hers. Yet he still seemed to find her very desirable.

I'm not sure one night is going to be enough, he'd said.

Not enough for her either, she suspected, if this was his idea of foreplay. What next? she wondered as an erotic tremor trickled down her spine to where her tightly held buttocks were quivering with anticipation.

He suddenly pressed himself up against her back, his left hand dropping from her shoulder to take possession of her left breast, whilst his right hand slid across to push her hair back from her face and neck. Her head tipped sideways when he put his mouth so close to her ear that his hot breath made her shudder.

'I think,' he murmured, 'That it's time to go to bed now. What do you think, beautiful?'

'I can't think at all,' she returned shakily. And wasn't *that* the truth!

'God, but I love seeing you like this,' he ground out, cupping her chin and twisting her head far enough around so that their eyes could meet.

'Like what?'

'All hot and bothered.' His eyes glittered down at her whilst he moved his outstretched palm back and forth across her by-then exquisitely sensitised nipple.

A tortured moan escaped her parted lips. 'You *are* a libertine,' she accused breathlessly.

'Not quite,' he retorted. 'But I could easily become one to-night.'

Ryan struggled for control as he scooped her up and carried her over to the bed. He struggled to calm his flesh, which was clammering wildly for a quick release. Not just quick—savage. He wanted to throw her onto that bed, rip off her panties and just ram himself into her.

Rough sex, however, was not something Ryan ever entertained. He prided himself on being an imaginative lover, but always a tender one. He never indulged in anything which smacked of violence. The thought of making a woman cry out with pain was anathema to him.

Okay, so some women liked it rough, he reminded himself as he laid her down across the bed. But he couldn't imagine that Laura would be one of them. Clearly she had believed, up until this life-changing moment, that she needed to be in love to enjoy sex. Which was a fallacy, of course. Sex was a basic human function much the same as eating and sleeping; you didn't need to be in love to enjoy either of those. Ryan had never been in love in his life and he sure as hell enjoyed all three.

Despite knowing deep down that he was making a big mistake taking a work colleague to bed—*business and pleasure don't mix, remember?*—Ryan told himself that he might actually do Laura a good turn by proving that sex and love didn't have to be joined at the hip. After all, it wasn't healthy for her to continue living without a man in her life. Her responses tonight had already shown him that she wasn't the ice queen she'd been pretending to be with him these past two years. Far from it.

By the time he sat down beside her on the bed and reached

for her left foot, Ryan had almost convinced himself that what he was about to do had a noble side to it.

Almost...

Laura clenched her teeth hard in her jaw as Ryan slowly undid the ankle strap on her shoe then eased it off her foot. Where did he learn to touch a woman like that so softly and so gently? She would have thought a goalkeeper's hands would be harder and rougher. But, no, they had the sensitivity and the skill of a surgeon. Every time one of his fingertips touched her flesh, an electric current ran up her legs.

'I've always admired your dainty feet with their slender ankles,' he said as he dropped the shoe onto the bedside rug and moved onto her other foot. 'And, whilst I adore these particular shoes, I can't risk leaving them on right now. The thought of your digging their lethal-looking heels into my back does not appeal.'

When an image popped into Laura's head of exactly how she might manage to dig her heels into Ryan's back, her heartbeat went from a fast trot to a wild gallop, her mouth falling open as she sucked in some much-needed air. But when the second shoe was dispensed with and his hands started travelling up her legs she found herself holding her breath once again. By the time he made it to the tops of her thighs, she had to breathe or die.

Her gasp brought his eyes to her flushed face.

'These have to go as well, Laura,' he told her, hooking his fingers under the sides of her panties and peeling them down her legs, all the while holding her eyes.

At last, he looked at her there.

By then Laura found it impossible to speak.

She was dying for him to touch her more intimately, but dreading it too. She knew she would be wet down there. She could feel it.

'Ryan,' she managed to blurt out when his finger moved perilously close.

Too late. He was there, and it felt incredible.

Her moan brought his eyes back to hers.

'You have a problem?' he asked, but without stopping. He was still using just the one finger, but it knew exactly where to go and what to touch, an erotic weapon of total seduction.

Her face twisted into a grimace which reflected her dilemma. She was going to come. And, whilst she was dying for release, it was not what she wanted. She wanted to come with him inside her.

'I...I... You have to stop!' she cried out.

He stopped. Just in time.

Laura shuddered with relief.

His head cocked to one side as he frowned down at her. 'Would you like to tell me why I had to stop? It wasn't because you weren't liking what I was doing. I could tell.'

She gnawed at her bottom lip and looked away.

'I won't know what you want if you don't tell me,' he said softly, and quite sensibly.

So she told him, her voice faltering and her face flaming with embarrassment.

'Is that all?' he said, sounding and looking pleased. 'Just give me a minute or two.'

He stripped off with considerable speed, chucking his clothes onto a nearby chair and not stopping until he was down to his underpants. At that point he did hesitate, first to go over to put another log on the fire then to search through his jacket pockets for his wallet, out of which he extracted two foil packets.

Laura could not believe that she hadn't thought of protection herself. Just as well Ryan wasn't so silly. But then he wouldn't be, would he? she thought ruefully. Not a man of his extensive experience!

Laura did her best to put her sensible head back on, but it was all to no avail when Ryan stepped out of his underpants. Oh dear, oh dear; she'd known he would be built like that. He was seriously impressive. His body was the sort of body that you saw on billboards advertising jeans or male Y-fronts. He could easily have made it as a male model. And he was all hers—for tonight, anyway.

This last thought brought excitement, but apprehension as well. Despite knowing she was way beyond changing her mind at this critical stage, Laura could not dismiss the niggling feeling that going to bed with Ryan would change her life in ways which might not be all good. She might have given the consequences of tonight's impulsive actions some more thought if a naked Ryan hadn't joined her on the bed at that point.

'Only got two of these, I'm afraid,' he said as he placed the condoms next to the lamp on the bedside chest. 'But they'll be enough. For now...'

When he pulled her round and rolled on top of her, Laura gasped at the weight of his body. But, as soon as he propped his upper body up on his elbows on either side of her chest, the feeling of pressure lightened considerably.

'Open your legs wide, Laura,' he commanded, 'And lift your knees up. Yes, that's the way, sweetheart. This could take a few seconds.'

Without using his hands in any way, he angled himself at her entrance but he didn't push himself in. Instead, he rocked back and forth and rubbed himself against her until she was almost at screaming point. She could feel her whole insides squeezing tighter and tighter, desperate to feel his flesh filling hers.

'Oh please,' she heard herself beg at last. 'Please...'

Only then did he enter her. But still not very far.

'Lift your feet and wrap them high around my waist,' he ordered her. 'That's it. Now rock back and forth with your hips. Hell, yes, that's the way.'

Laura followed his instructions until he was buried in her to the hilt, his flesh filling hers like a sword in its scabbard. Only then did he start to move, repeatedly pulling back a few inches before surging forward until he could go no further. Each thrust brought a gasp of pleasure from her lips, along with an increase in the most maddening frustration. As her body twisted tighter and tighter with sexual tension, her nails began clawing at his back, her heels digging into his buttocks. He responded by thrusting into her even more powerfully, and suddenly she came, her head thrashing from side to side as her flesh convulsed wildly around his. She'd never experienced anything like it before in her life. It was incredible!

'Yes, *yes*!' she cried.

And it was whilst her head was still whirling with the wonder of it all that Ryan came too, his whole body shuddering as it found release. He cried out as well, a loud, raw sound which reminded her of a creature from the jungle— Tarzan, maybe. Or possibly something less human.

So this was sex at its most primal level, Laura realised dazedly as she clung to his shuddering body. The kind animals indulged in. She could not pretend there were any fine emotions involved in their mating. They weren't in love. They barely liked each other.

No, that wasn't true any more. Not for her, anyway. She did like Ryan in a perverse kind of way. But she wasn't in love with him, despite having given him her body.

This last realisation came as a great relief. Maybe she would survive having a strictly sexual fling with him after all. Maybe she wouldn't do anything so foolish as to fall for him. She'd already fallen for two Mr Wrongs in her life. A third could prove fatal, if not to her sanity then at least to her soul. Because falling for *her* would never be on Ryan's agenda. He'd spelled it out for her already in no uncertain terms. He didn't do love, or marriage, or long-term commitment. Sex for him was just a physical pleasure, to be indulged in regularly, the same way he regularly ate and slept. Okay, so he did stick to only one bed partner at a time, but he always moved on. *Always.* She should never forget that.

Finally, his head lifted from where it had dropped down on the bed just above her left shoulder.

'Amazing,' he said with an almost surprised look on his face. 'Was that as good for you as it was for me?'

What could she say? It was way too late to be coy with him.
'It was wonderful,' she said truthfully.

He smiled. 'Tired?'

She shook her head.

'Great,' he said, and after giving her a brief peck on the lips
he abruptly withdrew, his reverse action forcing her legs to un-
wrap from around his waist and drop back down onto the bed.
'Have to go to the bathroom,' he said. 'Don't go away, now.'

Laura could not help it—she laughed. Wild horses wouldn't
have been able to drag her out of this bed. But as she lay
there, waiting for Ryan to return, her infernal female mind
did start worrying about how she might feel in the morning.
Not ashamed, she decided with a surge of defiance; she wasn't
doing anything to be ashamed of. Ryan had broken up with
Erica, after all. There was nothing to be ashamed of in con-
senting sex between two free adults.

Nevertheless, she found herself reaching for some bedclothes so that she wouldn't be lying there spreadeagled and
stark naked when he returned. Which was really quite hypocritical of her, Laura realised after she pulled the sheet up over
her breasts. Because, in truth, she'd rather liked being naked
in front of him. Had liked seeing the admiration in his eyes.
But she kept the sheet up all the same. Maybe she needed him
with her to be bold.

The sound of water running strongly in the bathroom soon
brought a frown. Maybe he intended to have another shower.
Hopefully, it would be a quick one. She didn't trust herself not
to start regretting what she was doing if she was left alone for
too long.

Unfortunately, time ticked away and still the taps ran.

So did her worrying thoughts. It actually wasn't how she
would feel tomorrow morning that bothered her, Laura finally
accepted, but the future in general. What would she do if Ryan
wanted to extend their affair beyond this weekend? Hadn't he
said that one night might not be enough? And, whilst she'd
been both thrilled and flattered by his words, she wasn't sure

that to keep sleeping with him would be wise. She might not be in love with him at this stage, but how long would it be before her emotions did become involved? She really wasn't one of those women who would be content with nothing more from a man but his body.

At least, so she thought, until the running water suddenly stopped, the bathroom door was yanked open and that absolutely gorgeous male body walked back into the bedroom.

CHAPTER EIGHTEEN

'WHAT'S with the sheet all of a sudden?' Ryan demanded to know as he strode towards the bed. 'I thought we'd got past that.' His hand reached out to grab the sheet out of her grasp, flinging it aside before bending to scoop her up into his arms.

Ooh, the feeling of being held naked against him; it was delicious. And so very exciting. Already she wanted him to make love to her again.

'I've run us both a bath,' he said as he carried her into the bathroom. 'Don't bother saying no. It's way too late for you to start being coy.'

She didn't say no—not to the bath. Or what he did to her once they were in the bath. She surrendered herself totally to his wishes, letting him wash her, caress her and position her this way and that so he had the easiest access to every erogenous zone she owned. His touch never seemed crude, yet he took liberties with her body which she'd never allowed before. And, whilst she was quickly desperate for another climax, she didn't come. A combination of his seeming to know when to stop doing whatever it was he was doing just in time, plus his telling her that if she held on until he was inside her again her pleasure would be greatly magnified.

So she held on, despite experiencing a level of frustration previously unknown to her. Constant caresses had extended her nipples to almost painful peaks, where even the slightest touch on them made her gasp. Her stomach was rock-hard with tension, her thighs aching and her sex dying to be filled. Every time his fingers slipped inside her down there, her internal muscles would grasp them tightly whilst her swollen clitoris throbbed with need.

'Ryan, please, I can't stand any more!' she cried at last when it all became too much to bear.

She was straddled across his thighs at the time, their bodies together like two spoons, Ryan's knowing hand rubbing a wet cake of soap back and forth across her burning nipples whilst his erection lay like an armed torpedo along the crease of her buttocks.

He could destroy me if he wanted to, Laura realised with real alarm. Make me ready and willing to do anything he wanted. She understood, suddenly, why that client of his had become obsessed with him. Ryan was the kind of lover who could easily obsess a woman.

Relief swamped Laura when he put aside the cake of soap and lifted her gently from the bath. She was so overcome with gratitude that tears pricked at her eyes. Only fear that he would stop making love to her altogether kept her emotions in check but it was a struggle, especially when he started drying her so sweetly and tenderly. Because by then she didn't want him being sweet and tender with her. All she wanted was for him to carry her back to bed and ravage her.

'What a pity,' he said as he rubbed the ends of her hair dry, 'That we only have that one condom left.'

She could not have agreed more, but couldn't bring herself to say anything so bold. Or so telling.

'Do you like oral sex?' he added, his eyes holding hers.

Laura swallowed. 'I...I can't say that I do.'

Brad hadn't been into anything but straight sex of the hard and fast kind. Mario, however, had been older and more experienced—or so she'd imagined at the time. He'd also been mad about blow jobs. She'd given him what he wanted because she'd loved him, and had thought he loved her; he'd said it often enough. But she'd never liked doing it.

'Why's that?' Ryan said. 'Most girls love it.'

'Do they?'

'The ones I've been with seemed to. Perhaps because I love doing it so much. Would you like me to try to change your mind?'

Laura finally realised he was talking about performing oral sex on her, not the other way around. Now this *was* alien territory for her. Brad had never ventured to suggest such a thing, neither had Mario. When she'd brought the subject up once, he'd said it was demeaning for a real man to do that. She'd believed him because she hadn't liked doing it herself. Now here was a real man claiming he loved it.

'I can see I've sparked your curiosity on the subject,' Ryan said, smiling a smugly satisfied smile. 'Come on, let's give it a whirl.'

'A whirl' was the right word for it. Within seconds he had her back on the bed, his lips creating havoc within her as they traversed her body at the speed of light from her mouth to her breasts, her navel and finally the smooth mound of skin which lay perilously close to her agonisingly aroused sex. She grasped great clumps of sheets in each hand as he came closer and closer to that spot that was screaming for attention. And then he was there, not kissing her, but licking the swollen nub of flesh like a ravenous cat lapping a saucer of cream. Immediately, her back arched from the bed as her body raced blindly towards the edge of the abyss like some crazed lemming.

Immediately, he stopped, lifting his head so that their eyes could meet. Hers were wide whilst his seemed perversely calm.

'Not so quick, Laura,' he told her. 'It'll be better if you wait a while.'

'But I don't want to wait!' she cried out in despair.

He laughed. 'But I'm going to make you wait, my darling.'

'I am not *your darling*,' she snapped, feeling angry with him, and even more fiercely frustrated than she had in the bath.

'I thought you said you didn't like oral sex,' he went on,

propping himself up beside her and teasing her breasts mercilessly with wickedly knowing fingers.

'I was referring to fellatio,' she bit out, trying not to groan. But it was hell, the way he now tugged at one of her nipples. Not roughly, she had to admit. But still...

'Ah,' he said, the tugging changing to a slow, twisting motion. 'Well, that is a different matter entirely. But I would imagine a girl of your intelligence would enjoy the sense of power that fellatio would give you. Wouldn't you like to see me squirm as I'm making you squirm at this moment? Wouldn't you like to make me lose control? Think of it as the ultimate triumph over me. Because I can promise you this, lovely Laura—I won't be as cool or as calm as I am at this moment. For those few mad moments, I will be totally yours. Now, isn't that an appealing thought?'

Laura stared up at him. *God, yes.* But it also presented her with a not so appealing thought.

'Is that why you agreed to sleep with me tonight?' she threw at him. 'To triumph over me?'

His fingers stilled on her breast, his eyes becoming thoughtful. 'I have to confess that sleeping with you has given me great satisfaction. And great pleasure. But triumph? No, I can't say that was my train of thought, though you would present a tantalising challenge to any red-blooded man. From the moment you told me what you wanted, however, my main goal tonight has been to give you the kind of sexual pleasure which it's obvious you've never had. Clearly, the man who hurt you was a complete incompetent in the bedroom. I can only imagine he was very young and inexperienced himself.'

'No,' she told him. 'Mario wasn't young at all. Brad was, though.'

'Who the hell is Brad?'

'My first lover. He was a fellow law student who pretended to love me so that he could have free room and board. I found out the truth when I came home one day and found him in bed with someone else.'

'Charming. And the dastardly Mario? Why did he pretend to love you?'

Laura was truly taken aback. 'How do you know that's what he did?'

'Didn't take a genius to figure that one out. All I need to know is why? No, don't tell me, I can guess—he was a client of yours, wasn't he? Right. He was on trial for something sticky and he wanted his defence lawyer to pull out all stops to get him off. Who better than a woman who loved him?'

Laura shook her head. 'I think you *are* a genius.'

He smiled. 'If you say so. So what was he on trial for?'

'Tax evasion. If he'd lost, it would have cost him millions.'

'But he didn't lose, did he? You won the case for him.'

Laura sighed. 'Yes.'

'And then he dropped you.'

'Like a hot cake.' Looking back, she could see that Mario had been a sadist of the first order. He'd enjoyed telling her outside the court house that he'd used her. Enjoyed seeing her hurt and humiliated. At least Brad hadn't been that wicked. He'd looked quite guilty when she'd found him in bed with that girl. Guilt was something Mario would never feel. He was totally conscienceless.

Laura hadn't been at all sad when she'd heard last year that Mario had finally ended up in jail. As for Brad... She'd heard over the legal grapevine that he was considered unemployable as a lawyer after having been fired a couple of times for 'questionable' behaviour. Leopards didn't change their spots, it seemed, something Laura would have to remember about the man she was currently in bed with.

'It's no wonder you went into sexual hibernation,' Ryan said. 'But their loss is my gain. I have to confess that I haven't had this much fun with a woman in years.'

'Fun!' she exclaimed, not sure if she should feel flattered or flattened. Calling sex with her 'fun' was hardly romantic. But then she didn't want him to romance her, did she?

Not really. But she didn't much like him calling what they

were doing 'fun'. It seemed demeaning. 'Sex for you is just a game, isn't it?' she threw at him.

'Now, Laura, don't go getting all hoity-toity on me. I've just shown you that great sex does not have to have any connection with love. Not that being in love ever gave *you* great sex in the past,' he pointed out somewhat ruthlessly.

'Sex, my sweet, can be indulged in strictly for pleasure, without the complications which emotional involvement inevitably brings. But I wouldn't say I think of sex as a game. More of a wonderfully satisfying pastime, one where the degree of pleasure involved improves with time and practice.

'Let me assure you that over the years I have devoted much time and practice to perfecting my skills in the bedroom. Trust me when I say that there's so much more that I can show you, and do with you. As I said earlier, one night is not going to be enough. If you'll agree, I'd like to continue our affair when we go back to Sydney. After all, we've crossed the line now; we might as well take full advantage and thoroughly enjoy ourselves.'

Laura stared up at him. Dear heaven, but he was as good a seducer with words as he was with his body. Such thinking reminded her suddenly of Brad and Mario, who'd both had silver tongues. Looking back, she saw that they'd seduced her more with what they'd said than what they'd done. Why had she fallen for their lies about loving her so readily? she wondered now. *Why?*

Because she'd *wanted* to be loved so very, very much. Because she'd been an emotionally needy little fool.

They hadn't even been good lovers. Just good liars.

At least Ryan was a good lover and, though persuasive, he wasn't a liar.

His head dipped to nuzzle at an earlobe, making her shiver uncontrollably.

'Do you agree, lovely Laura?' he whispered in a low, incredibly sexy voice.

What else could she do but nod?

'In that case,' he went on after reaching for their last condom, 'I think we've done enough waiting for tonight.'

Laura thought the first time he'd made love to her had been
incredible. But there was something even more magical the
second time round. He took his time once he'd entered her,
setting up a slow, sensual rhythm with his hips, his eyes holding hers. Her mouth fell open as the tension built and built, her
breathing becoming fast and shallow. Yet there was no anxiety in her, only the warm, sweet pleasure of his flesh rocking
back and forth within hers. At no point did she fear she might
not come because she knew she would. And when she did he
came too, their bodies in perfect physical harmony with each
other.

Laura found the experience quite overwhelming. Sexually,
they seemed made for each other. But as she clung to him, their
bodies still pulsing as one, she realised that emotionally they
were as different as chalk and cheese. Laura accepted that at
this point in time all she wanted from Ryan was more great
sex. But she suspected that if she kept up this level of physical intimacy for too long she would probably fall in love with
him. For that was how she was made.

Life was very cruel, Laura decided ruefully, always to
make her attracted to men who would never give her what
she wanted.

But at least this time she knew the nature of the beast in
advance. Ryan wasn't trying to fool her in any way, shape or
form. All he was offering her was a strictly sexual relationship,
without caring or commitment of any kind. And, whilst Laura
still could not understand why he was so adverse to love and
marriage, she had to accept that that was how he was made.
There was no point in becoming upset over it. If she wanted
to keep experiencing what she'd just experienced, she would
have to accept him on his terms, without hoping for anything
more.

Of course, it meant risking her heart again and her happiness. But it was impossible to walk away from what Ryan

was offering. Already she was addicted to the excitement he engendered in her, the wild pleasures he gave her, not to mention the fabulous orgasms which seemed to last for ever. Her body was still throbbing. And so was his.

She sighed a deliciously sensual sigh.

'I'll be back in a moment, Laura,' he murmured at last before gently disengaging her arms and legs from his back and waist.

She groaned, her limbs going to jelly as they flopped back onto the bed. A languor had suddenly taken hold of her whole body. Her brain too. She didn't want to fall asleep, didn't want this night to end. But as soon as Ryan left the bed Laura rolled over onto her side and fell fast asleep.

Ryan smiled wryly when he returned to the bed and found Laura out like a light. So much for his erotic plans for the rest of the night.

Though perhaps it was just as well. He too was weary. It had been a long day. A strange day. Who would have believed that it would end with his sleeping with Laura? Even more strange that he would enjoy it so damned much. Ryan pulled some bedclothes over her before getting back into bed, careful not to disturb her. He didn't want to wake her now. He wanted to think, a much easier process when he wasn't aroused. Or, worse, frustrated.

It didn't take Ryan long to figure out that he'd probably made a big mistake tonight. Not only was Laura a work colleague, but she was nothing like the hard-hearted career woman he'd always believed her to be. If she had been, he'd have no worries about continuing his affair with her. Unfortunately, underneath the tough-girl façade she wore seemingly with ease, Laura was actually a sweetie. And a softie. And sexy as hell!

Which was where the real problem lay: Laura's sexiness was different from the kind of sexiness Ryan usually went for. He liked his women a little wild and wanton. Very experienced, too. Liked them to know their way around a man's body. He never went for the shy, retiring types who needed seducing on every level. And he never, God forbid, took a virgin to bed.

Not that Laura was a virgin. But she might as well have been, from what he'd seen tonight. Perversely, he'd loved that about her, loved it that she was so inexperienced. Her responses to the things he'd done were wonderfully fresh, full of surprise and the most enchanting gratitude—not to mention passion. Her orgasms had been very intense.

It irked Ryan considerably that Laura had loved not one but two total bastards in her life. But then, that was the nature of love, wasn't it? It didn't make sense. It was both irrational and sometimes self-destructive, in his opinion, especially where women were concerned.

Which brought him to his major problem where Laura was concerned.

What if she fell in love with him?

There was no use pretending that it couldn't happen, just because Laura didn't overly like him. Women fell in love with men they didn't like all the time.

Ryan didn't want to hurt her. Hell, he'd spent most of his life trying not to hurt women. Not that he'd always succeeded. But he had never deliberately set out to hurt any of them.

Would he hurt Laura if he continued sleeping with her?

That was the question he had to answer before morning came. Which meant before he surrendered to his own tiredness and dropped off to sleep.

Ryan frowned. Maybe he would hurt her more if he stopped. Clearly, she'd loved the sex tonight. Loved it all. If he called it quits tomorrow morning she might think she'd done something wrong, or that he'd already grown bored with her. She would take it as a personal rejection. Women were quick to blame themselves when a man dumped them. To do so after just one night together would be cruel.

On top of that, there was no guarantee that Laura would become emotionally involved with him. She was thirty years old and a lawyer, for pity's sake. Hardly a naïve little thing. She already knew the score where he was concerned, knew that he was not husband material. All he was good for was some fun and games, something which she was in dire need of, in his opinion.

If she continued to sleep with him, then the risk was hers, wasn't it? Her future happiness was not his responsibility. She was an adult who could decide for herself what she wanted to do. He wasn't about to force her to continue their affair. It was up to her. But he would ask her again in the morning if that was what she wanted. Give her a chance to change her mind.

Feeling marginally better, Ryan stretched out and closed his eyes. But they immediately snapped open again. Of course, if Laura did decide to continue their affair—and he was pretty sure that she would—he would have to get himself a new lawyer. He would make that very clear indeed.

Never mixing business with pleasure was one rule Ryan didn't intend to break!

CHAPTER NINETEEN

RYAN woke before Laura. Without thinking, he snuggled up to her still sleeping form, curving his body around hers from behind. His arousal was instantaneous and extremely corrupting, banishing any thought of giving her either the opportunity or the time to change her mind about continuing their sexual relationship. Already he was stroking her bare breasts, stirring her back to consciousness, wallowing in the way she started moaning with pleasure.

And then he remembered—no more condoms.

Swearing with frustration, he leapt out of the bed and marched off to the bathroom where he jumped into a cold shower, staying there till he was ready to behave himself. By the time he emerged, well wrapped in a towel, Laura was wide awake and sitting up in the bed, a sheet thankfully clutched over those beautiful breasts of hers.

'Sorry about that,' he muttered, striding over to the wardrobe where his clothes were hung. 'Forgot we'd run out of protection.'

Laura was sorry too—sorry that he'd stopped.

'The bathroom's all yours,' he threw over his shoulder. 'Though I'll have to go back and shave at some stage. I'd leave the stubble on today in other circumstances, but I have a suspicion that Cynthia would not approve. Or your gran, for that matter.'

'You're probably right about Aunt Cynthia, but Gran won't mind. She likes macho-looking men.'

Me too, Laura thought as she admired Ryan's back view. She loved the wideness of his shoulders and the narrowness of his waist and hips. Loved the rippling muscles which framed his spine and bulged in his arms. Loved the length and strength of his legs.

He shrugged those gorgeously broad shoulders. 'In that case I won't bother.'

She stayed to watch him dress, even though she really needed to go to the bathroom. But she held on long enough to see him step into some sexy Y-fronts then pull on the black jeans he'd worn yesterday. A white T-shirt followed, over which he drew on a long-sleeved black shirt. What was it about a man in black, she wondered, that was so darned sexy?

He turned suddenly, his eyes thoughtful. 'Before I forget, there's something I have to ask you.'

Laura's heart contracted with immediate anxiety. 'Oh? What?'

'Are you quite sure you want to keep sleeping with me? If you would prefer to leave things as a one-night stand, I'll understand.'

Laura was truly taken aback, and a little dismayed. Was this his way of saying he wanted out?

She could only shake her head. 'I don't understand you, Ryan. I thought you still wanted me this morning.'

'I do.'

'Then what's the problem all of a sudden?'

'No problem on my part. I just wanted to give you the chance to change your mind. Sometimes things appear differently the morning after the night before. One's thoughts become clearer.'

'My thoughts are quite clear, thank you very much,' she said somewhat tartly. She hated it when men acted as though women were silly creatures who didn't know their own mind.

'You do realise that becoming my lover is not a permanent

position,' he went on firmly. 'And that it will mean the end of our business relationship.'

Laura was beginning to become quite impatient with him. There really was no need to keep reminding her what the score was. She already knew his track record.

'That's fine by me,' she bit out. 'I too have a life rule about having affairs with clients.'

His eyebrows lifted. 'Ah yes. I'd forgotten for a moment that you'd done that before. But of course you were in love with that particular client. Which is why it ended badly.'

The penny finally dropped for Laura. 'Oh, I see. You're worried that I might fall in love with you?'

'Something like that.'

'You truly are a most arrogant man.'

'Possibly,' he admitted. 'But not, thankfully, a libertine.'

'That's debatable at this point in time.'

He smiled. 'I rather like it when you get stroppy.'

'That's because it makes you feel safe!' she snapped.

He laughed. 'Nothing about you right now makes me feel safe, Laura. Which is why I want you to get that beautiful body of yours into the bathroom where I can't get at it.'

Laura tried to stay annoyed with him—but how could she when he'd just called her beautiful, not to mention admitted to an almost uncontrollable desire for her?

'You'll have to turn away then,' she told him with feigned haughtiness. 'I wouldn't want you to lose control at the sight of my beautiful *naked* body.'

His groan secretly delighted her. 'Must you remind me? Okay then,' he added as he spun round to put his back to her. 'Get going. And take some bloody clothes with you!'

'I can't. They're over there where you are.'

'In that case just get yourself into that bathroom the way you are. But I won't be here when you come out. I'll be downstairs somewhere, chatting up Cynthia!'

Ryan breathed a sigh of relief once Laura was safely in the bathroom. She hadn't been far wrong with her caustic remark about his losing control at the sight of her nakedness. He'd done his best to sound calm and reasonable when he'd given her the chance to change her mind—and when he'd reminded her that any relationship with him was never a permanent one. But underneath his cool exterior, he'd been struggling all the while to ignore the less-than-cool messages his body kept sending him.

He wasn't sure what he would have done if she'd said no, Ryan, I don't want to have any more sex with you. He suspected his behaviour at that point in time might not have been very noble. Only the knowledge that he could take her to bed tonight and on many more future nights had put some sanity into his head and some control over his wayward flesh.

Ryan shook his head as he sat down to put on his socks and shoes. It had been a long time since a woman had got under his skin the way Laura had. Actually, he could not remember it happening before at all. Ever!

Any other man might have imagined he was falling in love but Ryan knew differently. Romantic love was not an emotion he was capable of, not since he'd seen up close and personally what that kind of love had done to his mother. Ryan had only been twelve when he'd vowed never to fall in love, or marry, or have children. And nothing had happened since to change his mind on that score.

So, no, he knew he wasn't in love with Laura. It was desire which was possessing him at the moment, a desire which was heightened by her lack of sexual experience. He could not wait to show her everything. Tonight simply could not come quickly enough!

CHAPTER TWENTY

'THANK God you rang me,' were Alison's first words. 'I've been dying of curiosity all morning.'

'It's only ten-thirty,' Laura told her friend. 'I couldn't ring you before. I haven't had a minute to myself.'

A white lie, actually. She'd been alone upstairs for a good while before breakfast but had spent the time trying to get her head around things. As soon as Ryan had left the room and she'd been out of his corrupting presence, Laura had been besieged by doubt over what she'd agreed to.

So much for her much-vaunted pride! She felt disgusted with herself, not so much for sleeping with him last night—wild horses could not have stopped her from doing that!—but for agreeing to sleep with him some more without his offering her anything in return. He'd not even offered her the face-saving grace of becoming a proper girlfriend. He hadn't said a word about dating her, just about sex.

On top of that he expected her to waltz into work and announce that he was no longer her client? What excuse could she possibly give? 'Sorry but he's screwing me now and he doesn't screw women he works with'?

The man wanted his cake and wanted to eat it too, came the mutinous thought.

The trouble was she still wanted him on *any* terms. The shock and shame of this realisation was almost too much to bear.

She'd had to force herself to go downstairs for breakfast and to face not just Ryan but the rest of the family. She'd found them all in the kitchen being treated to one of Aunt Cynthia's over-the-top English-style breakfasts. Laura was never one for eating anything heavy in the mornings and would usually have refused, but this time she'd allowed herself to be fed bacon, eggs, baked beans and fried tomatoes with lashings of toast, because that way she hadn't had to talk much.

After breakfast, she'd helped her aunt wash up whilst Ryan had whisked Jane off on the promised drive in his convertible. He still hadn't returned half an hour later, which had given Laura the opportunity to go upstairs and finally ring her friend.

'You sound a little strained,' Alison said. 'Please don't tell me that nothing happened last night between you two?'

'Something happened all right.'

'Ooh. Do tell.'

Laura told her everything. Well, not in minute detail, but in broad strokes; some things were too private to divulge. And possibly too embarrassing. But she certainly told her every single thing about the chat Ryan had had with her when she had woken up, plus her decision to continue her affair with Ryan even though she knew it was heading nowhere.

'Please don't tell me I'm a fool,' she finished up, feeling drained all of a sudden.

'Far from it,' Alison said. 'If I were in your position I'd do exactly the same.'

'You would?'

'Yes, of course! After all, Laura, what's your alternative? You crawl back into an even more bitter and frustrated spinster cave where you hate all men and never have any fun?'

'But what if I fall in love with him, Alison?' she cried, voicing the worst fear she had about the situation. 'I can't afford to fall for another Mr Wrong. I just can't!'

'But this is different to the other two. Can't you see that? They pretended they loved you. Ryan wants nothing from you but your body.'

'But that sounds so cheap and nasty!'

'Not to me, it doesn't. To me it sounds seriously sexy. Go for it, I say. And, if you fall in love with him, so what? You might be sad for a while when it's over, but you won't be left feeling bitter and betrayed. You'll have some wonderful memories of a great lover who's made you see how beautiful and sexy you are. And, who knows? You might turn out to be the one.'

'What one?'

'The one who changes his mind about love and marriage.'

Laura laughed. 'You don't know Ryan.'

'Maybe not, but I'd like to. Why don't you bring him over next weekend for a barbeque?'

'I don't think he wants that kind of relationship.'

'You mean he just wants sex from you and nothing else?' Now Alison sounded shocked. 'No dates or anything like that?'

'I think so.'

'Now, that *is* cheap and nasty. You wouldn't settle for that, Laura? Surely?'

'That's what I'm afraid of, Alison. That I might settle for *any* arrangement with him.'

'Oh dear...'

'What do you mean by saying "oh dear" like that?'

Alison stopped herself just in time from telling her friend that it sounded like she was already in love with him. Nothing was to be gained by telling her, if that was the case.

But she had an awful feeling that this affair was not going to turn out well for Laura. There was nothing to be gained by telling her that, either. She was damned if she did, and damned if she didn't.

'I just don't like the thought of your agreeing to anything, Laura,' she said instead. 'Don't lose your pride over the man, no matter how good he is in bed.'

'A minute ago you were all for my having more sex with him!' Laura exclaimed, sounding exasperated.

'I am. Truly. Just...be careful.'

Suddenly, she wished she hadn't encouraged Laura to go to bed with him.

'I have to go, Alison. I can hear Ryan's car coming up the drive.'

'Ring me tonight, will you?'

'Maybe not till tomorrow,' Laura returned. 'I might be busy tonight.'

Of course, Alison thought sourly. *The lord and master of the bedroom will want another dose of what he'd obviously enjoyed last night.* And Alison knew what that was—relative innocence. That was what intrigued him about Laura, came the sudden, highly intuitive realisation. She wasn't like all the other Penthouse Pet types that playboys usually bedded. She was a lovely sincere girl with a warm heart who hadn't slept around, and who was way too vulnerable for the likes of Ryan Armstrong.

Alison grimaced as she wished she could take back all the stupid advice she'd given Laura, both yesterday and today. She should have realised that her friend wasn't cut out for strictly sexual flings. She was going to get hurt again and she, Alison, would be partly responsible. But it was too late now. The die had been cast and Laura would just have to roll with it. All Alison could do was be there when the end came.

But she wasn't looking forward to it.

CHAPTER TWENTY-ONE

'YOUR family's not that bad, Laura,' were Ryan's first words as they drove away from the house.

Laura sighed. 'They were greatly improved this weekend,' she admitted. 'But that was because of your influence. You had Gran eating out of your hand over lunch. What on earth did you say to her during that drive? She seemed much brighter than yesterday.'

'I hardly said a word; she did most of the talking. Told me where to drive. I just followed orders. She showed me the village and the church, the one near the Hunter Valley gardens. By the way, she said to tell you that that was where she wanted her funeral service to be held.'

'Oh, for pity's sake!'

'She wasn't being maudlin, Laura. Just practical.'

'But she won't die now. Not for ages. What else did she say? She didn't drop any hints about our getting engaged, did she?'

'Not directly. Though she did point out that they use that church for a lot weddings as well.'

'And what did you say to that?'

'Nothing, that I recall.'

'You must have said something to make her look so pleased with you.'

'I did promise to come to her eightieth-birthday party in November.'

'Oh no. Do you think that was a good idea?'

'I don't see why not.'

'Well, I mean, we might not last that long.' Laura's conversation with Alison had made her determined not to get any silly female hopes up where Ryan was concerned.

His sharp sideways glance startled her. 'My girlfriends usually last more than two months, Miss Cynical.'

Laura tried to remain looking cool but it was difficult when her heart had just turned over with a ridiculous burst of happiness. 'You mean you want to make our relationship a public one?'

Now he looked quite annoyed. 'Well, of course I do! What had you been envisaging? That I would keep you as some dirty little secret? Why on earth would I do that?'

Laura knew she couldn't tell him the truth—that she'd been imagining just that. 'I guess because I'm not the kind of gorgeous, glamorous female that you usually date,' she said instead.

'Good God, Laura, did you get a look at yourself last night? You are just as gorgeous and glamorous-looking as any of my previous girlfriends.'

'But I don't usually look like that on a day-to-day basis, as you well know.'

'There's no reason why you can't. All you have to do is go shopping for some more new clothes and wear a bit of make-up occasionally.'

'People at work will wonder what's happened to me.'

'So? Do you honestly care what they think?'

'Yes, I do,' she admitted. The end result of such a radical makeover was slowly sinking in. She didn't want her colleagues laughing at her behind her back. She would look a complete fool if she went in there all glammed up and told them Ryan could no longer be her client because she was dating him. They all knew what he was like. The women there had often made caustic remarks about his being a serial ladykiller.

'No, Ryan,' she said firmly, surprising herself.

He slanted her a startled glance. 'No *what*?'

'No, I don't want to buy a whole new wardrobe and, no, I don't want to be your girlfriend.'

The sudden silence inside the car was electric with unspoken tension. She saw his knuckles go white as he gripped the steering wheel; saw his shoulders rise.

'You don't mean that,' he said at last, his tone one of sheer disbelief.

'But I do.'

'You don't want to sleep with me any more?'

'I didn't say that.'

His head whipped round, shock written all over his face. Laura was pretty shocked herself—at herself, for voicing out loud what had suddenly entered her head. That it was *he* she wanted to keep as *her* dirty little secret, not the other way round.

When his car drifted dangerously close to the lane next to them—and the truck which was rumbling along at high speed—Ryan quickly returned his attention to his driving, swearing volubly as he righted the car, slowing down appreciably before he spoke again.

'You can't be seriously suggesting what I think you're suggesting,' he bit out, obviously not happy with being cast in the role of her secret lover.

Now that the initial shock of her suggestion had worn off, Laura found herself quite taken with the idea. How better to protect herself from future hurt and humiliation than by keeping their affair strictly sexual and, yes, totally secret? Not to mention brief. No one knew better than Laura that time and sustained intimacy—even that of a strictly sexual nature—would ultimately be her undoing. A week or two should be long enough to burn out a good degree of the lust that was still plaguing her, she decided. Long enough too to satisfy her curiosity over all those wildly erotic things Ryan claimed he could show her.

'It would be the best solution all round,' she said, feeling strangely exhilarated at having taken control of her destiny. 'You're a great lover, Ryan. Possibly the best I'll ever have in my lifetime. Which is why I want to sample some more of your incredible talent in the bedroom.

'But we both know you won't ever give me what I really want—which is a husband and a family. Added to that is the fact that I'm not getting any younger. Frankly, becoming your girlfriend, even for a few months, is a waste of my valuable time.

'The truth is I just want to have some more sex with you, but not for too long. A couple of weeks should do the trick. I appreciate my somewhat radical proposal might be a blow to your ego, but think of the plus side—you won't have to take me out anywhere or buy me expensive dinners. You won't have to meet my friends. All you have to do is—'

'Don't you dare use that word!' Ryan broke in savagely.

Laura found his outrage extremely hypocritical, something which he said he despised. 'I was only going to say *shag*,' she invented. She'd actually been going to say 'make love to me' in a momentary lack of concentration.

'I hate that word too.'

'Lord, but aren't we the sensitive one all of a sudden? And this from a man who had no qualms pointing out to me that all he was good for was sex. What would you prefer to call it then? Bonk? Screw?'

'I would prefer that you agreed to become my girlfriend for real!' he snapped.

Laura's back teeth clenched together hard in her jaw, as the temptation to say yes was almost overwhelming.

'Sorry,' she bit out. 'No can do.'

'*Sorry?*' he retorted, throwing her a savage glance. 'I don't think you're sorry at all.'

'And I think you should keep your eyes on the road,' she said when the car drifted once again.

He swore, using the four-letter word he hadn't wanted her to say. He didn't apologise, however. Instead, he fell silent and sped up, the car eating up the miles as only a powerful sports car could. Laura fell stubbornly silent too, determined not to weaken in her resolve to retain control of her life and this affair. They'd crossed the Hawkesbury River Bridge and were drawing near the outer suburbs of Sydney before Ryan spoke again.

'Right,' he said abruptly. 'Now that I've calmed down, this is the way I see the situation. I'm sorry if I gave you the impression that all I want from you is sex. I like you, Laura. Like your company and your conversation. I would enjoy taking you places and buying you expensive dinners. I would especially enjoy seeing you throw off that ridiculously tough façade you've been hiding behind and become the warm, beautiful, sexy, sophisticated woman which I know you could be.

'As for my wasting your valuable time, I don't believe any time you spend with me would be a waste. Life should not always be lived for the future, but sometimes for the here and now.'

He paused for a long moment, perhaps waiting for his quite seductive argument to work its magic on her. But Laura wasn't at all convinced. She did not believe in that live-for-the-moment rubbish. Unless fate stepped in with an unfortunately terminal accident or disease, the future inevitably arrived, during which you had to live with what you'd done in the past. It was all right for him; he didn't fall in love. But she did! And she wasn't going to. Not this time!

'I see,' he said with a rueful glance at her unmoved face. 'Obviously what I believe is irrelevant. Look, I'm not in the business of trying to change a woman's mind. But neither am I going to agree to such a ridiculous scheme. At the same time, I still want you, Laura—with a rather irrational desire, I am discovering. So I will stay with you tonight and endeavour to give you lots of the only thing you want from me. But, come tomorrow morning, that will be that. Our ways will part, never to be crossed again. That's my counter proposal. If you don't agree, then I'm afraid it will be quits today at your door.'

Laura sucked in sharply, her emotions in immediate disarray. So much for her façade of cool control!

Fury that he'd accused her of callously using him mingled with panic at the possibility that she would never be with him again. Which would be the case if she didn't agree to his 'counter proposal'. But how *could* she agree now? He'd already made her sound like some sex-crazed fool who'd thrown away any chance of a real relationship in exchange for a fortnight's sex. To agree to just one night of the same seemed so much worse.

She wasn't *that* desperate, was she?

'I'm sorry you think so badly of me,' she said, her voice sounding calm despite a trembling starting deep inside. 'I was just trying to be honest with you with my proposal, and not hypocritical. I don't think you can blame me for suggesting a sex-only affair when you yourself said you couldn't offer me any form of commitment. But I can see now that such an arrangement won't work for me, even for one more night. It is far better that we call it quits today, then you can move on the way you say you always do, and so will I. Hopefully, the next time I find a man I fancy, he'll want more than a temporary relationship.'

Ryan clenched his teeth down hard in his jaw as he listened to her quite stunning rejection of his proposal. And there he'd been, thinking she would not dare knock him back, not when she'd virtually admitted she was mad for him. He'd imagined that he'd backed her into a corner where he'd be the one in control and she would come begging for more. Which was what he wanted—more of Laura, naked and willing, in his arms. But on his terms, not hers. A man did have his pride.

Unfortunately, pride did have its downside. *He* was the one backed into a corner now. And there'd be no begging from *his* corner.

'Fine,' he bit out. 'We'll call it quits today.'

It was like a physical blow to Laura. She struggled not to cry out, then not to cry. Oh God, what had she done? Suddenly even one night with him was better than this…this emptiness.

'I will leave it up to you to arrange for another lawyer to be sent to me every Friday afternoon,' he went on, his voice sounding bitter. 'I don't care what excuse you give.'

'All right,' she said, her own voice sounding bleak.

'Now, if you don't mind, I don't want to talk any more.' And he turned on the radio, at the same time pressing whatever button it took for the roof automatically to go back into place.

Laura's heart sank. The roof closing was like a sign that everything was over. *They* were over.

She turned her face away towards the passenger window so Ryan couldn't see the tears filling her eyes.

CHAPTER TWENTY-TWO

IT STARTED to rain not long after they left the motorway, a grey drizzle which reflected the condition of Laura's emotions. She ached to say something to take away the horribly strained silence which had permeated the car since their argument, but could not seem to find the courage to speak up.

Or was it common sense keeping her quiet?

If she were brutally honest, Laura suspected that if she opened her mouth she would start apologising wildly, then agreeing to whatever Ryan wanted just so that he wouldn't drop her at her door. The thought of never seeing him again was appalling, so appalling that she began to wonder if she'd already fallen in love with him. It seemed unlikely, but why else would she feel so devastated? Surely it couldn't still be just lust driving her feelings?

But, even as she speculated on the reason behind her despair, her eyes slid over to where Ryan's hands were wrapped around the steering wheel. His hands were large, with long, strong fingers which had no doubt helped make him become a success as a goalkeeper. But none of that mattered to Laura. All she could think about when she looked at his hands was how gentle they'd been on her. Gentle, yet knowing. They'd explored all her orifices with stunning intimacy. She could feel them now, inside her, stroking, teasing, arousing.

Oh God, she thought as her body was suddenly overwhelmed by the most intense longing; her belly tightened as did her nipples. *At least now I know,* she thought wildly as hot blood roared around her veins, flushing her cheeks and making her break out into strangely chilling goose-bumps. Not love—still just lust.

She almost died of shame when he glanced over at her at that precise moment. It was impossible to hide the telling evidence of her flaming face. Impossible to look anything but what she was: desperate for him.

Yet he didn't say a single word. He just stared at her for a long moment before returning his attention to the road. But she saw that his knuckles had whitened, and she could feel an answering tension in him. He knew what she wanted, and he wanted the same thing.

Not a word was spoken when he pulled up outside her house. They climbed out in the most appalling silence. Ryan helped her to carry her things up onto the front porch. Rambo didn't make an appearance, which surprised her. Possibly he was curled up asleep in the neighbour's rocking chair which was something he liked to do when she was away. She was left to fumble with her keys. Once the door was open, she turned to face Ryan, terrified that he would still leave, and equally terrified that he wouldn't.

'Ryan, I—'

'Just shut up,' he broke in, his face and eyes tormented as he dropped everything he was holding onto the verandah and pushed her inside the hallway, kicking the door shut behind him.

There was no question of fighting him, or even protesting, because she wanted him to do what it was obvious he was going to do. The trembling had already started inside. The trembling and the wild, uncontrollable excitement.

Yes, yes, slam me up against the wall, she urged silently as he did exactly that. *Kiss me till I can't think. Rip my clothes off. Ravish me.*

'God help me!' she cried out when he finally surged up into her.

It was a manic mating; raw, rough and totally beyond reason. Beyond everything in this world which smacked of common sense and control.

And she revelled in it, her mouth gasping wide as he plun-
dered her depths with the most primal passion. He came first,
the fierce spasms of his flesh triggering her own cataclysmic
climax. Laura's release was so intense, so overwhelming, that
she started to sob afterwards, tears streaming down her face as
her arms flopped down by her side and her legs went to jelly.
She might have slid down to the floor if Ryan's body hadn't
been holding her up.

'Oh God, Laura,' he groaned, then clasped her tightly to
him. 'I'm so sorry. So dreadfully sorry.'

'It... It's all right...' she somehow managed to stammer between sobs.

'No,' he said, taking her by the shoulders as he levered his
body away from hers, his abrupt withdrawal bringing a startled gasp from her lungs. His eyes when they met hers were
haunted. 'It's not all right. What I did just now... It was all
wrong.'

His distress forced her to get control of her weeping so she
could reassure him that he hadn't raped her, if that was what
he was thinking. She'd been with him all the way. She could
have struggled, could have said no, but she hadn't.

'I'm as much to blame as you, Ryan,' she choked out, not
quite in control of her voice just yet.

'I can't accept that,' he ground out as he zipped up his jeans
then set about helping her with her clothes, which hadn't been
properly removed either, just enough to let him have his way
with her. 'I forced myself on you. And I didn't use protection.
What if you fall pregnant? I should be put up against a wall
and shot!'

'You didn't *force* me, Ryan,' she reiterated firmly. 'I have
free will and I wanted you to do what you did. I enjoyed it.
You know I did.'

He just stared at her.

'Let me assure you that my chances of getting pregnant are negligible,' she went on, thankful that she was one of those girls who kept dates pretty clear in her head—not that her head was all that clear at the moment. 'My period is due on Wednesday and I'm as regular as clockwork. It's a very safe time for me in that regard.

'Unless, of course,' she added, her heart jolting as another not very nice thought came to her, 'You're worried about my catching something far worse than a baby.' There was no use pretending that he wasn't a player with a stream of partners behind him. Maybe he'd done this kind of thing before—had unsafe sex, and with someone not as safe as she was.

He looked genuinely shocked at her enquiry. 'You have my word that your health is at no risk from me. I have never before had unsafe sex. Not once. This is a first for me, believe me.'

'Really?' Laura couldn't help it. She smiled at his admission. There was something perversely flattering that she'd been the one and only woman to make him lose control like that.

'Yes, really, Miss Smug.' He cocked his head on one side and gave her a long thoughtful look. 'I take it, then, that you won't mind if I stay the night?'

'I...er...was actually hoping for more than one night,' she said, well aware that she wasn't strong enough to send him away. Not yet.

Rambo bolting down the hallway towards her was a thankful distraction from the telling heat that was suddenly threatening to engulf her.

'Hi, sweetie,' she said. 'Did you miss me?'

He miaowed once, then sauntered over and rubbed himself around Ryan's ankles. When Ryan scooped him up into his arms, Rambo began to purr.

'He likes you,' Laura said, trying not to feel jealous.

'He's a very nice cat. Even with only one eye. His fur is incredibly soft.'

'He's very spoiled.'

'I can imagine. Does he sleep on your bed every night?'

'No. He likes to roam at night. I've tried locking him in, but when I do he just sits at the window in my room and cries. It's easier to just let him do what he wants.'

'Smart cat. He's trained you well.'

'I love him,' she said somewhat defensively. 'When you love your pet, you can't bear to see it unhappy, or hurt.'

'Hence the three-thousand-dollar vet bill,' Ryan said.

Laura refused to be irked by the dry amusement in his voice. 'I would have spent ten thousand dollars to keep Rambo alive! Now, if you don't mind, I have to feed him or he'll be a pain later on. And we wouldn't want that, would we?' she threw at him snakily.

He smiled a wry smile. 'Glad to see that some things about you haven't changed. Here,' he said, and handed the cat over. 'He's all yours. By the way, after you've fed him, is there a chance of some coffee? You pointed the kitchen out to me yesterday.'

Only yesterday? Laura thought with amazement as she carried Rambo down to the kitchen. One short day and so much had changed. The twice-bitten-forever-shy Laura of yesterday would have worried herself sick over where her affair with Ryan was heading. This morning's Laura had still been a little concerned.

The Laura who'd just had wild but fantastic sex up against a wall now looked at things very differently. No longer was she going to worry about falling in love with Ryan and ending up with another broken heart. She was going to embrace the lust which was still raging within her and live for the heat of the moment. The long-term future could go hang itself. The only future she cared about was the immediate future. Which was tonight.

Her heartbeat quickened as she realised that she would soon be back in bed with Ryan. Back in his arms, back experiencing the most incredible pleasure. She could not wait to be totally naked with him once more. To have him touch her everywhere. To touch him everywhere as well. Her head swirled at the thought of going down on him. Not reluctantly, but avidly. And certainly not because of some silly idea of sacrificial love. She wanted to feel that power which he'd described to her last night, wanted to make him lose control, all because of *her*.

It was a heady thought. Heady, intoxicating and thrilling.

Rambo's impatient miaow snapped her back to the present.

'You wouldn't understand, Rambo,' she muttered as she went about getting him the special treat she always fed him when she wanted him to settle. 'You've been de-sexed. Now, here, eat up. After which I want you to be a good boy and don't bother me for the rest of the night.'

'I hope you're not talking about me,' Ryan said as he strode into the kitchen, his beautiful blue eyes glittering with amusement. 'Because I don't intend to be good. And I am going to bother you. But not till I've had some coffee. Strong coffee. I suggest you have some as well; don't want you falling asleep on me.' He glanced around. 'I like your kitchen. The wood's a nice colour.'

'It's oak,' Laura said as she dropped the empty tin in the garbage. '*Real* oak.'

'It's classy,' he said, and pulled out one of the two wooden stools which fronted the small breakfast bar. 'Like you,' he added.

Laura wasn't sure what to say to such a compliment, so she settled for a simple, 'Thank you,' before turning away from him to put the kettle on and get everything ready for coffee.

'I only have instant, I'm afraid,' she said as she busied herself with the mugs.

'No problem; I'm not fussy. Just make it black and strong, with no sugar.'

'I don't know how you can bear drinking coffee without milk and sugar.'

'I learned when I had no milk and sugar,' he returned dryly.

She frowned as she turned back to face him. 'Were you really that poor once?'

'You have no idea.'

'No,' she agreed thoughtfully. 'I guess I haven't. I may have been unhappy as a teenager but I was never poor. I certainly never went hungry. That must have been horrible.'

Ryan shrugged, as though he no longer thought about it. Or cared. 'It made me appreciate things once I could afford them. And it made me work hard so that I could afford them. But enough of such talk. I never like talking about the past. It's a waste of time.'

'But the past is what makes you what you are today,' Laura said, curious now to find out more about him. She realised that he'd revealed only scant details about his early life to her family yesterday. Though Gran had picked up on the fact that his childhood couldn't have been easy.

'Yes I do know that, Laura,' he replied a little impatiently. 'But I don't subscribe to analysis of any kind. It does a person no good at all to rake over the past, especially when the things they're raking over are usually wretched and made them miserable. It just sets off old problems again. Far better to put things behind you and move on.'

Laura almost said that was much easier said than done but decided to let the matter drop. She didn't want to say or do anything to spoil the rest of the evening.

'Speaking of moving on,' he added dryly. 'So come with me, woman. Bed awaits.'

CHAPTER TWENTY-THREE

LAURA still fell asleep, but only after a lengthy sexual marathon where they made love over and over and over, in every position Ryan knew, including up against the wall again, though in the shower this time and with Laura facing the wall.

He didn't succumb to sleep, however, despite feeling drained. His mind would not let him rest, plaguing him with the things Laura had said earlier about how much the past influenced the present, and the person one eventually became. As he'd already told Laura, he did actually know that. Ryan understood full well why he avoided love and marriage. Why he avoided emotional involvement of any kind with the opposite sex.

He'd always believed that nothing would ever change that. That no woman alive was capable of unlocking the iron cage he'd fused shut around his heart the day he'd come home from school and found his mother dead on the floor and his father curled up in a corner, sobbing that he hadn't meant to do it, that he loved her.

Ryan had lived a long time since that day—twenty-five years to be exact. Not once in all that time had a woman touched his heart, let alone his soul.

Until now...

Was this love he was finally feeling? He wondered as he frowned down at Laura's sleeping form.

He wasn't sure, since he didn't know what romantic love

felt like. All he knew was that sex with Laura was different from anything he'd experienced before. He could not seem to get enough of her. Usually, his desire lessened sharply after a couple of times, his days of wanting sex all night long a thing of the past. Not so with Laura. Already he wanted to feel that special feeling again, the one which jolted him every time he entered her, then grew in intensity, culminating in waves of rapture. He'd never felt anything like it. Hell on earth—would he never be satisfied?

This can't be love, he decided as he rolled over and stared down at her naked bottom with its peach-like buttocks. True love would be less sexually driven. It was still just lust. A more obsessive form than usual, but just lust all the same. Give it time and these cravings would fade.

But not yet, he accepted when he reached out to touch her.

Laura woke to the delicious sensation of Ryan stroking her back. She was lying face down, on the bed, her arms bent upwards, her hands under the pillow that her head was resting on.

'Mmm,' she murmured sleepily, her mind not yet fully awake.

It soon snapped to, however, when his hand abandoned her back and started paying her more intimate attention. Today, she was just all excitement. She'd abandoned embarrassment as a lost cause; Ryan didn't have an embarrassed bone in his body when it came to sex. Everything in his view was natural and healthy, every part of a woman's body put there for his pleasure. And her own.

After a while, however, Laura didn't want to just lie there, letting him do what he was doing—though it was lovely. She wanted to do things to him for a change. With a small moan—it *was* seriously tempting just to stay where she was and let him have his wicked way with her—she rolled over abruptly. Pushing her hair out of her eyes, she sat up and met his somewhat startled eyes.

'You can do that later,' she said breathlessly. 'It's my turn now.'

His eyebrows arched. 'Your turn to do what?'

'Will you please stop talking? Oh my goodness!' she gasped when she pushed him down onto his back and she saw how aroused he already was.

'How long was I asleep?' she asked him in amazement. After all, they'd already made love quite a few times before she had dropped off, including that incredible time in the shower.

'Long enough,' he growled.

'Obviously,' she said, unable to stop herself from reaching out to touch him.

When she encircled him in her hand, he sucked in sharply, sending her eyes to his. This was the one thing she still hadn't done. Up until now it had been all him doing things to her.

'Do you like women going down on you?' she asked him, her voice thick with excitement.

'I do if they do,' he replied, his voice sounding strained. 'You said you didn't—like it, that is.'

'True. But that was before and this is now. I think I *will* like it with you.'

He groaned when she began to bend her head, groaning again when she put her lips to him in a tender kiss before slowly, ever so slowly, licking the head all over.

She didn't just like doing it, Laura realised dazedly by the time she drew him fully into her mouth. She *loved* it. Loved the feeling, not of power so much, but of knowing how much he was loving it. He'd given her so much pleasure; now it was her turn to give him pleasure. *Lots* of pleasure, by the strangled sounds he was making. She didn't care if he came in her mouth. She wanted him to come. Wanted him to stop struggling for control—which she sensed he was—and just let go. Determined, she picked up the pace, lifting and lowering her head to the rhythm of the thudding drumbeat her own blood was making in her head.

But, just when she was sure he was about to come, he

grabbed her and dragged her upwards, his strong hands lifting her up over him then lowering her down so that she was straddled across his hips.

'I want you with me,' he growled. 'Here, put this on me,' he ordered in gravelly tones, shoving a condom into her hands. 'Hurry,' he snapped when she hesitated.

She had a little trouble sliding the protective sheath over him but managed at last, amazed when he slid inside her with shocking ease, her internal muscles automatically taking hold of him in a vice-like grip.

'Hell on earth, woman,' he choked out, his face twisting.

Laura's face fell. 'Am I hurting you?' This was the first time she'd ever been on top in her life. Mario and Brad had both been the kind of males who would never allow a woman to take the reins during sex. 'I'm sorry. It's just that I...I haven't done it this way before.'

He stared up at her. 'You've never been on top?'

'No. Never. I'm so sorry.'

'There's absolutely no need for you to apologise.'

'But I *hurt* you!'

His smile was rueful. 'There's a fine line between pleasure and pain, Laura. I promise you that what I'm feeling is more pleasure than pain. Now, this is the way,' he said, cupping her buttocks with his large, strong hands and moving her.

She gasped. Oh, how heavenly it felt. She soon didn't need any help, riding him all by herself, faster and faster. His hips began to lift from the bed, pushing him even deeper inside her. She moaned and leant forward, her breasts swinging free of her chest wall, her bottom lifting slightly. Incredibly, the level of her pleasure increased with the change of angle, each forward thrust sending electric shocks charging through her body. Her climax hit with such blinding force that she cried out. Ryan cried out as well, his body spasming wildly within hers. She collapsed across his chest, her head coming to rest over his madly galloping heart.

It was then that she began to weep, her whole body suddenly surrendering to a storm of emotion that she was yet to understand.

'Hush, my darling,' Ryan crooned as he wrapped his arms around her back and held her tightly against him. 'Hush. There's no need to cry.'

'I know,' she choked out. 'I'm being s...silly.'

'Not silly at all,' he murmured. 'Just...over-tired. Time for you to get some proper sleep, I think. And time for me to go.'

Her head shot up off his chest. 'But you promised to stay the whole night!'

'I've changed my mind about that.'

'I don't want you to go,' she wailed.

'Don't worry. I'll be back,' he said, and firmly put her to one side whilst he sat up and swung his feet over the side of the bed.

She only just stopped herself from grabbing him to make him stay, but couldn't help asking, 'When? Tomorrow night?'

He sighed. 'I know I shouldn't but, yes, I promise to come back tomorrow night. Unless, of course, you've changed your mind about becoming my girlfriend for real,' he added, glancing over his shoulder at her. 'Then I could pick you up from your office, take you for drinks and dinner then back to my place for a very pleasant evening.'

Oh, how tempting it was to agree to his offer. So, why didn't she?

Because all the reasons why she'd rejected his original proposal were still there: he didn't love her. He would *never* love her. The fact that that realisation cut even deeper into her heart reinforced her decision to keep her affair with Ryan as short as possible. It worried her sick that she was already falling in love with him. How easy it would be to surrender to her emotional nature and just go along with whatever he wanted.

Don't do it, Laura, the bitter voice of experience insisted. *Stay strong!*

'I haven't changed my mind,' she said much more firmly than she felt.

'Fine,' he bit out as he climbed off the bed and reached for his clothes. 'But don't go thinking you can have it all your way indefinitely, Laura. I'm not happy with this arrangement. Not happy at all.'

'Really?' she couldn't resist saying. 'I would have thought it was right up your alley—all fun and no responsibility.'

The look he gave her would have frozen mercury.

Laura might have panicked if it had lasted. But slowly the ice in his eyes thawed and a sardonic smile lifted one corner of his mouth. 'I can see you would have been one hell of a criminal-defence lawyer. You really are wasted in corporate law. Which reminds me, don't forget to tell them at work that I'm no longer your client and that they'll need to send me someone else.'

Dismay curled her stomach. 'But what excuse will I give them?'

Now his smile turned a little cruel. 'That's your problem, Laura.'

CHAPTER TWENTY-FOUR

'No!' Alison exclaimed in shocked tones for the umpteenth time.

Laura suppressed a sigh. Lord only knew how her friend would react if she told her the whole truth about her ongoing affair with Ryan. She'd actually contemplated lying when Alison had rung her first thing this morning, barely five minutes after she arrived at work. But in the end she'd decided that a sanitised version of the truth would still save her pride, at the same time satisfying Alison's by-then rabid curiosity.

So she'd confessed to having sex with Ryan again when they'd returned to Sydney yesterday, but made it sound like it had been her idea that he eventually go home rather than stay the night. But when she confessed that she'd refused to become his girlfriend for real, opting instead for a brief sexual fling, Alison's reaction had still been negative.

'And you honestly think you can handle a strictly sexual affair?' Alison went on eventually in a calmer vein. 'That might suit lover boy but it's not you, Laura.'

Laura refused to let her friend think Ryan was to blame for everything. 'Try not to forget, Alison, that I've been a willing partner in all this. I want sex from Ryan as much as he wants it from me.'

'He must be damned good in bed to get you into this state. You've never cared for sex all that much in the past, not even when you were madly in love. But, of course, he *has* had a lot of experience,' she added tartly.

'Yes,' Laura agreed, wondering if Alison could be just a tad jealous. She was always saying that one's sex life went out the window when you had children.

Alison sighed. 'You know, I envy you, in a weird kind of way,' she admitted, confirming Laura's thoughts.

'Not as much as I envy you,' Laura retaliated. 'I'd give anything to have a loving husband like your Peter and two gorgeous children. You have a fantastic family, Alison.'

'I guess I do. It's just that… Oh, never mind. Look, don't take any notice of me today. I'm suffering from PMT; you know what it's like.'

'Indeed I do.' Laura frowned as she realised that she didn't have any of the symptoms yet.

Feeling slightly panicky, she went over the dates in her head again and came up with the same result—her period was definitely due on Wednesday. It occurred to her that maybe PMT went away when you were having a fantastic sex life. Maybe her body had become more relaxed. Stress could do dreadful things to one's health. Or so she'd read.

'What you need to do,' she told Alison, 'Is to have more sex.'

'Huh! And when exactly do I have time for sex? Those gorgeous kids of mine run me ragged.'

'Make time, Alison. I'll mind your kids next weekend and you go away with Peter.'

'Honestly? You'd do that?'

'I've minded them before.'

'Not for a whole weekend. You know, I think that's a great idea and I will take you up on it—eventually. But not this weekend. There's no point; I'll have my period.'

'You and me both,' Laura said dryly. 'Look, I have to go, Alison. I have heaps of work to do.'

Which was not strictly true. But she had to think up some plausible reason why she could no longer be Ryan's lawyer. It was sure to be the first thing he would ask her that evening.

But, as it turned out, Laura couldn't think of a reason—

not one she felt happy with. Already she was feeling hyped up about tonight. Hyped up and turned on. Thoughts of sex filled her head all day, so much so that by the time Ryan arrived on her doorstep shortly after seven she'd forgotten all about not having organised another lawyer. All she could think of was being with him. One look at his hotly glittering eyes and she knew he felt exactly the same.

They made it into the bedroom, but not the bed. And Ryan almost didn't use a condom—again! She was the one who reminded him just in time. When he swore, she laughed. Then he laughed. The delay was exactly what they needed to catch their breath and move from the hard wooden floor to the comfort of the bed. They even managed to remove their clothes before a burst of uncontrollable passion overtook them again.

Laura came the moment Ryan entered her, his own climax swiftly following. After his body stopped shuddering he collapsed across her, his weight almost crushing. When she pushed at his shoulders, he levered himself up onto his elbows and glared down at her.

'I can't keep this up, you know,' he growled.

Her brain felt as glazed as her eyes. 'Keep what up?'

'Waiting all day to be with you. I nearly went insane this afternoon.'

'Oh…'

'Is that all you've got to say? *Oh*?'

'I don't know what you want me to say.'

'Say that you feel the same way. Say you'll stop this nonsense and agree to be my girlfriend for real. Then we could spend lunchtimes together and have proper dates. And weekends away.'

Again, she was tempted to agree. But the bottom line was that he still only wanted her for sex with some company thrown in. There would be no proposal of marriage at any stage.

She said the only thing that she knew would stop him in his tracks. 'If I become your girlfriend for real, Ryan, I'm sure to fall in love with you.'

Ryan could not believe the crazy thoughts which ran through his head—mostly that he didn't care any more if she fell in love with him as long as she let him spend more time with her.

God, how selfish could he get?

Ryan rolled away from her, staring grimly up at the ceiling and wondering what the hell he should do. He didn't like it that he was becoming possessive of her. It worried him.

Laura could not believe how forlorn she felt when he abandoned her body. Forlorn and alone. He was lying right beside her yet he seemed such a long way away. She hated that feeling.

'I'm sorry,' she said suddenly, not really knowing what she was apologising for.

He turned his head to look at her. 'For what? Being honest? I like honest people. And I like you—very much so.'

'I...I like you too,' she said, choking on the words as she realised what an understatement they were. Because, of course, she didn't just *like* him any more. She *loved* the man. It wasn't the thought of no more sex with him that terrified the life out of her but of never seeing him again.

It was a shattering realisation. Laura quickly turned her head away lest her face betray the truth.

'I doubt you'd fall in love with me, Laura,' he said at that most ironic moment. 'By the way, what did you tell your boss about why you couldn't be my lawyer any more?'

Laura cleared her throat. 'I...er...haven't told him yet.'

'Then don't.'

Her head whipped round to stare at him. 'But why?'

'I don't want another lawyer. I want you.'

'What about your rule about sleeping with work colleagues?'

He shrugged. 'Rules are meant to be broken.'

His nonchalance infuriated her, especially after all the fuss he'd made. 'You can break *your* rule,' she snapped, 'But I have no intention of breaking mine. You're my client now and I do not have relationships with clients.'

He speared her with cold blue eyes. 'But you don't have a relationship with me, Laura. You're just having sex with me. Which reminds me, I take it you don't want to call it quits to-night either, do you? You want me to come back tomorrow night as well.'

Laura's teeth clamped down hard. He was deliberately try-ing to goad her. But she refused to be goaded. 'I guess that's up to you, Ryan. I can't force you to come.'

'But you want me to.'

She lifted her chin in a defiant manner. 'Yes,' she bit out.

'In that case, I'll be here tomorrow night. But after that I suggest we have a week's break from each other. That should stop us growing too attached.'

She wanted to hate him at that moment.

'What about our appointment on Friday afternoon?' she asked waspishly.

'The contracts can wait another week. Things are a bit slow at the moment. Now, I really must go to the bathroom. Meanwhile, I suggest you go get that bottle of white wine that I saw in your fridge door last night. I could do with a drink.'

'I was going to have that later with dinner,' she threw after him.

'Good God,' he said mockingly as he strode from the room. 'She's going to feed me as well. What a lucky fellow I am.'

Now she did hate him.

But not as much as Ryan hated himself. He scowled at his reflection in the bathroom mirror. What right did he have to say nasty things like that?

If you don't like the 'strictly sex' arrangement Laura wants, then you should just keep on walking, right out of her life.

So why didn't he?

Be honest, you hypocritical bastard. It's just your pride lashing out. You really want to stay.

By the time Ryan finished washing his hands, he'd resolved

to stop being stupid and just give Laura plenty of what she wanted. But he wanted to make love to her; that was the truth of it.

Ryan shook his head at himself in the mirror. It was as well that he'd suggested they have a break from each other; he was becoming way too involved. He also revised his idea about keeping her on as his lawyer. But he wouldn't tell her that just yet. He'd tell her tomorrow night.

CHAPTER TWENTY-FIVE

LAURA'S period didn't arrive on Wednesday morning, or Wednesday afternoon, or Wednesday evening. When Thursday morning came and still no sign of a period, her stress levels soared. Suddenly, she was thankful that she and Ryan were not in contact for a week. No phone calls, or text messages; no emails. Nothing until the following Tuesday when he'd be dropping round after work around seven.

The last time she'd seen him he'd said they both needed time to think, which was certainly true. Because by then she was more in love with him than ever, so much so that she was reconsidering accepting his offer of being his girlfriend for real and to hell with the consequences. She'd almost said as much when he had gone to leave. She might have done so if he hadn't opened his mouth to say he'd changed his mind about keeping her on as his lawyer.

'Don't worry about finding a replacement immediately,' he'd added. 'That can wait a while.'

It was a well-timed reminder that nothing had changed for Ryan. Any secret fantasies she'd been harbouring about his feelings for her having deepened went out of the window. So, yes, she definitely needed time to think about what she was going to do when she saw him the following Tuesday.

By Friday, Laura's period still hadn't made an appearance. It was a huge relief that she wasn't in contact with Ryan, because he might have asked her about it. This way, she didn't have to explain things. For Lord knew how he would react. He might think she'd lied to him and had somehow been trying to trap him with a pregnancy. As if she would!

But she could not deny that strangely, as soon as the thought entered Laura's head that she might have somehow conceived Ryan's child, by some perverse twist of fate, the idea of having his baby brought a zing to her heart. But the zing did not last, fading to a deep dismay when she realised it would definitely mean the end of any relationship with Ryan. Because he didn't do love or marriage or, God forbid, fatherhood.

That night she actually prayed for her period to arrive. But her prayers were not answered, not for another few days. Perversely, she cried when it did arrive the following Tuesday morning—cried and cried and cried. She was so distressed that she rang work and said she would not be in. Several times that day, she picked up her phone to call Ryan and tell him she didn't want him to come over that night. But each time she put the phone back down again. Love made one weak, she accepted despairingly. And there she'd been, thinking she was over being a victim to love.

Laura thought about what she would say to Ryan all afternoon, determined not to let him come inside. She even began to hope that he might not come at all. But he showed up, looking impossibly handsome in a suit and tie. Her resolve faltered when he smiled at her— Faltered even more when he said, 'God, but I've missed you,' then pulled her into his arms.

She didn't object to his kiss, telling herself that this was her goodbye kiss. But, oh, inside she was already dissolving.

'I'm sorry, Ryan,' she said when he finally let her come up for air. 'But you have to stop. I...I've got my period.'

'Still?'

She looked into his eyes and saw surprise, not scepticism.

'No. It... It didn't arrive till today,' she admitted.

Now he looked shocked. 'But you said...'

'I know what I said,' she swept on angrily, knowing exactly what he'd thought for a split second. 'I don't know what happened. I was so worried about being late that I actually went to a doctor yesterday and he told me that sometimes ovulation is delayed from stress. He asked me what had been going on in my life, and when I told him about Gran's accident he said that might have done it. Anyway, he said it was too early to test for a pregnancy but it wasn't impossible that I might have conceived. You can imagine how I felt at that moment!'

'No,' he said, looking oddly at her. 'How did you feel?'

It angered her even further, that coolly speculative look in his eyes.

All the distress of the last week welled up inside her, goading her tongue to strike out at him.

'How do you think I felt?' she snapped. 'You don't think that I wanted your baby, do you? Good God, I'd have to be insane to want that! It's bad enough that I let myself be seduced into a disgustingly futile affair with a man who offered me nothing of himself but his body—if it turned out I *was* pregnant, I think I would have jumped off the harbour bridge!'

'You don't mean that,' he ground out.

'I do indeed,' she returned fiercely, all reason abandoned with her loss of temper. 'What decent woman would want your baby? You'd make a terrible father. Why, you are the most selfish, self-centred, screwed-up man I've ever known! Even Mario was a better man than you. And that's saying something!'

He just stared at her for a long moment, his eyes haunted. And then he nodded. Slowly. Sadly. 'I couldn't have said it better myself,' he agreed.

The horror of her words finally sank in to Laura, bringing with it an almost unbearable shame. She had no right to hurt him like she just had. No right at all. As she'd said to Alison, she'd been a willing partner in all this. Besides, not wanting marriage and a family didn't make Ryan a bad person. He had every right to live his life as he saw fit, and it wasn't as though he hadn't been honest with her.

But it was too late now. The words had been said and she

couldn't take them back. Though, heaven help her, she wanted to, wanted to throw herself back into his arms and beg him to forgive her. Instead, she took a shaky step backwards, her fingers curling over into fists by her side lest her arms moved without her brain telling them to.

'I do apologise if I have behaved badly,' he said bleakly. 'I honestly never meant to hurt you. I think you are an incredible woman and I'm sure that some day your Mr Right will come along and give you what you want. Please tell your family I'm sorry things didn't work out between us but I wish them well also, especially your gran.'

His mentioning her gran tipped Laura's emotions into dangerously weak territory.

'Ryan, I…'

'No, Laura,' he cut in, whipping up one hand as a quite savage stop sign. 'You've said quite enough. Let's leave it at that. Bye, Rambo,' he added when the cat suddenly appeared at his feet. 'Look after your mistress for me.' And, whirling, he was gone.

Laura stood in the open doorway, staring at the empty path for what felt like an eternity. This time her tears were silent, spilling over and running down her cheeks, dripping from the end of her nose onto her top. No doubt it was being ruined, yet she didn't care. Laura suspected she would not care about anything for a long time to come.

The sound of her phone ringing and ringing eventually forced her to turn and walk down the hallway towards the kitchen, a disconsolate Rambo trailing behind her. Probably a telemarketer, Laura thought wearily; they always rang when people got home from work. Sighing, she snatched a handful of tissues from the box which she kept on the counter, wiped her nose then reached for the phone.

'Yes?' she said in a decidedly dead voice.

'Oh—Laura,' Aunt Cynthia choked out down the line. 'Oh my dear…'

Laura's already breaking heart shattered into tiny pieces,

for she knew immediately what had happened. And there she'd been, naïvely thinking nothing could possibly make her feel worse.

But she hadn't bargained on this.

Life wasn't just cruel she realised as her insides crumbled in despair—sometimes it was downright sadistic.

'What happened?' she asked in hollow tones. 'A heart attack, I suppose?'

'Yes, we think so. Jane had gone to lie down after lunch, as she always did. I went to wake her around five and she was just lying there, unconscious. We called the ambulance but there was nothing they could do. She was already dead by the time they arrived. She didn't suffer, Laura. She looked very… peaceful. Happy, even.'

'That's good,' was all Laura could manage to say, tears threatening once more.

'You know, I thought I wouldn't be this upset when she went,' her aunt said with a sob. 'But I can't seem to stop crying.'

Laura knew how she felt.

'I'll have to ring you back, Aunt Cynthia. I can't talk any more just now.'

Hanging up, she sank down on the floor, put her head in her hands and began to sob.

CHAPTER TWENTY-SIX

RYAN could not remember the drive back to the city; his mind was in total disarray. That he made it back to his apartment building without incident was a minor miracle. It was a struggle to concentrate on the road when his head was full of such distressing thoughts, the main one being that he would never see Laura again. Never hold her in his arms again. Never make love to her again. Even worse was the physical distress which accompanied these thoughts. His stomach was churning, and his chest muscles were so tight around his heart he imagined he might go into cardiac arrest at any moment.

As soon as he closed the door behind him, Ryan headed for his drinks cabinet and poured himself the largest straight whisky he'd ever had in his life, downing it quickly before pouring himself another. Before long, the alcohol did what his normally strong will could not, calmed his body and shut down his brain.

The following morning he rang his PA and told her he wouldn't be in for the rest of the week. Then he turned off his phone so that no one could bother him. For the next three days, he watched movie after movie, eating delivered pizzas and drinking himself into oblivion until he fell asleep in the lounge. Same thing on Saturday. By Sunday morning, he couldn't stand his own company any longer, or the way he looked when he happened to catch a glimpse of himself in the bathroom mirror.

A shower and a shave went some way to brightening him up, plus a litre of orange juice and a couple of aspirin for his hangover. Afterwards he went for a long walk around the nearby botanic gardens, during which time he thought and thought, mostly about the past, the kind of thinking Ryan was not well acquainted with. He put such activities in the same category as psychological analysis or, even worse, group-therapy sessions. He'd survived so far without the help of anti-depressants and in-depth counselling, well aware that people in this modern day and age would think him something of a dinosaur regarding his attitude to mental health.

Ryan had no doubt that if he went to a doctor and confided the truth about his childhood he or she would be amazed that he'd lasted this long without cracking up entirely. His grandmother had actually taken him to a psychiatrist not long after his mother's death—or perhaps it was a psychologist; he couldn't be sure now, it was so long ago. But Ryan hadn't liked the man. He certainly hadn't wanted to tell him all the shameful details of his mother's life—and death—and hadn't wanted to keep reliving any of it.

He'd decided then and there to survive his own way. Of course, if it hadn't been for his grandmother's support and love, he would not have survived at all, let alone become a success. Ryan could also see that shortly after her death he'd been in real danger of losing it for a while. Only by hardening his heart even further against emotional attachment of any kind had he managed to continue living.

And it had worked for him up until now…

As Ryan walked endlessly around the garden pathways, he forced himself to face the astonishing fact that Laura had somehow stolen past his defences and melted his cold heart. His pretending that it was just lust he felt for her was just so much rubbish: it was love, pure and simple. Well, perhaps not so pure or so simple, but love all the same. Nothing else could explain the devastation he'd felt when she'd verbally savaged him the way she had the previous Tuesday.

But his falling in love with Laura was the ultimate irony, because she didn't return his love. Anyone could see that. Her disgust at the very thought of having his baby had been obvious. Though startled, deep down he'd actually not been displeased by the possibility—another light-bulb moment, if he'd been smart enough to recognise it at the time.

But he recognised it now.

By the time Ryan made it back to his apartment, he'd made a few decisions and got back some of his fighting spirit. Okay, so he probably didn't have a great chance of ever convincing Laura that he was a changed man. But he wasn't about to live the rest of his wretched life without giving it his best shot.

Winning a woman like Laura was not unlike winning a soccer match against a top team, he conceded. You couldn't just barge back into her life, running around like a chook with its head cut off. You had to have a decent strategy. A plan.

By Monday morning Ryan still wasn't sure what to do. He could hardly just ring Laura up and tell her that he loved her; that wasn't going to work. He needed more time to think. At the same time he needed to get back to work. Unfortunately, three days out of the office meant he had a lot of calls to return, one of them to Laura's boss.

'Ryan Armstrong,' he said when Greg Harvey came on the line.

'Ryan, so glad you called. I gather you'll be needing a new lawyer now that Laura has left us.'

'What? Laura's *left*?'

'You didn't know? I thought she would have told you. She resigned late last week. For personal reasons.'

'What kind of personal reasons?'

'I guess there's no reason you shouldn't know. Her grandmother died. Apparently they were very close.'

Ryan suppressed a groan of dismay.

'We offered her time off,' the man rattled on, 'But she said she needed a complete break. We're sorry to lose a lawyer of her ability but life does go on, doesn't it? Look, there's a young chap who's just joined us. Brilliant legal brain. What say I send him down to meet you, see what you think? His name's Cory Sanderland.'

'Sounds perfect, Greg. But not right now. I have to go out shortly and I won't be in for the rest of the day. Leave it with me and I'll give Cory a call later this week.'

'Fine.'

'Have to go, Greg,' he said, and hung up.

But he didn't leave the office straight away. First he tried ringing Laura's mobile but it was turned off. After pacing around for a few minutes, he charged out to his PA's desk.

'Judith,' he said. 'I want you to contact Laura Ferrugia's PA and find out the phone number of Laura's best friend. Her name is Alison—that's all I know, I'm afraid. I know it's an odd request but just do this for me, will you?'

Judith, who was a sensible woman who liked her job, didn't argue. 'Fine.'

Five minutes later, she handed Ryan a piece of paper with a phone number written down on it.

'She didn't really want to give it to me,' she said. 'You didn't tell me that Laura no longer worked there. I had to say it was an emergency.'

'It *is* an emergency,' he told her.

'Care to tell me more?'

'Not right now.'

'Just as well I'm not a curious type,' she said, and went back to her desk.

He called the number straight away, his heartbeat quickening as he waited for someone to answer. At last, a woman's voice said, 'Hello?'

'Is that Alison?'

'Yes? Who is this?'

'Ryan Armstrong.'

He heard her sharp intake of breath. 'What on earth are you doing ringing *me*?'

'I just heard about Laura's grandmother,' he said swiftly.

'I've been trying to ring Laura but her phone's switched off. I was hoping you could tell me if her grandmother's been buried yet. I'd like to go to the funeral.'

'Laura wouldn't want you there.'

'I'd still like to go.'

'Oh, for pity's sake, give the girl a break, will you? And just stay away from her. She doesn't want any more to do with you.'

Ryan decided then and there that if he wanted to win Laura he also had to win her best friend.

'She doesn't want anything to do with the man I used to be,' Ryan said. 'She might want to have something to do with the man I am today.'

'And what's that, pray tell?'

No doubting the cynicism in her voice.

'A man in love.'

Now he heard an even sharper intake of breath.

'I love Laura, Alison. And I want to marry her. Now tell me when the funeral is.'

'Oh Lord, it's today. In a couple of hours.'

'And you're not there with her?' he threw at her somewhat accusingly.

'I would have been but my little boy isn't well. He's asthmatic, you see, and has a bad bout of hay fever today. I daren't leave him.'

'I see. Is it being held at the chapel near the Hunter Valley gardens?' he asked.

'Yes. How did you know?'

'Never mind. I have to go, Alison, if I'm going to make it in time.'

'Yes, yes. Just go. And Ryan?'

'Yes?'

'For what it's worth, I think Laura loves you too.'

A wild joy flooded Ryan's heart. 'What makes you think so?'

'I've thought so from the day after she went to bed with

you. Laura only has sex with men she loves. She's that kind of girl.'

Ryan smiled. That was one of the reasons he loved her.

'Have to go, Alison.'

'Hurry, Ryan. Laura needs you.'

Yes, he agreed silently as he grabbed his suit jacket and headed for the door. Just as much as he needed her. They needed each other, two lonely, seriously screwed-up people whom life had hurt but whom life hadn't totally beaten yet.

Laura sat in the front pew of the chapel, trying not to look at her gran's coffin, or the masses of yellow roses which covered the lid. Every time she looked at the yellow roses she wanted to cry. They had been Jane's favourite flower. When Laura had left school and started living in her parents' house at North Manly, her gran had bought her several yellow rose-bushes to plant in her garden to remind Laura of her.

As if I would ever need reminding, Laura thought as tears threatened once more.

Panic joined her tears, for it was her turn to speak. Uncle Bill and Aunt Cynthia had asked her to give the main eulogy, claiming they were both poor public speakers whereas she was used to it. She'd shied away from doing it at first before accepting that it was the last way she would be able to express her gratitude to Jane for all she'd done for her. She'd written down what she wanted to say, lest she forget it. Now she stared down at the piece of paper on which she'd written the inadequate words, seeing that it was nothing more than a twisted crunched-up mess in her lap. It was impossible to straighten it out.

When Aunt Cynthia nudged her in the ribs, she rose and stumbled up to the podium. Somehow she managed to relate the story of Jane's early life from memory, dry facts really, about where her grandmother was born and where she went to school. She spoke of Jane's love of country life and of gardening. She then mentioned her marriage, complimenting her on being a loving and loyal wife, and a devoted mother.

But the moment she came to where she wanted to say how wonderful a grandmother she had been, her mouth went bone dry and a huge lump filled her throat. She looked down and tried to straighten out the crumpled sheet of paper but it was all a blur. Dying of embarrassment, she was staring down the only aisle of the small church when suddenly, through the blur, striding towards her with forceful steps, was the last man on earth she expected to see at that moment. My God, she thought wildly as her heart whirled and her heart lurched. What on earth was Ryan doing here?

He didn't hesitate, crossing the strip of carpet that still separated them, stepping up to stand close to her and slide a strongly supportive arm around her waist.

'Sorry I'm late,' he said gently as he pulled her against him. 'Got a bit lost without Jane's splendid directions.'

Laura blinked up at him, having been rendered even more speechless than before.

'I take it you're having a spot of trouble,' he whispered, having glanced down at the still-crinkled paper. 'As you can see, folks,' he continued in full voice, 'Laura is slightly overcome with the situation. Which is understandable, given how much she loved her gran. So I'm going to finish speaking for her. For those of you who don't know me, my name is Ryan Armstrong and I'm Laura's boyfriend.'

Ryan hoped like hell that she hadn't said anything to her family about their having broken up. He suspected that she might not have done so just yet. She was proud, his Laura. He felt reassured by Cynthia's eyes, which weren't looking at him with shock, or even surprise—reassured also by Laura's acquiescence to his arm around her.

'Now, I didn't know Jane all that well,' he went on. 'We only met once, over one short weekend. But that was long enough for me to see she was one of those grandmothers that make the world a better place to live in, especially for their grandchildren. I know something about grandmothers like that. I had one myself. I know how Laura feels, and on her behalf I'd like to thank Jane, as well as all the other amazing grandmothers in this world, for their sweetly giving natures, their unconditional love and their wonderful wisdom.

'I'm sure if Jane could speak to us today, she would tell us all gathered here in her memory not to be sad. She would want us to celebrate her life, not mourn her death. I know she was extremely proud of Laura, and all her family. Bill, Cynthia, Shane and Lisa: she loved you all dearly.

'She was also proud of where she lived. She recently showed me the Hunter Valley Gardens, along with this very beautiful little church, saying this was where she wanted her funeral service to be held. Both Laura and I hoped that such an event would be many years in the future. But it was not to be. Let me just say that it was a privilege to know Jane. Goodbye, darling Gran. Rest in Peace.'

Ryan's arm tightened around Laura as he led her back to her seat, sobbing now, taking a guess that she'd been sitting next to her aunt and uncle in the front pew.

'Well said, Ryan,' Bill complimented, his own eyes shimmering with tears. Cynthia was incapable of saying anything, a handkerchief held up to her face as she wept quietly into it.

Ryan found himself quite choked up too, feeling genuine grief—and some more remorse too, for not flying back to Australia and speaking at his own grandmother's funeral. If only one could go back in time…

But he could still remember how alone he'd felt at the time, thinking that the one and only person in his life that he could count on was gone. Laura was probably feeling the same.

He had to make her see, however, that she *could* count on him, that he wasn't the feckless fool she imagined him to be. She was still weeping quietly when they left the church. Ryan was thankful that they weren't going on to some wretchedly

dreary graveyard, Bill quickly explaining to him outside the
church that his mother had requested that she be cremated privately and her ashes sprinkled on her beloved rose garden. It
seemed a much better ending, in Ryan's opinion, than being
buried. But each to his own.

'Where's the wake being held?' he asked Bill.

'Back at the house. I presume Laura will be going back in
your car, Ryan?'

'Yes, of course.'

'See you back there shortly, then.'

When Ryan steered Laura over to where he'd parked his
car, she didn't argue with him, a testimony to her distressed
state. But shortly after they joined the long lines of cars heading back to the house she pulled herself together and glanced
over at him with a deep frown crinkling her forehead.

'I still don't understand how you knew about Gran's funeral,' she said. 'Or even why you came.'

Ryan supposed he could make up a plausible lie—that he'd
seen a funeral notice in the paper. But he didn't want to do
that. He wanted to be totally honest with Laura from now on.
It was the only way she would be able to trust him.

'Greg Harvey told me about your gran's death this morning when he rang to offer me a new lawyer. I tried to ring you
straight away but your phone's turned off. So I rang Alison
and she told me when and where the funeral was.'

'Alison? But you don't know her number.'

'I made it my business to find it.'

'But *why*?' There was total confusion in her voice.

'Because I love you, Laura,' he said, turning to look her
straight in the eye.

Laura's mouth fell open, her eyes widening at the same
time.

'I love you and I want to marry you,' he added, knowing
that a declaration of love was not going to be enough. For how
many men used false words of love to seduce women back
into their beds? He had never been guilty of such tactics but

he imagined other men had. Certainly dear old Mario and Brad had.

'You want to marry me?' she echoed, clearly in shock at his proposal.

'Yes. And have children with you. I want it all. I've been thinking about it for days and that's what I want with you, Laura. I'm hoping that's what you want too.'

Laura could hardly believe what she was hearing, or contain the joy that washed into her until then despairing soul. For she knew instinctively that Ryan would not lie about something as serious as marriage and children. Love, yes; he might lie about that. But not the rest.

It came to her suddenly that he must know about her falling in love with him. Alison would have told him something. Dear, romantic-minded Alison who could not resist a happy ending, no matter how unlikely the couple.

'Did Alison tell you that I loved you?' she choked out.

'She said she thought you did,' he admitted. 'But I would have come today even if she hadn't said anything.'

Somehow, his knowing that she loved him momentarily burst her bubble of happiness. It brought doubts as well. Laura needed more understanding of his dramatic change of heart before she could blindly say yes to his amazing proposal. She needed the comfort of knowledge.

'But you said you would never fall in love, or get married and have children,' she pointed out.

'That was before I met you, Laura.'

'No, you said it *after* you met me. You said it more than once. You warned me.'

'I didn't realise then that I would fall in love with you. I didn't know what falling in love felt like. I didn't think I was capable of it.'

'But *why* would you think that? Everyone is capable of love.'

'I know that now. But till I met you I refused to let it into my life.'

'You have to tell me why, Ryan. You have to make me understand. I do love you, more than I ever thought possible. But I can't marry you unless I know why you felt like that.'

He sighed, then nodded. 'You're right; I know you're right. It's just so damned hard to talk about it, that's all.'

'If you truly love me, Ryan, then you have to trust me with your past. I promise I will never tell another living soul. Not Alison. Not anyone.'

Laura could see the difficulty he was still having, opening up to her. What terrible trauma had he endured as a child, she wondered, that would make him retreat from emotion as he had? She hated to think he might have been abused in some way, but what else could it be?

'I love you,' she repeated. 'I will always love you, no matter what you tell me.'

He still didn't speak so she just sat there and said nothing further. The long line of cars was making slow progress on their way back to the house, giving him enough time to decide whether to confide in her or not.

'My mother didn't die of cancer,' he said at last. 'She was murdered.'

Laura only just managed not to gasp in shock, for it was the last thing she was expecting.

'But not by any stranger,' he added in a rough, emotion-charged voice. 'By my father. Her *de facto* husband. The man she said she loved. The man who claimed *he* loved *her*, even as she lay battered to death at his feet.'

'Oh, Ryan…'

'I found her, you know, when I came home from school. Lying next to the kitchen table in a pool of blood.'

'Oh my God…'

'She'd cooked me a cake. It was still on the table. It was my twelfth birthday.'

Laura closed her eyes. Lord in heaven, no child should have to endure that. She'd thought she'd had it bad when her parents had been killed. But it had been an accident. They hadn't been murdered.

'He was sitting on the floor next to her, crying. I...I...'

When it was obvious he could not go on, Laura reached over and placed her hand gently over his, which was suddenly gripping the wheel like a drowning man holding on to a piece of flotsam. 'You don't have to tell me any more right now. I can see you had good reasons to reject love and marriage and fatherhood. We'll talk about it later.' *Much* later.

Ryan shook his head. 'No, I want to tell you now. I want you to understand. It had been going on for years—the violence. The beatings. Not me, just Mum. The only times he hit me were when I tried to protect her. Even then he would just push me aside. He was insanely jealous of her. Wouldn't let her go to work, wouldn't let her leave the house or have any more babies. When she became pregnant once—I think I was about seven—he accused her of having an affair, then he punched her in the stomach over and over till she miscarried.'

'Oh my God! That's appalling, Ryan. But didn't people know what was going on? Your neighbours? Your grandparents?'

'Domestic violence was very common where we lived. A lot of the men were unemployed. My father did work occasionally, but he was unreliable. He was a drunk, you see. We mostly lived on welfare, in a housing-commission place which should have been condemned.

'As for relatives, Dad refused to have anything to do with any relatives, especially Mum's. Though I knew my Mum's mother was alive. Mum told me her name and where she lived and said if anything ever happened to her that I was to go to my grandmother's place. She even hid some money in a secret place which she called my escape money. Many times I thought about taking it and just going, but how could I leave her to him? I begged her to come with me but she wouldn't. She said she loved him. I could never understand that. It made no sense to me.'

'I don't think she loved him at all by then, Ryan. She was

simply scared to death of him. I had a battered wife as a client once. She stabbed her husband in the end.'

'I thought about killing my father several times. I wish I had.'

'I can imagine. So what happened to him? I presume he was arrested for murder?'

'He pleaded guilty and got twenty years. But he was bashed to death a few months later in jail. It seems the other prisoners don't take kindly to wife killers.'

'I can understand that. And I can understand you now, Ryan.' Very much so, the poor darling. It was no wonder he never wanted to talk about the past, and no wonder he'd rejected love for so long. 'I really appreciate your confiding in me, but you know what? I think we've done enough talking about the past for today. I would much prefer to talk about the future.'

He glanced over at her and smiled. 'A woman after my own heart.'

'Oh yes,' she said, smiling back at him. 'I *am* after your heart.'

'You already have it, my love.'

Her own heart turned over. 'I'm still coming to terms with that.'

'You're not the only one. When I realised I loved you, I wasn't sure what to do because I thought you would never love me back. I mean, how could you possibly love such a selfish, self-centred, screwed-up individual like me?'

Laura groaned. 'I hated myself afterwards for saying that, because I don't think that at all. I think you're a fine man, decent and kind, with a warm, loving soul. Look at the way you talked about grandmothers at the service just now. It was beautiful, the words you said.'

Ryan's heart squeezed tight at her sweet compliments. 'Can I take it, then, that you *will* marry me?'

Her eyes shone as she looked over at him. 'Whenever and wherever you would like.'

'How about first thing in the New Year, up here in Jane's favourite chapel?'

Laura smiled. 'Sounds like a good idea to me.'

EPILOGUE

'I CHRISTEN you Marisa Jane Alison Armstrong,' the minister said, the same minister who'd pronounced Ryan and Laura man and wife eleven months earlier in the same church.

'She was so good,' Alison complimented Laura when she handed the baby back after the ceremony. 'Not a peep out of her, not even when the holy water was poured over her forehead.'

'She loves water,' Ryan said proudly. 'I've got her booked in for swimming lessons when she turns six months.'

Alison and Laura exchanged amused glances.

'And when is she going to start playing soccer?' Alison's husband asked with a twinkle in his eye.

'Never too soon, Pete,' Ryan replied. 'Four or five is a good age. That way she can be a striker and not a boring old goalkeeper.'

'A striker,' Laura murmured, rolling her eyes and shaking her head. She still found it hard to believe just what a besotted father Ryan had become. As soon as he had found out she was pregnant, he'd turned into a real mother hen. When she'd suffered from morning sickness during her early weeks, he'd insisted she stop applying for new jobs and take it easy at home, a move which hadn't entirely displeased her; her own priorities had changed by then. But *she'd* insisted she at least remain *his* lawyer, to keep her hand in. She loved coming to his office every Friday afternoon at three p.m., though nowadays she was dressed a little more stylishly. Sometimes they didn't get much work done.

'Everyone back to the house for drinks,' Cynthia chimed in.

'Everyone' was not a large group, the only guests at the christening being Alison and Peter, along with Lisa and Shane, Bill and Cynthia. Their wedding had been a much larger affair with lots of Ryan's old friends and clients attending, followed by a slap-up reception at a local five-star resort.

But they'd decided to keep the christening much more private and personal. Alison's two children were being minded by their grandparents for a couple of days, giving Alison and Peter the opportunity for that romantic getaway that they had been meaning to have all year and not got around to. Ryan had booked them into the same five-star resort they'd spent *their* wedding night in—his treat, he insisted. The four of them had become close friends during the last year, with Ryan liking Peter's easy-going nature a great deal.

'I suggest you follow me,' Ryan told Peter as they made their way to where their cars were parked. 'It can be a bit tricky finding Bill and Cynthia's place. I'll drive slowly so you won't have any trouble keeping up.'

Ryan still took his time loading their precious cargo into the carry-cot in the back of his new family-friendly car, a four-door Lexus which he'd bought a few months back. His willingness to trade in his much-loved BMW had displayed to Laura more than anything he said just how much it meant to him to become a father. And how serious he was taking the role.

'They're a nice couple,' Ryan said when they were finally on their way. 'But their kids can be murder. I feel sorry for their grandparents.'

'Sibling rivalry,' Laura said, thinking of how she'd been with Shane, who'd been a kind of sibling to her.

'Spoilt, more like it,' Ryan said dryly. 'Have you seen how many toys they've got?'

'I don't think you can talk,' Laura pointed out. 'I can see

already that you're going to give Marisa everything her little heart desires.'

'Oh, no I won't. She's going to learn the value of money. And of hard work.'

Laura groaned. 'You're not going to be one of those fathers, are you?'

'And what kind is that, madam?'

'Pushy. And bossy. And controlling.'

'Absolutely not! I hate controlling people.'

Laura laughed, then so did Ryan. 'You're right. I am a bit controlling. But I can change. I've changed a lot already.'

'You have indeed,' Laura said with warmth and love in her voice.

Ryan glanced over at his beautiful wife and smiled. 'I have one suggestion to make which might eliminate my spoiling our little princess back there.'

'Do tell.'

'We could have another baby.'

'So soon?'

'Why wait? Life is short, Laura.'

For a split second, Laura thought of her gran. And then she nodded. 'You're right. Another baby would be a good idea.'

'All my ideas are good.'

'Oh Ryan,' she said with a soft laugh. 'You are incorrigibly arrogant. But that's all right. I love you just the same.'

'That is why I love *you* so much, my darling.'

'Oh?'

'Because you love me just the same.'

* * * * *

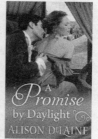

The Anointing Breaks the Yoke

Pearl Coleman

New Wine Press

New Wine Press
PO Box 17
Chichester
West Sussex PO20 6YB
England

Unless otherwise stated all Bible quotations are from the Authorised Version.

Amplified Bible © Copyright 1965 Zondervan Publishing House, Grand Rapids, Michigan MI 49506, USA.

NKJV New King James Version of the Bible. Copyright © 1983 Thomas Nelson, Inc.

ISBN: 1 874367 14 0

Typeset by CRB (Drayton) Typesetting Services, Norwich
Printed in England by Clays Ltd, St Ives plc

Dedication

This book is dedicated to John Brown and Dan Cippico, two men of God from whom I received such brotherly love and encouragement.

Pearl Coleman

Contents

Acknowledgements

My deep and abiding love go to the team and intercessors of 'City of God Ministries' for their faithfulness. I never cease to give thanks to the Lord for them all. My love and warmest thanks to Emma who helped me over a hurdle with secretarial work at a time of severe illness.

This book was written during six weeks of severe debilitation, through the blessing and undergirding of the Holy Ghost. My love and appreciation go to Faith who was led by the Spirit to manuscript the book with such excellence in just fourteen days. At the greatest crisis in my life He was my Jehovah Jireh and I experienced servanthood all around me. Praise His Holy Name.

With all blessings and thanks,
In His love and service,

Pearl Coleman

Chapter 1

The Anointing

Following my return from a visit to Israel on 8th June 1992 and during a time of considerable infirmity, I set aside one hundred days to be before the Lord – simply fasting, praying and listening with listening ears as never before, and taking Holy Communion daily.

There was something my Father desperately wanted to communicate with me and it concerned the anointing. He wanted me to realise how golden and precious a treasure He had given me, and to know why in His mercy He had allowed me to retain it, and what in future could cause me to lose it. For by the Spirit He was saying to me:

> 'Now that you are finally listening to Me, to appreciate in detail your anointing for My purposes, any disobedience on your part will cause the anointing to diminish and even cease. Therefore, my daughter, I seek to cause you to treasure the anointing, for it is costly, but as it is written *"For unto whomsoever much is given, of him shall much be required; and to whom men have committed much, of him they shall ask the more."'* (Luke 12:48)

He went on to remind me that what I had asked for I had been given and I could not be released from it at my own whim! Read my first book *Go and Do Likewise* to

9

find out that I asked to be used in particular against witchcraft, freemasonry, and in healing the broken-hearted.

He showed me that the anointing is a pouring in and pouring out of His Spirit, and that if our response to His love is prayer, time with Him and paying attention to His Word for every situation, then the anointing is there when you are buying a tin of soup in the supermarket, just as it is when you are standing before the Body of Christ in ministry. Walking in the anointing is walking in the Spirit, it is listening with listening ears and casting aside the spirit of the fear of man, and not being intimidated by those who, for whatever reason, disapprove of your ministry.

My friend Ernest and I were visiting the Old Mill at Gomshall for lunch one day and I could not take my eyes off an American couple seated at a table the other side of the room with an Englishman. I did not want to be rude and stare but it was as though my vision was drawn to them as a pin is to a magnet. The American gentleman, who was very tall indeed, got up to examine a piece of antiquated agricultural equipment fastened to the wall, and I jokingly said: 'It's no good, you can't take it with you!'

He turned to me with the most beautiful smile on his face and we exchanged a few pleasantries before he returned to his seat. We met up again in the low-beamed boutique above the restaurant. The gentleman was having difficulty manoeuvering his head under the low beams and joked about it. I cannot recall my exact words but they were something like: 'Praise the Lord for your height and all the advantages it gives'.

There was a pause and his wife looked at me with her eyes shining. 'So you are . . . ' I never let her finish.

'I thought you were.'

In a moment all five of us were circled with arms around each others' shoulders praying in the Spirit. There was the anointing. I had not the slightest idea how many shoppers passed around us whilst we were praying in the Spirit, but I do know that what we felt was the very presence of His Spirit there in the unity and love of Christ Jesus. Afterwards we sat at a table outside in the courtyard and shared the Lord for well over another hour. These sorts of situations are continually arising in my life and I give Jesus all the glory for that.

To retain the anointing, sit under the anointing and do not remain where teaching or preaching is done in the flesh. If you cannot leave quietly, sit and pray in the Holy Spirit, who will lead you into all truth. Then come apart. Remember that those who would intimidate you not to pray for others or set the captives free spontaneously are operating under satanic control. Intimidation seeks to render you ineffective for Christ, then manipulate you into doing nothing, from which follows domination and control. And there is plenty of it about, believe me!

Those who intimidate are usually locked up in their own fears. They need deliverance and are blinded in part to this realisation, for many such are, alas, those who believe they are committed to Christ and doing His work! Upon whatever grounds, restraining those with a genuine heart to minister is not of the Lord, who prefers people to step out and be ready to make mistakes and be a fool for Jesus. I encourage all the babes added to my team to just get on with it. Some move fast, some are slower but none is stagnating. Stagnation leads to spiritual death, and indeed we know that when the physical body stagnates in any area of function, a disease state is produced. Stasis leads to disease.

The fruit and the gifts demonstrate the anointing. Those who receive from you under the anointing must be seen to bear fruit – and, believe me, this is so delightful to witness. It is such an encouragement to soldier on with the Sword of the Spirit. The anointing may fall upon you from another just as it transferred to Joshua upon the death of Moses (Joshua 1:1–5) and the mantle of Elijah passed to

11

Elisha (2 Kings 2:13). Let the anointing of the anointed rub off on you!

How Do I Know if I Have the Anointing?

This is a question one is frequently asked. Please do not look for goose bumps, tinglings or the like. They could even be deceptions of the flesh!

My personal response to this question is that I have an awareness that I can do all things through the One who empowers me within (Philippians 4:13). That is the direct translation from the original Greek. Also the anointing will be manifest in the fruit.

The anointing produces power and conviction; it is defined by the enabling or impartation of God's ability upon and through a totally yielded vessel. Like electricity the anointing can be stored and released at times of need.

If you have a heart for God and are desirous of servant-hood to the Body and to the unsaved, and you stick around the anointed, then expect to receive the anointing! I did!

In this hundred days I became deeply aware that everything I ever did in ministry depended upon the anointing which I could have to a greater or lesser degree. The anointing is a precious gift given to those really seeking God's face in servanthood. The anointing brings a repulsion of worldly pursuits – even things that were formerly enjoyed, pale into insignificance as priorities in life. You start to realise 'I do not mind if I never do that or go there again'.

I have been caused to go back to the time I was in the world and into the pursuits I enjoyed, ballroom dancing, opera, theatre, London theatre, local theatre, concerts, visiting stately homes, window shopping, driving to the coast at weekends, etc., etc. Ugh! Now I cannot visit a stately home without discerning all the occult, and what is the point of looking at things you have no intention of buying? It all seems such a waste of time compared to God's glory.

I look back quite shocked at what filled the empty spaces in my life. I know that as one grows spiritually and the Lord becomes a reality in omnipresence and omnipotence, there are no empty spaces to fill because He actually fills them! Praise the Lord!

Jesus said:

> 'The Spirit of the Lord is upon me, because he hath anointed me to preach the gospel to the poor; he hath sent me to heal the broken-hearted, to preach deliverance to the captives, and recovering of sight to the blind, to set at liberty them that are bruised. To preach the acceptable year of the Lord.'   (Luke 4:18–19)

There is the authority to preach the Gospel, to heal and set free in Jesus' name. It is also written that you have an unction i.e. an anointing to function,

> 'But ye have an unction from the Holy One, and ye know all things.'   (1 John 2:20)

Look at verse 27:

> 'But the anointing which ye have received of him abideth in you and ye need not that any man teach you; but as the same anointing teacheth you of all things and is truth, and is no lie, and even as it hath taught you, ye shall abide in him.'

There are those anointed for teaching, but you do not need a vicar or a pastor or Pearl Coleman, or anyone to teach you, for you have the master teacher, the Holy Spirit ever present. If you want Him to teach you He will.

Don't tell me you cannot memorise scriptures. You can if you wish to. In the worst crisis of ME He taught me all of James 1 in about one hour! I cried out 'I really want to learn this but I can't do it, my memory is awful, but You can teach me!' And He did!

John 3:34 tells us that those whom God has sent have the Spirit without measure; it is unlimited! The anointing is a *'well of water springing up unto eternal life'* (John 4:14).

If you desire the anointing, check out by the Spirit who influences you, who you associate with and your environment, e.g. where you sit and walk, who you spend time with. Do not sit under the law where traditions prevail, old rules and regulations are clung to and the Holy Spirit is quenched. We have to worship in Spirit and in truth, for *'it is the Spirit who gives life, the flesh profits nothing'* (John 6:63 NKJV). So if the Spirit gives life, churches not operating in the spirit are **dead**. What is dead cannot impart life or restoration to the perishing.

Ask yourself this question and be honest with the reply; be before God when you respond: Have you travelled to church and back X number of years, to arrive home thinking, 'So what!' Have you felt unfed, or as it used to say on the buses during the war 'Is your journey really necessary?' If this is so, come apart and seek God's face in your closet. Make your Sabbath holy by reading the Word, singing a psalm or song to Him in your private place. Fall down on your face and worship Him and you will find that you will *'be transformed by the renewing of your mind'* (Romans 12:2). Pray for Israel. Then have a day of peace and tranquillity. Get some fresh air, walk His glorious countryside praying in the Spirit. If you are in town, get out of it for a while, or find a public garden, square or green space and commune with Him there, or go home and put on some good teaching tapes. These are only ideas.

I know many people being called apart to do just this. In a few months they have usually read at least the whole of the New Testament, the Psalms and the Proverbs – and started to use a concordance.

I love to dance before the Lord at home. I go from room to room leaping about with pure joy. I sing love songs to Him in the Spirit. Remember, *'where the Spirit of the Lord is, there is liberty'* (2 Corinthians 3:17). Truly if there is no liberty to flow spontaneously in the Spirit in your church you must be inclined to doubt the presence of the Holy Spirit, and if He is quenched – all is null and void and of the flesh.

Seek for holiness, for you cannot be an evangelist without the anointing of holiness, which is the fear, awe and reverence of God. We desperately need the authority only holiness will give us and we need the compassion of Jesus for others. We do not need sympathy. Sympathy agrees with your dilemma or situation or sickness – compassion does something about it. Love with the heart of Jesus.

Do not preach and teach unless you can lead people on into healing and deliverance. One follows the other automatically. Apostles and prophets need the anointing on the Word and spiritual revelation from the Word. They need to spend real time with God because He will not reveal His mysteries to those who are only prepared to give Him fleeting attention. Please ask yourself 'Am I in the right place for my ministry?' because if you are not it is a very serious thing. If the anointing God has given you is being stifled by a pastor with a spirit of fear, or you are sitting in an unbelieving church, you must ask God if He wants you to stay there. God may want to move you on. Do not remain where you should not be. Be courageous – *'for God has not given us a spirit of fear but of power, and of love, and a sound mind'*.

I know of an increasing number of holy people who are being led out of churches where the Spirit is not moving (Revelation 18:4). A common factor is that they have remained there for some years because of a dozen or so really lovely people they have been praying with for change. It's tough but God does not want you staying for lovely people, but for Him. And you will not, I assure you, lose such fellowship through leaving.

15

Let me share this true story. A beautiful lady, infirm for many years, received treatment for Candidosis at the Clinic two years ago. Since following a new diet, she has found that her brain has cleared and she has become very healthy and positive in outlook. She started to use my tape library. It has an abundance of tapes by Lance Lambert, Derek Prince, Bill Subritzky, Johannes Facius and others. In a short time she bought a concordance and an Authorised Version Bible plus an Amplified Bible as well and got stuck into the Word, following guidance from her tape teachers. If they said 'Do a study on wisdom', or 'do a study on stiff necks' etc., she obeyed, and learned much. Then she was called upon by her church to vote on the finances for the re-arrangement of the pews and an extension to the church building. The congregation were told to pray and ask God how they should vote. By this time she had had an extension built on her own home to have a sanctuary to house all she was collecting and where she could be quiet and pray without interruption or interference from the children, and study the Word of God. She got before the Lord from about 10 a.m. to 3 p.m. daily and could not get an answer on how to vote. So she fasted and still no answer came. So she called out to God and said: 'Lord you are *not* telling me how to vote and I will not leave this place until you do, however inconvenient.' As quick as a flash the reply came:

'I am not telling you because you are not going to be there. Leave.' In common with many of us she could not believe that the Lord would take her out without telling her where to go! Neither can her Vicar! What God has told her to do is to continually watch and pray, especially for Israel, and keep on sending parcels for the immigrants.

Frankly she is blossoming into a sensitive woman of the Word. Now this is absolutely true and what is more her resistant-to-the-gospel spouse is coming into the Kingdom. Hallelujah!

I share with many that the Bride of Christ will go underground in the End Times. I have seen beautiful men and women of God lent by Him to churches for a season and removed by Him when what He had sent them in for and with, was refused or ignored.

RELIGION = NO CHANGE – remember that.

Be a breath of fresh air to all you meet and stir stagnant waters wherever you go, but expect the smell which can initially result!! Get a team around you who are in unity and prayed up, and enjoy and move in a corporate anointing. The anointing is also for the assembly, be it large or small. The anointing also abides in you for any moment of need.

Exhort and encourage each other. Love builds up – it does not tear down. Watch out for 'slaying in the spirit' counterfeited by Satan! The devil will put people down so they cannot get free! When you minister under the anointing manifestations in themselves do not count, so do not seek them! There may indeed be many. I've had both, none or many, and I now do not mind which it is as long as I am aware of the anointing. Be accountable always to God first. Do not 'possess' the ministry God has given you. Be ready to loose it and let it go. Be ready for God to change your ministry and receive the blessing of fresh anointing for obedience. This happened to me recently.

I received in the closet that He wanted to do a new thing in me. Then I received an unexpected letter from a pastor with a prophetic ministry. Then three men of God of three different nationalities arrived one Clinic day quite unexpectedly. They prayed and prophesied over me. I knew it was from God. I was also told in the prophecy 'do not be tempted my daughter, when confronted with a certain situation, to deal with it as you have formerly done. Do not despise what you have done in the past because all that you have done and know I have taught you. But I am moving you on in a new direction to a higher place. Listen to me and I will tell you each time what to do. Your

17

confidence will be in the authority of the anointing I have given you.' I heeded this and I have had my spiritual ears really pinned back. No wonder the Lord gave me a new ear drum in Israel!

I have been astonished at the brevity and simplicity of recent ministry. I praise God that I have seen fruit of healing and deliverance as never before – and it is all less intense and much quieter and quicker. Yes, I did have such times of brevity in the past, but now it all seems so quickly over. Praise the Lord – it has to be, for the queues of God's hurting ones grow longer and longer.

We have an infirm Church! I am feeling in my Spirit that generally speaking for the most part God wants us to stop making a meal of things and to get on with it, to cut away all the frills and trappings, the pomp and ceremony, the focal points in Churches and Fellowships, and to get back to the focal point of our services being Jesus Christ, and the leader of the service being the Holy Spirit.

If one day you arrived and the musicians had not got any songs prepared and the pastor had not received a word to teach on – would you be shocked? Or would you be delighted and get on your face and worship Him in Spirit and in truth, or bask in the stillness listening for the Word? I've been in a church in Penang where that happened. What followed was dynamic. It certainly changed my life.

Do be careful if you are ministering, to take your own musicians or make yourself familiar with the players. Music will bring the anointing that is biblical, but crash, bang, wallop and beat drives the Spirit away. If you have ever listened to a group called 'Wellspring' you will know what the anointing on musicians is – but alas many groups in churches actually quench the Holy Spirit through copying secular decibels.

Do you *really* believe you have an anointing from God to get on and obey the Great Commission and be of service to your fellowship or church? Do you have to sit trembling and frustrated trying not to see the sick needing

18

the Word you have been given, and to ignore the demons of grief, fear and infirmity manifesting in the Body? Do you receive a Word and are fearful of bringing it? Do you long to dance to the Lord surrendering all your members to him in worship but feel someone will think 'there he (or she) goes again, showing off?' If this is you, you need to liberate yourself in Jesus' name. I have lost count of how many times beautiful Christians stifled in churches operating under manipulation and control have, in pouring out their hearts to me, said those very things. And yes, I know, because I've been there, I know that feeling and what is more, if you churn and do not make yourself available unto the Lord, and you go on ignoring these yearnings in the Spirit then **you may become sick**. Please hear what I am saying. The anointing is a pouring in and a pouring out of what God has given. You need to discharge it.

In the *physical*, if patients do not discharge the static electricity from their bodies they can get sick, not only physically but mentally. The *spiritual* discharge of the anointing is essential to your wellbeing. Usually it is a gradual process. God's people start to feel weepy, especially in church. They often want to cry, and may feel a sort of deep grief rising inside them, sometimes accompanied by increasing malaise, lack of energy, weakness and exhaustion. Then real pains can come, vague at first, then persistent.

On page 110 of my second book *Fruit Abiding in the Vine* in chapter 23 *Hindrances and Failure to Walk in Deliverance* I list the reasons for this. No. 10 says 'Being part of a larger battle requiring corporate action. People made ill by wrong or strife in churches.' That was something I learned about some ten years ago from the teachings of Derek Prince. Many of my Christian patients actually have an illness, a very real illness in their physical bodies or minds which is rooted in rejection, crushing criticism, or suspicion of them in churches. Quite often these sad and distraught people have the pastor or elders saying to them 'And what do you think the Lord is saying to you in all this?' What he should be saying is 'Am I responsible for the condition of this member of my flock?'

Shepherds lead the flock, they do not push them from behind. Shepherds feed their sheep, they do not starve them, but lead them to green pastures. *'Woe be unto the pastors'* (Jeremiah 23:1). Some versions say *'Woe to the shepherds.'* Read Ezekiel Chapter 34 NKJV, especially verse 4: *'The weak you have not strengthened, nor have you healed those who were sick, nor bound up the broken, nor brought back what was driven away, nor sought what was lost, but with force and cruelty you have ruled them.'* This chapter is actually headed 'Irresponsible Shepherds', and don't say this was just for Israel!!! (Jeremiah 8:11). *'For they have healed the hurt of the daughter of my people slightly, saying, peace, peace, where there is no peace.'* In the Amplified version it reads *'lightly and slightly.'*

There are a lot of shepherds, alas, bidding their sheep goodbye at the end of the Sunday service with a smile and a 'bless you', when with any discernment they would see the blood pouring out of the wounds, and the sores of their festering sheep!

Pastors need to take responsibility for the health of their sheep. The warnings in the Scriptures are true!

Chapter 2

The Wearing Out of the Saints

How does it happen? Pressure – including pressures to minister. Long private sessions are to be a thing of the past unless the Holy Spirit directs and I don't minister now unless I am specifically directed to do so. This rules out any doublemindedness and the desire to let the feeling that you are sorry for people determine what you actually do.

Yes, there are people who battle not to take God's 'NO' for an answer, who will implore, plead, even threaten! But 'NO' means 'NO', if Jesus is to be glorified and the spirit of the fear of man not entertained. That 'NO' may well mean there is no repentance, or the person is quite unready for deliverance for some other reason where the Spirit must convict. So often I experience that those who accept that it is not God's timing, or the wish of the Holy Spirit to minister and exhibit patience and acceptance, quickly receive ministry in a very unexpected way which amazes both them and me.

During my last visit to Penang, the Church prophet, a man given to infrequent prophecy, blessed me for the second time. The prophecy included a caution that God wanted me to seek Him only and not the advice of men, and to rely only on the Holy Spirit. Time and again I have seen that this direction by the Spirit was of lasting value and spiritual reality, because even the most mighty men

21

and women of God, and also myself of course, have a blind spot, a chink in our armour, whereas the counsel of the Holy Spirit reigns supreme.

On some really very serious issues in my life I have received counsel from men and women whom I really esteem in Christ Jesus, and discovered later to my horror it was wrong counsel. I am not alone in this experience! I have also found that a jewel of wisdom and counsel and might, can come from someone who appears to be a very insignificant member of the Body. I should say too, that I have received Godly counsel from the very poor and meek. We ignore the supreme counsel of the Holy Spirit at our peril. This is not to be critical, neither is it to judge, but it is an alarm bell to trust and lean entirely on the Father,

> 'For cursed be the man that trusteth in man and maketh flesh his arm.' (Jeremiah 17:5)

I now cut myself off daily from all binding and soul prayer, that is people praying in the flesh as to what they feel I should do. It is quite a release! The Lord also is inclined, I find, to remove people from your path who you may love dearly but who are subtly blocking your ministry because of idolatry. One thing is for sure, God does not allow *me* any idols. The very moment I get to the point of idolising someone, they are whisked out of the way. It can be very painful. He is a jealous God! Also I do not want anyone idolising me, thank you, because I am bound to fall off the pedestal. Love me by all means, but accept that I am not flawless, that I do not have all the answers, and if I do not know – expect me to say so, and do not be disappointed.

'Can you get me a word, sister?' It is a common cry.

I tend to respond, 'No, you get one for yourself!'

Now that I have explained how the Lord has spoken to me about the anointing, let me tell how I believe it came about.

In my weariness I had been looking at the scripture which tells us that we shall do greater things than Jesus because He was going to the Father. I thought it such arrogance, that I should think I could do anything greater than the Lord Jesus, and yet that is what the Word says.

> *'Verily, verily, I say unto you, He that believeth on me, the works that I do shall he do also; and greater works than these shall he do; because I go unto my Father.'*
> (John 14:12 NIV)

In recent months, I suppose I've had a faith lift because I believed this scripture with all of my heart. In those first hundred days at the Holy Communion I told Him straight: 'Now I'll not settle for less than the greater things. Oh God! Let my shadow fall on people and heal them. Let me see healings I have never seen before. I want it all!'

I am tugging at the hem of His garment and I will not let go until I get what I want. I do not care how long it takes but I am serious. I was further convicted by Ephesians 3:20 which tells us that *'God is able to do exceeding abundantly above all that we ask or think according to the power that works in us.'*

I believe that power is the anointing, the unction to function.

I know too that we do not win anything through the dynamism of our own personalities, but through our availability unto the Lord as a follower of Christ willing to be obedient to God's calling on our lives.

> *'For we are to God the aroma of Christ among those who are being saved and those who are perishing.*
> *'To the one we are the smell of death; to the other, the fragrance of life. And who is equal to such a task?'*
> (2 Corinthians 2:15–16 NIV)

I want with all my heart to be equal to the task and I

know full well that the whole key is abiding in Christ. Abiding means obedience, faithfulness, trusting, loving and listening intently to what the Holy Spirit is saying. I am also convicted that there is very little time to get my act together! So little time, so little time!

It is in the light of this revelation, that in this third book I share with you ministry experiences only made possible by the anointing which abides within. I thank those of you who have sent so many appreciative letters, and also for your prayers and intercession.

Just a word of warning on prophecy. I have been overwhelmed with prophecy for decades. Always check it out. I have a rule now. I check it out in prayer. If I get a 'No' from the Holy Spirit then the prophecy is scrapped, forgotten. This usually disposes of 90 per cent of what I am given. If I am not certain 'Yes' or 'No' I type them out and look at them four years later. If I see that things have come or are coming to pass I keep them. I have in all six prophecies given since 1987 which are totally accurate, and I have not had cause to dispose of them, but rather to trust those who brought them spontaneously and unexpectedly. There was one which for all its blessing and exhortation contained a warning of a deception that I may encounter – and it came to pass. When my Pastor was praying for me concerning this matter to be loosed from it, he said graciously,

'Don't condemn yourself, Pearl, we've all been there.'

That was the balm of Gilead to me, I can tell you, because he was in an excellent position to say 'I told you so.' I praise God that he did not do this.

Do watch out for pride, even pride that you cannot be deceived! It's no comfort at the time that someone illustrious, and in your opinion spiritually superior to yourself, has been deceived. It's lovely to see more men and women of God renouncing the doctrines they have publicly preached the world over. Praise God for Benny Hinn's admission of theological errors in his book *Good*

Morning Holy Spirit. In February 1992 European Christian Books time journal, he's reported as saying 'Brother, I am teachable.' Bless him, bless him Lord, we all need to cry out for teachable spirits!

Isn't it wonderful to recall afresh daily that if we do stray, forgiveness is only the prayer of heartfelt repentance away. I actually enjoy my Father's correction. Do you know why? Because when I receive it, confess and repent of blindness or being slow to obey or whatever, He always gives me a reward. I always get a prize and I love it. Have you ever given your child a reward for being good? Do you know, if you will really become acquainted spiritually with your Father in heaven you may expect blessings. Abba, Father!

It is my experience from treating thousands of sick members of the Body of Christ that there is a subtle wearing out of the saints caused not by Satan and his cohorts but by the persecution of Christians by each other. Some seek to block the ministry of others by the quenching of the Spirit. 1 Thessalonians 5:19 states quite clearly *'Quench not the Spirit.'* Verse 21 goes on to say:

> *'Prove all things, hold fast that which is good.'*

1 John 4:1 exhorts us:

> *'Beloved, believe not every spirit, but try the spirits whether they are of God: because many false prophets are gone out into the world.'*

How can the Body, or anyone else for that matter, test a ministry of office in the gifts if it is not allowed to operate and be corrected if it is not in order?

Whatever happens we need to look at fruit, but quenching of the Spirit decrees that fruit is not allowed to bud and blossom. It is my finding, and I am not alone in my experience, that where the Spirit is being quenched in churches and fellowships, sickness and grief which results in infirmity can prevail in the Body. Many religious pastors are overly concerned that their congregations may go over the top if let off the restraint of legalistic worship. One can sympathise to some extent with the viewpoint when one sees the irreverence of some so-called worship in our churches, where our Holy God must be deafened by drums and rock beat rhythms. I know of one large church where everyone avoids the first three rows on the side of the church were the musicians group, and it is considered a penance for latecomers to sit there!

A real problem for us in leading people to Christ is where to send them to fellowship. Not having been through the system, and newly born-again through the non-religious presentation of Jesus, they are not expecting to enter a congregation where undoubted unholy restraint by intimidation is exercised. I see many sons and daughters of vicars who alas, cannot sit in the congregation of their own fathers for this reason, and are icily treated in their domestic situations as a result. Even more extraordinarily, I have patients who have never been able to talk about Jesus to their fathers in clerical office.

Any pastor worth his flock should surely be prepared to allow the lambs to gambol and sing in the Spirit. He can always stretch out his crook and yank them in if there is disorder. Since most young people get born again and receive the gift of tongues quickly and are told that it is the perfect way of communicating with their Father, they are very disappointed to find this gift not used in fellowship, and not infrequently let this precious gift stagnate as a result. I praise God that when I received the gift of tongues I was attending an Anglican Church worshipping in Spirit and in truth. I recall how I used to love the singing in the Spirit, the graceful dancing and the prophesying in tongues with the interpretation following. I was very excited indeed as I used to wait with eyes shut tight and prayerful lips for the interpretation to come, whilst marvelling at this wonderful new life in the church.

I had attended Church since the age of three and this first experience came in my early forties. Keep your eyes open for churches where the Body meets an hour before the service to pray in the Word in the Spirit.

Stifling of the flock in this area of using the gifts amounts to accusation and distrust of the Body. It raises suspicions in the minds of the innocent. It causes dis-ease in the congregation and corporate grief.

In 1991 at the Ellel Grange Brighton Conference on Healing and Deliverance, Bill Subritzky said from the platform: 'Those who accuse those under the anointing of the Holy Spirit as having power from another source are guilty of blasphemy against the Holy Spirit.' Isn't that a heart cry for wisdom?

So saints, if you are sick because your shepherd feels your anointing is of the flesh and your indwelling Spirit is being quenched – move out and on! Remember, His grace is sufficient.

Chapter 3

Response to
FRUIT ABIDING IN THE VINE

In my second book *Fruit Abiding in the Vine*, I stated in Chapter 15 that I was writing in response to the deluge of mail I had received when my first book on the ministry of deliverance *Go and Do Likewise,* was published in 1990. We experienced a great deal of problems in the preparation of the manuscript of the second book. Firstly, the computer operator complained that the chapters on deliverance ministry kept being wiped off, or came out muddled. Then the printer found that the binding machine chewed up books and we lost 15 per cent of the print run. In over 50 years of printing millions of books they had never had such a bad problem before! We came to the conclusion that it had to be demonic activity!

In his foreword to the second book, Bill Subritzky said that it would minister to tens of thousands. That foreword has been almost prophetic! Yet again there has been such a continuous stream of correspondence, often comprising ten A4 sheets of small handwriting to decipher, and telephone calls at every conceivable hour, that I have had to protect myself from intrusion into my very existence.

I have, of course, among my spiritual mentors, many men with long years of experience in deliverance ministry, who at the onset gave me much counsel of wisdom and might, indicating that I would need to protect myself from such pressures and demands if I were to remain fragrant and anointed for His purposes. I found myself one Sunday after church, literally flat out with exhaustion in my garden on a sunbed – a rare treat indeed for me – only to be confronted by a lady who actually walked round to waylay me on my own lawn. I knew then, that the time had come to take stock of this threatening situation. This lady had travelled on the off-chance from London, to see me about her spirit of gluttony!

I could relate many such incidents and have long ago seen why many mighty men of God make themselves unavailable unless they are actually teaching and ministering at conferences, and also protect themselves by disappearing as fast as they can afterwards! As one who in the past often felt that it was such a pity, I can see that it is a matter of self-preservation, to say the least! I do praise God for the response to my books, and bless those who have written in such detail about their particular agony. What I find less of a blessing is the huge pile of letters arriving without the courtesy of a stamped addressed envelope by which to respond to their twenty questions!

Readers of my other books may recall that the Lord caused me to yield the Clinic to Him in the spring of 1990. I had to close it and rely on Him for my supply – and then He gave me the Clinic back pressed down and running over with patients, who had to be filtered through on one day a week, since the Lord had charged and required me to take monies only on one day a week. Not for deliverance ministry of course! The remainder of the time was to be devoted to the ministry, and to the prayer time needed for such a calling. At one point it began to look as though what I did earn, once all the rising overheads were paid for, was going to be spent on stamps and secretarial expenses, to respond to those letters unaccompanied by stamped addressed envelopes! Also I used to receive requests such as 'Will you write and tell my friend about your testimony against homoeopathy, because she hasn't read your book?' There are no prizes for guessing my response to that one!

Seriously, though, I do sense a problem here for many Christians. Does the Holy Bible not say, *'He who sows sparingly will also reap sparingly, and he who sows bountifully will also reap bountifully?'* (2 Corinthians 9:6, NKJ). When I look and see how the Lord has blessed me in every direction, and daily loads me with more blessings (Psalm 68:19), I can only surmise that it is due to obedience to His Word. There is no other explanation. Naturally speaking it would be impossible to run and maintain the Clinic on earnings one day a week, were I not blessed by His provision. I am certain too that blessing the Jews as I was moved by His Spirit to do in January 1991, has in no small measure contributed to the fact that I continue to be more than solvent.

I do recommend the tapes by Derek Prince on 'The Christian and His Money' (Bromley, 6.10.88). Derek discusses the principles of right giving and the fact that money is important to Christians. He tells us that money is part of our worship and, on another cassette, that God does not need our loose change. He always says that, 'When God touches your heart He invariably touches your pocket!' I can truly say that it has been like that with me. I have always believed that our money is to be used for the Kingdom of God and that money saved in various accounts or building societies is so that we can sow the interest in the Kingdom. What else can it possibly be for? Nothing we have is our own – it is all on loan. So let us give cheerfully and generously. Praise the Lord! God loves a cheerful giver (2 Corinthians 9:7).

There is no doubt that everything goes up in cost all the time. Water, rates, gas, electricity and telephone bills are now exhorbitant. Car thefts and burglaries are causing increases in insurance. It was 34 per cent last year on cars, I am told, due to joyriding amongst other things. Yet in all this I have managed to keep my Medical Clinic fees the same now for four years, because of sensible economies and blessings from the Lord. For example, when I obeyed and reduced to a solitary Clinic day, He sent me by His Spirit voluntary staff who work here as a gift of time and labour for His work. I was able to cancel very expensive advertising bills, for the Lord sent people in droves by His Spirit. The hefty bills for maintenance of this old property have been miraculously met by love offerings, and in any event I always seem to be sent really excellent workmen who charge half the usual rates! So I can continually sense God's hand on all that happens here, and I am so grateful to Him and thank Him fervently for His manifold blessings and provision.

You know, our Father loves to be thanked – gratitude is prayer. Every time I drive through my gates I say from my heart:

> 'Thank you, Father, for the beautiful home and Clinic you have given me. Thank you for my beautiful garden and the privacy here in this noisy world. Thank you for my lovely car, my clean sheets, hot water and nourishing food. Thank you that I can just buy any Bible I want and read in it how all these blessings are received. Thank you for all the faithful men and women of God you have placed around me,' etc., etc.

Well, to get back to the mound of correspondence. I was most curious and interested to discover a particular pattern in so many of the heart cries. It concerned the suffering of patients with myalgic encephalomyelitis (ME), also known medically as post-viral fatigue syndrome (PVFS), and this is one of the matters that I have felt I should share with the Body of Christ at this time – in what I hope will be a much smaller book! Since I want my writing to be led by the Spirit under the anointing, I am open to having such plans changed or added to.

31

On page 258 of *Go and Do Likewise* I have appended a note which says, 'Since writing this book I have been delivered from the spirit of ME and I am healed. So has my receptionist, Praise God.' On page 144 her testimony is set out exactly as she wrote it, in the chapter on 'Examples of Release from the Curse', and I shall be referring to this case again in my analyses of ME patients.

When I ministered to her I confess I had absolutely no idea of the depths of her suffering and family miseries. She herself states that I was unaware that her own born-again General Practitioner had told her she had a spirit of infirmity. She was set free after a Clinic Teach-in, through a word of knowledge given to me so fast and very unexpectedly, following the removal of her pierced earrings. Her deliverance illustrated for me yet again that although people will beg you to pray against this or that, it is not glorifying to the Lord or effective unless one is directed by the Holy Spirit. Don't allow people to pressurise you into fleshly prayers! Offend man rather than the Holy Spirit.

Chapter 4

What is ME?

I will use the abbreviations for myalgic encephalomyelitis (ME) or post-viral fatigue syndrome (PVFS) in the forthcoming chapters of this book.

I believe I can do no better than to quote the Myalgic Encephalomyelitis Association for an accurate description of the illness. One can see that there is a real emphasis on the need to rest and rest and rest, and also not to feel guilty about resting. From my own experience a lot of patients, including myself, after the initial fever do not look at all ill because of the rest they are forced to take, and if you have been active, onlookers simply cannot appreciate the agony of the debility of hardly being able to walk at all. This association was set up in 1976 and received charitable status in 1980. It is run by a central committee of volunteers and organised locally into self-help groups. I will now quote from their leaflet, *Guidelines for Sufferers*. There is very little in this sensible and realistic advice I would not agree with, and I would confirm exacerbation of allergies, especially to grains and dairy products, in all ME patients.

What is ME?

'ME is a syndrome which develops, in the majority of those affected, after a virus infection. The patient fails to make his/her expected recovery owing to an abnormal immune response to the virus. The virus then persists in the muscle cell and probably the nervous tissue interfering with normal cell function and causing symptoms characteristic of ME. Usually the patient recalls a specific triggering infection but sometimes ME has a slow, insidious onset.

'The NHS and DHSS now recognise ME as a debilitating and distressing illness. However ME can be difficult to diagnose. Routine tests reveal little unusual but recent research has implicated enteroviruses in many of those tested. The glandular fever virus (EBV) has been demonstrated in some cases. There may be other viruses involved that have yet to be identified.

What are the Symptoms?

'Initially you may have a flu-like illness with respiratory or gastro-intestinal symptoms. There follows undue muscle fatiguability, exhaustion and a feeling of being generally very unwell. You may get muscle pain, headaches, nausea and bowel upset. Focusing of the eyes may be difficult and sleep pattern is often disturbed. Sweating, coldness of limbs and low body temperature are common. You might find it hard to concentrate, find the right words and memories. There can be distressing psychological effects and at times you may feel emotionally quite fragile.

'As the symptoms of ME resemble those of other debilitating illnesses your doctor will want to exclude other possible causes of your symptoms.

'Almost all sufferers describe conditions which increase their symptoms or cause setbacks, e.g. physical or mental stress, further infections, alcohol and extremes of temperature. A characteristic of ME is its fluctuating pattern with good and bad periods, symptoms also varying from one time of day to another.

Management of ME

'So far, there is no evidence that any particular treatment is widely effective but some things, together with time, increase the likelihood of spontaneous improvement.

'Early diagnosis is an important step not only in reducing stress for the sufferer and family, but in ensuring better disease management. Misdiagnosis can lead to wrong advice. Referral for active physiotherapy or "exercising yourself to better health" will probably leave you feeling worse and set you back.

'Sufficient rest especially in the early stages and during setbacks is advisable. On the other hand prolonged bed rest beyond the acute stage has its dangers since it is possible to become trapped in a vicious circle of immobility and weakness. Within these general guidelines you will need to determine your own levels of rest and activity by experiment and experience.

'Setbacks often follow on from sufferers doing too much, too soon, once they feel a little better. ME is particularly hard on children, those on their own and people with energetic temperaments who have to "accept" the illness with its limitations and adopt a pattern of life within those limits.

'Sometimes there are setbacks and improvements which cannot be easily explained but which are part of this naturally fluctuating disease process.

'Most sufferers in time do recover, some even after years of ill health. A small group remains chronically ill but continual deterioration in symptoms is not the normal pattern.

How Can You Help Yourself?

'Most people feel more fulfilled if they can positively contribute to their own health care. You may find the following helpful:

　　Read and understand what you can about ME. Learn

35

to pace and not overcommit yourself, recognising what your body tells you it can or cannot do. Avoid the temptation to "catch-up" on jobs just because you feel a little better. Try and find a balance between rest and exercise which works for you.

Avoid or think seriously about conditions or activities which make you feel worse. General anaesthetics, antibiotics and vaccinations, while sometimes necessary may increase symptoms in some sufferers in the short term. Avoid infections if you can but don't cut yourself off from others more than necessary (particularly important for children).

If you think you have developed sensitivity to some foods since becoming ill discuss this first of all with your doctor. Aim to maintain a balanced diet eating fresh rather than processed foods. Limit drinks or foods with additives.

If you are depressed or anxious don't keep it to yourself. Understanding and support from others, whether your family, fellow sufferers, friends or your doctor, helps in coping with ME. If you feel suicidal consult your doctor immediately. Counselling can often help and/or medication may be advised as a short term measure in treating depression.

Seek your doctor's advice for distressing and persistent symptoms such as insomnia or excessive pain. Complementary medicine may also help relieve some symptoms for some people. Unfortunately there are no clear guidelines on treatments since what can help one person may not help another.

Keep hopeful. For everybody there are now more reasons for optimism. Much has been achieved and we are learning more about ME all the time. Your Association is pursuing research to improve diagnosis, to test treatments and to find a cure for ME.'

Suicidal feelings are common in ME patients, and many

do actually commit suicide. In born-again Christians it is essential to call out the suicidal spirit and get the sufferer to proclaim Psalm 118:17:

> *'I shall not die but live and declare the works of the Lord.'*

Also Psalm 107:20:

> *'He sent His Word and healed them, and delivered them from their destructions.'*

Loss of independence and self-confidence is a real problem for sufferers and added to this, one has to cope with the disbelief amongst friends and family that the patient simply cannot snap out of it and do what they used to do. For those who have been used to entertaining this is such a blow. I know many find, as I did, that the thought of filling a kettle and hearing a car arrive unexpectedly at the house bringing someone expecting tea is enough to treble the symptoms of weakness – and fear. I shall be dealing with the attendant spirits in this disease later. Clare Francis, the valiant yachtswoman who made two single-handed crossings of the Atlantic as well as skippering a yacht in a round-the-world race, spoke of the total inability to convince friends that she was sick. In a report to the *Independent* newspaper Clare told reporter Penny Jackson how her characteristic strength militated against her – friends could not believe someone so capable was so helpless. She said, 'Because I was having so much sleep and eating healthy food I looked so blooming and it was impossible to convey even to close friends how ill I was.'

I recall being terribly hurt when a sister in Christ whom I loved dearly wrote to a brother in Christ saying, 'Have you noticed Pearl doesn't finish her sentences now?' as though it were demonic confusion. I have to say that Christian ME sufferers often take on board the spirit of the accuser of the brethren (Revelation 12:10). Yes indeed, a formerly dynamic personality, being able to take control or organise, really goes against the sufferers of ME.

Again, a most useful pamphlet has been issued by the ME Association on how to care for a sufferer, as follows:

How to Care for a Sufferer

'ME is an extremely variable illness which results from **not** recovering after a virus infection. It may have such features as extreme fatigue with slow recovery, disabling pains, confusion of thought and changeable moods. Although not terminal, it can be extremely debilitating, and great patience and understanding are needed from those who are caring for the sufferer.

'This leaflet has been prepared to help relatives or friends who are caring for a sufferer from ME.

The Problems

'The basic problems are the great muscle weakness, muscular pains and tenderness, lethargy and mental debility.

'All these are made very much worse by physical and mental overactivity and recovery is greatly prolonged.

'Any sufferers who have previously led normal active lives experience great distress in becoming dependent on others and losing the ability to direct their own lives as they would wish.

'There is generally a serious loss of self-confidence when this happens and consequently, a need of understanding support.

'ME can cause rapid mood swings. Symptoms can be bizarre and unpredictable.

'New infections and local or general anaesthesia can cause setbacks.

'At its worst, the illness can be very devastating and can cause the sufferers to become severely depressed.

'The immune system may in some cases become hyper-sensitive, and allergies and sensitivities may develop to various substances in the environment such as food or fumes, etc.

How to Help

'It is important that the sufferer can be assured of your belief and be confident of your support. A GP who is aware of the disorder and who is understanding is important, especially if he is able to liaise with the Association's medical advisers. A diagnosis of ME. is most important and to obtain a positive diagnosis reassures the sufferer and convinces the doubters that the disease process is organically determined. A diagnosis is also necessary if the DHSS are to be involved, especially if the illness prevents the sufferer being able to work and maintain an income or if further financial support is required in the form of supplementary benefits or sickness benefits of various types.

Loss of Independence

'Be very sensitive about the problems of becoming dependent on others. Respect the sufferer's individuality and avoid being patronising or inconsiderate.

Self-Confidence

'Build the sufferer's confidence as much as possible by such means as encouragement with maintaining personal appearance (hair, dress, etc).

'Include the patient in any decision-making as a full member of the family.

'Encourage any valid activities which would be within the patient's capability and would give a sense of achievement or useful helping.

Mood Swings

'Recognise these as part of the illness and help family and friends to see them in this light also. Try not to be impatient and be philosophic about unexpected changes of plans.

Further Infections

'Complete mental and physical rest are needed to help a patient recover from a further virus infection.

'Keep the patient's surroundings as cheerful and pleasant as possible and try to avoid any excessive noise or stress.

'Encourage the sufferer to take some fresh air in the garden or short trips further afield as soon as possible when enough strength and courage return. Such changes build the expectation of improvement and discourage brooding.

Depression

'Encourage the patient to talk about ME and relieve some frustration in this way, but also try to enlarge the sphere of thought and conversation.

'Visitors can be very welcome as good listeners. They also cheer the sufferer with their concern and lessen the sense of isolation.

'If the sufferer's depression does not lift, a great deal of patient encouragement will be needed.

'Do not be insensitively breezy and cheerful on one hand or tell the patient to get a better grip on things on the other.

'Do not denigrate any form of help the patient wishes to try. "Fringe medicines" may help, and the patient's wish to do something positive is very important in itself. (I would add – make sure they are not occult – Pearl.)

'Persistent, deepening depression should be treated with great care. Seek medical advice.

Allergies

'In observing the patient on a day to day basis, try to notice things which help or hinder recovery. Any substances which might be causing reactions should be avoided. These substances can be almost anything from food and drink to cleaning substances, toilet preparations or fumes from cars, gas, paint etc.'

Further information about the ME Association can be obtained from:

The Secretary,
ME Association,
Stanhope House,
High Street,
Stanford-le-Hope,
Essex, SS17 0HA

Tel: (0375) 642466

Chapter 5

How it all Began

The history of ME dates back to 1955, when it was first named 'Royal Free Disease'. It was given this label because the first recorded outbreak, which was written up in the British Medical Journal as 'mass hysteria' occurred at London's Royal Free Hospital. Many doctors and nurses suddenly succumbed to this unidentified viral infection, and endured prolonged ill health subsequent to the onset. This was often dismissed as neurotic – and indeed in some cases that definition has continued to distress such patients for many years.

Evidence has accumulated to show that patients do suffer genuine organic illness. The worst aspect is that previously energetic and lively people are reduced to a state in which they will often refer to themselves as the living dead, feeling like death warmed up, a walking corpse, a zombie or half dead, and so on. Readers will see why I mention this prior to looking at spiritual ramifications. Also, spiritually we accept in deliverance ministry that panic or mass hysteria in crowds, such as occurs at football stadiums and in tube stations resulting in tragedy, is simply the transference of a spirit of fear.

GP Dr Charles Shepherd, himself a sufferer, wrote an article for *Pulse* magazine answering ten questions he is often asked about 'a controversial and perplexing condition!' Part of this report follows.

Who Gets ME?

'Often previously fit adults, especially females in their late teens to their 30's.

'Long term sufferers often seem to have been conscientious, active individuals without previous emotional or psychiatric problems, who "soldier on" in the early stages of the illness, which seems to be an important factor in worsening the outcome.'

What Causes it?

'Possibly an immunological failure to deal with a particular viral infection. The risk factors may be multifactorial.'

What is the Pathogenesis?

'The hypothesis is that the virus persists in nerve, muscle and white blood cells, interfering with their normal function and causing the characteristic neuromuscular symptomatology.'

What are the Symptoms?

'Patients may recall a non-specific "triggering" infection with myalgia, lymphadenopathy, pyrexia, upper respiratory tract symptoms and occasionally a marked vertigo.

'The two key diagnostic features are muscle fatigue, which patients may describe as "tired, aching muscles which seem to wear out easily." This rapidly increases during physical exertion till the sufferer reaches a point of weakness/exhaustion. Myalgia and fasciculations may accompany the fatigue.

'Second, "encephalitic" features: patients lose concentration easily.'

Dr Shepherd mentions many symptoms suggesting more widespread involvement of the central nervous system, such as lack of co-ordination; I certainly used to walk into walls. Sensory disturbances, autonomic dysfunction, hot or cold sweats may occur, cold extremities and intolerance of heat or cold, fainting spells and tinnitus.

We know that patients experience a worsening of their conditions or indeed a relapse, when exposed to stress, infections, alcohol, temperature extremes and general anaesthetics. This includes dental injections for fillings or extractions.

So there is often a combination of distressing physical symptoms.

Dr Shepherd reports that in diagnosing ME he needs to take a detailed clinical history to exclude other causes. Clinical examination usually reveals no abnormality, and patients do not always present with exhaustion, although if even slightly exerted they may become exhausted.

Routine blood tests are not much use, but a search for antibodies indicating persisting enteroviral infection (e.g. coxsackie B) will support the diagnosis.

Like so many other doctors dealing with ME, Dr Shepherd feels that adequate rest in the early stages enables patients to recover more quickly, and some indeed fully. But there are alas, some patients who remain chronically unwell, and this may continue for many years.

We know that early and accurate diagnosis is of great benefit; with no explanation the sufferer may otherwise be labelled as neurotic or malingering, although this is less common in recent years.

Dr Shepherd states that 'There is no scientifically proven way of altering the course of the disease.'

Again, in this article it is stressed that patients should take adequate rest, especially in the early stages – and not exceed limits of physical or mental capacity too frequently, or to the point of exhaustion. Also changes in lifestyle are vital in cases of prolonged illness.

Mentioned for further reading by Dr Shepherd is 'Postviral Fatigue Syndrome. The Saga of Royal Free Disease,' by Dr Melvin Ramsay. Available from the ME Association.

With grateful acknowledgement to *Pulse* medical journal and Dr Charles Shepherd for permission to quote in part from *Pulse*, 22/29 August, 1987.

Chapter 6

Appointment in Jerusalem '92

I left for Israel on June 30th, 1992 suffering from complete burnout. I was travelling with Rufus Adu, a team member, and Marilyn, my personal intercessor for six years, in a party from Christian Friends of Israel. My mind was overloaded with questions I had been turning over for at least twelve months. The Shavuot Conference at the Hilton Hotel, Jerusalem, was to last four days, following which we were to have four days led by the Holy Spirit about what to do in Jerusalem. I should say that my sister in Christ was also exhausted, having spent several months nursing a relative with an acute condition needing much supervision. Marilyn happens to be a Gold Medallist SRN, which you will see is quite relevant.

A few weeks previously Marilyn had brought me a word constantly received for some time before she gave it. The word was 'professional Christianity'.

Now I cannot say this was a shock, but since I was overtaken by a computer, as marvellous and orderly as everything had been with so many neat forms printed for all occasions, numerous prayer sheets with pretty borders, and even the odd cartoon thrown in to bring a lighter side to the deliverance ministry God had involved me in for His purposes and glory, I had been asking myself: 'Is this what God wants of me? Or is it a time for change?'

The only problem has been that Satan made certain that

I never had the time really to pray this thing through! I became aware, as many in deliverance ministry do, that there is real danger of being swamped by the deluge of persons, all with very legitimate needs for healing and deliverance, so that one's own personal needs are constantly set aside, leaving one totally drained of energy and reserves.

Anyone who has read my books will know that the Lord spoke to me through Romans 15:1 some years ago. Only my closest friends know that six months ago, following an evening of praise and exhortation unto the Lord, I was very clearly given Mark 6:31 (New King James Version).

However, constantly overtaken by the events of the needs and despair of others, this command got shelved and I had grown more and more exhausted. I should say that it is only the fear of the Lord that had caused me to 'hang in there with the ministry', for I had long wanted none of it. But at every turn, in every place – restaurants, car parks, on trains and planes, in taxis and public places everywhere – God has caused people with needs to crop up.

I have always been an intercessor of sorts, and at the second Brighton Conference organised by Ellel Grange, I answered a call to be birthed into intercession and to drop the ministry of deliverance. God, however, had other ideas, and showed me very precisely that was not His intention. Also my Father made it plain that in the flesh I cannot set aside what He has anointed me for. This is not pride. I know that I was anointed for this ministry, and as readers of my books will have read, I determined it always as a vital part of the Great Commission.

Then I read in Mark 6:31–32 that Jesus spoke to the apostles, telling them to *'come aside to a deserted place and rest awhile, for there were many comings and goings, and they did not have time even to eat.'* I had a real witness in my spirit. I could look back on certainly eight years of burned, skipped or improperly digested meals, which have

47

not infrequently messed up my metabolism. This has made a mockery of the instructions I give my patients. Physician heal thyself!

In 1984 I was in intensive care through burnout after years of calamity and stress, and was told 'Pearl, there are no dead heroes,' when I protested that I could not afford to take time off from the Clinic. As a deserted wife I was battling to keep my home and the Clinic, and I was not at that time launched into deliverance ministry.

Anyway, I will not elaborate unduly. That I am foremost a servant of the Lord Jesus Christ, I pray none will doubt. Unfortunately I had also become a servant of the Post Office, the telephone and the computer with all its demonic entities. Suffice it to say that I have had a real yearning to break these bondages and still be effective, even more effective for Christ. I have long been in pursuit of holiness. Holiness fades into non-existence without a constant closet prayer life. Satan loves to snatch this away and will overburden you with time-wasting and harassing spirits, and folk who pressurise you in all directions to be at their service in preference to the Lord's.

This has now stopped! In common with many doing the same work I have stopped all private ministry, which takes up so much time and inclines the receivers to be self-centred and selfish. I am saying 'no' unless absolutely led by the Spirit to do otherwise. I have indeed done this for some two years where deliverance is concerned, though I have rarely refused to pray for people. The Lord has shown me that I am to go right back to the position where I wouldn't even go to the supermarket without checking it out with my Father.

My Father wants my eyes on Jesus – not on a team of helpers, not on postal duties, but on Him alone. He wants me yet again to rest, wait on Him and do only what he instructs, whether it offends or pleases. I have to stop and arrest forces which are trying to get me running around in circles, and walk straight ahead. The path is narrow but the way is to Him. His burden is easy and his yoke is light. I am to stop holding people up, and to hold myself up into the light and truth of His countenance.

David Noakes said long ago that he felt the Lord wanted me to 'teach many and minister to few', under the Moses principle. I have always believed this was of the Lord, but I have allowed myself to be pressurised into other directions. No More!

These are End Times, and there is little enough time to be obedient to the Lord in any event.

We have seen incredible fruit abiding in the vine from the Clinic and the ministry. I believe I am being pruned back for vigorous growth and luscious fruit, and I am having a healing time now with Jesus, just He and I alone. It is just how it was when I used to take daily Communion, before that precious time got squeezed out by so many other things.

The team as it formerly existed is changed, but those servants of Christ are still available if there is a need. We are back to being a united group – I may say big isn't always beautiful. We shall now have fellowship not only when we minister, but we shall meet simply to pray and share Jesus as the Holy Spirit leads, and to share what the Lord is teaching us. Most of the others are under similar pressures as myself, with business and family demands, and we are all aware of the need to pray for the peace of Jerusalem.

I am right now on a three-month sabbatical unless the Holy Spirit gives me a command. This does not mean I shall be idle, but I shall be working for Him, in the closet or wherever, and trusting that all those who intercede for me will continue to do so, and those who assist from time to time in financing work for the Kingdom will also continue to do so, knowing that all the frills have been cut away.

When I come into line my Father always does something good to bless me, and to instruct me clearly as to His purposes. He certainly blessed me and confirmed the ministry He anointed me for in Israel. I was blessed to receive ministry for myself upon arrival in Jerusalem. I was crying out for it. 'Emotional Rape' was a strong spirit which had to go in Jesus' name. A lot of transference of spirits which had gained entrance through exhaustion was dealt with. I know that Satan seeks to wear out the saints!

Upon arrival in Israel our hotel was not ready because we had an unexpectedly silky-smooth journey through Israeli customs. So we went to a beautiful hillside kibbutz for breakfast and met for prayer on the terrace afterwards.

I immediately noticed an elderly lady in agony with a finger which she kept shaking. She was clearly in distress and said she had not had the pain when she left home that evening. Her face was quite contorted. I believe it was a whitlow, and we know how such a septic finger at the nail rim can suddenly develop and swell up to abscess-like proportions so that it needs lancing.

I moved over to her and she proffered the finger. I took her hand and asked:

'Do you believe that Jesus can heal you?'

Her response was a brisk affirmation. I continued,

'Are you ready to receive your healing in Jesus' name right now?'

Again she said emphatically, 'Yes!'

'Be healed in Jesus' name,' I told her.

And she was. The pain and problem melted away and she testified to this fact. At the end of the trip she confirmed that she had remained well.

I believe in that small incident God spoke to me about a change in my ministry, which was to become quick and simple in the name of Jesus. But more of that later.

I went out to Israel resolute that I would not pray for, or minister to anyone. After about 24 hours in Jerusalem, the Lord made it very clear that I was to minister to a certain lady and she was mightily set free by the Lord Jesus. Likewise I was led to a gentleman whose head was constantly in a black cloud as I looked at him. He was from a far distant country and I was able by God's grace to bring the Word against a curse over his life since a young boy and direct him to freedom. Both of these encounters were quite exceptional and I regret that confidentiality makes it impossible to share, but Jesus gets the glory anyway.

We had another appointment in Jerusalem. During a worship time Rufus was given the vision of a very unusual red shirt with a stripe on it, a peculiar double stripe. Later, without telling us, he found the man in the shirt, who turned out to be part of the second Exodus, a Messianic Jew from the USA. Now unknown to Rufus, God had centred my attention on a Jewish gentleman who I could see was sold out to our Lord and very anointed. It was a large crowd – I would think it varied from 1,000 to 2,000 people at different meetings – yet I constantly stumbled over this man, and I was drawn to his devout worship. He seemed totally unaware of anything but Jesus.

When Rufus told me he would surreptitiously point out this man, it turned out to be the very one the Lord seemed to be indicating to me. Rufus had shared with him, and there was certainly a plight there through his obedience in returning to Israel. Rufus felt he should bless him financially, and had received in his spirit a sum. I was able to confirm the actual figure, but did not know at first if it was in pounds or shekels. The Lord sorted that out. Our two sums agreed in value, though Rufus was given the amount in pounds and I had it in shekels! I cannot divulge details, but we had a triple agreement and confirmation to pray for the man. He was with his wife, whom we had not seen at this point.

Rufus directed us to where they sat. After the evening session the Lord had given me a word. I had no idea what I was talking about, but gave it, after which the wife broke down sobbing and the man's eyes filled with tears. We immediately took authority over a spirit of grief and mourning and the lady was instantly set free by Jesus. The lady also suffered from asthma which clearly wasn't

51

demonic, which was why the Lord said to me as I prayed 'diet book'. Anyway, that was deliverance number three, brief and to the point. We left the conference room overjoyed in Jesus. Subsequently a beautiful letter from these beloved ones, told us that our obedience had opened the door to their abundance and that it was flowing in, and their financial problems had ended. Praise His Holy name!

Deliverance number four was on the seventh day in Israel. By this time I was really enjoying the reality of real prayer time and being obedient. I was still very weak indeed, but the Lord caused me to be suddenly strong for these occasions. I had to miss quite a few of the sessions with exhaustion, but I did not allow guilt or pressure to enter in, and really enjoyed the time waiting on the Lord in my room. On Sunday morning Marilyn went to Christchurch. Rufus stayed in his room to read the Word and to catch up on sleep.

It was a hectic schedule with three sessions daily, then the local warfare afterwards and some trips out. I decided to go down to the grass verge surrounding the pool. I should not have been amazed at the world gathered there, since it was the weekend of Shavuot (Feast of Pentecost), and a public holiday. I felt too tired to return to my room, and desperate for fresh air, I found a space and lay down with my Bible. After praying for about a quarter of an hour I raised my head to find a much larger space around me, so I put my head down and continued in inaudible prayer for another three quarters of an hour.

A few days previously I had occasion to ask Marilyn, my long term intercessor, 'Marilyn, are you afraid of me?'

It was quite a loaded question because I had been asking everyone close to me, especially those who work with me at the Clinic, or on the team, and those I have long fellowshipped with. This question of my boldness has come up again. Those who read my books will know that I have got fed up with being referred to as a 'strong woman'. I've always felt that if one is to be a leader one has to be strong, but God has melted me down certainly over the years, and this has been commented on by very many people, male and female. When it rears its head, which it hasn't for a couple of years, I always get bored with it. I discussed it with Rachel, my clinical assistant of some four years. She is a very tough former YWAM missionary, yet for all her organising ability she is really feminine. She said,

'Why is it that as soon as women organise and dovetail everything, and assume leadership roles, they are accused of domination or control? If nobody leads, nobody follows,' or words to that effect. I should say Rachel has had plenty of experience in this area in churches ruled by Jezebel spirits. Remember too, that Jezebel spirits are not confined to females!

Initially I was quite alarmed when Marilyn said,

'Well, yes I suppose I am a little, but then I am afraid of everyone and everything.' I was amazed, because we had ministered over six years against so much fear in precious Marilyn, a victim of incest, rape, torment, brutality, rejection and so much humiliation from her alcoholic father and schizophrenic mother who died of senile dementia. Marilyn had been a gold medal nursing sister and an air hostess, both par excellence. Her survival had been like mine, the reality of a miracle of the Lord.

She went on to explain how she was still fearful of folk in church, in shops, in the street, nervous in so many areas, fearful of giving offence. Thus I had been lifting her up in prayer on the grass that Sunday morning.

Then the Holy Spirit said,

'Call out the dead, all of them, and spirits of the walking dead, and cut her off from the angel of death.'

Now one of the speakers at the conference, a former surgeon, Dr James van Zyl, who laid down his profession for the Lord Jesus and was given a healing ministry and became a fisherman, had mentioned the angel of death. He explained how the angel was invited when a death sentence was spoken over a person. This happened to me when I was 30, when a hospital consultant told my former husband not to hope for my life as I was so deeply unconscious, with my son three months in utero, following a very definite suicide attempt, my third and last. The first was at eleven years old. The second was when I was fifteen with a broken heart. On all occasions I was deeply unconscious.

We also had explained to us that fear accompanies those troubled by the angel of death, fear of death and dying, but then multiplied fears can get on board as we know. I then recalled that as a small child, from birth to eleven years, I lived over an undertakers in a grotty flat. We were very poor and the seven of us lived in a very few rooms. I remember always being terrified in this house, and seeing things, because the private chapel was in the hall under the stairs! We had to pass the coffins to get to our rooms. I recall a particular coffin at the age of about seven years, which had the lid off for viewing, and our flat stank to high heaven of embalming fluid. I recall wiping disinfectant around all the cracks in the doors so the smell wouldn't get in. To make matters worse, when the gas went out we had to go downstairs to the hall to put a shilling into the meter. That night my parents were at the pub next door and the gas went out. We all sat terrified in the dark, too terrified to confront the body in the hall downstairs to get at the gas meter!

All this was given to me in Jerusalem, as I lay on the grass. I couldn't think why I was receiving all this. I'd had my ministry and I was cut off from the angel of death anyway.

Suddenly Marilyn appeared on the grass beside me.

'Marilyn', I said, 'did you handle many dead bodies as a nurse?' She groaned and told me gruesome stories of being called out at night when sister in a nursing home, to give mouth to mouth resuscitation in a loo where a lady had collapsed, of frequently having to lay out corpses quickly who had died upright, of a constant flow of corpses being wheeled to the mortuary, and of lining them up with others. She was also attendant in operating theatres where babies were being vacuum-suction aborted, and had the horror of disposing of foetuses.

What ample opportunity for transference of spirits in all that, I considered.

Marilyn was wanting to be cut off from several things anyway, and Rufus and I decided that we should minister to her before supper. I could sense a strong anointing in all my weakness. Marilyn had ministered in love to me, and now it was her turn to receive. We returned to our rooms, hot and sticky, to rest, wash and pray. Then we met in my room for ministry.

Marilyn is a very anointed handmaiden with a real appetite for being set apart with the Word. She has been such a faithful prayer warrior for me, bless her. I had quite a lot of repenting to do concerning Marilyn, because eighteen months ago I allowed myself to be cut off from her, and removed her from the team without any real explanation. She was dreadfully hurt, and I have been so ashamed because I had become controlled, though I did not realise it, by a lady from abroad. This is a long and costly story, but I have confessed and repented on my knees before God, and He forgave me, as precious Marilyn did. This same influence was connected with Silva Mind Control and Astral Projection, and all the team had to be cut off from it. Having cut Marilyn off from it in Jesus' mighty name, I cut her off from the angel of death.

I had been given a *'spirit of bondage again to fear.'* The Lord caused me to read Romans 8:15–17 and Galatians 5:1 over Marilyn before we started. Like me, Marilyn has a long history of infirmity, and this helps the angel of death to hang in there! I called out the spirit of bondage again to fear, and then, 'Every spirit of the dead and the walking dead, come out in the name of Jesus.'

To my utter horror, Marilyn, the most learned of all our

55

group, started to pray in the Spirit, and she would not stop. I looked at Rufus, and he was amazed. I kept stopping her. I put my arms around her shoulders and said, 'Marilyn, Marilyn, can you hear me? You must not pray in the Spirit, dear, you know that,' but off she would go. I sensed she could not hear me, and several times we had to go back to the beginning. We laid hands on her, almost in desperation, and bound every spirit of confusion, exhorting her to breathe out. She finally obeyed, and smashed down on the floor. But first she was suspended, bent backwards on her toes, like a bow. I was amazed she did not fall. Eventually she fell, her arms above her head, and I knelt beside her with the oil.

She was in real distress – there was something wrong with her ears and her jaw. I put my fingers in her ears and commanded the demon to leave. It left. As I looked at her jaw, I saw it being moved up as though to be tied up, as one quickly does to a corpse when the chin is tied up so the mouth does not fix open.

'Loose her and let her go!' I commanded. Her jaw was so odd and she was having a difficult time.

'What is it, Holy Spirit?' I asked.

'Rigor Mortis,' was the prompt reply.

'That's it, that's it,' I said, and commanded this spirit to leave in Jesus' name. Marilyn breathed it out hard, about three times. By this time I had anointed her forehead and ears. After the last breath she sprang to life, literally. With her arms above her head she was lifted to her feet as though raised from the dead. I spoke the words, 'Marilyn, come forth,' and just like Lazarus she came forth. As she got up she said she felt the grave clothes fall away and heard the words, 'Marilyn, come forth' in her spirit. Initially, I had also called out the spirits of the morgue, the coffin and the shroud. I had a picture of Lazarus being raised from the dead as she arose.

Now that's not all. The joy on Marilyn's face was real, such as I had never seen before. We got on our knees and wept with joy and praised His name. As I was on my knees I got the words, 'Royal Free Hospital,' and I felt the Holy Spirit was telling me that ME is, or is linked to, the angel of death. It almost blew my mind! Yet I knew that I was really under the anointing.

My mind was racing back to my medical journalist days. In my spirit I was shown an article from *Pulse* Medical Journal, 22/29th August, 1982. Would I be able to put my hand on it?

'Lord,' I said, 'if this is from you, let me find it quickly!'

Upon arrival home I went straight to it. I have quoted it in the previous chapter. As you will know, tens of thousands are sick with ME which totally debilitates people so that they are indeed like 'walking dead.' It costs the nation millions in lost working hours, legislation to register patients as disabled, and drugs which are of little avail. I cannot tell you how many who come to me with ME are nurses or members of the medical profession.

Why did the Holy Spirit give me 'The Royal Free Hospital?' I had a strong witness in my spirit as I was on my knees praising with Marilyn and Rufus that the angel of death is ME or linked to ME. We are told there will be an increase in demonic powers and End Time pestilences as the age draws nearer to the return of Christ. Look at the New Age medicine for example. Be that as it may, I am aware, as a former ME sufferer, that pathological evidence may or may not be found and medical opinion differs in how soon after the initial virus infection one needs to look to find it.

Immediately my journalistic training was urging me to check hospital records for abortion rates in 1955. But the Holy Spirit did not want me chasing this one, but rather to receive simply from Him that the angel of death passed over that hospital in 1955, and those who were open to be invaded for whatever reason, involvement in abortion, disposing of foetuses or even ignorance, got it. It may be a curse on the medical profession, since so many nurses, doctors and medical orderlies succumb to it – and the 'innocent' in fear are captured, just as innocent people get AIDS, which was firstly a curse on homosexuals. I don't know.

What I do know is this – that I would like to see as many ME patients as possible, cut them off from the angel of death and call out the spirits of the dead (all of them) and the walking dead. Also, can anyone write and positively tell me if Death and Hades is the same principality as the Angel of Death? Many ME patients have been set free when released from the curse of Jezebel, which includes Death and Hades and Anti-Christ. Bill Subritzky advises me that there might be more than one angel of death. And that's not all. Our plane from Israel had a severe fault and we had to return to Israel and wait five hours for another plane. This was after the horror of getting permission for an emergency landing and seeing all the fire-fighting apparatus speeding towards us. We had to sit where we were and were not released for some time. All in all that added to quite a few hours of tension and delay – babies on their last nappy etc.! I believe about 90 born-again Christians praying in the Spirit kept us up in the secret place of the Most High. Marilyn and I got some very relevant Psalms in agreement. Praise the Lord for Bibles on our laps!

When I arrived home more than seven hours late my throat was very dry and sore, and so was Marilyn's, though I did not know this until a week later. When I went to bed I had a quick peep at my throat, and boy what a sudden infection! This went quickly into a high fever. I painted it with myrrh and fell into bed at 1 am. I knew nothing until fifteen hours later, except that I had come to, on and off and wanted to get up but hadn't been able to move.

Then at the end of this period I heard the Holy Spirit say, 'Remove the shrouds,' which I was told were in the immersion heater cupboard which is in my bedroom. I was convicted at once. Two were covering the damaged water heater cylinder. One was folded up in the bottom of the cupboard with clean dust sheets. The story is that my former cleaner and caretaker, whose husband worked at a crematorium, brought some lovely white plastic sheets when she did some decorating for me. The padded jacket round the cylinder had been shredded up when my former cat got shut in, and we had re-covered it with these shrouds!! Of course, I hadn't realised at the time. Next, feeling quite weak, I was scrambling in the loft where I keep all the decorating sheets. I found two more, used three years ago when my bedroom floor was excavated with dry rot. So there I was, surrounded by five large shrouds. I cannot tell you how quickly I got rid of them!

Ever since I got back I have been so weak and sleepy, with no muscle power, soldiering on inasmuch that I'm not actually sick, just so weak. But 100 days have passed now at the time of writing this chapter with no respite. Since I returned from Israel I have taken Holy Communion every day and mostly I have been alone with the Lord, resting in my garden in the lovely sunshine. I tried to walk but was a bit of a flop. Most of you know I love to stride out in the countryside. I just had the strength to change my bedding (ten days after returning home), and to cook a meal – which I did not want. I prefer to eat raw. At that time I was not meeting the demands of anybody. I just wanted to be re-established in my golden relationship with Jesus. I need more wisdom and more holiness, and these are daily requests from my heart.

I had asked the Lord that if what I received regarding 'the angel of death' was correct, he would send me an M.E. patient directly. This letter came the day after I prayed. I will not give her real name, and the only date I will give is June 1992.

'Dear Pearl Coleman,

First I would like to thank you and praise God for your highly enlightening book *Go and Do Likewise*. I could not put it down. I've been a born-again, tongue-speaking believer for eight years and belong to E/K Christian Fellowship. I have three young boys and my husband is also a committed believer in every sense of the word.

I am 30 years old and for the past six years have suffered from ME quite severely, in fact the first three years I could barely walk or brush my hair and to verbalise these last six years and the trauma of bringing up three little boys is almost impossible. In the early years I was completely deserted by my brethren as they did not want to understand the disease. The more I believed the Lord for healing it seemed the worse I got.

Prior to the ME I was used by the Lord in discerning spirits, and was totally committed to Jesus in just about everything, as was my husband. In fact we were training for leadership and seemed to be being used powerfully for Jesus! There was tremendous jealousy toward us from some brothers and sisters in Christ, as we are also quite musical. When my downfall came the result was that many of our so-called close brothers and sisters seemed to rub their hands in glee, saying we must have done something very wrong for this to happen to us.

I was distraught as I could barely manage my babies without collapsing in a heap and a whole range of other ME symptoms. My husband had been counselled that this was all in my mind, even though I had been medically diagnosed by six consultants. I was totally alone in my plight except for Jesus, but He could not lift or change my babies' nappies. I was housebound and so were my children. At evening my husband would come home from work disgusted at this former spiritually strong wife in a heap and in tears.

One very close friend who stood by me and myself prayed without ceasing about this illness (this was five years ago). The Lord told us it was 'Organic' but was rooted in End Time pestilences. I knew this was from Jesus as at that point I didn't know what organic illness was. However, since then I have become very educated in a lot of the illness you describe in your book, due in part I believe to the Holy Spirit and my desire to be healed.

Also at that time He told us ME affected the 'Hypothalamus' and the 'Mitochondria', things we had never heard of, and guess what, recently they have discovered this is so. We feel highly honoured. However I do believe Satan is at the core of this pestilence. As you will know it affects your mind and soul, leaving one weak to the core of one's being.

I've been delivered from a lot of stuff, i.e. witch-craft, spiritualism and other curses. But I do still feel there is something intrinsically demonic about ME and I still have not quite found out what. I would be interested how you got free and if there is anything the Holy Spirit showed you. I should like to say that the Lord has been progressively delivering me and bringing about a slow gradual healing, but there is something still blocking that complete release.

I will go on with my story. Our marriage did break down, although we did not separate as I could not have made it to the bus stop. My husband had to give up work to help me with the boys, but he had nothing but hate for me. My illness had ruined his life. He would frequently abuse me mentally and the church support was nowhere to be seen. It seemed they felt I had no faith otherwise I would be healed, and after three years I was beginning to believe them. I became a pathetic, lonely, emaciated figure and I literally held on to God by the fingernails pleading for physical respite, totally stripped of everything, love, health, money and every kind of happiness. I felt as though Jesus had taken me out to the wilderness and dropped me there abandoned, although I could not let go of him. He was my only help. I spent long months in hospital, separated from my little ones. I often thought of ending it all, but I knew I'd be cut off from Jesus so I continued to hope and hold on for dear life. Anyway this situation continued for five years, until something quite dramatic happened, that I would rather not recall, but maybe I should as I've been forgiven.

We went to a new church in the hope of a new start, but Peter wouldn't come along. At first he did, but then began abusing me emotionally worse than before. There were days when no matter how hard I tried I could not deal with the kids as my muscles would not allow it (bad relapses). This particular day Peter came into the bedroom and cleared the contents of the window sill on my face. The humiliation and guilt I felt were overwhelming. I felt I'd let God down, Christians down, and my hubby down and the kids by not being healed. It was a constant battle not to let this overtake me. In an ME haze I was not even physically able to cope and as it affects the brain clinically, I was low anyway.

To cut a long story short I got friendly with a divorcee ten years my senior. One evening after Peter had knocked me to the ground over something he did not agree with, I got a taxi to this man's home in desperation. (I should have listened to the Holy Spirit.) The man was the only one who seemed to care humanly. When I got there he began to say the things I had longed to hear from Peter, and put his arm around me and began to kiss me. I'm sad to say after a short refusal I succumbed and this liaison became a bondage I found almost impossible to break for three months.

Eventually the Holy Spirit gave me a dream in which I was going down in a vehicle to Sheol with a demonic corpse in the passenger seat. I realised it was time to repent and come clean, which I did, and I sadly had to reveal this abomination to Peter who to my surprise wept and begged my forgiveness for his cruelty. But it took me another month to realise the enormity of the sin and for true repentance to come and believe me, it nearly finished me off. Thankfully I'd never had sex with this man although in my heart I'd committed adultery a thousand times.

God forgave me, Peter forgave me and it took me months to receive the forgiveness myself. I'm in no doubt why God hates this sin as it is so destructive. The man concerned went on to speak the most lying filth about me for months afterwards and God quite simply told us to 'be quiet' and let Him vindicate us. The pastor of the church said I had seduced this man and that he was a man of God and I was basically a whore. During this time God was so merciful and loving to us, and began to repair a completely broken marriage. We went back to our old fellowship where our pastor lovingly repented of his treatment of the ME and the desertion of the church on our behalf.

I still have symptoms of ME although God is healing me. I still don't get much support if any from the brethren (although my pastor and an elder are now marvellous). I am still walking in faith for forgiving the injustice of ME and the disbelief I encountered, and having read your book I found that the chapter on Freemasonry made me feel very strange. My father's and mother's side are steeped in it. It was my pastor who gave me your book and I'm meeting him next week to have the freemasonry thing dealt with. I would like to add that most of these things (illnesses) happened prior to the affair when we were walking strong in the Lord. I find it amazing that this happened to us.

For the past three years I've been getting attacks in

my sleep when I'm aware of the time, where I am, and I'm pinned down by something unseen. I come round screaming Jesus' name, but it takes ages. My pastor has been seeking Jesus on this for ages. I've repented of everything I know of. I just want to get free, for I know God has a calling on our lives. Things are abating.

I felt strongly to write to you. I've never done this before or opened my heart in this way to anyone. Please pray for me. Jesus told me last night 'No matter what it takes I will free you'! I love the Lord. Thank you for your precious book.

Love in Jesus
Penelope'

Now, I believe this is an extraordinary confirmation. Her story of utter weakness and despair is what we former ME patients know to be descriptive beyond measure. I have received many such letters in the past. Two of my team members suffered it. One was a nurse. The other, a former missionary, was definitely expected to die from an injury on the mission field in Africa, and a vigil was kept for her. Marilyn, a nursing sister, handled the dead and was always sick. After we returned home she confirmed that when she was so desperately ill on various occasions her father, who despised her, used to stick his head round the door and say, 'Definitely rigor mortis setting in.' A curse spoken with the authority of a father!

The strong fears in a former secretary of mine used to appear and disappear along with the chewing of the inside of the mouth, and I recall that as a student nurse she was most distressed when she had to put the foetuses from spontaneous abortions into jars of preservative and label them for medical purposes. I believe everyone concerned should ask the Holy Spirit to convict them if deliverance is needed, especially if they are fearful of people, including those whom they love. Marilyn reports that despite the setback of the virus, she is totally changed and not nervous of saying what she wants to anyone. Praise God, praise God, praise God!

I believe the enemy has tried with a vengeance to stop me getting this down on paper. I want the Body to test out what I have received.

Eighteen months ago I heard from the Lord to take communion daily. I started doing this, but stopped because of so many pressures. I know it was a request from my Father to bless me, and Satan won't snatch it away again – no way! And guess what, I learned from that lovely South African Doctor, Dr James van Zyl, that the late Smith Wigglesworth did it, and Derek and Ruth Prince do the same. This is time of change for me! I must wait quietly and listen prayerfully, and I am expectant that God has some amazing news for me.

It is clear to me that many committed Christians are receiving the same message, to repair, retreat and come closer to Jesus than ever before, and to keep Israel burning in our hearts. With the prayer support of some members of my church, the team and intercessors I'm doing just that. Praise the name of Jesus!

Bills for photocopying, postage, printing costs for 'Give aways' have got completely out of hand. God is really speaking to me about simplicity, spontaneity of action, and teaching. He wants me re-entrenched in the Word with my Bible, my utmost important asset. I believe I quote Corrie Ten Boom when I say '"KISS" – keep it simple, stupid!' Amen to all the trappings falling away and the priority of a relationship with Jesus overriding all other considerations. I am not settling for less, and it means the arrows will be sharper against the enemy.

I know that I personally am suffering from 'the wearing out of the saints!' No more! The Lord has emphatically confirmed the ministry. I've been praying for Him to take it away. We have invitations to teach and minister, and I shall wait on Him to see what He wants, when and how.

Right now it is a sabbatical outside the ordinary run of the mill work entailed in earning a living at the Clinic. I thank God to have Rachel at my side, she is a tower of strength and so wise. There is confirmation from many I trust to be at peace and rest.

Chapter 7

More Evidence of the Angel of Death

When patients suffer ME it is an obvious entrance for companion spirits. All three of these spirits are mentioned in the Holy Bible. They are fear, infirmity and grief and mourning.

Fear, we know, embraces many areas. Fear of man, fear of failure, fear of sickness and so on. Infirmity invites another group; despair, weakness, self-rejection and exhaustion. Grief and mourning brings in broken-heartedness, in this case for loss of health. Often unforgiveness is rooted in grief. I would like to mention that unforgiveness contains a desire to punish the offender. In the cases of ME one is mourning for the energy and vitality one has lost, as much as we mourn for the deceased loved one or the deserting spouse. In many cases of ME. I believe these root spirits have to be dealt with.

There is another spirit too which prevails in born-again Christians with ME. It is anger against God who 'allowed the sickness.' We know that God does not put ME on people but He will use such sickness to get our attention when immobilized by ill-health. It is a time when God puts a magnifying glass on our lives! In that way many character traits and ungodly attitudes may be dealt with, one of which is impatience. The Scriptures tell us, *'But let patience have her perfect work, that you may be perfect and complete, lacking nothing'* (James 1:4, NKJV). Every ME patient needs to hang on to that scripture. I love the Authorised Version: *'But let patience have her perfect work that ye may be perfect and entire, wanting nothing.'* Also there is a promise in James 1:3: *'Knowing this, that the trying of your faith worketh patience.'* That is also from the Authorised Version, and needs to be known really well by ME sufferers. One thing I do know is that nothing tried my patience like the debility of ME!

Those three master spirits, fear, infirmity and grief and mourning often bring in their wake a death wish, for example a suicidal spirit or simply a longing to die. One dear sister in my team had a spirit of the fear of living. It was discerned by a brother and manifested in ministry. She feared life with this uphill battle.

When born-again, Spirit-filled Christians who are walking in obedience and doing all they can for the furtherance of the Kingdom suffer this crippling health problem and do not seem to progress despite prayer, fasting, good diet, vitamin and mineral supplements, prolonged rest and the pursuit of Godly habits, they can also harbour unforgiveness of God. Many call out to God to know why He allowed this terrible attack on their brains and central nervous system. We saw this in the letter quoted in the previous chapter – the writer expressed this need to forgive God!

I know from my own personal experience that to struggle against the illness is futile. Somebody wrote that we have to have the grace to accept the things we cannot change. I would not agree with that. I prefer to say we must have the grace to accept the things which God CAN change! For it is written, *'For with God nothing will be impossible'* (Luke 1:37). Frankly I believe the greatest spiritual weapon we have against ME is to call out to God for mercy (Hebrews 4:16). I shall be dealing with that later.

I was, as I have already stated, desperately ill and delirious for some fifteen hours on my arrival home from Israel on June 8th 1992. One thing I was sure of was that Satan did not want me to get the revelation on ME down on paper to inform the Body of Christ. I came home to the loss of my computer, my secretary, my gardener and odd job man and the loss of my health. I also came home to a queue of patients both for physical treatment and for deliverance, mostly a combination of both.

My handwriting, it is agreed by one and all, is quite dreadful and I knew I needed first to get someone to type it out roughly so I could then get it in manuscript. This job fell onto the shoulders of Sharon, a lovely young woman who came to the Clinic in the spring of 1992. She was, despite being sick and tormented, like a breath of Spring. She had a beautiful baby boy she was breastfeeding, and two small girls, whom she seemed to be able to juggle with ease! A really natural mother in a crisp cotton dress, with lovely fair hair, blue eyes and such a gentle voice.

For all her calm in this respect, she was nevertheless disturbed, confused and tormented. In pursuit of a drugless, antibiotic-free upbringing of her children she had fallen prey to New Age medicine, and her children were all in the clutches of a macrobiotic diet.

I will never forget that first visit because I had Raj Kumar from Malaysia staying with me at the Clinic. He was the former heroin addict I met in Penang, who had been healed by Jesus. I also had dear Ernest, who is mentioned a lot in my second book, helping downstairs. Two school teachers were in the waiting room: Nigel, who is now a trainee with the team, and Rufus Adu, whom I now refer to as my right hand man on the team.

I sensed such an anointing as Sharon sat in front of me and as I started giving her the gospel. So I called Rufus, Nigel and Ernest upstairs. I knew it was an important time.

Sharon was born again and baptized in the Holy Spirit

on that first consultation. I knew she had been snatched from the jaws of hell, and her babies also. As I led her through confession and repentance to the Lord I was aware that all the men were weeping. Tears were streaming from their closed eyelids. It is times like this, with such a moving of the Holy Spirit upon all present, that I feel such overwhelming gratitude to God, not only for the power vested in me as a believer, but for His placing around me such fine and stalwart men of God.

Sharon comes to the Clinic as much as she can, when her two little girls are at school, and her mother will look after Samuel, her son. She loves to be with us and is soaking up the Word. It was on one such visit that she offered to type, with two fingers, a letter I had written to my team.

On June 28th she returned the rough copy with a letter as follows, exactly as she wrote it:

'Dear Pearl,

Please find enclosed the rough typed copy of the ME letter, "Appointment in Jerusalem". It was quite a feat for me to tackle as a two fingered typist, but I've enjoyed it, and I do believe I was meant to do it. So much of what you have learned has so much significance for me. I felt I must tell you that I was meant to type that report.

My history is as follows: I worked in one of the oldest mental asylums in the country for three years. Whilst there I witnessed a change in my own personality, and had to deal with the most deranged people, schizophrenics climbing the walls with the voices they heard, manic depressives, murderers, homosexuals, child abusers, every form of perversion known, attempted suicide victims, transvestites, psychopaths etc. etc. I witnessed people who had mutilated themselves, slashed wrists, throats, and of course I had to deal with the dead and the dying, and lay them out when they had died.

The hospital had a certain "feel" to it. The long, high walled corridors were eerie, and we used to hate to have to walk down there at night. Knowing what I've learned now I assume these to be spirits about the place. I also lived in the nursing home in the hospital grounds. My bedroom faced the mortuary, and every one of the staff who lived there had problems. It was well known to the local police for its suicide attempts, fights, drug abuse, wild parties, fires etc. They used to say that the doctors and nurses were more insane than the patients!

Why did I go there? Rebellion I suppose, to get away from my mother who was jealous of my father's attention towards me, and the usual teenage problems I encountered, and that was the only residential nursing course available at the time. That place was Hell on earth. I witnessed things that nobody would believe unless they were there. Patients jumping from three storeys up to the ground with "the voices", physical abuse toward patients from the older, long-term "institutionalised" staff.

It's while I was there that I met Philip (a trainee nurse), who was the most unstable man I have ever met, insecure, an alcoholic, who abused me, broke my jaw, and emotionally tormented me. Yet I felt sorry for him and put up with it. I don't know why. I was so miserable, and even left the most generous kind man I was engaged to for two years for him. My parents and friends thought I had gone mad, and said so! Well, to cut a long story short, we planned to marry, booked the wedding and I bought my dress, and bridesmaids outfits etc. Then one day just before the wedding, he turned up at a flat I had moved to temporarily, but couldn't afford. He told me he had never loved me, knocked me out, pulled the phone off the wall and knocked over the electric fire. Luckily I awoke to find it smouldering. I finally realised I could take no more, and phoned my Dad, who promptly collected me and brought me home, first trying to find Philip who had conveniently disappeared. (I'm afraid of what my Dad would have done if he had found him!)

As I had become qualified I immediately applied for a job locally, and thankfully got it (in a psychiatric outpatient clinic, another long story). It was then I found out I was pregnant. I so longed for a baby. It was all I ever thought about from being a young girl through into adulthood. Then the doubts set in. Would Philip plague me for life? Would I ever be free of him? By now he was ringing my home to talk to me but my parents put the phone down. I was also getting support from Paul (now my husband), who learned I was home and had been a friend before, and I didn't want anything more to do with Philip.

Well, Philip and I met up. He told me he loved me and wanted me back, but my parents could see through him and told him to go, which he did, saying "I'll give you some money for an abortion if I really have to." The rest is history now. Everyone felt it was for the best. Oh! The price I had to pay, as you know, that day when I first came to the clinic. Well, then I married Paul and had Hayley, and was so thrilled I'd been given another chance to love a child of my own. But I don't know what has gone wrong with Hayley, why she is so emotional and rebellious. When I got into New Age to "find the answers" I was told Hayley is probably the spirit of your dead child reincarnated. Oh, the lies of the enemy! I was told "Your dead child's spirit is with you in your aura and manifesting in Hayley now", that's why she was probably angry, because she was letting me know she was here. I know that I rejected her with my mixed up emotions and self pity.

Pearl, I've really got carried away. I'm sorry. I

know you have enough long letters, but I did ask the Holy Spirit to help me write this, and a lot of things have surfaced, and I've never really asked for His help before. But I do want to be soaked with His presence and knowledge. Yet still more is surfacing but I'll write off now. My own constant ill health started after I left that hospital, with tiredness, acute depression, emotional insecurity and terrible anguished state of mind, and especially when I turned to New Age medicine.

Please call me if you need any assistance with this report. I must admit I wept through most of it, especially where the abortion was mentioned. Praise the Lord, He has healed me of my broken heart regarding that.

Thank you for your constant support and help.

Love,
Sharon'

I had quite forgotten Sharon was a nurse before she married. On July 14th she was delivered of the Angel of Death. It was for real.

Sharon had also been plagued with threadworms for a number of years. The next week, using God's promises in Psalm 91 that *'no plague shall come near your dwelling,'* I reminded God that Sharon's body was the temple of the Holy Ghost. I cursed the threadworms in the name of Jesus and that was the last of them. Praise His mighty name!

Chapter 8

The Mercy of God

I said in the previous chapter that the mercy of God was the greatest spiritual weapon we have against ME.

It is real wisdom to support the immune system with a wholesome diet and to check for imbalance of chemicals and vitamin and mineral deficiencies. As in the treatment of candidosis, written about in my previous books, it can dramatically change the quality of life for sufferers. Indeed I have never experienced in my 23 years as a clinical practitioner a case of ME or MS without underlying candidosis and resultant allergies, stemming from a perforated gut.

I dealt with all this in my previous two books so I will not repeat it here, except to say that the Holy Spirit long ago revealed to me that candidosis was the curse of mildew (Deuteronomy 28:22). I am certain that ME is an End Time pestilence and as such has demonic roots. I believe also that the Lord uses such illnesses to cause a time of self-examination for the saved, and a desire to receive salvation for the unsaved.

There is no doubt that the medical profession does not have the answer or a cure for ME, and with respect, is not really able to help persistent sufferers of candidosis. Whatever way you care to look at it, this state of affairs really throws one on the mercy of God. It causes one to come to the end of worldly assistance and indeed the end of self.

If one has a born-again Christian doctor to assess one's treatment, then one is already experiencing the mercy of God, believe me!

Now as I am writing this book I have had quite a shock to be diagnosed as having PVFS and I might add that it is affecting me rather more badly than the first time. Never did I expect to go through it all again! As my lovely born-again Christian medical adviser gave me the diagnosis he said, 'And in your case, Pearl, it is *not* demonic.' He knew of the revelation I had received and was emphatic. Because he is a praying man of great spiritual integrity, I felt inclined to agree with him, but I was not sure. Also I am aware that I have been disobedient in not 'coming apart' as the Lord clearly directed me six months ago.

Please do not rush about calling out a spirit of ME unless you have discerned it, because it only makes mockery of what the Lord requires. I have always taught that deliverance is not a guessing game. Alas, I see increasingly, a moving out in the flesh, of Christians desirous of the ministry of deliverance. It's a right and scriptural desire, but there are requirements of fasting and prayer for this ministry. I do not only mean fasting food, but fasting television and other worldly pursuits! Again, a little more of that later!

I am concerned too at an increase in manifestations of the flesh, which appear demonic and very real, but are nothing more than a piece of theatre. Deception is everywhere, and the Body of Christ needs to get its act together if we are to fulfil the purposes of Christ in the End Times.

How I appreciated Lance Lambert's groaning recently on the state of the Church. 'It's a good club,' he said, 'and there are some saved members!'

Two of the End Time priorities for believers are to repent on behalf of the Church and to pray for Israel. The Church is not meant to be a social club for coffee mornings, jumble sales and dinner parties. Derek Prince says that if the Church only used the power vested in it, the whole scenario could be changed. Our Father must really be weeping. It is no good just feeling cosy in our own little churches. We have to look at **The Church, God's Church Worldwide**.

Again we are back to the mercy of God. I'll quote Derek Prince again, from his tape 'True and False Church': 'Do you know why many of us do not receive God's mercy? Because we don't ask for it.' He adds, 'Mercy is something that God rarely refuses.'

Funny how the Lord causes me to pull out old cassettes .at such a time of debility, and there encased in a teaching is such a precious jewel.

Now let's look at some familiar scriptures on the mercy of God:

> '*The Lord will perfect that which concerns me: your mercy, O Lord, endures forever: do not forsake the works of your hands.*'　　　　　(Psalm 138:8, NKJV)

The verse in this beautiful psalm reminds us that our Father actually created us. He is the manufacturer, and when our worldly possessions break down we always refer to the manufacturer's handbook to see what has gone wrong. The Holy Bible, as I am constantly saying, is the manufacturer's handbook and tells us in Psalm 139:14–16 (NKJV):

> '*I will praise you for I am fearfully and wonderfully made; marvellous are your works, and that my soul knows very well. My form was not hidden from you when I was made in secret, and skilfully wrought in the lowest parts of the earth. Your eyes saw my substance, being yet unformed. And in your book they all were written, the days fashioned for me, when as yet there were none of them.*'

Doesn't that make you gasp in wonder, and put the Rolls-Royce manufacturers to shame?

Does that mean, I often ask myself, that God knew we were going to be ill, to be tested, maybe beyond endurance? I suspect it may do. That is my opinion of course. I am trying to point out some scriptures of real help and comfort to the believer and sufferer of ME.

Look at the promise in Psalm 136:1 (NKJV):

> '*Oh give thanks to the Lord, for he is good! For his mercy endures for ever.*'

Also the much-loved Psalm 103:11–13:

> '*For as the heavens are high above the earth, so great is his mercy towards those who fear him;*' (note who the mercy is for!) '*As far as the east is from the west, so far has he removed our transgressions from us. As a father pities his children, so the Lord pities those who fear him.*'

There is the promise then of mercy and pity so long as we have the fear of the Lord – which we all know is the beginning of wisdom and indeed knowledge (Proverbs 9:10 and 1:7, NKJV). Who has not done a study of fear and wisdom from the Scriptures? One could go on for months. If you haven't ever done such a study – doing one could heal you! Why? Because paying attention to the Word brings healing and medicine to all our flesh (Proverbs 4:20–22).

Yes, I know we Christians all know about the fear of the Lord, the need for wisdom, the promises of mercy. But do we really avail ourselves of His promises daily, if not hourly? And when I go on like this I'm addressing myself also. I know I am guilty of being squeezed out of existence sometimes by demands and pressures upon me. I keep trying to do better. I am in search of holiness, and the more I search the more diligence I realise I need, not to get sidetracked!

Again, at this time of physical disability, I find myself guilty of having had a spirit of the fear of man. I am not actually afraid of people but I am afraid of hurting them, of appearing to be short-tempered or to have no compassion. But am I afraid of the Lord, to hurt Him by ministering when He has said **no**? I cannot be both! Quite tough!

It's not my business why He says '**no**' – but it usually means the person is not repentant, or it's a cop out to avoid making an effort or crying out to God on their part. Misplaced ministry, the Lord has been showing me, is a horror to Him. No one person has a right to ministry from any minister; they do have a right of entrance to the throne room and to get on their faces. He says, *'Call upon me – and I will say, "Here I am"'* (Isaiah 58:9).

Hebrews 4:16 says, *'Let us therefore come boldly to the throne of grace, that we may obtain mercy and find grace to help in time of need.'*

The beautiful scripture Jeremiah 33:3 promises that if we call on Him, He will *'show you great and mighty things, which you do not know'* (NKJV).

If one fears the Lord then one does not disobey Him. I was certain that I was in obedience, but now I am restricted in movement I see that I was definitely not – and on two very important matters.

Firstly, He told me to come apart and rest. Of course I knew I needed rest. It didn't occur to me that He might have something so special to say that He wanted my full attention – and He surely did! He wanted to speak to me about a future husband, and about a change in the direction of my ministry. What could be more important than that!

What is more, almost eighteen months ago I was told to take Holy Communion daily. I made a start – it lasted all of 19 days. Then I had someone come to stay with me, and I felt they didn't want to join me so this devotion faded out.

What my Father really wanted was for me to have time

alone with Him and to press on doing what He had instructed me to do, regardless of what anyone else wanted to do. What a dimwit I was! I had to go all the way to Israel to buy a little booklet written by a South African GP, Dr James van Zyl, in which he wrote how the Lord told him to take Holy Communion daily, and all the blessings he had received as a result of his obedience for himself and his family. What is more, as I have already mentioned he just happened to mention that after he did this the Lord confirmed the instruction to him through a tape on which Derek Prince said that he and Ruth took communion daily. Then, reading the life of Smith Wigglesworth, he found that he also did likewise!

No prizes for guessing who my two mentors are (not idols, please note!). When I think what I had been missing! Anyway I got started immediately I arrived home. I am now on my 110th consecutive day as I write this chapter, and I cannot tell you what a privilege and joy that special time with the Lord has been. There's nothing ritualistic about it, in fact really it's a little different each day. But boy am I listening! I'm also getting a few nasties about myself – but I am so pleased to be put under His magnifying glass and to be able to correct them speedily.

After all the Word is for correction, reproof and training in righteousness. It's not a 'bless me' club we belong to. I know I'm being pruned but I'm not resisting it. Never have I accepted disability as I do now. Don't misunderstand me. I hate it. The concertina legs, the lack of coordination, the dry eyes, the difficulty sometimes in finishing sentences – but I am also receiving information I was deaf to because of the pressure of ministry.

The Lord is also telling me to be aware of false prophets and I know there are going to be even more about. So we must be finely tuned in our discernment. I am throwing all these things in as it were for spiritual discussion. ME is a time for self-analysis if it is a time for anything.

I am also shouting out to God daily for His mercy,

something I have never really called out for. I think calling out for mercy is a sign of having come to the end of self. Really I'm quite pleased to be there. It's been a long journey, and the road to this self-awareness has been so rough. I only have myself to blame.

How I identify with the cries of Johannes Facius in his furnace of affliction, crying out to God! His wonderful book of humbling *God Can Do It Without Me*, should be read by all sufferers of any disease. That word 'humbling' is also frequently overlooked by the Church, of which I am a member.

> **If** – note *'If my people which are called by My name will humble themselves, and pray, and seek my face, and turn from their wicked ways, then I will hear from Heaven, and will forgive their sin and heal their land.'*
> (2 Chronicles 7:14)

If we do a study on humbling ourselves, we find that God gives grace, honour, salvation and mercy to the humble, then He exalts them!

Would *you* think that arrogance is a problem in the Church and that the Church is rather short on humility? According to Derek Prince,

> 'Spiritual pride and arrogance is the greatest problem in the charismatic Church.'

During this time of searching the Scriptures, words like grace, mercy, humility, wisdom and fear of the Lord have taken on a new meaning for me. Oh yes, I knew about them before, but it is as though they have been etched on my heart as being the roots, the core, the essence of freedom and abundant life. You know, I thank God always for chastening and pruning. Without it I would be nothing more than a blancmange!

One man of God brought some comforting words to me

at my bedside recently. He said, 'Do you know that God does not prune branches unless they have already borne fruit?' I had, I confess, never really seen it that way, and yet the Scriptures tell us that branches that do not bear fruit are lopped off! (John 15:2)

John 3:30 is a scripture which really got my attention about two years ago: *'He must increase, but I must decrease.'* I can see quite clearly that I am not small enough yet! Amazingly, though, all through my ministry life He has said, 'Be bold, be strong. Don't lose your boldness,' and at the same time told me to have a meek and quiet spirit. It's a balance like that needed for walking a tightrope. Lord, bring me to the other side, please!

Quite recently I was mulling this over on my face before the Lord, and He showed me that the atom, although so very microscopic, harnesses a power that is positively explosive! Hallelujah!

Chapter 9

Television

It is no secret that television has always been an abomination to me. I was probably the last person in Britain to own one. It is a very small coloured portable given to me by a patient I treated for several years without charging.

He said, after my former husband had ransacked the house, 'Pearl, you must have a television. How will you know about the news now you have cancelled your newspapers?'

He wasn't a Christian, so explaining that the news is in the Bible wouldn't have helped. And yes, since I had been led to cancel my newspapers after fasting them for a few weeks, it was nice to see the news – and indeed, being an ardent lover of countryside and the Lord's creation I did enjoy those wonderful natural history films.

In the early stages and novelty of having a 'box' I was aware of the control it tried to have over me. I found myself guilty of watching rubbish, often quite fascinated by its awfulness. To fascinate means to bewitch. Like so many I would flick that handswitch from programme to programme to find the lesser rubbish, often ending up seeing nothing all the way through and going to bed too tired to read my Bible.

Now come off it – don't say you haven't all been there! It is obvious that many Christians feel that the scripture

'Without vision my people perish,' means without television!

Well, I do not wish to appear proud, but I was always very alert to the manipulation and control exerted over Christians by TV when I heard various pastors from the pulpit or from the platform refer to characters in programmes I had never watched, in their sermons. I realised I didn't know who they were talking about, so I couldn't get the message!

Derek Prince says the TV is the most common source of witchcraft operating in homes. Television can manipulate people into wanting articles they do not want or need and cannot afford, and indeed can isolate family members. The advertisements can affect the appetite and the thirst, a lesson I learned when my small son was loaned his pal's portable TV set whilst he was on holiday. It was a mini black and white set and he fixed it up by his bedside. I'm reflecting on what happened some forty-seven years ago.

I had no qualms about allowing him to have his pal's TV set on a small wheeled table at the end of his bed, and enjoying the novelty of it. What I didn't bargain for was the fact that it was going to cost me about £5 extra in housekeeping that week.

It must be obvious to those who have read my books and articles that I am a persistent advocate of whole, unrefined, fresh food, and a despiser and non-consumer of the instant cardboard junk variety of nourishment, so it goes without saying that this is what my lusty lad had been reared on since birth.

The first night of owning his pal's portable TV my son, prone to dodging bedtime to potter in father's workshop where he had his own bench, or visit friends to share a variety of interests, retired to bed early, luxuriously, with the set.

For the most part he was entertained by ITV, and at regular intervals he announced from his bedroom that he was 'peckish, hungry, famished and starving', in that order. Invariably the hunger pangs passed as I failed to produce what he was fancying – crisps, sweets, curly wurlies, scented biscuits which smell like the bath salts counter in Woolworths, or other rubbish.

This tack succeeded on day one of the borrowed portable, but not on days two, three, four, five or six. At intervals which grew more frequent each day, he clamoured for sustenance, even heeding my advice of 'Get it yourself,' in case he thought he was going to idle between the sheets while I played waitress!

Gradually the week's supply of fruit disappeared from the fruit bowls, refilled many times from the larder. The dried fruit and nut jars, even those containing the varieties he quite disliked, emptied rapidly. Boxes of wholewheat cereal disappeared into thin air, with lashings of 'extra pintas.'

'He's a growing lad,' his father kept telling me, as I vainly searched for food to quell those hunger pains, which would not satisfy the desires undoubtedly created by the advertisements for bars which would help you work, rest and play (certainly he was resting alright), mints with holes (which mean teeth with holes), and much sugar-coated temptation.

There is no doubt in my mind at all that my son was not hungry enough to peel the oranges he loathed at 10 o'clock at night, to gobble in front of the box. He had been hypnotised, mesmerised into believing he was needing this food, and in one week he had gained half a stone in weight.

Now I mention all this because such effects are not confined to hungry little boys. They also apply to adult males, and females, including Christians.

In 1978 I was an established journalist with a prolific output of some millions of published words to my credit, on every conceivable subject, although I specialised in journalism concerning health and the environment. That year I wrote an article for a magazine called *Prevention*, entitled 'The Audio-Visual Villain'.

In 1980 I wrote an article for *Epoch* quarterly journal, entitled 'The Plug-in Drug', for which I had to supply a cartoon. I enlisted the help of a couple of art students from the local technical college, and gave them an idea of what I wanted artistically produced. It was a large TV set with two devil-like horns sprouting from the top and a hand growing out the side, holding a pronged trident. Pictured on the screen was a gunman about to blast somebody's brains out. In front of the screen, anchored by a ball and chain, were two children, surrounded by an army of sweets, fizzy drinks, crisps, peanuts and so on. The door of the TV room was half open to reveal the parents with hats and coats on, clearly just off to the pub whilst the children sat mesmerised, not even bothering to say goodbye.

Amazingly enough, another student produced a design I had not required, but I felt it was so apt that I used it. The cartoon depicted a very modern TV in front of which were three teenage robots glued to the TV with beams directed from their eyes to the screen.

This article contained well-researched evidence into the varying effects of TV upon viewers, such as violence, and I noted a case where a judge sentenced a violent teenager to a period of time without television.

I had a reputation at that time for writing on the side effects of drugs, with titles like *The Obscene Drug Scene* and *The Affliction of Addiction on Prescription*. In 1980 I had written:

> 'The side effects of drugs are constantly being conveyed to us via the mass media and our medical and scientific journals. Iatrogenic has become almost a household word and nobody can deny that a public information service, manifesting itself in many forms, now exists to protect people from dangers which perhaps a decade ago they were unaware of or not warned about. All credit must go to those responsible for bringing about this healthier situation.

'I think, however, that whilst we are actively concerning ourselves about the side effects of pharmaceuticals, we are less aware of the side effects of what could well be described as a more insidious drug, namely "the opiate of the people," that plug-in drug, the television.

'Accepting that "the box" could be described as a hypnotic, sedative, tranquiliser, stimulant etc., etc., should not the same concern be given to overdosing with it as to the pill form causing such effects? I feel that it should, and maybe General Practitioners being made aware of the dangers could write on their EC10 forms, "I prescribe less television for this patient."'

Now you may be wondering what all this has to do with ME or the Angel of Death – but I promise you I'm getting there!

This article, along with many others I wrote on the detrimental effects of TV was picked up by the London Broadcasting Corporation, who operated a phone-in programme called 'Nightline'. I was contacted by LBC, as being considered something of an expert in this field, to take the phone calls from Mr and Mrs general public on a programme entitled 'TV, is it a drug?'

I have to chuckle because I recall the shock when I arrived just before midnight to be wired up and was asked if I would like a coffee. I refused. 'No thank-you,' I said, 'but I would like somewhere to pray.'

I had quite a time with the precious Holy Spirit before going live, and indeed the programme provoked such an encouraging response to what I had felt in my Spirit about the 'box'. With phone-ins one must expect to have the odd caller tearing you to shreds, but not only was I able to mention Jesus, I had a real confirmation of the evil of this piece of sitting room furniture: children who failed exams until the TV was put in the loft, infants ceasing to have nightmares when removed from its influence, and improvement in eyesight with reduced viewing.

Over the following decade I was able to confirm these problems as facts in many cases of unhappy children seen at my Clinic. But what transpired more recently came I admit as a little bit of a surprise.

Chapter 10

Television and the Church

Following my return from Israel on June 8th 1992 and succumbing to that peculiar virus which had such a sudden onset and left me totally debilitated and was eventually diagnosed as PVFS, I was forced virtually to withdraw from society. I did the occasional Clinic day, most weeks aided by Rachel, but in the main I was just around below stairs to help if spiritual assistance was needed. I was on a self-appointed three month sabbatical, unless strongly led by the Holy Spirit.

One of those days, feeling very well, I was sitting at the table in the office downstairs where patients pay their bills. It is actually my large dining room which converts to an office on such days.

Rachel brought a lovely school teacher patient down after her appointment had concluded and took the next patient upstairs to the consulting room. As the lady was paying her bill I felt the Holy Spirit rising within me. I wondered if I were going to minister. The receptionist took the cheque and Ernest, one of my helpers, was standing nearby.

The words were put in my mouth. I'll call her Gina. I asked, 'How are you, Gina?'

Rachel, poised on the stairs with the next patient, spoke out, 'Well, she is making progress, but it's slow.'

Gina told me that she was definitely better than when

she first came, but was very debilitated, and had been for nine years, with what, she didn't know. To be honest I believe she could easily have been diagnosed ME.

Then this curious array of questions uttered from my mouth.

'How much television do you watch, Gina?'

'Oh, quite a lot,' she responded.

'How many hours each day?'

'Oh, it must be quite a few.'

'How many?' I found myself pushing the questions home quite strongly.

She continued, 'I suppose I do watch a lot. It is my only relaxation.'

'How many hours a day? Four, five, six?'

'I suppose it must be that amount,' she replied.

The Holy Spirit indicated that I should test her to the rays of TV and fluorescent tubes. I placed her in front of my small TV, putting her on a wheeling stool she could place in the identical proximity to her viewing chair at home. I tested the strength of her deltoid muscle and found it quite strong.

I then switched on the TV for a few moments and told her to look into the screen. After about 60 seconds I tested the muscle strength, repeating it at intervals of increased exposure. The patient grew weaker and weaker, until she was unable to hold her arm out at all.

I then did the same with fluorescent tubes. As a teacher she is under them at school. There was a strong reaction.

These patients will tell you that they cannot be in shops and stores for ten minutes without having to go outside. It is my experience that a damaged immune system cannot tolerate radiation from such sources. Many are allergic to the quartz batteries in their watches.

I have always realised the problems for hospitalised patients or those in old people's homes, stuck in front of this monster without choice. I also realise that the TV is the only entertainment for exhausted ME patients who can do little in the way of exercise or movement, and whose brains are often not clear.

But the reality of the issue as far as the Church is concerned suddenly struck me. This course of least resistance is keeping Christians out of the Word. When a Christian is ill it is often a time for the Lord to speak to them, and many will say it is nice to have time for the Bible. But once a sick person plonks himself or herself in front of the TV we have a combination of hypnotism and mesmerism. Those patients are placed in a position of no resistance and enormous fatigue the longer they are exposed. We know that both ME and MS patients experience eye weakness and visual disturbance. How much is this exacerbated by incessant TV viewing?

To sum up, those who really do not need exposure to TV are the sick and those who get such exposure, are frequently the sick. Those who are sick really need the Word to become flesh for them and yet they are actually likely to have less time with their Bibles. Also many Christians will complain of tiredness at the end of the day, making it an excuse for not opening their Bibles!

I asked Gina how many hours a day she read her Bible. It was alas minutes, not hours.

Well, the Lord has prompted us to make this a part of our questionnaire. We have a question on activities. Lisa, my receptionist, suggested that we list TV as an activity because most patients only think of walking, painting, swimming or golf etc. to qualify as an activity – and passive viewing, which takes up so much of their time, does not get a mention!

Now readers take the test. Do not cheat! Write down for one month the hours spent viewing the TV and hours spent studying *'to show thyself approved unto God, a workman that needeth not to be ashamed, rightly dividing the word of truth'* (2 Timothy 2:15). The next step is of course confession and repentance and exercising masterly control in Jesus' name over the ON/OFF switch.

Try fasting the television and see what you achieve in terms of spiritual growth, improved eyesight and energy. Maybe you will not become one of those who, as Barry Smith predicts, will be monitored by fibre optics and the fish eye lens!

Addiction to TV is about as socially acceptable to the Christian as alcohol or drugs. Only my opinion of course, but check these things out for yourself. Bless you. However, if you do have ME, switch off indefinitely – and whatever viewing you may do, sit outside of the beam.

If your TV is black and white, the beam disappears through the floor over a distance of about 15 feet. Watch out for the old black and white TV in the children's bedroom upstairs radiating to you below stairs whilst you carefully avoid the beam of your coloured set!

Seducing Spirit

A secular study was conducted in the USA on how to sell to born-again Christians as opposed to others. There are 50 million committed Christians in the USA – that is approximately one-fifth of the population, so it would be quite a market to capture! The research was carried out to see what lures and entices Christians into purchase etc., etc. The results of this study showed that Christians are no different! They are subject to the same enticements and seductions as the world. They can be influenced to purchase goods by the same methods causing others to buy.

Now that I am carrying out my own research on the viewing hours of Christians, this result does not surprise me. The word 'bewitch' means to smite with the eye – so we can see a lot of bewitching with TV goes on as far as Christians are concerned. And of course, that which seduces, is witchcraft.

Whichever way you look at it, this is not good news for the Church, when ten minutes a day seems to be the average time spent in reading the Bible, as opposed to four hours of TV viewing! Dare I say that if the reverse were true it would revolutionise the effectiveness of the Body of Christ in world affairs.

Of course the survey I am doing is not yet complete but I feel that so far we have an accurate barometer of the way things are going. When we hear from Barry Smith that fibre optics and a fish eye lens are going to enable Big Brother to monitor our every activity at home, one realises that Satan must be well aware of the existing situation.

Please conduct your own survey. Make these lists of daily totals:
1. Time spent in prayer.
2. Time spent in reading the Holy Bible.
3. Time spent in viewing television.
4. Time spent in fasting (if you are brave enough).

The Strong Man

The ruler over the television was pointed out to me by the Holy Spirit some while ago when ministering to a television addict. He is the 'Prince of the Power of the Air' (Ephesians 2:2). That same ruler takes control of those who cannot do anything without a background of music (and it does not have to be pop), who walk around with earphones permanently connected to their heads, and drive the car with radio blaring.

Can I ask you a question? Who do you think ultimately takes over the wheel when uncontrolled 'noise' surrounds the driver in that confined space? Please hear what I am saying, *not* what I am *not* saying. And yes, I do have Christian teaching tapes on sometimes when I drive, and I do sing praises when I drive. Ask for wisdom in your car as elsewhere.

Why do you think supermarkets and chain stores now invariably have piped music going as you stack your trolley? It is my opinion, I stress *opinion*, that some market researcher has shown that it takes shoppers' minds off the prices and lessens the concentration so that they omit to notice how much everything has gone up, and that they also purchase more.

Alas, people in numerous professions are constantly propped up by background music. What makes them think *you* want it? Have they actually asked you? I have spoken to many people who, like me, simply want to be quiet – and they are not all Christians.

I do not even want praise and worship tapes going on all the time. I want to listen to hear what the Lord is saying to me by His Spirit. That silence is, as the old adage says, 'Golden'.

Much of the Body of Christ now hides behind praise and worship and music groups. Imagine going to church and hearing your Pastor say, 'We are not going to sing, dance or praise tonight, but we are going to get on our faces and listen.' Would it empty the church, do you think? No. Some would have to be treated for shock, but most of the Body would love it.

Chapter 11

Testimony of Healing from ME No. 1 Emily Woods, Somerset

Emily came to see me on August 6th 1991, very severely debilitated. According to my notes she had been definitely diagnosed ME in June 1989, following prolonged illness.

At the first consultation it was definitely established that she suffered from Candidosis and general yeast allergy. Also I see that I wrote 'grief and mourning, frustration and desperation,' on her initial notes. These were spirits of course. As is customary she went straight onto the diet in my handbook and was provided with a selective vitamin and mineral therapy to boost her immune system.

As we got to know each other it emerged that her mother was extremely dominant and also that the grief inside her was from the loss of the opportunity to give expression to what I discovered later was incredible musical talent. Her voice was both angelic and different. Emily was 72 years of age, and due to problems in her church, was unable to use her gift – which caused despair and frustration, especially since in her illness this would have provided an outlet for pent up feelings.

Emily grew very much stronger and on September 17th 1991 the Holy Spirit led me to minister to her in some depth. By this time I had discerned that she was under Jezebel – a part of the unholy trinity which I learned about from Bill Subritzky. The unholy trinity are Jezebel,

Antichrist and Death and Hades. This trio are clearly defined in Bill's very useful handbook on *How to Cast Out Demons and Break Curses* (available from New Wine Ministries). Also cast out were exactly 72 demons, one for each year of her life!

I always have a counsellor to jot down what is dealt with to go in the file, because patients will sometimes come and ask for deliverance of a particular spirit and one naturally does not retain details of ministry – the Lord does not want that. It provides a good check point in case patients ask for something to be done and one knows for sure it was dealt with. This enables us to see that patients walk in deliverance from their own efforts. Deliverance and walking in it requires a two-way and ongoing co-operation with the Holy Spirit.

Emily's testimony is given below, exactly as she wrote it.

Testimony 17.9.92

'My troubles really started when we moved from London to the country in 1984, and I found it very difficult to adjust to a different church and way of life. As I was then 65 years old, I was not so resilient, although I loved the country and our home ... However, my church life was *very* important to me, and I missed the many Christian friends and wide range of activities I was used to. My husband and I had received the fullness of the Spirit, and been involved in Charismatic renewal since 1973, and our lives had been transformed by this.

'When we came here, it was rather like having been to university, and then going back to kindergarten. We are both musical and had been widely used in this area, but found this outlet somewhat blocked, and I received wounds and hurts, and feelings of rejection which went much deeper than I realised. (As I had been rejected as a child this was particularly bad for me.)

'In October 1988 I became ill with a constantly recurring swelling in my eyes, a severe rash all over my face, pains in arms and shoulders, and severe swelling and discomfort in my stomach. I also became increasingly exhausted, so that every few weeks I had to stay in bed several days, after feeling unwell for about a fortnight. This would all recur again in four weeks or so, and the cycle went on until I wrote to a naturopath in Scotland, who kindly sent me herbal medicines to rebuild my immune system. I later visited him, and he diagnosed Epstein-Barr virus (a type of ME) and continued to treat me by postal communication. My health did improve a little, but it was obviously going to be a long business.

'In August 1991 I visited Pearl Coleman and she advised the Candida diet, and many natural supplements, which I started on 2nd September. I visited her again 17th September, and was tested for further allergies.

'However, I became convinced that I needed deliverance very badly, and Pearl very kindly agreed to see me the following week as she felt led of the Lord to do so.

'During the deliverance I was sobbing and crying uncontrollably, and very loudly, and Pearl discerned spirits of grief, mourning and death. (I had already written out a request for hymns to be played at my funeral!) Certainly my feelings of grief were deep and desperate. There were also spirits of resentment and rejection, and these evil spirits came out with loud cries, and eventually I was peaceful within and Pearl anointed me with oil and I received the infilling of the Spirit again. Praise the Lord!

'From this time on my symptoms diminished very rapidly, and I am told I look wonderfully well, and indeed I am. I am still on the diet which in any event is very healthy, a little modified, and at 73 years old I am careful not to over-exert myself, but life is very different now and I praise the Lord for His goodness to me. My singing voice has returned and the Lord gives me spiritual songs with which to glorify Him.

'My problem was obviously both physical and spiritual, and I have been able to acknowledge that my resentments and unforgiveness were *sins*, unacceptable to a Holy God, and I have been given strength to ask forgiveness of those I have resented.

'I look upon the world with new eyes again, and feel love and understanding and friendliness to all my fellow creatures. I am deeply grateful to God for guiding me to visit Pearl and for all the work she does in this area of healing of the body, mind and spirit.'

I think we can agree that there is certainly evidence of the Angel of Death in Emily's history – since she actually wrote out the hymns she wanted for her funeral. Many ME patients cry out to die as it would be for them easier than living.

I anointed Emily's forehead and feet after ministry and cut her off from witchcraft at the feet where ancestral demons are not infrequently tied to make people return to places of witchcraft. I'm not saying this was so in Emily's case, but both her mother and aunt were demonised and I believe it went back much further than that.

When Emily rose to her feet she sang unto the Lord in the Spirit such a song that Raj, who was ministering with me, and I and even people in the waiting room and reception wept. If anything was angelic and offered up as incense it was Emily's praise and thanksgiving. After that joy, I felt I would like to close the Clinic for the rest of the day.

Emily believed afterwards that it was the finished work. She and her husband were further blessed by attending a teaching I did in Dorset and she looks incredibly young and healthy. I discharged her on April 14th 1992, after eight months' two-monthly visits, leaving her to use wisdom over her diet. Most patients are reluctant to return to junk food or sugar binging diets after such experience of what diet can do for the spiritual body – which is the temple of the Holy Spirit, not to be filled with garbage or given into carnally.

A very high proportion of my patients come to really enjoy water and very simple food. I do feel that we may all be being prepared for leaner End Times in this respect.

Chapter 12

Testimony of Healing from ME No. 2 Henri Hillier, Suffolk

Henri was a very beautiful blonde twenty-two year old who first visited the Clinic on April 7th 1992. When she was four years old she suffered great shock and trauma from the near drowning of her little brother when the car he was in went over a cliff. She had been involved in all manner of the occult and had some very hair-raising accidents. Her grandfather was a freemason. There was a suicide attempt at nineteen years old, and she also heard voices at the onset of ME.

Accompanying Henri was her husband of some eighteen months, a shy, handsome young man complete with one earring. He informed me that after reading both of my books, it was put in for the visit, to see if I would make him remove it. Warren was full of inhibitions and phobias and clearly not head of the house. They were a very likeable couple.

The onset of Henri's ME was definitely in Hong Kong, as you will see from her testimony, but she was also suffering from a great deal of guilt and rejection. Her father is an Anglican vicar. I will let her tell her own story in the unaltered testimony which follows:

'I had spent my childhood and early teens involved with the supernatural and the occult – my greatest

100

wish was to become a witch. God however, had other plans for my life and in 1984 at the age of fifteen I became a Christian. I think I was probably like most other Christians. I joined a lively church, did a bit of witnessing and carried on living my life. Then in 1988 I decided I wanted to do some voluntary work. I ended up going to Hong Kong to work with Jackie Pullinger, a Christian missionary who is involved with helping drug addicts.

'I arrived in March 1988 after a 28-hour flight, exhausted and very ill after having had all my injections on the previous day. I soon recovered and was allocated a job to do. This involved taking reformed drug addicts (known as brothers because they are brothers in Christ) to dentists and in some cases hospitals. One of these brothers had cancer and I used to take him for regular check-ups. Unfortunately his health deteriorated and he died. I remember attending his funeral; he was laid out in a coffin and we walked in a circle around the body, "paying our last respects". I thought at the time how strange it was doing this and I felt a little uncomfortable; it was the first dead body I had seen and it was someone I knew.

'It was soon after this that I became extremely ill, about June 1988. One of my friends found me in bed with a high fever. She went to get help and I was carried into the air conditioned hospital room. I am not sure how long I was there – it may have been a fortnight. I was very weak and the nurse said I was too ill to move. I strongly believed I would get well through prayer, after all I was seeing drug addicts healed from their addiction every day. Many people prayed for me but nothing happened. I had to be taken to the bathroom in a wheelchair. It is difficult to remember pain but I know it was severe, stomach cramps, migraines, sore throat. No-one knew what it was. When I did recover I went to a Chinese doctor

101

and he said it was extreme exhaustion and asked me to rest and not to become stressed! This was impossible as I had gone out to Hong Kong to work.

'When I later returned to England in July 1988 I slept for days and after a holiday in France I was taken to the doctor for a check up. I was still having migraines, pains in my body and was crying all the time. After examining me thoroughly he told me he thought I might have ME. I had blood tests but they revealed nothing conclusive. I was due to begin teacher training college in September and I could not face the idea of being ill with ME so I dismissed it from my mind and did not return to the doctor. A friend of mine also suffered from ME and she was convinced I had it as I had the same symptoms.

'In September I started college and was convinced it would be the end of all my problems. However, it was not the end of them. Sometimes I thought I was going mad and I think others did too. It was difficult to know who I could trust. The hard thing was that Christians seemed to think it was all in my head. At one point I thought I was going to be taken into an institution.

'From 1988 to 1992 I suffered from bad bouts of depression, sometimes lasting for weeks. My symptoms would keep recurring – everything seemed such an effort, even thinking about what I had to do in the day seemed a major task. There was a continuous battle going on inside my head. All I wanted was to die but I believed that as a Christian I could not commit suicide and still have eternal life. It did not stop the feelings of torment and blackness and total despair going on inside me.

'I had decided to leave college after only two terms as I no longer wanted to teach. I went from job to job, from the town to the country but I could not find the peace I so desperately needed. I saw a Christian psychiatrist, my pastors and teachers prayed, laid hands on me, but still all I could see was darkness. I could not understand why I was suffering so much. I was a Christian, I studied God's Word and I asked for healing, but nothing happened.

'In September 1990 I got married to a wonderful Christian man and we went to Australia for a year. I was so happy but things just did not improve. There was very little work so we had to clean for a living. I was exhausted and would collapse every night. I had migraines, terrible pains in my legs, continuous sore throats and an ongoing frustration with myself and my life. I still longed to die.

'In March 1992 we were staying with my parents in Suffolk and I had another relapse. I could not even hold a glass up to my mouth. My mother was suffering from ME also, and my father could not accept the fact that I had it too. That was it – both my husband and I had had enough. We had recently read an article about Pearl and her work and we knew I had to see her. We prayed for weeks before my appointment that God would speak to Pearl about my situation. I went to see her in March and she confirmed that I must have ME.

'We were just about to leave when Pearl stopped us and said that the Holy Spirit was telling her to pray for us! It was truly amazing. God healed me in the most incredible way. Pearl ministered for quite a long time as I had to be released from many curses and spirits, in particular the spirit of death, the spirit of fear, the spirit of unforgiveness, the curse of witchcraft and the curse of the vagabond. There seemed so many things. It is hard to explain in words the sense of peace and freedom which I felt. It was as though a dark shadow had been taken away from the top of my head and I felt lighter, even in weight! It was as though I had been a bird in a black iron cage with an open door but I was so paralysed that I could not go

103

through the door. Now God had led me through the door and I was free. I don't know how to begin to thank God for freeing me and my husband; and Pearl for being so faithful to God and for being such an important channel for God's healing. She told me that the anointing became so strong as we were about to leave, that she knew it was a command to pray.

'Praise God that I am now free from pain and that I feel energetic and full of life. I am *completely* healed of ME!'

I believe there is definitely evidence here that infirmity opened the way for the Angel of Death through transference of spirits from the dead addict. In the coffin they all had to walk around the body, all the more grotesque from having facial make-up which gave a mask-like appearance.

Henri was very shocked having to walk past this coffin. Shock and terror are two of Jezebel's children. Subsequently we see that she entertained a real death wish. The Angel of Death never needs a second invitation to invade.

When Henri and her husband came downstairs from my consulting room and were at reception I could not take my eyes off them as a couple. They seemed so helpless, she sick, and he unemployed. Her mother was also an ME patient and Henri was so concerned about her.

The Holy Spirit said 'minister' just as they were about to make their exit. I was quite staggered but obeyed.

I led them together in the prayer to be free from the fifteen curses, and spirits which execute those curses. Since that time the Holy Spirit has revealed an additional curse, that of insane violence.

There were marked manifestations in both of them, even more so in the husband. I then bound the unholy trinity and cut them off at the feet. They both fell genuinely under the power of the Holy Spirit. I say genuinely because a lot of folk will fall in the flesh.

The Holy Spirit has shown me not to be too bothered about falling in the flesh as long as the ministry has been in order.

When people fall in the Spirit, they fall without fear and go down as straight as a die. They do not crumple or stagger back. Some do the latter in resisting the Holy Spirit, but when the Holy Spirit falls on a person, fear is out – fear of falling, fear of damaging the furniture etc. I do not believe people are hurt falling in the Spirit whatever they fall on!! I have no proof of any of this, but a real witness in the Spirit that it is so.

The miracle of that ministry was not only Henri's instant recovery, but when Warren got up he was head of the house. Praise the Lord!

I love these two and they often visit the Clinic out of real interest and helpfulness. They are both powerful witnesses and know how to witness. God will use them mightily I am sure. The first time they stayed on after an appointment was to help me minister to a lady with a death sentence upon her. She brought her common-law husband and he got saved. The witnessing of these two young people had far more to do with it than I did.

I praise God for His mercy and grace unto us who are saved and those being saved.

We are now seeing Warren for physical assessment because he too has candidosis. A lot of cross-infection goes on in married couples.

I know that they are both so free, the physical problems will be dealt with quite quickly. Meanwhile as newlyweds they are learning the wisdom of correct nutrition. Bless them both.

Chapter 13

Freedom from Curse and Spirits of Curse

In the previous chapter I mentioned the curses the Holy Spirit has revealed to me and added to over the years.

Although this subject was dealt with in my 1991 book *Fruit Abiding In the Vine*, since that time I have learned a great deal more on the subject – and when I lead people in this prayer at public meetings it is a life-changing event, believe me.

The Holy Spirit has shown me the curse of Eve works in all female problems. The curse of the Vagabond worked out in the descendants of those involved in piracy, thieving, wandering around with no fixed abode (e.g. tramps, gypsies, nomads). Also this curse comes through rendering evil to those who have done you good. And please note, if you gossip and run down and malign someone from whom you have received Jesus or effective ministry, you fall into this category even if you are cosily established in the stockbroker belt, secure in your position and residence! So beware!

The Curse of Eve and the Curse of the Vagabond cassettes are by Robert Ellender, Harvest Christian Fellowship, N108 W. 17376 Lilac Lane, Germantown, Wisconsin 53022, USA.

The Holy Spirit then showed me the ancestral curses of lust, alcohol, insanity and insane violence. These latter two are decidedly not the same curses. Some insane folk would not harm a fly, they are so feeble. Others are violent and murderous through insanity.

One of my team, a very, very tall gentleman and head of a university department had felt for some years that there was still a spiritual problem in his life. There was a history of insane violence, with terrible damage inflicted upon family members in years past by the perpetrator. One day I discerned this so strongly in my brother in Christ I agreed to minister to him. His main deliverance has been some years previously.

The whole team were assembled for this time of prayer and Raj was with us. I believe my brother is 6′ 4″, I am 5′ 2″ and when I broke this curse and called out the spirit which executed the curse it looked as if I would be strangled, and I saw Raj jump into position to ward off the attack if need be, because my brother's enormous hands came out towards my throat with such a roaring and eyes so wild. I am known to stand and not back off at such times claiming the blood and authority of Jesus Christ. The hands with spreading fingers stopped just short of my throat and the demon came out. Phew! It was a bit nerve-wracking I must admit, but greater is He that is in us! A little shock is not surprising when such a gentle loving brother acts so completely out of character!

The prayer set out as follows should suffice for all your needs:

The Prayer

Remember you are praying to the Head of the Church — the Lord Jesus Christ.

Lord Jesus Christ, I believe that you are the Son of God, and the only way to God, that you died on the cross for my sins and rose again from the dead. I renounce all my sins and I turn to you, Lord Jesus, for mercy and forgiveness. I believe that you do forgive me and from now on I want to live for you. I want to hear your voice and obey. In order to receive your blessing, Lord, and to be released from any curse over my life, first of all I confess any known or unknown sin committed by me or my ancestors or those related to me. (Confess your sins and any known ancestral sins; do this audibly but quietly.) Lord, I thank you, I believe you have forgiven everything I have confessed and, Lord, now I say that I forgive all other persons who have ever wronged me. I forgive them all now as I would have God forgive me and I forgive myself. In particular I forgive (name persons, speak out quietly). Furthermore, Lord I renounce any contact by myself or any related to me with Satan or any occult power of any form or any secret society.

Also Lord, I commit myself to remove from my house and my person any kind of occult objects that honour Satan but dishonour Jesus Christ. With your help Lord I will remove them all – and now, Lord Jesus, I thank you further, that on the cross you were made a curse, that I might be redeemed from the curse and receive the blessing, and because of what you did for me on the cross, I now release myself from every evil curse and every evil influence and every dark shadow over me or my family from any source whatsoever. I release myself now in the Name of Jesus. Amen. Amen.

Now, Lord Jesus, because of your people's prayer, I, as your anointed representative take the sword of the Spirit and I break in the Name of Jesus any ancestral curse over them.

I break in the Name of Jesus the curse of **witchcraft**,
I break in the Name of Jesus the curse of **freemasonry**,
I break in the Name of Jesus the curse of **incest**,

I break in the Name of Jesus the curse of **poverty**,
I break in the Name of Jesus the curse of **infirmity**,
I break in the Name of Jesus the curse of **accident prone-ness**,
I break in the Name of Jesus the curse of **rejection**,
I break in the Name of Jesus the curse of the **root of bitterness**,
I break in the Name of Jesus the curse of **rebellion**,
I break in the Name of Jesus the curse of **humiliation**,
I break in the Name of Jesus the curse of **Eve**,
I break in the Name of Jesus the curse of the **vagabond**,
I break in the Name of Jesus the curse of **alcohol**,
I break in the Name of Jesus the curse of **lust**,
I break in the Name of Jesus the curse of **insanity/insane violence**.
I seal over the windows and doors of their memories from all past hurts and wrongdoing with the Blood of Jesus.

In the Name of Jesus, I pronounce the forgiveness of sins for your ancestors and yourselves, and I say to you all in the Name of Jesus come out from under the curse and receive the blessing of the Lord which maketh rich. I pronounce in the Name of Jesus that for your shame you shall have glory. Now – Praise the Lord, you are free from curse and ancestral curse, you are forgiven.

Now turn to someone and tell them 'I believe that I am free from curse'.

Now exhale deeply and slowly the spirits executing each curse.

In the Name of Jesus Christ I call out the spirit that executes the curse of **witchcraft**,
In the Name of Jesus Christ I call out the spirit that executes the curse of **freemasonry**,
In the Name of Jesus Christ I call out the spirit that executes the curse of **incest**,
In the Name of Jesus Christ I call out the spirit that executes the curse of **poverty**,

109

In the Name of Jesus Christ I call out the spirit that executes the curse of **infirmity**,

In the Name of Jesus Christ I call out the spirit that executes the curse of **accident proneness**,

In the Name of Jesus Christ I call out the spirit that executes the curse of **rejection**,

In the Name of Jesus Christ I call out the spirit that executes the curse of the **root of bitterness**,

In the Name of Jesus Christ I call out the spirit that executes the curse of **rebellion**,

In the Name of Jesus Christ I call out the spirit that executes the curse of **humiliation**,

In the Name of Jesus Christ I call out the spirit that executes the curse of **Eve**,

In the Name of Jesus Christ I call out the spirit that executes the curse of the **vagabond**,

In the Name of Jesus Christ I call out the spirit that executes the curse of **alcohol**,

In the Name of Jesus Christ I call out the spirit that executes the curse of **lust**,

In the Name of Jesus Christ I call out the spirit that executes the curse of **insanity/insane violence**.

Now raise your hands in the air and say, 'I praise you Lord that I am free.' Give Jesus all the glory and to this daily for a month, as you step out of bed in the morning.

Chapter 14

The Baby

It was the morning of September 15th 1992. I was single-handed in the consulting room and facing a busy day. One of my patients arrived with the eldest of her three small children, a very hyperactive child. Because I do not care for other small children in the room when I am assessing such infants I had asked the mother not to bring her baby and the second daughter. So I was astonished to see her propping a baby up in the back seat of her car when she turned into the driveway. I stared hard through the window downstairs as I saw her giving the baby a bottle, thinking how peculiar since I knew she was breast feeding her little son. Then I saw that it was in fact not her child. I was a bit concerned about the baby being left in the car and clearly so was she. My receptionist opened the front door and I followed behind her immediately sensing agitation in the mother.

'Oh dear!' she apologised, 'I am sorry, I am minding this little baby and I simply could not get anyone to take him as they were having my own two.' She explained that she was also a foster mother and that this baby was hers for six weeks.

'It is an emergency,' she told me.

By this time the Clinic was twenty minutes behind which I loathe. Henri, the young woman who was healed of ME was wih me as she had been coming on Tuesdays with her

111

husband, Warren, to sit in on Clinic activities. I had amassed a whole pile of filing and other things for Henri to do, and I felt quite put out as I said to the relief of my patient's mother,

'Look you had better go and get the baby and Henri will just have to hold him for half an hour.'

We went upstairs to the consulting room and I hurriedly made a start on the examination of the elder child. Meanwhile Cynthia was busily chattering away explaining that knowing I wanted to see her alone with her daughter, she had gone everywhere for someone to mind the child but they were unwilling. She explained that this little scrap of a boy, so small and so sad looking was the result of an unsuccessful abortion. Apparently his mother arrived all bloodied and unsuccessfully aborted in a complete mess at the hospital. Once the baby was born the mother left him saying she did not want him. I felt sick inside. He was so very small, like a compact little doll in one of those one-piece stretch towelling suits. As we descended the stairs to the office, the Holy Spirit told me to minister to the child. I went and plucked him from Henri's arms. Now we really were late and the next patient was waiting to come upstairs. As I held the baby I began to weep. I was cuddling him up very close. I had no idea what I was going to do, certainly I had no idea I would be weeping copiously and showering him with my tears.

Henri, Warren and Lisa jumped up and gathered round me. I asked Lisa to get me some water. I called out to the Father for mercy for this little boy.

'Father, he has nobody, you knew him before he was even conceived in his mother's womb and that an attempt has been made to murder him. Help him Father! I am going to baptize him now into Your Son Jesus.'

This I did and prayed in the Spirit over him, then I heard again:

'Minister to him.'

The anointing was so strong. I found myself taking

authority over the spirit of rejection, the spirit of murder and the spirit of abortion. I bound them in Jesus' name and commanded them to leave in His name. As I did this the small boy gave an enormous sigh and he turned his face up to mine and smiled. We all saw it and rejoiced. Don't tell me demons are not real!

I then prayed his adoption by the Father, we all laid hands on him and Cynthia took him home. Cynthia rang me later and said:

'I knew it was God's intention as I hunted around for someone to have him, for him to come to the Clinic. Now I know why!'

That was another situation in which I thanked my Father for the anointing. All day I felt so happy that this little sweetheart had been claimed for Jesus.

'Suffer the little children to come unto me.'

This small baby was brought to see me two weeks later. An orphan spirit was quickly dealt with in Jesus' name and he responded in the identical way with a sigh followed by a smile.

As he chuckled and smiled at me Cynthia told me that he had been totally transformed by his initial deliverance and there was good news that he was to be adopted into a Christian family.

I can tell you that I really wanted to keep him myself!

Another baby has now been brought to the Clinic following abandonment at birth by his mother. I prayed deliverance in exactly the same manner, and the baby was set free. I have now directed the foster mother to bring to us any babies she is fostering!

Chapter 15

Deuteronomy 27:17

A lady wrote to me from the Isle of Man about her friend who had returned recently from a long vacation in Australia. She arrived to find that a neighbour had fenced off part of her garden and taken it over. The lady who wrote said she had just read *Go and Do Likewise*, and what could her friend do as the lawyers seemed unable to help?

It's quite amazing the questions I am asked sometimes, but in spite of being swamped with mail I was led by the Holy Spirit to reply, especially as she enclosed that delight, a stamped addressed envelope! I was in fact able to share with the correspondent my own story.

One day over a bank holiday with Christian friends visiting, we arrived back from a lovely country walk to find that my neighbour had hacked the roots of a conifer hedge at the rear of my property. These beautiful trees had been planted and established over some nineteen years. They had replaced fencing covered with ivy and honeysuckle, which had blown down in a storm. These particular conifers were chosen for their shallow bowl like roots and beautiful green and yellow tipped foliage. They also screened my kitchen view from a very ugly collapsing wooden garage constructed onto a concrete base, and the very untidy dilapidated garden next door, sadly neglected in pursuit of golf! Apart from this, the hedging was always full of nesting birds which gave me such delight because with the bird table near the window over the kitchen sink, I could have a never-ending treat of seeing the birds making a short trip to their nearest food supply. I am certain that I have written many times that my garden is a bird sanctuary.

We all gazed in disbelief at the conifers leaning dangerously towards the house. They were about fifteen feet tall and nicely trimmed into hedging. Attached to each tree was a white postcard which read 'These trees have to be removed by Monday (it was the Saturday of a bank holiday) or I will take them down and leave them on your lawn.' The neighbour must have trespassed upon my property to fasten these notes in such a position! Shaking with a mixture of shock and indignation I rushed next door to confront my neighbour.

I was extremely friendly with his wife who actually worked for me at a time when I would employ nominal Christians. However, for some peculiar reason the husband was always a bit cool towards me. They had been neighbours about ten years. At that time I had resided some twenty one years at the property. His wife stayed on after I got born again and was amazed at the happenings. I felt not to dismiss her although she did not meet the new Holy Spirit requirements for staff. She was getting very keen and impressed by what she saw and confessed herself to be the daughter of a freemason and said that her Scots grandmother also dressed up in some regalia with a big hat. She was due to have ministry the same week as this incident occurred, and of course Satan stole this release from her.

Upon challenging the husband he informed me that a new garage was to be built in place of his old one, made in concrete slabs, and that the roots of my trees were infringing his land by two inches! What is more, that I already had an extra two inches of his land! The area referred to ran behind his old garage and another even more broken down shed adjoining it, and a sort of waste tip for junk, fortunately screened by my own garage.

116

As I looked into his coal black eyes I wasn't really expecting to see demonic activity. But there it was, a raging jealousy and hatred! I had no idea what it was until much later.

I was a single woman with a very immaculate property and garden and this highlighted the ramshackle condition of his own premises where the grass was rarely cut, the garden rarely weeded and heaps of junk lay about in piles to be taken away but never was – bits of old fencing, scrap metal and tiles from an old bathroom, lots of logs and an assortment of plastic buckets and old garden crocks. Frankly I was always glad I couldn't see too much from where I was.

It was a grand old house with much potential and quite honestly on the few occasions I went inside, that wasn't much better than the outside, being greatly in need of decorating and modernisation.

What was the problem here? This affluent man had two idols – golf, and his BMW which was his firm's car really, but he kept it immaculate. He would stride around gazing at it, and his wife would often joke 'No money for decorating, only for golf and BMW's.' I believe really it was her lament.

She was a busy working lady with children, doing what she could in the time she had, with very limited resources. They had arrived to live next door at the time my former husband had ransacked the house, and my neighbour saw me refurbish everything and maintain the property to a high standard, in spite of the departure of a very industrious and capable spouse. He of course, did not realise that what God had given me had to glorify Him, and that the Holy Spirit helped me all along the way to refurnish. I wasn't dealing with a Christian I could reason with! The man was very threatening and I was dealing with the shock of what I was seeing in a neighbour whose face I had never had the opportunity to really look into before. His wife had told me that he was very unsociable and I had

117

accepted that. They did come to a dinner party once with some neighbours and medical friends and it was not at all an unpleasant time. This was when they had not long moved in and I wanted to make them feel wanted.

This tree saga went on. I kept claiming God's protection and that the trees were rooted and grounded in love. My lawyer came personally and advised me that my neighbour had stolen land from an established boundary. However, he claimed that boundary disputes can go on forever and advised me not to proceed because of the costs involved. He said, 'You'll just have to establish a new hedge with some fast growing shrubbery a few inches in.' This meant digging up my crazy paving at the rear of the property at my expense, getting the trees now endangering the property carted away at my expense and buying more trees or shrubs also at no small expense. But there was worse to follow. The trees ultimately died and were dangerous in spite of much propping up. They did not need much digging out as they were very shallow bowl roots the size of which indicated to anyone that they had indeed not constituted a problem for the new garage that they changed for the old. In any event the same base was to be used. So there had to be another explanation.

Remember, all the time I was calling out to God, speaking the Word over the situation. In that year I was still very much into the faith and prosperity message, I was naming it and claiming it for all I was worth. Was God deaf? Many others stood in agreement with me. Finally the trees were cleared and the old wooden garage removed revealing nothing more than a back garden resembling a scrap yard. I was informed that there was no point in putting up a fence as the men would want to walk around to paint the new garage which would be erected within ten days.

No prizes for guessing! The builders did not come on time, and apart from the eyesore I had to contend with, a dog arrived to trespass on my land, chase my beautiful

Burmese brown cat and foul my lawn. A few pathetic strings were strung across the area when I complained, but they were no match for this athletic crossbreed. What he couldn't get under he jumped over and his tunnelling instincts made the average mole look like an apprentice. Also this dog was noisy. It wanted to explore my garage, my potting shed, even the house, entering through the French windows with its great tail lashing delicate ornaments off low tables etc. etc. My beautiful silky Sable, gentle and loving, established without question within my boundaries for some fifteen years, was terrified of this intruder.

I adored Sable. Yes, that was shown to be true, and adoration of animals is not permitted by the Lord any more than adoration of men or motor cars! She was the silkiest good natured cat who was constant when all else dear to me, had been eroded away. She loved me. She would sit draped around my shoulders whilst I wrote, and curl up on my lap at every opportunity. In winter she became a furry hot water bottle for my feet and would purr all night under the duvet. I recall decades ago I used to say to my son, 'No cats in beds!' I often wondered what he would have thought to see me at that time succumbing to the wiles of this enchanting, entertaining cat. So great was my idolatry that because she wouldn't eat if I was away ministering, I used to pay someone to come and stroke her three times a day! Yes, I know it was ridiculous, I did the same with my Russian Blue cat who died at the age of twenty three. She had been rescued from ill treatment.

I am writing this because ultimately I was convicted when I heard Derek Prince say that inordinate love of animals could constitute witchcraft. This was only two cats of course!

The final straw was when this four footed creature next door cornered Sable in my garage. There was still no sign of the proposed garage being erected! Following being rescued Sable hid under my bed and literally would not come out for days. I lay on the floor at all angles trying to reach her. I was not unkind enough to poke her out with a broom!

From that time onwards she was reluctant to eat or drink. Later the vet explained that severe shock had sent her into renal failure. All this misery on top of the eyesore from my window and damage done by the dog to my property, and useless appeals from me for decency, made me wonder where the Lord was. Then one day whilst praying after Sable's demise, I heard the words so clearly,

'Vengeance is mine: I will repay, saith the Lord.' I knew it was God, so I shut up petitioning and left it to Him. He also led me to Deuteronomy 27:17 *'Cursed is the one who moves his neighbour's landmark. And all the people shall say "Amen"!'* I felt very encouraged. Then one day whilst waiting for God to act, I was visited by a pastor and his wife. I was walking them around the property when the wife enquired, 'What about your neighbours?'

'You might well ask,' I replied, revealing the whole unpleasant story.

She looked at me and asked, 'Have you blessed them, dear?' Groaning inwardly I replied, 'No, I jolly well haven't.' Elsa started to bless them and I found myself joining in, albeit with unspoken protest. Then I vaguely recalled a scripture somewhere in the Bible which said *'Bless those who despitefully use you and the Lord shall reward thee.'* Remembering this promise I prayed with more fervour and continued to do so. Elsa had also asked me if they might move and I had told her 'Not a chance'!

Now this is what happened in the order of the events:

1. The man was made redundant.
2. He lost his BMW and had to use his wife's tiny mini.
3. He had to resign from the golf club as he had no money for fees.

4. He continued in unemployment, and one could almost sense him wishing he had not spent money on the new garage.
5. A storm came, blowing down part of his fencing on all sides of his property except the side adjoining mine. His car port was demolished and roof badly damaged.
6. He had to leave to go to work hundreds of miles away and the property would not sell. Finally it had to go for a pittance.
7. His lovely wife got cancer and had to have surgery, and the children had to leave private school.
8. The house remained empty for months and months and was finally occupied by a lovely responsible family who are diligently licking it all into shape.

I was not delighted at what happened, but gasped at the awesomeness of God's Word. I could give many other examples of God being the judge and jury on my behalf. I finally contacted Faith, part of whose garden had been illegitimately fenced off by her neighbour. She told me that he was into martial arts and agreed it felt like spiritual warfare. We prayed against this strongman and because of this lady's love of the Lord I know He will act on her behalf as she stands and claims Deuteronomy 27:17. What happens will have to go in my next book. Blessed be the name of the Lord!

Chapter 16

Letter to the Team and Intercessors

It has been customary for me to circulate the team and intercessors following public meetings. The exhortations that follow later in this chapter, went out to those beloved brothers and sisters who stood with me so faithfully in a corporate anointing on January 29th, 1992.

We now have a very expert ministry team operating in South East London, consisting mainly of African brothers and sisters. Since we see a lot of Africans it has been wonderful to see the Holy Spirit establishing their ministry.

Upon arrival at this meeting in Dorset I was greeted by an officer who informed me that the Vicar who organised the meeting was totally debilitated with an unknown virus. I knew this dear brother had been severely under attack since he commenced organising the meeting on healing and deliverance but I was shocked because I had spoken to him only forty-eight hours previously. His wife whom I had not met informed me sadly, 'Pearl, if he could have crawled here he would have done so.'

I must say I was not only disappointed and dismayed but I had a real sense in my gut that this could not be the Lord's will when his servant had struggled against all odds and much persecution to put on this meeting. Before I took the platform to open the meeting, I was asked to pray for Mrs Ponnampalam of Ipoh, West Malaysia. This lady was the mother of Raj Kumar the guitarist pictured on the front of my second book *Fruit Abiding in the Vine*. She had suffered terrible head injuries and paralysis and haemorrhage following a road accident in which she was catapulted through a car windscreen. A daughter travelling with her was killed, one son badly injured, whilst her son Raj escaped with severe shock of which he was not delivered until some twenty years later at the Clinic! There was severe brain damage to the central nervous system, but the church prayed and she was miraculously raised up. As a result her unbelieving husband got born again.

In 1991 a cancer of the eyelid was discovered and the eldest son rang the Clinic where Raj was with us for rehabilitation following heroin addiction. He too was healed by the Lord after 12 years addiction. Raj was told by his brother that the cancer was believed to have infiltrated the cranium and in order to prevent it reaching the brain, part of his mother's face would have to be removed and reconstructed, and she was to be admitted to hospital for surgery.

'No, do not receive this,' I told the brothers. 'If it is established in the eyelid, we can curse it and command it in the Name of Jesus to be confined to that place and not to spread.'

We got into agreement, I cursed the cancer and under the anaesthetic it was found to be confined simply to the eyelid. A new eyelid was constructed successfully with plastic surgery. The sight in this eye had been waning for some time, and Mrs Ponnampalam asked if she could be considered for a lens to be implanted. However the eyeball was so misshapen, thought to be due to the accident all those years ago, that it could not receive a lens. The surgeon said that he would have another look when the making of a new eyelid had been completed and the surgery had settled down. The Monday following the Saturday meeting the surgeon was to investigate the possibility of a lens again. I was asked to pray that the eyeball would be made normal to receive a lens. Also Sister Rachel at the Clinic asked us to pray as the Church for a very sick missionary in France. He became desperately ill whilst investigating and exposing the occult in French schools. He developed myasthenia gravis, cancer of the heart, suffered respiratory failure, and had to have a tracheotomy. Finally he had been six months on life support at the time we were asked to pray. His wife was told that he would never go home again.

Rachel's church had been involved in intercession for his life because her husband went to visit him in France and the missionary conveyed to him that he believed his sickness was demonic and if the Church prayed, God would raise him up. So with those three heavy loads I ascended the platform and as I was welcoming those gathered in a hall packed to standing capacity, God spoke to me very clearly, 'Pray for the vicar and I will raise him up.'

At the same time a voice said so clearly in my ear, 'You'll look stupid if you pray and he doesn't come.'

I was in no doubt at all to whom the second voice belonged! I was being challenged. I addressed the gathering as 'Church'. I said that I was going to pray in faith and in agreement with them as the Church and that God was going to raise up the vicar and get him to the meeting. Then I prayed for Raj's mother and the missionary.

The Lord was so good. The vicar was raised up and arrived at the meeting to a tumultuous reception. I anointed him with oil and was almost in tears myself. Tears of pure joy. Later I heard that under anaesthetic Raj's mother's eyeball was found to be normal and she received a new lens and consequent sight. Then I heard that the missionary was miraculously off life support, the cancer of the heart disappeared and he was home with his wife, to the doctors' astonishment.

We give the Lord Jesus all the praise and all the glory

for these wonderful healings. I feel that the agreement of so many of God's people counted for much, but I know that much spade-work was done by Rachel's prayer warriors also. Praise the Lord!

In the small hours of the morning, prior to that meeting the Lord had me scribbling down a revelation which I will share in the next chapter. There follows my exhortation to the team and intercessors on January 29th, 1992.

'Beloved,

So many letters and comments have reached me concerning the meeting on the 18th January, that I have really had some special time thanking God for you all and for the anointing and miracles He gave us all that day.

It is not new for me to comment on the love of Jesus which binds us together and causes great and real compassion to be in us for those to whom we minister God's grace and healing. We all know that the same **love** is the most powerful message of the Gospel – and that the love of Jesus is quite unconditional.

I found myself reflecting yet again on the teaching of my former Pastor and Bible School Teacher Rod Anderson. Rod always used to remind us that it is God's goodness which draws us to repentance (Romans 2:4, Amplified Bible), and His goodness to us all that day certainly inspired me yet again to seek holiness and obedience above all things.

Just look at Ephesians 1:2–5 in the Amplified Bible:

2. *May grace (which is God's unmerited favour) and spiritual peace (which means peace with God and harmony, unity and undisturbedness) be yours from God our Father and from the Lord Jesus Christ.*

126

3. Blessing (praise, laudation and eulogy) be to the God and Father of our Lord Jesus Christ, the Messiah, who has placed us in Christ with every spiritual (Holy Spirit given) blessing in the heavenly realm!

4. Even as (in His love) he chose us – actually picked us out for Himself as His own – in Christ before the foundation of the world; that we should be holy (consecrated and set apart for Him) and blameless in His sight even above reproach before Him in love.

5. For He fore-ordained us (destined us, planned in love for us) to be adopted (revealed) as His own children through Jesus Christ, in accordance with the purpose of His will – because it pleased Him and was His kind intent;

These verses surely illustrate His love, that He picked us out and that we are accepted in the beloved. Everything God does is planned in **love**. Hebrews 11:6 – *He that comes to God must first believe that He is*. We need so much to understand the character and nature of our heavenly Father.

One has to understand the Word to bring forth fruit. The Scriptures tell us this. We read in 1 John 4:18 that perfect love casts out fear and this includes fear of man and fear of rejection from which so many Christians suffer.

We must have **faith towards** God **not** faith in something.

The only way this faith can be cultivated is by spending time with Him **alone**. Yes, it is good to have corporate prayer – but the danger here is that we prop each other up too much. Personally I was taught, and I feel so deeply, that corporate prayer should in the main be in the Holy Spirit, e.g. praying in tongues, which not only builds us up – but is a prayer of agreement by the Body. It is the perfect will of God being prayed over people's lives. We must beware of going to God with a shopping list. "Please will you do this for Aunty Ann and that for Joe Bloggs." *Maybe God doesn't want to* – and Father knows best!

Attitudes register before the Spirit of Almighty God. Paul, writing to the Church at Corinth on incest (1 Corinthians 5) was writing these things to test their attitudes. He advised that such offenders should be expelled. If the Spirit is dealt with, the flesh must come into line. Jesus Christ dealt with hearts and attitudes. Attitudes towards the Word must not become mechanical or religious because we are familiar with it. Rod Anderson used to tell us that he loved to "hang around with God all day." I know exactly what he means, there is nothing mechanical about it. It can mean what Rod used to call having "2 minute lovelies" with the Father all day!

Praying in the Spirit one hour each day does not qualify us for spirituality. Naturally walking in the Spirit does. The habit of prayer must not be the source of our faith in God. God is not a habit; we are communing with a Father whose Spirit dwells within us to quicken our mortal body.

When the truth and Spirit of Scripture is alive in our lives we are able ministers of the Spirit which brings life. The letter does not bring **life**. (Read 2 Corinthians 3.)

Yes, we need to be able to quote the Scriptures but that is not just parrotting them, but having the Spirit of the Word so deep within, and the reverential fear of the Lord calls sin **sin**.

A rebuke which wins over is a rebuke which comes from **love**. Authority that functions and works is one that has been achieved through having established a relationship with Christ. Earthly knowledge only produces arrogance.

Just look at Ephesians 2:1–4 which concludes with the "*wonderful and intense love with which He loved us.*"

Fellowship with our Creator has to be first on the list of priorities. On a tape recently, I heard Derek Prince speaking of God having spent the last three years "dealing with Ruth concerning her attitude towards me" (Derek). She had received to put Derek second. I know it is easy for me to speak now as I am single. But how many of you are putting spouses *before* the Father when He does not want to be second in line?

Somebody preached recently that duty to families can even be a cop out! My former Pastor was eight years a heroin addict. He used to tell us of his frustration if he could not get the time he was used to with the Father, that withdrawal from God was like withdrawal from heroin. It is hell if you are used to spending time with God. I realised that this has been one of my problems during the last year. I got scratchy and irritable – not being with Him as much as I was used to.

The Father just loves to have your company. With his intense love towards us (Ephesians 1:4) He does not have a check list with which He is waiting to zap you before He will move into your life. Understand who He is. He is **your Father**.

Rod told us that one day when he was wailing before God about his own shortcomings, that he couldn't be blessed because of this and because of that, the Father spoke clearly in his ear, saying:

"Son, I wish you would recognise this. There is a lot more right about you than there is wrong."

He said it really set him free. I must say it set me free too – so if you are dosing yourself with self-condemnation – stop it. Understand who **He** is.

Release your shortcomings. We often have great faith in the negative and God by His Spirit will convert that to the positive. Heartfelt prayer will strengthen and increase your relationship with the Father. The prayers of the righteous are short!

The ministry God has blessed us all with, is effective only in direct relationship to the amount of time we spend 'getting to know our Father!' *Before you can touch people you have to first touch God*. Otherwise it's just a bunch of Christian works! The time we spend with God affects and effects ministry – not praying about the ministry or our business. See Ephesians 2:6 Amplified Bible of the *"joint seating with Him."* **Wow**!

1 Thessalonians 5:17 exhorts us to be unceasing in prayer, Luke 18:1 to pray and not to faint or turn coward.

Warning

No gifting from God can stand for long without the backing of intercessory prayer and a personal relationship with the Father. Faith must not be in the gift but *the giver of the gift*. Eloquence, gifting, is obsolete without **love** which can only come from having a genuine relationship with the Father. True spiritual maturity is defined by how much of God flows through your life towards the lives of others. Such love is free from judgment and condemnation of others. Yes, we need to be alert for deception, rogue ministries, false prophets and doctrines spreading like wildfire through the Body of Christ in these End Times – but our protection is getting on with establishing a right relationship with our Father and making Him number one even before our loved ones.

Derek Prince says **anything** which comes before God is **idolatry**. **Anything!** Three weeks ago I was on my knees confessing idolatry. I called out to God "Oh No, God! Not again! How could I?" I just saw so clearly something had inched in to prise me away from time with my Dad! All so legitimate too! I just

130

got rid of that thing so fast I can tell you – and He renewed a right spirit within me. Praise His Name. Don't be hesitant to keep on spring-cleaning yourself out, beloved. Always recognise demonic activity as a time-wasting spirit, a harassing spirit, diverting you from time with the Father. Heartfelt prayer keeps us ahead of the devil. Lack of prayer time brings ultimate defeat.

I was speaking to a worship leader from Kensington Temple recently. She said, "there is simply no time left other than to get on with what God tells you to do and to be first accountable to Him." I would add that if we wait for the approval of men we are in danger of doing nothing!

Well that's got that off my chest. I have brought it to you following fellowship with my Father.

I love and bless you all,
Pearl.'

Chapter 17

Revelations Prior to the
Dorset Meeting

Star of David – Occult?

During the fasting and prayer time prior to the teaching
and ministry of January 18th, 1992, I believe that I had
revelation from the Lord on the occultism behind the Star
of David. It is a question I am often asked at question
time. 'Is it alright to wear the Star of David?' My answer is
always '**no**'. I have quite a few experiences that have given
me dis-ease of some consideration – including ministry to a
Jewess in Israel, where relatives had died in death camps.
The Lord would *not* allow me to proceed before the Star
of David, a heavy gold one, was destroyed. It transpired
that the lady herself was uneasy about it, and I know
several men of God who have felt the same dis-ease.

I was thinking about Rev. David Pennant's comment
concerning emphasis on worship time in many churches as
I was studying Amos. See chapter 5:3, 6:6 and read verses
25 and 26 of Amos 5 (Amplified).

I believe the star God referred to is the Star of David.
Pray about it and let me know how your spirit witnesses.
Thank you. When I visit Israel with my personal intercessor we both feel very uneasy with the Star of David on
just about everything. One lady I know was healed of a

serious throat problem when she removed the gold star of David she wore round her neck permanently.

Twin Spirits – Perverse and Foolish

The second revelation I received was on the twin spirits of perversity and foolishness. We are aware of other twin spirits of course. The commonest seem to be fear and torment, rejection and lying.

The Lord commenced by reminding me of the spirits of excellence in Daniel:

> *Because an excellent spirit, knowledge, and understanding to interpret dreams, clarify riddles, and solve knotty problems were found in this same Daniel, whom the king named Belteshazzar. Now let Daniel be called, and he will show the interpretation.*
>
> (Daniel 5:12)

> *Then this Daniel was distinguished above the presidents and the satraps because an excellent spirit was in him, and the king thought to set him over the whole realm.*
>
> (Daniel 6:3)

I was shown that wisdom is the twin to excellence and that we cannot have one without the other: e.g. excellence = wisdom; wisdom = excellence. It seemed that I was being shown that foolishness was the opposite of wisdom and perversity the opposite of excellence.

I then did a study of the perverse spirit and found that it nearly always is mentioned with foolishness. There are many examples in Proverbs of a perverse spirit, perverse lips, tongue, heart, etc, for example Proverbs 4:24, 8:8, (that is headed the proverb of excellence and wisdom) 11:20, 12:8, 14:2 (verse 3, 7 and 17 refer to fools or foolishness) 17:20, 19:1 (perverse and foolish coupled together) 21:8, 28:6. These are just a few.

Other scriptural references are Numbers 22:52 The

Angel of the Lord called Balaam perverse *'Your way is perverse.'* In Deuteronomy 32:5, Moses called the Israelites in the Song of Moses *'A perverse and crooked generation.'* In verse 6 he says *'Oh foolish and unwise people.'*

1 Samuel 20:30 the Bible speaks of Saul's anger against Jonathan. *'You son of a perverse and rebellious woman.'*

Isaiah 19:14 proclaims against Egypt *'The Lord has mingled a perverse spirit in her.'*

Proverbs 8:8 – see excellence and wisdom.

Proverbs 14:2–3 links up between foolishness and pride.

I looked up **perverse** in Webster's dictionary.

Perverse

1. Turned away from what is right and good.
2. Corrupt, improper, incorrect.
3. Contrary to the evidence or the direction of the judge on a point of law.
4. Obstinate in opposing what is right, reasonable or accepted.
5. Wrong headed arising from or indicative of stubbornness or obstinacy.
6. Marked by peevishness or petulance.
7. Contrary.

These are the basic meanings.

Foolish

Marked by or proceeding from folly. **Folly** = lack of good sense, normal prudence or foresight.

A fool = can lack in common powers of understanding – even be harmlessly deranged.

So there is a curse of dimwittedness or stupidity here – and how often in demonic activity do we say 'Why can't they see what Satan is doing to them?'

Satan blinds eyes, but if someone had a foolish spirit it could block the exit of perversity.

Anyway I hope you can see what I am getting at. I

couldn't bring it all to the meeting, there simply was not enough time. However, it was clearly given to me for some folk present, one young man who was delivered of the spirit of perversity, as an ex-Satanist had 'I am perverse' on his sweat shirt! I've *not* seen that one before!

When I bring these things to the Body of Christ it is so these others may check or comment on them. It is what I believe I have received from the Holy Spirit and I expect and advise those around me to test out everything coming from me and I really welcome any comments or observations others have.

Testimonies continue to arrive concerning 'Wednesday's child (full of woe),' in the demonic nursery rhyme about the days of the week one could be born on. See Chapter 31 of *Fruit Abiding In the Vine*, for me such a remarkable testimony.

Chapter 18

A Visit to Mayday Ministries

In early September 1992, a magazine entitled *Healing and Wholeness* arrived in the post sent by one of my intercessors. She had ringed round an article 'Healed from ME' for me to read. They were all very moving testimonies, but what really caught my eye was a little square at the foot of the page which was entitled Mayday Ministries. A single paragraph stated that this ministry, linked up with Sozo Fellowship in Romsey, had ministered to at least twelve people with ME although initially they had not even known what ME was and they had all been totally healed.

Now my interest was really aroused! Also a commentary by the Editor, headed 'Editor's Note' read,

> 'No member of our editorial team has yet had the opportunity of visiting and assessing Mayday Ministries for Healing and Wholeness.'

An idea began to take shape in my mind! How about if I donned my investigative journalist's hat and went along to sniff the air? I also liked the name Mayday which is the SOS signal 'Mayday, Mayday' given by ships who are sinking, and my little vessel was certainly floundering in rough seas!

I shared both the article and my idea with the team and

we decided to test the waters for my seemingly leaking boat!

Three of us fasted for seven days on water and travelled to Romsey on the sixth day. I must admit I was feeling a little weak and the ME was certainly not in remission! However, the precious Holy Spirit undertook and I drove us there with comparative ease. We took Holy Communion before we left and I told Rufus and Nyakwera that I was going with a completely open mind to see if there was something there for me to receive.

As I drove I was suddenly aware of the anointing stirring an excitement in me and also bringing a most incredible peace. I was sensing that my brother and sister in Christ were feeling the same and both of their faces were shining with an incredible radiance. We arrived at Mountbatten School in Romsey in plenty of time and Nyakwera and I swiftly made our way to the cloakroom. We had been consuming large amounts of water during the fast! As we refreshed ourselves, various ladies and children started to come in to use the school lavatories and I must confess I was surprised to see so many children. They certainly didn't appear sick. As I was drying my hands a lady came up to me with a beautiful smile on her face and bade us welcome.

'Oh, hello,' I said. 'How long does the service last?' The service commenced at 2.30 pm. 'That depends on the Holy Spirit' was the welcome reply, 'but we certainly do not expect people to travel for such a long way for a couple of hours.'

It was then explained that worship took place for about two hours, then the children made an exit whilst the Word came forth, then there would be ministry until 6.30 pm or thereabouts, after which there was a break. During this time refreshments were able to be purchased and a bookstall visited and fellowship could take place. After this private counselling was available if needed, but people usually received in the assembly.

Now I was getting excited and so were my companions. A meeting led by the Holy Spirit, somewhat open ended, but orderly and where people did not normally need private counselling. This was all music to my ears, and wasn't it what God had been speaking to me about during those months of closeness with Him? Indeed it was! Praise His Holy Name!

We entered the large school hall and assembled ourselves near the front to the left. Placing my Bible and notebook in front of me on the floor, I sniffed the air and there it was, the fragrance of the Holy Spirit. And the anointing upon me at that self-same time was so electric I felt I could have marched down those rows and scattered the enemy. But I was not present for that purpose.

I could sense my companions aware of the holiness around us. The children seemed to have a special composure. I discovered much later that some of those little ones were very anointed indeed. Tiny tots were allowed to toddle around freely. Normally this would have concerned me, but I felt an incredible peace. I was well aware that I had come to test the waters and I recall I turned to Rufus sitting on my left and told him, 'I don't think I need counselling, but I'm going to receive anything going in the assembly.'

In a short time I could witness that nothing was allowed to cut across the anointing. I was wondering why I had such an anointing since I was there simply to receive. My Father certainly knew. We worshipped in Spirit and in Truth for almost two hours. I could sense my Father's delight as He smiled down on us. There were people there from as far away as Yorkshire and Cornwall. What is more, the lady who had greeted me in the ladies' loo was Marion Daniel who ministered! She was lovely, she had the anointing, and she was certainly uncompromisingly righteous. No, I am not given to flattery nor am I given to idolatry, but when I recognise the anointing I will say so and I will eagerly and expectantly sit under it and that's what I did.

I felt that I was floating and shining and then I went up for prayer. I received ministry, which was swift and simple. Marion asked me some pertinent questions which revealed a definite spiritual insight and discernment. The Word that was given before the ministry was so simple and based on four Scriptures, Scriptures I knew well but which in the busy and demanding schedule of ministry without respite to others, had slipped away and become unreal.

I began to identify with Johannes Facius author of *God Can Do It Without Me* even more, as the reality and eternal truth of those precious scriptures came sharply into focus. The scriptures were,

> *'Death and life are in the power of the tongue.'*
> (Proverbs 18:21)

As Marion spoke of the creative power of God's Word and our total dependence upon Scripture, something I point out time and again to anyone I am counselling, I was convicted in my spirit beyond measure that when I was enlightened concerning the faith and prosperity message in 1988, I actually threw out the baby with the bath water, in my concern not to be deceived. It was a time for personal confession and repentance and I got on with it quickly.

The next scripture was Romans 12:1–2 especially the words in verse 2 – *'And be not confirmed to this world: but be ye transformed by the renewing of your mind.'* Marion quite rightly pointed out that when Satan attacks us as he does through our minds, we have to have a scripture in them to counteract his lies. So when he comes at us with 'You're sick and weak and cannot function' you reply,

> *'I can do all things through Christ which strengthens me.'*
> (Philippians 4:13)

And when Satan tells you that you are going bankrupt, that you cannot pay your mortgage, the gas bill or the school fees you tell him,

> *'But my God shall supply all my needs according to His riches in glory by Christ Jesus.'*
>
> (Philippians 4:19)

or remind Satan that your Father owns

> *'The cattle upon a thousand hills.'*　　　(Psalm 50:10)

The next scripture was Luke 13:14,

> *'And the ruler of the synagogue answered with indignation, because that Jesus had healed on the sabbath day, and said unto the people, There are six days in which men ought to work: in them therefore come and be healed, and not on the sabbath day.'*

Dear me, how the revelation came to me that day, for indeed I had become a victim of the wearing out of the saints (Daniel 7:25) through the pressures of ministry and not coming apart as the Lord had instructed me. How I had allowed the demands of men to squeeze me until I had no reserves to refresh and regroup. It was indeed only through the mercy of God that I survived. But there was to be more revelation on Luke 13:14 during the next month!

Finally Marion showed us that the key to healing and wholeness was abiding in the vine.

> *'Abide in me, and I in you. As the branch cannot bear fruit of itself, except it abide in the vine; no more can ye, except ye abide in me.'*　　　(John 15:4)

> *'Ye have not chosen me, but I have chosen you, and ordained you, that ye should go and bring forth fruit,*

and that your fruit should remain: that whatsoever ye
shall ask of the Father in my name, he may give it you.'
(John 15:16)

Marion told us that abiding was obedience, faithfulness, trusting, loving and listening. Wasn't that what my second book *Fruit Abiding in the Vine* has been all about? What then had happened to me?

She also pointed out very strongly that 'Jesus was a confronter'. As I studied Luke 13 later that week I realised that Jesus was indeed a confronter and that His confrontation was in the synagogue on the Sabbath day. What was God saying to me? In Luke 13:16 Jesus clearly states to the ruler of the synagogue that the woman whom Satan had bound for eighteen years was to be healed on the Sabbath. And how many times had God clearly told me to loose people in the name of His son Jesus on the Sabbath in Church? The lady who sat behind me for weeks in church in a wheelchair, and the Lord said 'Tell her to rise up in the name of Jesus and she will be healed.' I had shaken with fear because I knew my Pastor disapproved of my ministry and thought I was in the flesh when indeed the anointing was so strong, rising up within as a burning fire that I had to quench, and quell, and quench, week after week, until I became sick; infirm through compromise and disobedience and fear of man. Then when I finally plucked up courage to move, she no longer appeared in church. She was too disabled to attend anymore, but I was told 'we are all praying for her.'

I tell you it was a very terrible time for me as I fasted and prayed those next few weeks and the Holy Spirit showed me sternly that the only place I never ministered healing and deliverance was on the Sabbath day in the church (synagogue)! It was with considerable groanings and travail that I realised in that situation I entertained the spirit of the fear of man! Oh yes! I could pray on the telephone, in the Clinic, in the street, anywhere and if

God told me to pray and He would raise someone and deliver them, He always did. I would do it at public meetings, confident and under the authority of Christ, but in church – no way! I felt condemned because the Lord had given me a special ministry, yet the Bible says that *There is therefore now no condemnation to them which are in Christ Jesus, who walk not after the flesh, but after the Spirit* (Romans 8:1).

It is at such times that one realises that years of persecution in church, when it becomes known that you are moving out in the Spirit, can scar you deeply almost for life. But as Marion said to us that day, 'Your walk is your responsibility.' And so it is.

We know that the apostate Church will persecute the true Church in the End Times. End Times are here! Hallelujah! Praise the Lord!

Blessed are we when men speak ill of us and persecute us – as it is written,

> *'Blessed are they which are persecuted for righteousness' sake: for their's is the kingdom of heaven. Blessed are ye, when men shall revile you, and persecute you, and shall say all manner of evil against you falsely, for my sake.'* (Matthew 5:10–11)

Chapter 19

So Much in Common

As I looked over the bookstall on my first visit to Mayday Ministries, which I learned were to be birthed as Sozo Ministries, I was rather startled to see books on herbs, and many other guidelines for a healthy body also displayed amongst the literature. As I perused I saw that here was another garlic advocate and someone who felt that we should make it our business to learn what was edible in the countryside as a preparation for the End Times, when if we do not take the mark of the beast we may starve if the Lord does not provide for us supernaturally.

I have always preached that we cannot feed on junk food and expect a good performance from ourselves physically or mentally and that this affects our spiritual growth. I believe that thousands of our Christian patients would testify to that effect as the one emanating from the Clinic for 24 years. Here was another sister in Christ giving out the same message. So it wasn't only me who had heard such things! Praise the Lord!

I have had confirmation over two decades now that the Lord wishes us to look after our bodies which are the temple of the Holy Spirit.

'What? know ye not that your body is the temple of the

*Holy Ghost which is in you, which ye have of God,
and ye are not your own?'*   (2 Corinthians 6:19)

Quite frankly I would not be in business if we did not have an infirm Church! It is sad but true! Clearly Marion had spent much time in libraries to become informed on Psalm 104:14 and I admire anyone who does their own research. I have certainly had to do mine, and much more since environmental or alternative medicine became fraught with the deceptions of New Age Medicine, making some of us look as green as the green image New Agers hope to convey, as they infiltrate every area of medicine that Christians who are seeking restoration for their infirm bodies without resorting to drug therapies, would maybe try out.

The New Age medicine cult is of course being ushered in under the disguise of green imagery and protection of the environment, forming the cultural basis upon which the New World Order will be formed when the world economy collapses, as it surely will. There will then be a combining of paganism, multi-faith and all manner of occult and such works of the flesh which allow for the proliferation of idolatry and of evil. See Galatians 5:19–20 for the works of the flesh. If you want to know where the headquarters of New Age Medicine is, it is in the pit operated by satanic networks.

We shall then see and hear cries for unity which will consist of nothing more than a famine of the truth, particularly in churches who have chosen to deny and ignore the Scriptural command to pray for the peace of Jerusalem (Psalm 122:6). *'Pray for the peace of Jerusalem; they shall prosper that love thee.'*

Readers of my second book *Fruit Abiding in the Vine* will have noted in Chapter 38, entitled *Weep for Jerusalem*, how I was unexpectedly made to publicly weep for Jerusalem whilst teaching in Denmark – and I have

146

been weeping ever since, though if I cried every tear in my body it would not be enough.

My weeping has in no small measure been at the ignorance and stubbornness of the Church in general, if not in particular, to ignore the responsibility we have to pray for God's chosen people. Churches who are committed in word and in deed, in prayer and in fasting for God's people will be mightily blessed – be sure of that!

I decided quite definitely that I would like to know Marion as a person not only as an able minister of God's Word. As our friendship grew she was very quick to discern a curse over my life which had not been dealt with. I have to confess that I was astounded, truly believing that all curses had been laid to rest in Jesus' Name. In a telephone conversation she told me,

'Pearl I've read both of your books. I read *Go and Do Likewise* when it first came out. I was so grateful because the chapter on the demon of nicotine really witnessed to me on smoking. As a former smoker I had been soft-pedalling on cigarette smoking when it came to deliverance ministry, believing that if we got all the other rubbish out of the way first, giving up smoking would follow – whereas in your book you said the opposite, which I can testify I have found to be quite true. However, having just met you I felt that I should read your first book again and the second consecutively.'

She added that she had to be very careful because she did not read many paperbacks since they would keep her out of the Bible. Amen to that! Something else we had in common.

'You know, Pearl, I believe there is a curse on your relationships with men, because Satan already fears you single, and knows what a force against him you would be if you were married to a man of God.'

I didn't wait a minute.

'Let's do it now please.'

Marion agreed, I went to the telephone by my bedside,

opened the Bible in front of me and got on my knees. I was set free in the mighty name of Jesus and I give Him all the glory. I am also grateful to my Father for putting me in Marion's path. As I am always saying, in our Father's vocabulary there is no such word as coincidence. This was all part of his perfect plan for me. Hallelujah!

Chapter 20

The Birthing of Sozo Ministries

Clearly the Lord was using Marion mightily for His glory, as He has used me. Clearly also she has received much persecution from Church leaders who found her ministry threatening, but probably more than I have.

You know, if pastors and church leaders find the anointing threatening, they do not know perfect love. The Bible says, *'perfect love casts out fear'* (1 John 4:18).

If pastors are not tormented by having you around then they know that perfect love! If they doubt your anointing, they should at least allow you to move out in it, and then they can jump on you if you are wrong and correct you with the Word, not with their own opinions. But may God forgive them if they are quenching the Spirit of God! They are answerable to Him, and such understanding of the Word in this respect gave me the peace to move out to the extent that I have and not be a man-pleaser. I have only ever been a member of four churches in half a century of Christian walk, and I praise God for the places I have been allowed to move out in the Spirit, for it blessed me. To be trusted in this way makes one very sensitive to the Holy Spirit, and very careful not to be out of order in any respect. I asked Marion how she got started and she gave me the following in her own words.

'I was office manager at Mayday Personnel Services, a recruitment agency. My boss Beryl, was an "ex"

Jehovah's Witness and searching again for the truth. At the same time I was searching my heart to make a deeper commitment to Him and pondering full-time service for Jesus.

During this time Beryl got born again and gave her business to the Lord in 1985. Beryl and her husband Bob divinely offered to release me on a daily basis from office duties until I had five days a week ministry and then I could disappear from the office! This birthed Mayday Ministries. Beryl had learnt that she needed to tithe from God's abundance, so I remained on the payroll until such times that the ministry totally supported me through all God's people giving faithfully in tithes and love gifts.

During my time working for Mayday Personnel Services I was growing in the things of the Lord and very involved with the local Anglican Church. My ministry then was to travel the south coast encouraging churches to use movement/dance in their individual and corporate worship.

In 1983 I developed back problems and it was diagnosed that it was the effects of 'trauma' from a car accident – as I was at the time in a dance ministry, I didn't *think* this was God's best for me, but knew no other teaching other than, "sometimes we have to suffer physically!" To cut a long story short I heard the teaching that "God wants you whole" and not only did I receive a miracle in my body I also got fired up and started praying for people simply on the strength that *"They shall lay hands on the sick* (my bit) *and they shall recover* (God's bit)." Jesus died on a cross that I might be saved, healed and whole.

Someone who had a gynaecological problem asked for prayer and got saved and healed. Beryl and I were thrilled and had found that "**it works!**" Her friend with deep depression saw the change and also asked for help. This lady had been involved with the occult

150

and we saw a mighty deliverance coupled with salvation, and so the fruit increased and we soon had a group of new converts in one area so we started a house group. My parents, George, Joan, and other friends helped with this and various people came, many in need of salvation and healing. Later we started the "Ready for Ministry" courses at our offices, and saw many 'birthed" into ministry.

Many doors also opened at this time to preach the gospel in schools and colleges and other areas of the ministry developed. We saw that Mayday Ministries had the role of **pioneering**, hence the various areas we have moved into over the years. It has also been valuable training ground for our present ministry.

We were fellowshipping with many people who were spiritually homeless for various reasons and decided to meet once a month for praise and worship. This developed into a very fruitful group. Little did we know God was preparing us all for something greater than any of us could have dreamed of. We outgrew our meeting room and Sozo Fellowship was born. We had no idea then that the Lord was building a fellowship of people who are the "core" of this new vision. He was raising up musicians, teaching us how to worship – giving me more practise to preach, and everyone more experience in counselling.

In 1989 Bob and Beryl purchased a holiday village in North Devon and we used it for our first seminars on wholeness and victory. It was later we saw that the Lord just "transferred" the people and their anointing to North Devon. **Amazing strategy**! Only **He** could think up that one! Can you imagine arriving "cold" with no contact or familiarisation with each other and just launching into the seminars – 150 miles from home!?

We have continued to grow enormously and learn many new things together, and the key has been the anointing of love and the **unity**. The ministry has grown rapidly and continues to, with Sozo Centres and house groups birthing in towns where people's lives have been touched with the Sozo message through Britain.

Since 1989 we have had a special anointing to ME sufferers and have seen dozens miraculously set free alongside others in our times of worship and ministry. Each year we have wholeness and victory seminars. In 1993 we have several seminars planned in the North and South. If we can help in any way or if you would like more details of our ministry please write to: Sozo Ministries, PO Box 29, Romsey SO51 0YU.

The Birthing of Sozo Ministries
(Formerly Mayday Ministries)

Sozo Ministries, previously Mayday Ministries, is a ministry bringing wholeness to the world through Jesus. Sozo in Greek means *saved, healed, and whole.*

Marion Daniel supported by her parents and family, has formed a team of people including musicians and counsellors who minister the whole gospel and the revelation that God delivers and heals as His people praise and worship Him in holiness and in Spirit and in truth. Our aim is to take people into the Holy of Holies in worship and to see signs, wonders and miracles following the preaching of the uncompromised Word of God.

To make people confident in their inheritance to receive wholeness in Body, Mind and Spirit, thus enabling them to walk in **victory**.

Finally to give people a life changing experience to share with others!

The following areas of ministry have just unfolded at the Lord's direction.

Wholeness and Victory seminars/conferences throughout the year – seeing many miracles and healings.

Team Visits to various towns and cities by personal invitation throughout Great Britain, preaching "God wants you whole" (the whole gospel).

Video Ministry throughout Great Britain with local people inviting others to hear the *whole* gospel.

Courses regularly available throughout Great Britain on "Preparing for Ministry" for those wishing to minister for Jesus Christ.

Birthing and supporting the vision of **Sozo Fellowships and Centres** in four counties so far.

Where We Meet

Romsey Fellowship and Sozo Centre, Hampshire meet every third week as a fellowship and centre where Marion and her Team are available (dates and details available).

Sozo Centres

After the seminars it was apparent that there was a need for people to have follow up ministry, bringing their wholeness to completion through the power of the Holy Spirit. From this need the Sozo Centre vision was birthed. There are special days set aside for the ministry team to be available to counsel etc. etc. to those in need, and some centres meet reguarly each third Sunday as a fellowship ministering the healing of Jesus.

Other Sozo Fellowships and Sozo Centres

Launceston Sozo Centre, Cornwall
Rotherham Sozo Fellowship and Centre, South Yorkshire
Tiverton Sozo Centre, Devon

Send for details and dates of your nearest venue. Kindly enclose a large stamped addressed envelope.

Sozo Ministries has produced a small booklet full of testimonies from people healed of ME. Please enclose £1 to cover the cost of photocopying.'

Marion has met many of our team and some of the intercessors. We feel led by the Spirit to come alongside her in prayerful support, because of the anointing upon her and her helpers.

David Noakes speaks often of God making little oases everywhere in preparation for these End Times. The Clinic has often been referred to as an oasis and I am certain that the Sozo meeting places are such. We who minister God's truth to obey the command in obedience of the Great Commission, also at times need places of refuge, especially when persecution hots up and we need a re-emphasis of the everlasting arms! (Deuteronomy 33:27). Do not be ashamed if when you are a worn-out saint you need to lift up your shield of faith with another soldier. That is what the Body of Christ is for! The definition of the Body of Christ is wherever Christ is the head and there is unity of the same Spirit. This can be a large number of people together but mostly I would dare to comment that it is few. Big is not always beautiful but it is frequently bloated!! With Pride!

What do I mean by that? Swollen with the pride of its numbers! Jesus said *'make disciples'*, not increase membership! The concentration should be on making disciples.

Chapter 21

The Fear of the Lord

I had long passed that hundred days set aside to seek God's face in so many areas of my life, during this time not only reading the Scriptures and singing to the Lord, but enjoying that wonderfully private time with Him daily at the Lord's table. Far from becoming a ritual, this quiet time with Him was not only to pour out my heart and tug at the hem of His garment for the full powers vested in me as a believer, to cast out demons in His name and heal the sick, but to share my problems and seek direction for that day, that week, something I had backslidden in to do.

Sometimes this meeting with the Lord was short, sometimes extremely long so that many other things I planned to do did not get done! These things could be things I really needed in the natural to do, or places I needed to go. Like the dentist! Often it was sacrificed but always there resulted a blessing. The accent on those times was one of listening and listening and listening. One conviction certainly emerged and it was that what Dr James van Zyl preached in Israel about the Lord's table had proved an absolute truth. For me there was a greater anointing, and an increase in the ability to discern spiritual matters. What is more I shared both Dr van Zyl's tape entitled *The Great Physician* and his little book entitled *The Lord's Table and Healing* with many Christians as the Lord led me, particularly those whom God was clearly setting apart to speak to Him. (Available from Faith in the Word Ministries, PO Box 112, Stanger, 4450, South Africa.)

Each and every person who has met with the Father, the Son and the Holy Spirit daily in this way have told me of the increased peace, revelation and harmony in their affairs since they undertook to set aside time to commune with the Lord, however hard pressed they were. This I do believe. If one receives a word of advice or recommendation from one of the Lord's anointed servants and obeys, this very obedience brings great blessing.

I recall the advice of Bill Subritzky to have a balanced diet of the Word daily, e.g. to read chapters of both the New and Old Testaments and a Psalm and a Proverb daily. I accepted these recommendations as being from a servant of God and as a result I have read more of the Bible since then than ever before. Why? Because I never wanted to stop after one chapter or one psalm, or one proverb! I found I couldn't put the Bible down once I had picked it up! But I also could be certain of something else, that Satan would always do his level best to prevent me opening the Word. I have now made it a policy to have a Bible in each room of the house so that I can grab one quickly wherever I am. Even a walk down the hallway to the bedroom to get my Bible can present a distraction which leads me into the kitchen! Satan is many things we know about because they are written, a thief, a liar, the son of perdition etc, but he is also a distractor!

During one of those precious times with the Lord, He spoke to me by His Spirit about not bringing to the Body the various words and visions he had given me. I told Him quite categorically that I had already brought things which were either ignored or not commented upon. He informed me that it was not His intention as yet that I should stop. I noted the 'as yet' because I had been up that road before, and it was a road I did not care to travel again. He challenged me with the scripture that Marion Daniel had challenged me with, 2 Timothy 1:7: *'For God hath not given us the spirit of fear, but of power, and of love, and of a sound mind.'* I was wriggling in my spirit when Marion said that if God did not give me a spirit of fear, where did I think it came from? I felt great shame when I recalled the hundreds and hundreds of people I have jubilantly given that scripture. I knew for certain that this fear only existed in one area of my life and I knew also that this one area had to be dealt with.

The Lord showed me so clearly through his Word that I was being manipulated through fear and I hated every moment of that revelation! As they say in the world 'the truth hurts'. I was given the scripture Proverbs 29:20. *'The fear of man bringeth a snare; but whoso putteth his trust in the Lord shall be safe.'* A snare is a trap. Yes, I felt in such a trap because I have never enjoyed such wonderful fellowship where the Lord has placed me, and I have a deep commitment to those brothers and sisters, even though I am not allowed to minister to them in freedom and spontaneity as the Holy Spirit would lead me. Wherever I have worshipped I have always felt free to fall on my face, to sing in the Spirit, to dance before the Lord, even to prophesy and never has a pastor had to summon me and say, 'Sister, that is not of the Lord.' Rather I have had the joy of hearing men of God confirm that they felt what I had brought was of the Lord. This is always such encouragement to listen carefully to the Holy Spirit.

There was one exception to this, when I brought the word on witchcraft in the church and was smartly asked to leave. It was an unpleasant experience that I know I share with many members of the Church! Again, we must expect persecution, and know we have the truth when we are persecuted for righteousness' sake. The Lord also showed me that I had ceased to publicly pray for Israel in church. He showed me that Israel is going to be the plumbline for the true Church, nothing else. He reminded me of Isaiah 61:1, *'The Spirit of the Lord God is upon me; because the*

Lord hath anointed me to preach good tidings unto the meek; he hath sent me to bind up the broken hearted, to proclaim liberty to the captives, and the opening of the prison to them that are bound.'

The Lord had shown me before I went to Denmark that my first love should be Israel and God's chosen people the Jews. He also gave me a very unpleasant reminder from Psalm 137:5–6, *'If I forget thee, O Jerusalem, let my right hand forget her cunning. If I do not remember thee, let my tongue cleave to the roof of my mouth; if I prefer not Jerusalem above my chief joy.'*

This again really spoke to me. In the church where I worshipped I was speechless, and also my right hand writes my books of which I have concrete evidence that they are blessing thousands. I do not say this in pride, but with a thankful heart to the Saviour. One lady wrote from Malaysia, 'Sister Pearl, God has given you the gift of penmanship.'

So many wrote words to the effect that they never finished a paperback but could not put my books down. I received so many letters in this vein, that I thought it right to start thanking the Lord for this gift, for indeed I would be blind if I could not see His blessings from my writings. Thank you Jesus.

He also gave me Psalm 118:6

> *'The Lord is on my side; I will not fear: what can man do unto me?'*

That did it, I had to go back to Sozo and get delivered in the assembly there. I knew it was what God wanted. I went in repentance and humility and on that wonderful day I was set free in my spirit. I danced before the Lord in total surrender and to my amazement prophesied over the assembly, which I learned later blessed many. On the way home the Lord showed me in my radiance that if one has the fear of the Lord one cannot have the spirit of the fear of man and there is no half and half situation to be the Bride.

I spent many, many hours with my Bible and certain scriptures were highlighted for me. Many were scriptures which spoke to me in my sickness in Israel when Lance Lambert spoke anointedly on this very subject, 'The Fear of the Lord is the beginning of Wisdom'. I have many cassettes on this subject collected over the years, but this message available from Christian Friends of Israel, Shavuot 1992 Conference Jerusalem Tape SC05 is a jewel.

I share a conviction with many in the Body, that those who choose to stand with God's chosen people, the Jews, and to bless them and pray for Israel will actually be as persecuted as the Jews were by the apostate church. The root of all sin is to do our own thing. Doing our own thing means that we are not obedient to the directive of the Holy Spirit. Isaiah 53:6 puts it quite succinctly:

> 'All we like sheep have gone astray; and turned every one to his own way.'

Adam started it at the Fall and we have continued in this way, if we are honest. But if we seek after holiness which will only follow our submission to the refiner's fire we have to will to cease doing our own thing, and to do His, that Jesus might be glorified in our lives.

We need to bring to the dying world such an aura of holiness that those who see it bow the knee to Jesus or flee into the darkness. And please do not be amazed if people back off from you, when you really haven't done anything wrong. It is one of the first things I learned in ministry, that one is not popular with demons ruling in people whom they control and hostility may be expected. I praise God that there are those with such humility and discernment that they know what's making them dislike and mistrust you and will stick around and get rid of it! Here again is an unpleasant truth. People will not mind at all being delivered of fear, grief, brokenheartedness, etc. but confronted with witchcraft they will back off. That is because witchcraft intimidates, manipulates and controls, in that order.

Unfortunately the moment the fear of the Lord (such a healthy fear), is mentioned, people get scared and associate that fear with heaviness, damnation and punishment. Yet unless we can grasp the victory in having the fear of the Lord, we could not possibly be able to make ourselves ready as the Bride of Christ.

Let me give you some scriptures on the fear of the Lord to delight your heart, to comfort and encourage you to seek and cultivate that fear as an essential part of your spiritual growth.

> *'The fear of the Lord is the beginning of wisdom: and the knowledge of the holy is understanding.'*
>
> (Proverbs 9:10)

Now we are exhorted to seek wisdom in the Scriptures and we can learn from the Word that we can never proceed to get wisdom unless we first get the fear of the Lord.

> *'The fear of the Lord is the instruction of wisdom; and before honour is humility.'* (Proverbs 15:33)

Here we are clearly being taught that wisdom requires the fear of the Lord to attain it.

> *'The fear of the Lord is the beginning of wisdom: a good understanding have all they that do His commandments.'* (Psalm 111:10)

Again, keeping His commandments involves seeking wisdom and understanding and the means to such attainment are through the fear of the Lord.

> *'Behold, the fear of the Lord, that is wisdom; and to depart from evil is understanding.'* (Job 28:28)

In other words, without the fear of the Lord one would continue to do one's own thing, whatever one fancied to do, because of the absence of the fear of the Lord. Yet when that fear becomes automatic, I repeat, automatic, departure from evil is automatic also.

Please do not say, 'but I do fear God, yet I keep on doing this.' My response is that obviously you do not fear Him enough! So get that fear cultivated to the perfection of not daring to disobey.

I recall I have always been fearful of electricity, a fear nurtured in me by my former electrical engineer spouse. Clearly my fear was not sufficient because I would wipe the dust off a two-bar electric fire we had when we first got married whilst switched on, with a damp cloth! I was what one would describe as a damp duster! I always dusted with a slightly damp cloth. When I first married it was not automatic that we owned gadgets like vacuum cleaners! Yet my fear of electricity was not completed until, whilst foolishly damp dusting one cold winter's day, I could not resist the smear on the shiny reflection of the electric fire. I got such a belt! The shock threw me across the room and my fear of electricity, my healthy respect for it, was perfected!

> *'The angel of the Lord encampeth round about them that fear Him, and delivereth them.'* (Psalm 34:7)

That is why I can sleep alone in an isolated dwelling place, in an unlit lane on the ground floor with my window open. Before I was born again, even with two men in the house I would insist that *all* windows both upstairs and downstairs were sealed tight and all the doors double locked. Yes, I actually expect God to take care of me because I fear Him.

> *'By mercy and trust, iniquity is purged; and by the fear
> of the Lord men depart from evil.'*　　(Proverbs 16:6)

Be certain of this, if you trust the Lord, He will protect
you and show you His mercy.

> *'For wisdom is better than rubies.'*　　(Proverbs 8:11)

Since we cannot, according to the Scriptures, obtain
wisdom without the fear of the Lord, then the fear of the
Lord is also priceless!

> *'The fear of the Lord is clean, enduring for ever.'*
> (Psalm 19:9)

This means that the fear of the Lord is a sign of purification. Do not resist the refiner's fire, for the purification
process is not possible without the fear of the Lord and
who are those wholehearted towards the Lord unwilling to
be put in the crucible?

> *'Blessed is the man who feareth the Lord.'*
> (Psalm 112:1)

The opposite to blessed is cursed. Which are you going
to opt for?

> *'The secret of the Lord is with them that fear Him and
> He will show them His covenant.'*　　(Psalm 25:14)

This means that the Lord will open up His treasures and
secrets to those who fear Him. He will reveal things to
those He trusts with revelation, because they fear Him. To
fear the Lord puts us in an incredibly privileged position of
sharing.

'The fear of the Lord is the beginning of knowledge, but fools despise wisdom and instruction.'

(Proverbs 1:7)

So here we have fear described as the beginning of knowledge, e.g. spiritual wisdom. Proverbs 3:7–8:

'Be not wise in your own eyes; fear the Lord and depart from evil.

'It shall be health to thy navel and marrow to thy bones.'

The marrow in our bones we know gives them their strength. The navel we know is where the umbilical cord has been tied for separation from our mother at birth, so we can leave the womb and become an individual in our own right. Now if that separation has not been a healthy one, it will mean later in life one may have to be cut off from one's mother spiritually. It is the same type of deliverance as when ungodly soul ties are cut between people.

I believe the words in those verses of Proverbs 3 are very deep and instructive.

'The fear of the Lord prolongeth days but the years of the wicked shall be shortened.'　　　　(Proverbs 10:27)

Not only is this fear an ingredient for the recipe for long life, the absence of such fear of the Lord means shortened life. Now do not write to me and say that you know a wicked old man of a hundred, or a lovely holy lady who died at thirty three. A life is in fact as long as its quality. Ask the Lord to show you what that means if you have not grasped it already! This was given to me by Holy Spirit revelation.

'The fear of the Lord is strong confidence; and His children shall have a place of refuge.'

(Proverbs 14:26)

These words confirm the covering for those who dwell in the secret place of the most high (Psalm 91:1).

'The fear of the Lord is a fountain of life, to depart from the snares of death.'   (Proverbs 14:27)

The fountain of life keeps you like a watered garden with a spring of water whose waters fail not (Isaiah 58:11). The fountain of life is therefore continuous and everlasting if it fails not. I believe this is why some people do not appear to age! I proclaim Isaiah 58:10–11 over myself daily since the Word was given to me in May 1988 by Dr Joy Seevaratnum. People are always saying, 'you look younger each time I see you' and frankly I am delighted. I've needed that restoration, believe me!

'The fear of the Lord tendeth to life; and he that hath it shall abide satisfied; he shall not be visited with evil.'
(Proverbs 19:23)

I believe that this satisfaction the verse speaks of is the contentment Paul refers to in whatever state we are in. The contentment that comes from knowing that the Lord is with us and if He is with us it matters not a jot about the rest!

'By humility and the fear of the Lord are riches, honour and life.'   (Proverbs 22:4)

Three very desirable attributes, wouldn't one think?

'For he that feareth God shall come forth from them all.'   (Ecclesiastes 7:18)

This phrase speaks of victorious emergence. Whoever is your persecutor, your enemy, your assailant, whatever your satanic situation of adversity, you will triumph over them. Hallelujah!

> *'And I will make an everlasting covenant with them,
> that I will not turn away from them, to do them good;
> but I will put my fear in their hearts, that they shall not
> depart from me.'* (Jeremiah 32:40)

This truly is for the backslider, those who have met with
the Lord and subsequently fallen away. Yet I can tell you
truly that if you have been miraculously rescued from the
pit of hell by a sovereign visit from the Lord, then He had
a purpose for you. You may still not be certain what it
was, but I can promise you, that because He has put that
fear of Him in your heart you will not escape, and at some
time, sooner or later you will return to Him.

> *'Then they that feared the Lord spake often one to
> another; and the Lord hearkened and heard it, and a
> book of remembrance was written before Him for
> them that feared the Lord and thought upon His
> name.'* (Malachi 3:16)

This is confirmation for the walking in the light, the
fellowship that we have with believers united in Christ, not
steeped in division, being a body however small that the
Lord delights in and will listen to. It speaks of frequent
assembly, not Sunday Christianity. Of course you may be
commenting by this time that these verses are from the
Old Testament. I want to remind you that the Old Testament stands, not one word of it passes away, as it is written
and that the New Testament is a ratification as it were of
the Old Testament. But let us turn to 2 Corinthians 7:1:

> *'Having therefore these promises, dearly beloved, let
> us cleanse ourselves from all filthiness of the flesh and
> spirit, perfecting holiness in the fear of God.'*

This reinforces my earlier comment that there can be no
holiness without the fear of the Lord.

> *'Submitting yourselves one to another in the fear of the Lord.'* (Ephesians 5:21)

Again a confirmation of the need to fellowship with those of the same unity of Spirit. Where Jesus is head, the Body is in unity and fear of the Lord, there is the true Church. I suggest that one cannot submit to someone who does not fear the Lord if you fear Him yourself. It simply isn't on. You may consider this a matter of debate, but the Bible says, when two are agreed it shall be done! I take that to mean if two are not agreed it shall not be done!

> *'Work out your own salvation with fear and trembling.'* (Philippians 2:12)

That does not read, work out your own salvation with fear of your pastor, your employer, or your friend! It means with the fear of the Lord, who is our salvation, working in us as the next verse denotes,

> *'For it is God which worketh in you both to will and to do His good pleasure.'* (Philippians 2:13)

> *'Wherefore, we receiving a kingdom which cannot be moved, let us have grace whereby we may serve God acceptably with reverence and Godly fear. For our God is a consuming fire.'* (Hebrews 12:28–29)

Does it not thrill you to know that as fact our God shall ultimately scorch and burn away into ashes all that comes against His throne and His Kingdom?

Do you not want to be on the side of a powerful God for whom you have a healthy respect, for that is what the fear of the Lord is. It is not the craven, trembling, fear that causes you to cower in the corner shivering, but a fear that brings glorious reward and freedom from all other fears. Fear of the Lord leads us into the actual experience of His all surpassing love, that perfect love which casts out fear (1 John 4:18).

> *'So that we may boldly say The Lord is my helper and I will not fear what man shall do unto me.'*

Believe me, the fear of the Lord will bring you into the heart and will of Jesus Christ your Saviour, it will be a hedge of fire around you and your property, it will cause you to lay down all your idols and be blessed in your walk with Him.

I will be frank. There is no substitute for the fear of the Lord, and Satan and all his works came against me as I prepared this chapter to expose the costliness in terms of spiritual growth of harbouring a spirit of the fear of man.

I pray with my utmost fervour that you will be as blessed by reading it as I was by writing it.

With heartfelt thanks to Lance Lambert, Derek Prince and others who have taught me on this subject and inspired me to do my own studies.

Chapter 22

The Accuser of the Brethren

I am sorry to tell you readers that as well as the criticism and gossip referred to as the church-going demons in my second book *Fruit Abiding In The Vine*, we have another demon very active in the Church. He is in fact a ruler; his title is The Accuser of the Brethren.

Under this ruler, his minions, criticism and gossip will spread lies about members of the Body of Christ. They are warmongering, divisive, rumour proliferating spirits feeding on jealousy and strife. These are a criteria from which to draw a conclusion. As one would expect since they emanate from the 'Father of all lies' they are liars themselves. The main activity of this brigade is to sow bad seed about your brother or your sister in Christ and that seed is more often than not rooted in jealousy. Believe me I've had my share of it, and I am sure so have some of you, judging by the histories I glean from patients.

My old Pastor Rod Anderson, absolutely forbade anyone in the Liberty Christian Fellowship, to which I had the joy of belonging until it ceased to exist, to receive gossip about anyone, and that if we dared to do so we would be as disgusting as the perpetrator.

I tell you, this instruction concentrated the mind

wonderfully, and if you have never heard Rod Anderson's teaching on 'The Love Walk' (four cassettes still available from 0494 882878) then you should find them edifying. It was this teaching that I heard locally one day some years ago, that caused me to travel ninety miles each Sunday to sit under the Word.

We were expected to arrive well before the morning service to pray in the Word, and in common with those who also travelled far and wide to attend, we came home fed with spiritual food that had not evaporated by tea-time on the Sunday. It was a continuous feast. Upon reflection it was a place we also learned to laugh a lot; the joy of the Lord was really present in the gatherings.

I recall Rod saying, 'Don't you receive anyone else's garbage. You have enough of your own to dispose of!' In the main we who assembled there were the hurt and maimed of the Church, who had discovered this oasis of the Lord one way or the other. Our Pastor was a resurrected heroin addict. Funny how former heroin addicts seem to be important in my life!

Of course, being a Christian Clinic practising environmental medicine, which some people like to call alternative medicine (but I do not because it smacks of New Age involvement which I abhor), we are often faced with a barrage of questions as to what exactly we do. Readers of my first book *Go and Do Likewise* will recall that we actually changed our name from the Christian Clinic for Alternative Medicine to the Christian Clinic for Environmental Medicine after the destruction of my homoeopathic pharmacy in 1986 following revelation from the Holy Spirit that this form of medicine was in fact occult. It was a revelation which caused me great shock and only the fear of the Lord enabled me to cope with the destruction of this idol. For indeed I had also depended upon homoeopathy to a large extent for the curing of people's ills. Then hard on the heels of this revelation came the destruction of all my iridology books and discontinuation of reading the iris of the eye as a diagnostic technique. This really left me with a practice of diet and prayer, determining allergies and balancing vitamin and mineral deficiencies. As a long term well published journalist on matters of health and environment this did not pose as many problems for me as it did my patients who had grown used to their little homoeopathic fixes!

I remember as I sat in the Reverend Jimmy Song's office with the contents of my pharmacy and homoeopathic library in black plastic dustbin sacks ready for burning, he said 'Now that you are travelling light, having disposed of all that stuff, the journey will be easier.'

There is no doubt that those decisions which seemed so costly at the time have brought blessing upon blessing, fruit upon fruit and caused me ever increasingly to rely on the Lord.

But meanwhile, out there are a lot of accusing spirits in unforgiving Christians who simply refuse to believe that I am not engaged in occult medicine. It is not uncommon to have patients book in excitedly to see me and cancel when someone in their church says, 'Oh, didn't you know she is using homoeopathy?' when I haven't done so since 1986! 'And didn't you know she uses acupuncture?' when I wouldn't know one end of a needle from the other!

A lot of desperate Christians, who pluck up courage to come, having prayed about it will look furtively to see if my broomstick is propped up against the back door, or if there is a sack of frogs legs and eyes of newts waiting to be stirred into a cauldron tucked away in some corner!

I am always so thankful that patients do pray before coming, and I delight to hear a sister say, 'I've been before the Lord for some weeks since I read your book and the Holy Spirit convicted me to make an appointment to see you,' or 'Your book came at a time when I was seeking revelation and I was convicted to come and see you.'

As time has progressed much accusation has melted

away, but we have to be aware as practitioners of environmental medicine that a lot of alternatives to orthodox drug treatment go hand in hand with New Age, green imagery and all those sorceries.

My vindication is always with the Lord and the perpetual Clinic fruit which abides in the vine and itself brings forth fruit. Of course the abundance of fruit from the City of God Ministries which was incorporated into the Clinic a year ago, blesses us continuously.

However, there are times when one discovers that the enemy is preventing the captives from getting free through the offices of the Accuser of the Brethren.

Recently I learned that my first book which has apparently blessed the ministry on the African continent, was being considered for reprinting for Africa. At the same time I learned that a Christian ministry was no longer stocking my books because one of their counsellors had visited us and felt uneasy.

My assistant Rachel and I were aware long ago of the fear in the Christian Church over anything to do with alternative medicine and that they are in real danger of throwing the baby out with the bath water! Thus they are depriving Christians, who are not desirous of drugs and their horrific cumulative side-effects, the opportunity to avail themselves from side-effect-free medicine. I can assure you too that our infirm Church needs just such assistance due to ignoring so many of God's laws and instructions.

As the sales of *Go and Do Likewise* increase and a parallel increase of freed captives results, it is clear that Satan wants to block sales at crucial ministry opportunities. So where has he gone to place his poisonous seeds? Into the Body of Christ.

Anyone who applies to join our waiting list to become a patient must of necessity read our Clinic papers and sign a form to say that they have done so and understand them.

These are available to prospective patients for the price of a stamped addressed envelope.

I have done this for ten out of the twenty three years we have existed and found it helpful and effective in informing patients. Thus I feel that I should be confronted personally with any unease or criticism. If one can average such a thing I would assess that ten readers of each book get healed and delivered of a variety of ills, so one can see why Satan opposes me!

Anything, even orthodox medicine in the hand of an occultist is dangerous. I believe that the spiritual state of the practitioner needs much consideration. I believe the Lord always looks on the heart. I would not have anyone using acupuncture in my Clinic any more than I would kineisiology, because I oppose both, but I dare not judge Christians who are seen to bear fruit, especially when I do not entirely understand what they do! Ninety percent of alternative medicine gives me a real check in my spirit, which I prefer to be my guide, but still I may not judge my brothers and sisters in Christ, or spread rumours about them. If I am really plagued by thoughts about such people and their activities, the best place for me is in the closet seeking His face. Remember this, dropping bad seed about people cancels out the good seed you might be sowing. This is not to encourage a spirit of compromise, but to express the need to be very certain that one has one's facts right!

I have seen Christians almost mortally wounded by the fiery darts of their brothers and sisters in Christ and it makes me tremble because I pay a lot of attention to a subject not too well debated in the Body. It is the wrath of God!!

'But thanks be to God, which giveth us the victory through our Lord Jesus Christ. Therefore, my beloved brethren, be ye stedfast, unmoveable, always

*abounding in the work of the Lord, forasmuch as ye
know that your labour is not in vain in the Lord.'*

Blessed be His Holy Name.

Chapter 23

Amazing Amelia and Other Testimonies

I met Amelia Nathan Hill in 1979 when I was busily engaged as a medical and environmental journalist, with my own columns on health journals and contributing to medical publications. At this time having overcome crippling arthritis from diet, I was enjoying amongst other things, tearing around the medical lecture circuit, being seen in such illustrious places as the Royal Society of Medicine and The Royal College of Physicians. I was mopping up not only for the journals to which I contributed, but much information for those I sought to help.

Amelia is an incredible woman, one of the few people alive who survived Weil's disease caught from rats whilst swimming in a river near Rome. She had been sick from the day she had been born, with a list of diagnosed diseases enough to fill a medical encyclopedia and a list of undiagnosed mysterious illnesses which baffled all the specialists she saw. Her agonising story is told in her own book *Against the Unsuspected Enemy*.

Founding the world-wide renowned group *Action Against Allergy*, and supported and encouraged by many in the medical profession, Amelia, in spite of her debility, travelled the world winning numerous awards for her work as she sought to bring help and comfort to others suffering from allergies. If Isaiah 58:10–11, my favourite scripture, applied to anyone, it applied to Amelia, and I know that just as I have sown in tears and reaped in joy so will she.

And if thou draw out thy soul to the hungry, and satisfy the afflicted soul: then shall thy light rise in obscurity, and thy darkness be as the noon day; and the Lord shall guide thee continually, and satisfy thy soul in drought, and make fat thy bones; and thou shalt be like a watered garden, and like a spring of water, whose waters fail not.

As a journalist I used to be in receipt of the Action Against Allergy newsletter. In March 1986 Newsletter 26 arrived. By this time I was in the healing and deliverance ministry. As I gazed down the latest long list of recent diseases and attacks on her weak body, I scrawled across it in red felt pen 'Spirit of Infirmity, underlying curse through disobedience – sought supernatural experience, apart from having ME, rejection, lying spirit.' I wrote her a note to that effect, but do not recall a reply. I expect I sounded hard! I was so frustrated for her, knowing what I knew by then.

Amelia's Testimony

'Having spent most of my life bedridden through sickness, healing is something I had always been interested in. Living in Italy where I was born, it is customary to turn to the village priest or to one of the saints when you are ill. Very many different saints are famous for carrying out miracles there, but nobody explains how and why this can happen. Seeing a quantity of placards with dedications and thank-you tokens on the walls of most churches or on the diverse shrines of the road-side madonnas, gave me the hope that if I went there to pray, I would also one day be able to place a gold placard or a medal of thanksgiving there. In spite of all my inspired faith I did not receive any healing.

176

I was brought up very strictly and with little love. My mother, an actress, wanted me to become a socialite and actress and my father (a walking encyclopaedia), wanted a clever boy and also a learned pupil which a hyperactive and dyslexic girl like myself could hardly satisfy. There was no religion and mainly rows at each mealtime so far as I can remember.

At the age of seven my father had been posted to London, and when I was taken by my mother to give Christmas presents to sick children in a hospital, I decided that I was going to become a nurse.

I started nursing at the age of 17 in a children's hospital run by nuns, but after a while I had to give it up as I was catching all the illnesses which were going around. By then we were back in Italy, and we spent 5 years in hiding because of the war. I continued having life-threatening illnesses which I suffered from all my life. While working at the children's hospital, I became very fond of the nuns, especially the Mother Superior. I wanted to become a nun and be like her. I had to go to communion every morning but I really did not understand why or what it was all about. Often when in church I would feel faint and ill so I assumed that God did not want me there. It was only twelve years ago when back again in the UK that I found out that most of my illnesses were caused by an allergic reaction to foods and inhalants and only four years ago I found out that I was suffering from ME, (Mialgic Encephalomyelitis), an illness often unrecognised by doctors and which a professor of Rome University, Prof Lino Businco, claims causes the allergies. Having discovered all this after trying every type of cure possible as described in the book I wrote in 1980, *Against the Unsuspected Enemy*, this was of great relief as doctors often tended to come to the conclusion that my illnesses were all in the mind.

Dr Darrel Ho-Yen, from Inverness, Scotland, who specialises in ME, at a meeting organised by the association of AAA (Action Against Allergy), which I founded to try and help those suffering like I was, when asked, 'How do you know if you suffer from ME?' answered, 'You just know it. How do you know when you are in love? There is no other illness like it.' I had always believed in God and could not understand why I had been afflicted in this way.

After more than 50 years of consulting top specialists all over the world and spending all my money, I was told about Dr Ted Morter from America who professed that it is our attitude in life that can cause a lot of illness. In spite of feeling ill I travelled the world lecturing on allergies and won many awards for my work, but I still felt that something was badly wrong. I was interested in Dr Morter's theories mainly because he had sent me a tape of a Mr Randi Shumi, one of his very allergic patients who was bedridden. He was in a worse state than I was but he had recovered by thanking God and learning to forgive both himself and others. Listening to the tape and other Morter tapes over and over again made me aware of how bitter and unforgiving I was towards myself and towards those who misunderstood my illness. I had also been constantly upset for the many other patients whom I saw were often ill-treated by their doctors or their loved ones or both.

I broke my femur bone at that time and was laid up in hospital for over a year with little else to do except listen to tapes or read. Doctors did not think I would pull through and doubted that I would be able to use my leg again. Trying to put into practice what Dr Morter advocated though was very difficult, but it appeared to have rewarding results.

It was then that one of my AAA members wrote to me sending me an article about a fellow sufferer whom I knew well, Pearl Coleman. Apart from her long-standing illness ME, she had broken her arm badly but apparently she had been miraculously healed. I naturally rang her to ask how she had been healed. She suggested I went down to Woking to see her so that she could explain in detail what had happened to her. This I did in October 1991. I was a bit overwhelmed by the praying and speaking in tongues I witnessed there but I could not fail to see how happy everyone was, singing and praising the Lord and how well and full of life Pearl seemed to be. Pearl had turned her home into a 'Christian Clinic for Environmental Medicine'. I received ministry to be freed from curse and I gave my life to the Lord Jesus, and heard beautiful songs sung by Raj Kumar who was the guitarist and shared his testimony with me. The music was beautiful and the tape of his worship always uplifted me greatly. I had only ever heard hymns before. Pearl told me that I should go home and start reading the Bible daily. The Bible had always seemed like 'double-dutch' to me in spite of learning the catechism based on the Bible when I wanted to become a nun. With perseverance I carried out her instructions and I began to understand some of the passages of the Bible she had recommended. She also recommended many books for me to read. Also Mr Shumi's words on the tape regarding his healing by thanking God and forgiving and after six months, seeing the 'Morning Star', began to make more sense.

I continued trying to forgive and thank God but I did not feel any better, if anything, I felt worse. I went down to see Pearl again and this time she said that she thought I should be baptised in a full immersion. When she explained what that meant, I was horrified, as apart from the many other allergies, I had an allergy to cold and the thought of being immersed in water in a church filled me with fear. Pearl prayed with me again, but knowing how I felt, proved to be most understanding and said she would try and think of a way in which this could be done. In the meantime Pearl had introduced me to a friend of her's, Joy, one of the Clinic's Christian counsellors who came to see me from Esher once a week and to Chris from the local Wimbledon Baptist Church who also came once a week to have a friendly chat. Things were not easy however as I knew that at home there would be opposition to anything like this and there still is.

I was now walking again with the aid of a stick and because of my poor health doctors had suggested that I spend the winter in a less cold and damp climate. As the workmen were due to come and underpin our house, I had decided to go to the South of France where I had a bedsitter. I was due to leave on the 2nd March, 1992, and a few weeks before that I woke up one morning saying to myself, 'I have to be baptised before I leave for France.' I just could not understand what had come over me. But this thought became imperative.

I enquired if I could have it done, perhaps in my bath, and then settled for a small church. But Chris, from the local Baptist Church, told me they were going to have their monthly baptismal service at their church on 16th February. I asked him to ask his elders if I could be baptised there and they accepted. With fear in my heart and to the horror of the only friend to whom I could talk about these things, I was immersed and baptised in this big church full of onlookers. Not only was I frightened but felt unwell and had bad pains which did not make things any easier. After the immersion I was prayed for with laying on of hands but did not feel any different. I went home that night and went to bed relieved that I had achieved what I had set out to do. Next morning I woke up with no headache. I had suffered from headaches all my life, first migraine headaches every other day for which I took barbiturate painkillers. When I found out more about allergy I avoided the foods and inhalants I was found to be allergic to and the migraines disappeared. I was left, though, with daily headaches and the typical feeling ill caused by ME for which I took from two to six aspirins every day just to be able to function. I therefore was quite surprised when the morning after the baptism I had no headache especially as I had been under a lot of stress because of the worry about the baptism and because of the worry of having to travel and to cope all alone in France in my precarious condition. I naturally thought it was just chance. Rarely did I have a day or two of respite but I have not had a headache and I have not had to take a painkiller since that day, after taking painkillers systematically for over 55 years. This I can only call a miracle.

I then left for France where I stayed for three months and I was lucky to find a similar supportive church to the one in Wimbledon with a loving and caring congregation who continued to pray for me. In fact, after the sudden healing of my headaches, I began to find that other of my symptoms were slowly disappearing. I found I was able to eat virtually anything and go out without a scarf round my head without catching cold. I walk reasonably well and without a stick. Learning to be more in tune with God has made me realise that I had to stop trying to do things myself and learn to hand over everything to Him. So many changes have now come about in my life. I have found new friends whose love and understanding can only be given them by the Grace of God.

People ask me how I know I am healed and I can only answer as Dr Ho-Yen did at our AAA meeting regarding ME, 'You just know it. How do you know when you are in love?' Instead of desperation you feel joy and hope not felt before and is inexplicable in words.

So at the age of 73, after a life-long search, I have finally realised that all this time God has been trying to show me His way, but I was too wrapped up in myself and the illnesses of others to be able to understand or listen to Him. I know it is late ... but better late than never!'

Amelia Nathan Hill
London 14.10.92

Most wonderful of all is that Amelia's testimony in her widely circulated newsletter has reached many who are turning to Jesus for their healing. She is absolutely overwhelmed with people who want to know more about the miracle working power of Jesus Christ today. Fruit bearing much fruit. Isn't He wonderful?

I spoke to Amelia on October 17th, 1992, she tells me that she does not take a single medicine or even a vitamin, that she lives by Hebrews 11 and that the Lord has given her Revelation 22:1–3. What Amelia does not know is that those very scriptures were laid upon my heart in Israel in June 1992, and that she has confirmed what I am receiving and praying through right now. Her ribs have just broken, but she will not receive anything but herbs and her calcium through dissolving egg shells in lemon juice! I believe that she is an inspiration to us all, and that like myself the Lord will perfect her bones (Isaiah 58:11). We are going to meet soon as she can now use public transport. Praise the Lord!

Helen's Testimony

'As an anorexic I received deliverance in the name of Jesus from Pearl a few years ago. This led to my baptism in the Holy Spirit and the increase in my spiritual growth. Since that time I have walked in considerable freedom and certainly I have never been anorexic since. However, from time to time I feel a little fearful in spite of having received much deliverance of all manner of spirits of far. I can always keep on top of this and take authority over it as Pearl has taught me to in the name of Jesus, but when life gets a bit pressurised (I have my own busy dressmaking business), the danger lurks.

Whilst visiting Pearl recently she handed me an article about the Angel of Death. I started to read it and became more and more interested and amazed as I went on. It mentioned those who had close contact with death or those who wanted to die. I realised with horror that while being anorexic nine years earlier, I had longed to die. I remember driving my car very recklessly in an attempt to have an accident and hopefully to die.

After reading the article, I told Pearl how I felt and she ministered to me there and then cutting me off from the Angel of Death and decommissioning the spirit that I had invited with my longing to die. I fell to the ground, I am told, with my arms crossed across my chest (the sign of death) as though I was laid out in a coffin. I was freed in the name of Jesus. Since then I have felt calmer and more peaceful and more able to cope with life, whatever the stresses and I praise God for this new revelation given to Pearl because I feel it is very important for all cases of anorexia, whether nervosa or bulima, they all come very near to death.'

Helen

Helen does have a point there and I am also ministering to a large number of nursing staff who worked attached to gynaecological units where they were involved in abortions. They have had some pretty grim manifestations in virtually every case. But since we are dealing with Molech and the curse of blood guiltiness that's not surprising.

Do It Yourself Kit

Nothing delights me as much as receiving a letter which indicates that Christians have had the initiative and faith to minister to themselves. This means that it is always one less for me to see or to fit with a counsellor. This letter arrived on my desk at the time of writing this book, and it blessed me because its contents served to remind me of that first time I actually spoke a creative word. The lady in the first book that Faith refers to has never looked back and has been such a blessing to the Clinic since her healing some eight years ago, as a radiant counsellor bringing countless people to the Lord and teaching them about Jesus. God also provided her with a wonderful godly husband and she is truly enjoying restoration of the years that the locust had eaten away.

Faith Tamkin's application of the Word to heal her is as follows:

'Ten years ago my doctor wrote a certificate stating that I would be unable to do any full time work again because of a condition in my back called spondulitis. He said the only solution was an operation, but that only had a 50/50 chance of success, the down side being that I could end up in a wheel chair!

About four or five years later I attended a Christian teaching meeting at Hove Town Hall where the speaker called for someone with a back problem to stand. I had expected half the meeting to stand as back problems are so common, but only one other person besides myself stood up. I really believed I was healed at that time, and in fact went home and the following day managed to dig some of my garden which I had not been able to do for years, and I had no pain. I was at home full time, and helping young men who had become Christians in prison to find their feet in their new life in Christ, and so for a while did not try to find any work. About a year later I went for

184

a job as a courier driver, and found I was working long hours, often driving in and out of London and sometimes more than once a day, and my back started to ache again. I found that whilst I was able to do more than I did prior to the healing prayer made for me, there were still many things I could not do, and one of them was to kneel for more than a few seconds without leaning on something, or to sit without making sure my back was well supported with a cushion.

Whilst reading Pearl's book *Go and Do Likewise* I was struck by what she said about speaking the creative word for a new gut for someone, and I prayed along those lines for my back, speaking the creative word to each part of my spine with my limited knowledge of anatomy, following this self-deliverance. I can now kneel for long periods, sit where I want, and I can almost do the back bends that I used to do as a youngster! Praise the Lord!'

I would add a word of caution here, concerning ME. I feel it is wisdom to have someone who is very anointed and competent in this field of ministry, to deal with problems in this area.

At this stage of my experience, I definitely believe for evidence of a curse upon the medical profession as a tie up with ME but am not saying it is as simple as that, as this is a multifaceted area for further revelation.

I had further correspondence with the lady whose letter I quoted in the early chapters of this book, and she has written of her deliverence from the angel of death. A separate letter to me from her pastor confirms it. Praise the Lord!

Telephone Anointing

It is not unusual in the round of telephone calls and postal communications to receive a sudden and strong anointing rise up within me when I certainly was not expecting to minister.

I always try to keep calls as brief as possible and I am always grateful when letters are clear, brief and concise. Below is an example of a letter I received in August 1992. As I read this letter the anointing was so strong. Before I had read the contents I found myself writing 'classical witchcraft, the tongue, Jezebel' across the front page of her letter.

Lucinda (not her real name) had written,

> 'Dear Pearl,
>
> I am about half way through reading your book *Go and Do Likewise*. On separate sheets I have written lists of things that trouble me.
>
> I live in a small, inner city Christian Community House and want so much to sense the Lord in the power of His Holy Spirit, but I am so frustrated.
>
> On many occasions I have sought ministry for healing, renewing and empowering, with very limited results. I could weep from sheer frustration. Reading your book, I almost feel it was written with me in mind – has made my heart burn within me, and given me new hope. Please, please may I come and see you for ministry?
>
> Much of the ministry I have received seems to have been quick and superficial. If you can see me, and I pray to God it may be so, would you please let me know conditions, charges, etc. and if it is possible to get accommodation in the area?
>
> HELP!
>
> In Jesus name,
> from *Lucinda*
> Psalm 72:12–14'

Attached to the letter neatly set out were the following:

'Shadowy things from the past

Father. Over sexed, made mother's life a misery. Much poverty made worse by father's heavy drinking.

He was forced by his father to become a miner, though he was a claustrophobic. Always shouting, swearing, hitting us. No peace.

Mother. Very good, loving. Very afraid of father. She was a gossip – I've inherited it. Although she was a loving mum, I've always felt not really wanted, due to anxiety over poverty during pregnancy?

Sister. Sexually abused me as a young child. Very pretty, lively, intelligent. Always centre of attention, drawing admiring comments. I always felt like the thick, unlovely sister! Father continually told me I'd never be any good for anything. I hated him and left home at 18.

Husband. I said I'd never marry. Why did I? He used me like a prostitute. It was a nightmare. Mental, physical, sexual abuse and cruelty. Very promiscuous. Committed suicide when he was 30 because he'd got a 16-year old girl pregnant. Sometimes didn't speak to me for weeks at a time. Said he married me out of pity. I was so ugly no one else would have me!

Wrong attitudes. Lack of compassion, jealousy, envy, resentment, gossip. Can't seem to stop, e.g. I'll just share this with you for prayer! Lying (also included in list of involvements), hatred.

Things I have been involved in. Spiritism, fortune telling, ouija, yoga, adultery, masturbation (still), stealing, cheating, lying (still exaggerate now matter how hard I try), self-induced abortion.

Physical health problems in the order in which they are most troublesome.
Gluttony resulting in obesity
Irritable bowel syndrome and haemorrhoids
Thrush and soreness
Chronic catarrh and severe headaches

Arthritis – very painful in feet and toes
Incontinence
Hot flushes (for more than 20 years)
Spondulitis affecting top of spine
Stiffness in neck and shoulders
Jaw pain when chewing (cartilage worn away?)
Varicose veins
Fatigue/heaviness
Shortage of breath
Sometimes I find I'm holding my breath – why?
Feeling of panic in stomach – why?'

Looking back at her notes since she became a patient, I
see I wrote at the end of her lists 'Bless her for her
honesty, what a mess!' She also listed her physical problems under which I had scrawled 'Candidosis for sure.'

When I receive such letters which are filed away I never
really know if I will meet these people and of course most
telephone calls are dealt with by staff.

It was clearly the Lord's intention that I took this incom-
ing call on my day off, and I had not remembered this
particular letter, but later I realised that I had an identi-
cally strong anointing when speaking to her.

I got my Bible and ministered to Lucinda, binding up
quite a few things, and now knew she would be coming to
see me for a physical appointment.

Upon examination she was shown to have very severe
Candidosis which can affect the brain and mood very
easily. Her score in our *Assess Yourself For Candidosis*
booklet (£2 plus 8″ × 5″ stamped addressed envelope) was
one of the highest I have ever seen. She was in her early
sixties and had been ill for 50 years! Again, I wrote on her
consultation notes 'desperately ill, also needs deliverance.'

As she was leaving the Clinic, the Holy Spirit made it
clear that I was to minister on that day before she left.
Since I have a long waiting list, she was delighted.

Lucinda was set free in a mighty way and as led by the

Holy Spirit I also anointed her tongue and cut off the demons tied to her feet. What touched me about this lady was her simplicity and honesty, and clearly the Lord was also touched! Praise His Name for a restored life.

It seems that the Lord is blessing me with increasing authority to pray for women with an issue of blood and to curse cancers at the root. He is also giving me revelation on the curse of endometriosis and I will share one such case in the next chapter.

Chapter 24

Root of Bitterness

One of the most incredible experiences I have had is to know that I was under the anointing in a dream. I believe, as this testimony unfolds, many women will identify with it.

In a dream one night I found myself in an operating theatre. Apart from having a glimpse in such places, prior to a general anaesthetic for myself, I know exactly what an operating theatre looks like. As a young woman, when I worked at the London Stock Exchange and was longing to be a surgeon, I took full advantage of two students from Guy's Hospital, both of whom were competing for my affections, to be smuggled into a gallery with a glass floor where medical students could view surgery taking place.

I was thoroughly intrigued by such skills and little did I know that thirty years later I would be carrying out excision with the Sword of the Spirit!

In my dream I was standing at the anaesthetist's end of the operating table watching the surgeon with scalpel poised above the abdominal area of a lovely sister in Christ with whom I shared a warm relationship.

I first met her as a patient who consulted me with endometriosis, which is a disease facet of the Curse of Eve. Jane had the most apalling skin complaint. It looked like acne rosacea, but I felt it was not. Although her skin dramatically improved with diet as did her figure, these awful disfiguring angry hard lumps, not infrequently with a centre vesicle, red and inflamed, would crop up from time to time, making her self-conscious and wretched.

Jane started to attend my teachings and ultimately became attached to the team. She is a wonderful, gifted counsellor and totally competent in deliverance ministry. Although very quiet and gentle her authority over the demonic field is very evident and I praise God for the love and support she gives me.

I was astonished to see the face of the patient on the operating table was Jane's, as the surgeon made his precise incision in her flesh. He pulled the flesh back and out of the hole in her abdominal cavity emerged a long vile tumour. It was shaped like a serpent with a broad flat head.

I gasped. 'What on earth is it?' I asked the Holy Spirit in my sleep.

The reply came swiftly, 'A root of bitterness.'

Then I clearly heard the surgeon say as he made to cut it out, 'With this one we have to get right to the root.'

Then to my utter horror he sliced if off near to the attached end. I awoke sitting up in bed crying, 'Oh! He didn't get the root, he left the root.'

Well, I sat on this one for about three weeks. I did not want to make Jane fear she had a serpentine cancerous growth. Yet I felt it was so because of the sexual problems in her former marriage, when she became totally frigid because she felt defiled by the many affairs of the spouse she loved. How on earth could I tell this sweet gentle sister such a thing? Well I couldn't!

But the Holy Spirit had other ideas; and eventually tired of sleepless nights I climbed out of bed to ring her one Sunday evening. It was quite late.

Jane's testimony is below, told in her own words:

'My marriage had eventually broken up after 22 years. Throughout the whole of that time I had felt that my husband was never really fully united with me. His mother and sister had never made a space for me to enter into their family, and I felt very rejected by them. I also felt that they had a very strong hold over my husband. His mother made him feel guilty for marrying me, and his sister was very jealous of me. We finally parted because I had become sexually frigid towards him, and he could not live with that. My frigidity had been caused by him being unfaithful to me on many occasions in the first years of our marriage. The threat of 'other women' made me feel very insecure, and that stayed with me throughout the remaining years that we were together.

The sexual area of our lives, which had originally been so good, was not the seat of all the problems. I felt dirty if he touched me.

I so wanted to keep my family together, but I had been cornered by my sexual feelings not being free to flow because of rejection and insecurity. Underneath all this was a deep need in me to feel that he loved me without me providing the sex. Love and sex had become separate things to me. Sex was no longer the consummation of love. His unfaithfulness had sexually abused me.

This situation continued for many years and we were happy in our own way. Then the tension began to rise, it built up until it was unbearable, but also in the background was his family bringing news of an old girlfriend who was available again. I knew that he had always felt that things were unfinished between him and this girl. Eventually he said that he couldn't go on any longer and to separate was the only solution. It was a relief. Much better to know what was going to happen, than live on a knife edge.

He was nervous, but seemed to be looking forward to it. I had become ill with endometriosis. Some months after the separation I found that he was well into a relationship with his ex-girlfriend and that his family had been instrumental in that, urging him on to spite me.

In my eyes they had won! They had tried to tempt him away from me before with other women. They knew his weakness was sex. It seemed that anyone they chose would be better than me, in their opinion.

We had come through so many problems, but I could not fight him or his family any more. I was at the end of my resources, tired and ill. My husband and I had agreed not to divorce, just to leave it and go with the flow. But when I realised his family's part in all of this, I divorced him for adultery to 'get even with them'. They had undermined our marriage and been secretive. I was making sure that it was all out in the open and that I was going to 'play the last card'. It was my revenge.

The following years were hard work. Lots of healing to be done in me and my children. My outlook was positive and I recognised how blessed I was in many areas. I didn't want to be bitter, I had seen how destructive it could be, I was sure that bitter was the last thing I was going to be.

I was slowly coming to terms with my new life, and would be going along happily, when out of the blue, my now ex-husband would jolt me from my peace by playing happy families with our children and the new lover in his life. His family joined in this too, extending invitations and acceptance to his new partner. It hurt so much. I felt so abused, emotionally and sexually. I felt ugly. Where did my feelings count in all of this I wondered?

While his face was radiant with love for his lover, my face was coming up in sore itchy large red spots. I put it down to drugs that I was on for endometriosis, then down to allergies, but eventually I was no longer on the drugs, and not eating anything that would upset my system. Yet my skin still flamed up.

Then after a rather upsetting episode with my ex, my face came up terribly. The cause was now obvious. I felt I was out of control. What could I do about my emotions? It was as if the anger, resentment and frustration were burning me up. I could feel it now. I knew those emotions had to be dealt with. Because I had received ministry from Pearl earlier on I felt she was so busy, I went for ministry elsewhere for two consecutive Sundays. I was telling those who were to pray for me about my anger, resentment, and frustration, and they prayed, but it was not dealt with. I was still burning up.

On the second of those Sundays, I was sitting at home late in the evening when the phone rang. It was Pearl. Although we are good friends, I had not seen her for a while, so she did not know the conclusion I had come to about my 'angry spots'. Pearl said the Lord had got her out of bed to phone me. We talked a little and then she said,

'The Lord has shown me that you have a root of bitterness. Can you receive it?' she asked me.

Pearl knows me as a gentle loving and caring person, the bitterness was well concealed from both of us, and so she was gentle in her approach. Wow!

'I can receive that' I said, 'I have been going for ministry for two weeks, but it hasn't been dealt with.' We didn't have the root which the Lord had given Pearl, the root of bitterness.

Bitterness can be so subtle. The Holy Spirit showed me that even to think 'Why couldn't my ex-husband's family have accepted me as they had his new love?' was a bitter thought.

Jesus has taught me to see their pain, he has given me understanding, compassion and the ability to see through their behaviour. Many things have been brought to the light, and most of all Jesus has taught me to forgive.

I prayed during that last week of my bitterness and received a picture of myself being lifted high up on an operating table, and someone laughing with joy. I didn't know the significance of it until Pearl told me her side of the story.'

Jane came for ministry and spent time on God's operating table! I cursed this root of bitterness at the roots and excised it with the Sword of the Spirit. Since that surgery by Almighty God, I have watched Jane's skin clear completely and to say that her face has taken on a new radiance and beauty is an understatement. Praise the Lord! I get so excited about such things.

We know that the root of bitterness is the end product of the curse of rejection, but I am convinced that a major cause of it is sexual betrayal. When mine was excised in 1986 I was told it was about four feet long!

Chapter 25

Is There a Format for Deliverance?

In *Fruit Abiding In The Vine* Part II, pages 72–27 contained the teaching I give on the ministry of deliverance. More recently I was shown a paper where it was suggested that blowing out demons could be 'demonic and not Godly' and the question of a format for deliverance was discussed.

Now in answer to the question 'Is there a format for deliverance?' the answer has to be an emphatic '**No**'! For as I point out in Chapter 19 *Reliance on the Holy Spirit*, that such reliance must be absolute and we know that the Holy Spirit does what He wants, when He wants and how He wants, and praise God for that! Therefore if you are relying totally on the Holy Spirit and there is *no* other way to be involved in the deliverance ministry, you must be prepared for Him to change anything you are accustomed to doing.

For two years I ministered without the use of the outward breath, with a degree of success. Then I heard a tape entitled 'How to Recognise and Expel Demons' No. 6004, Keys to Successful Living Bible Teaching by Derek Prince. Derek's explanation of the method he taught made real sense to me. He taught that in Phillips translation of Mark 16:17 *In my name they shall cast out demons,* reads

'*In my name they shall expel demons.*' He goes on to say that the key word is *expel* which is to exhale. He teaches that to do either requires

1. A decision of the will.
2. Action of the muscles.

He then goes on to say that expelling an evil spirit requires the same decision of the will and action of the muscle, and that as believers who have met with the requirements for deliverance we have the authority to expel demons from ourselves.

We know of course as I also have clearly set out in my teaching that the requirements are confession, renunciation, repentance, forgiving all others and calling upon the Lord. Derek explains that in Hebrew the word 'spirit' is '*breath*' and in Greek '*wind*' so an evil spirit is an evil breath, just as the Holy Spirit is the breath of the Almighty. He says 'In the baptism of the Holy Spirit you drink in the Spirit of God. Jesus said, "*if any man thirst let him come unto me and drink.*" To expel is the exact opposite of drinking in, so when you've met with the conditions co-operate with the Holy Spirit. It may be that the first breath will be human breath, the second likewise, the third also, but, somewhere down the line, something other than human breath is going to start coming out.'

Well, I took this teaching to heart, it made sense, and the results were very positive so I continued in that way until more recently. I will explain that later.

It has been suggested that since demons can exit via any orifice or organ or limb, breathing out is telling them how to leave. Nonsense! In thousands of ministries I have never, never known a demon to exit other than where it decided to exit. So it is that when breathing out, that method can change into a cough, a shriek, a sob, a sigh, intensive yawning, choking, groaning, roaring or any other manifestation, such as the person falling down, curling into a foetal position, rolling about etc. In all cases, what freed the person being ministered to was *obedience*.

If you are submitting to the anointing in another, you are submitting to the Holy Spirit directing the person ministering. If you have no trust in the anointing or the person, forget it. Deliverance is out. So the answer to the question of whether breathing out is addressing the demon on how to leave is an emphatic 'No'.

Deliverance is a nasty subject at the best of times. So many in the Body are fearful of demons and totally oblivious of the authority we have over them. Many long to be involved, they are 'living' to make a start but fearful of initially doing something wrong. (Notice I did not say 'dying' to!)

If you are a teacher you have to lay down guidelines, rather than rules for beginners to follow, confident that if their hearts are with the Lord, and they are full of compassion to set the captive free and smack the devil on the nose, the gracious Holy Spirit, so gentle, so sensitive, will move them on to a different place when He is ready and He knows they are ready. The Lord has perfect timing, it will be different for us all, but everyone has to make a start somewhere.

Writing the foreword to my first book, *Go and Do Likewise*, Dr Tony Dale said that the Scriptures do not always give us a full description of what Jesus did; that we did not see Him naming the demons as I did, but that did not mean that He didn't!

John 21:15 says

> *'And there are also many other things which Jesus did, the which if they should be written every one, I suppose that even the world itself could not contain the books that should be written. Amen.'*

We need to really heed this verse of scripture before we criticise or condemn the ministries of others. The greatest ministry I ever had was from John and Elsa Linden-Cook. Anyone who observes this ministry knows that those submitting to it are often told to cough. I was given a bowl and told to cough into it. My initial reaction was, 'I don't want to cough I want to breath out,' but I was submitted to this ministry, I could sense the strong anointing on them both, so I obeyed and coughed and coughed and coughed. Nothing fell into the bowl, I tried to spit but couldn't really produce saliva, and I could hear Satan telling me it was all a waste of time, but I was fasted and prayed up, I knew his tricks!

Even on my way home he was telling me nothing happened, yet that day after three (if I recall) long hours of ministry the curse of rejection and personality spirits deposited in me were dealt with once and for all. I was totally transformed. That spirit which executed the curse of rejection over my life had been dug out and I tell you I still get plenty of opportunity to take rejection on board but it rolls off me, I do not receive it because the curse was broken at that ministry. Praise God!

Now I dare to suggest that if I had done a Frank Sinatra ('I did it my way'), I would not be free to this day. Hallelujah! Obedience to the Holy Spirit always pays. Again this question of conversing with demons often arises. We know that Jesus spoke to demons on more than one recorded occasion. Like Derek Prince teaches, I always caution on conversations with evil spirits, but I have told them to shut up and to name themselves. I have also said 'I recognise you' when one thinks it has given me the slip.

My greatest shock was to hear a woman with paralysis of the vocal chords say from her hospital bed, 'I am lust, and I'm sick and tired of you goody-two-shoes,' when in exasperation I asked it to name itself. Do you know that people bound by paralysis, amputation and wheelchairs not infrequently harbour appalling lust? Poor souls. Sex is often on their minds because of their inability to take part in this special and precious gift of life. So they think about it constantly and desire becomes lust, which eats them away. Smith Wigglesworth addressed demons, and he also regularly belted people in the stomach. I have done that sometimes. It does not hurt the person, you are hitting the demon. I do not advocate it, neither do I condemn it. We are back to the Holy Spirit leading and we must not pet demons. If I want to be like anyone who served the Lord without fear or favour it would be Wigglesworth, bless him. He said

> 'Be filled with the Spirit: that is be soaked with the Spirit. Be so soaked that every thread in the fabric of your life will have received the requisite rue of the Spirit, then when you are misused and squeezed to the wall, all that will ooze out of you will be the nature of Christ.'

The nature of Christ was not all ooey gooey, Wigglesworth knew that, but through him shone always the compassion of Jesus. We know he offended many. We also must agree that he delighted the Father!

Do you know I have such an intolerance for some types of witchcraft when I confront them, that I have to constantly remind myself of where I am at. I often offend because I will not let it get a word in edgeways. It likes to interrupt to talk over me and it will rant on indefinitely, always accusing me of not letting it get a word in! Sometimes these come on the telephone and I put the receiver down and walk away. I return ten minutes later and they are still babbling quite unaware that I have not been listening! I quite often say, 'Shut up and listen to me.' It sounds so rude, but there is a type of Jezebel like this who will run circles round you if you don't watch out. Beware!

Another question I get asked is do I like people breathing on me? My response is an emphatic 'no!' Jesus breathed on his disciples. I would be willing for Him to breathe on me, but wary of anyone else doing so because I know spirits do exit on the outward breath sometimes! Having seen my whole team almost demolished by someone who professed the anointing breathing on them and personally finding the idea disturbing I would not allow this, neither would I do it myself. Again, in all these matters there may be differing opinions. We have to look to the Holy Spirit and be watchful and prayerful in every situation of ministry. I have lost count of how many individuals and couples I have taught, and I do often throw them in at the deep end and marvel, yes and often weep with joy as I see them take off, putting the enemy to flight in the name of Jesus and under the anointing. Satan wants condemnation in the Body of Christ, but

> *'There is therefore no condemnation to them which are in Christ Jesus, who walk not after the flesh but after the Spirit.'* (Romans 8:1)

We need to pay more heed to this scripture and cover much more with love than we do.

Two of my team were quite upset reading the paper I have referred to and they began to feel that they were doing everything wrong, especially since some had noticed changes in my ministry. Satan wanted them fearful of doing anything. My personal opinion is that if people with a heart for this ministry are rooted and grounded in this method of expelling demons they are kicking off safely. Another advantage of this method is that it actually prevents hyperventilation. It is vital to instruct the person to breathe out from the gut low and slow, and we are all extremely careful to do that.

Since I wrote the second book I am being shown by the Holy Spirit how to minister more swiftly, but I am sure my grounding in heeding the ministries of men I trust like Dr Joy Seevaratnam, Derek Prince, and Bill Subritzky has done me much good and caused me careful spiritual growth.

I have in the early days of ministry often seen grief and mourning and humiliation loosed by cuddling the person alone. Likewise I recall ministering to a man who suffered a heart attack at the onset of ministry. Satan was trying to run me off and I reminded him that at the name of Jesus demons had to leave and some seventy left as I named them. The brother in Christ was transformed. So many infants will co-operate with this method and believe me I see the demons leave.

Just recently I ministered to a beautiful girl of eleven. There was yards of stuff to deal with. I held her in my arms addressing the strong man and told everything else to go in the name of Jesus. We had found this child to have serious multiple allergies. Following this ministry we tested her twenty four hours later and not an allergy remained. She is totally free! This makes a case for allergies being demonic. Often they are as in ME but at this stage I will not make a sweeping assertion.

Based on my experience of twenty four years with a Clinic and almost a decade in ministry I would say that most people who do not lose allergies are non-Christians, but that many deeply committed Christians do retain some allergy. I retain allergy to grains. Because I have heard people being loosed of such allergies I have attempted to address mine and get others to do so but it is no use. Ministry for the unusual must be based on discernment or a word of knowledge. Of course your heart leaps when you hear that someone with forty years wheat allergy loses it because Derek Prince got a word of knowledge. Do only what the Spirit says and remember there may be demons about which did not exist when the scriptures were written. Heaven knows what the names of the six thousand named legion in the Gadarene were, but there had to be quite a large herd of pigs to take this lot.

I am not naming demons like I used to and I see the ministries of some old timers around me having the same experience. I tell them, be guided by the Holy Spirit, He could be changing your ministry as He is changing mine. Move in the flow of it and be peaceful. I am quite enjoying the changes, the speed and efficacy of doing so little, but I know the grounding I have had has been essential.

Remember always if you are under the anointing and the Holy Spirit gives you something new or different to do. Obey. When I was told to tell a former team member to spit on mud and anoint his little son's eyes with it (the child was four and had a cancer behind the eyes threatening the sight), I said to myself, 'Lord give me something easy to tell him to do.' But I obeyed the Father trusting my anointing, and the cancer left. Praise the name of the Lord!

Twice when ministering to women with tycoon-like husbands I was given 'doormat spirit' and that was the healing of two marriages. I didn't stop and think 'I didn't read that in the Bible,' I remembered what was written in John 21:25. Later the Lord showed me Isaiah 51:23 right through to Isaiah 52:1–3. There it was, the doormat spirit!

In that final ministry for ME I lined up and began desperately blowing out as I was prayed for. The lady ministering said 'Don't miss it Pearl, stop' so I stopped. I knew I was breathing out in an act of desperation. I was submitted to her anointing, so I obeyed at once. The Holy Spirit also promptly convicted me to stop at that time. There is no room for pride in this business! Be humble, be teachable, even be stupid, but above all obeying what is received under the anointing. The Lord will bless you.

As a teacher there is much in me that allows the folks I am training to have their heads. We tend to learn from our own mistakes and frankly it is the best way to learn. The Lord bless all of your ministries.

Chapter 26

Still Weeping for Jerusalem

The last chapter in my last book was entitled 'Weep for Jerusalem', and yes I am still weeping. I am also weeping because in the main the Church is totally ignorant or has chosen to ignore what the Bible says our attitude towards the Jews should be.

In the United States of America we have just seen the defeat of President Bush and one catastrophe after another overtaking that once great land. We see Isaiah 60:12 being worked out.

> *'For the nations and kingdom that will not serve thee shall perish; yea, those nations shall be utterly wasted.'*

I am sad to say the same is looking to apply to Great Britain, who is turning away from the Lord. One of the revelations that the Lord has given me during this time with Him is that Bovine Spongiform Virus (Mad Cow Disease) is a curse upon our Scottish beef, 80 per cent of which is being slaughtered in the name of Allah!

There is no doubt that during two world wars Britain was sovereignly protected by our Father in heaven, to emerge through such a devastating period in history with her vast Empire intact. Alas in 1947–48 Britain opposed and sought, to her shame, to thwart the rebirth of Israel as a sovereign nation with her own State. I believe we can look back and identify the gradual decline in our own nation with that of a struggling second rate power, with our betrayal of God's chosen people. Psalm 122:6 exhorts us to,

> 'Pray for the peace of Jerusalem; they shall prosper that love thee.'

Well, are you doing this? I have done so daily, faithfully, and often, since I received the revelation that to ignore the plight of the Jews and their relevance to salvation means *spiritual* if not *actual* death.

The Bible says in John 4:22,

> 'For salvation is of the Jews.'

Without the Jews we would in fact have no Bible, no prophets, no patriarchs, no apostles and no Saviour. Jesus is *'The Lion of the tribe of Judah.'* Judah is the name from which the word Jew is taken (Revelation 5:5).

In Romans 11:30–31 Paul indicates very clearly that the gentiles should show mercy towards Israel. That mercy is wrapped in love! We need to love the Jews enough to pray for them constantly, and hedge Israel around with a fire hedge of protection in the Spirit as the hordes of Satan encamp around her borders, striving in the deception of 'land for peace' to squeeze her out of existence. Historically many so-called Christian countries are guilty by default in barely having uttered a word of protest as millions of Jews were exterminated in Europe by the Nazis. We need as a nation to repent before God and pray for Israel. The true Church will love Israel, stand with her and for her. The apostate church will not. It is as simple as that.

I personally feel so ignorant concerning Israel. I can only cry out to God in the Spirit for her, finance her survival as much as possible and lead others to do the

206

same. I will go as far as to say we are cursed if we do not favour and love and pray for the Jews through whom we are grafted into the Vine. Just a little warning though and I quote Derek Prince,

> 'I have discovered that making a commitment of this kind to pray for Jerusalem and Israel will definitely stir up a special measure of opposition from satanically inspired forces. On the other hand, I have also discovered that God's promise given to those who do pray in this way will hold true – *"they shall prosper that love thee."* This is a scriptural pathway to prosperity – not merely in a financial or material sense, but as embracing an abiding assurance of God's favour, provision and protection.'

I would agree absolutely with that statement in every respect. The persecution is certainly hotting up, but God's favour is also very evident.

I believe also that God is showing me by His Spirit that ministering freedom of curse to the Jews is vital to their receiving Jesus as Messiah, Jews also need deliverance. They are under the Curse of Blood Guiltiness, the Curse of the Swastika, the Curse of Anti-Semitism just for a start, and any Jews I minister to are cut free from these curses and the spirits executing those curses are decommissioned in the mighty name of Jesus the name at which every knee shall bow and every tongue confess as Lord! Jewish people not infrequently harbour a spirit of grief and mourning for ancestors lost in the holocaust.

In Matthew 27:25 we have the witness of a self-spoken curse over the Jewish people. When Pilate was declaring his innocence of the shed blood of Jews, the Jews replied:

> *'His blood be on us and our children.'*

That is the curse included in the curse of blood guiltiness. The other curse of blood guiltiness is the Curse of Molech which includes the spirit executing the Curse of Abortion.

I wrote in Chapter 6 'Appointment in Jerusalem 1992' quoting the heartbreaking letter from an ME patient I suspected had the Angel of Death over her. Finally, because she was so debilitated I sent the instructions to her pastor and a brother in the church she attends who were ministering to her. I sent them the up-to-date Freedom from Curse prayer given in Chapter 13 of this book and told them how to cut her free of the unholy trinity, Jezebel, Anti-christ, and Death and Hades.

Another letter from her arrived as I am concluding this book, and space does not permit me to print her long letter here. Suffice it to say that she is free and the description she gave seemed to be almost a carbon copy of Marilyn's deliverance (Chapter 6).

The Angel of Death also needs decommissioning over Israel, due to the incredibly high ratio of abortions there. Christian Friends of Israel reports

> 'There have been approximately 302,000 Israeli children killed by legalised abortion in Israeli hospitals since 1948. However, there have been more than 1,000,000 Israeli babies slaughtered by illegal and legal abortions altogether. The Minister of Health reported 60,000 abortions in Israel in 1975 alone, which means that the abortion rate was nearly equal to the birth rate in that specific year.'

I could go on forever. I have such a wealth of new spiritual experiences to share, but I must reluctantly conclude.

Could I ask those reading this book who are not convicted of their dire need to pray for Israel and support the Jews, to do two things,

1. Read Matthew 25:31–46. The scripture makes clear that all nations will ultimately stand before our enthroned Saviour Jesus Christ to be judged. That judgment day will be terrible for those who cannot grasp the scriptures as the sheep are divided from the goats. Verse 40 quickens the spirit, *'Inasmuch as ye have done it unto one of the least of these my brethren, ye have done it unto me.'*

2. If you are not 100 per cent certain that you are not being deceived on this issue, *dare* to pray the following prayer. You may of course use this to have anything at all revealed to you that is hidden, but don't be surprised at the results. I and others have had some pretty nasty revelations when praying this prayer daily. The comfort is that only *'the truth shall set us free!'*

Prayer for Revelation and Against Deception

'Come now, Holy Spirit, as it is written, you are the Spirit of truth guiding me into all truth and showing me things to come (John 16:13). Come now with revelation knowledge and unveil all deception around me – remove scales from my eyes and unstop my deaf ears so that I may hear and see what the Spirit of the Lord would have revealed to me.

Thank you Father that when I call unto you, you show me great and mighty things which I know not (Jeremiah 33:3). I am calling unto you now according to your Word, that you set an end to darkness, and bring all that is hidden to light (Job 28:3 & 11). Thank you that according to your Word there is nothing covered that shall not be revealed and hidden that shall not be known (Matthew 10:26).

Praise be to your name that it is written that you will give me the treasures of darkness and hidden riches of secret places (Isaiah 45:3), that you reveal the deep and secret things and know what is in the darkness and the light dwells in you (Daniel 2:22), for you are the God of heaven who reveals secrets (Daniel 2:28).

Thank you, precious Holy Spirit, for guiding me into all truth this day and always.

Praise be to the name of our God for ever and ever. Let every hidden thing be revealed according to His Word.

Amen.'

Note:

'*Me*' and '*I*' can be substituted with '*us*' and '*we*'

May the Lord bless you all, thank you for blessing me with your prayers and readership.

Chapter 27

Thank You Jesus!

Was I healed of ME? I am sure this question will be in the minds of many readers. The truth is that the manuscript was with the publisher at which time I was still extremely ill, and no, at that date I was not only not healed but in great despair about this non-event!

However, God in His great mercy healed me on Sunday November 1st around 5.30 pm. The manner of my healing confirmed much that I have been spiritually trying to put together on this disorder.

It was my third visit to Sozo Ministries in Romsey, Hampshire. There had been a long weekend seminar there from the Friday, culminating in the healing service on Sunday afternoon. I returned a third time because the Holy Spirit gave me a clear direction to do so, and because I am always so blessed in that assembly.

Following beautiful worship and Marion Daniel bringing the Word, those assembled were informed that over the weekend the Holy Spirit had confirmed an anointing for the healing of ME. I sat stuck to my seat thinking 'I cannot go up a third time.' I felt such a failure, such self-condemnation for my non-recovery in spite of all I knew to do both physically and spiritually. The week previously someone sent me a cutting from a medical magazine.

A Consultant Psychiatrist was declaring in print,

'My experience of ME sufferers is that they suffer triumphantly, and the claim that this disease has ruined their lives is not to be believed.'

He described a symposium he attended on the subject where in the audience 'pale and thin lipped ladies of vengeful appearance, waiting to pounce neurasthenically on those who dared to suggest that their sufferings were other than virally induced.' He said, 'ME offers not just an escape, but something better still: a cause. You can suffer and by joining one of the pestilential self-help pressure groups, believe that your suffering is not in vain, but is hoping to bring about a better world.'

The whole article entitled 'Myalgic Encephalomyelitis – My Eye' was a rhetoric of cold, utterly compassionless sarcasm. It was a disgrace to the profession, a parody of ignorance. On the other hand in the same journal the contribution by Dr Charles Shepherd, himself a sufferer for many years, provided a string of medical references giving conclusive evidence of structural damage to muscle mitochondria along with type 11 fibre atrophy.

Dr Shepherd made it quite clear, an experience I would share, that ME is not a condition confined to 'semi-intellectual middle classes', but all social classes. Personally I have treated ME cases of seventy years of age and nineteen years of age, and all the ages in between, both male and female. Having presented a string of medical references with a précis on each one, Dr Shepherd rightly concludes:

'Patients with genuine ME *do* have their lives ruined by this illness, and have every right to feel angry and upset when they still have to contend with the sort of prejudiced and sarcastic comments made by this doctor. The results are that they fail to receive practical advice on how to cope with a very disabling illness, the Department of Social Security refuses to pay sickness benefits, families and employers do not believe they are ill, and sadly for some, the only way out is suicide – which is where we currently obtain postmortem material for research purposes.'

Now, having studied both articles, I have to conclude that ME does indeed have a tentacle, or many tentacles attached to its diagnosis which constitute the traumatic effect on the immune system of such experiences as shock, terror, grief, anger, loss and betrayal. These could be described as very powerful human emotions.

We know for a fact that the onset of many diseases can be shock. The fact that people are known to have their hair go pure white overnight following trauma or shock surely is indicative of the visible effect on the hair. Could there not be such an invisible effect on the muscle mitochondria known to have their own DNA, which is susceptible to shock or viral interference? The medical evidence I have read would certainly support this contention absolutely. It is also a medical fact that shock causes confusion and memory loss in many victims, a common factor in ME. I actually had to write the date on my wrist because although I knew it I could not recall it from one minute to the next!

I suffered terrible emotional shock just prior to my illness and suffered a viral infection which gave me a fifteen hour delirium. Because I am strong in the Lord, I do not expect to succumb to anything, there could be a degree of pride in that of course, and certainly nobody ever expects me to be ill or tired!

I decided to go forward in the healing line. As I stood there in my guilt and shame of it, being the third time I had done so, tears streamed down my face in a flow I could not check. Marion prayed and I surrendered all my members to the Holy Spirit. I recall laying there, ice cold and desolate for a few moments. I am told I was there for about forty minutes altogether, but I have no recollection of this. I saw very definitely, as I fell, one exact quarter of the green casing of a horse chestnut. I had no idea what this meant. One of the team, when I stirred, came over to lift me up and I said very irritably, 'No, don't touch me, don't touch me.' I knew I sounded harsh but I did not want human contact. Clearly the meeting had ended and as is customary, people were scattered around the large hall in small groups either talking or praying.

Marion seeing me stirring came over. By this time I was sitting on an upright seat. She drew a seat alongside me and asked how I felt.

'I feel terrible, I feel really terrible,' I replied and down came the tears like a waterfall.

I am sharing this in detail because deep in my spirit I know it is going to minister to some victims of ME.

On the Thursday and Friday prior to that Sunday, Rufus came to see me in his half-term and we spent two days praying in the Spirit in the countryside. The autumn foliage of rust and gold and yellow was magnificent. I had been so longing for the great outdoors and to walk again. I have always been a ten to fifteen miler, and I have been in real despair at missing my exercise and the beautiful scenery it afforded me. The sweet chestnuts, swollen in their bristled shells were beginning to tumble off the majestic chestnut trees, many well over seven hundred years old. The infinite variety of the leaves of pine, fir, plane, oak, ash, cooper beech, holly and sycamore afforded an incredible background of forestry to the sheepleas. The sheep were scurrying about for tender grass beneath the fallen chestnuts, and pheasants and squirrels abounded on the forest floor alternately leaping and scavenging as our appearance disturbed them. I am always amazed that pheasants and partridges, prolific in that area, never actually fly away when disturbed, but run and leap about like frightened chickens.

Rufus and I alternated our walk with sitting on logs and praying. At the end of the second day he asked me how long I had been in actual ministry intensively. I was soon able to work out that when I started to hear from the Lord to rest I was commencing the eighth year. At this time a lady totally unknown to me telephoned me from Switzerland. She was very apologetic and said that for some months the Holy Spirit had told her to invite me to Switzerland and that it was a definite prompting. Not having had such an experience before, she was concerned that it might not be the Lord.

The story was this. Following reading my books *Go and Do Likewise* and *Fruit Abiding in the Vine*, this lady felt inclined to 'scoop up' her children and come to the Clinic for a consultation for herself and them. When praying about it the Lord said, 'Ask her here.'

She thought it so odd and for some weeks went on with this prompting. Finally she prayed to the Lord that if it was not of Him, would He remove my name from her mind. Far from doing this she got an even stronger inclination to invite me to Switzerland and then the words and scripture for the Sabbath rest. Because of the terrible experience I had concerning someone from abroad who persistently rang me up to tell me that the Lord had told them to come and minister to me, giving me no peace until I did, resulting in what was almost a calamity for the ministry, I politely resisted any invitations from this lady. I sent her letters around the inner ministry team and felt very disinclined to do anything, from the 'once bitten' standpoint. However, finally I prayed with this lady, (I'll call her Louise) and felt great peace when we prayed together asking the Holy Spirit for further revelation.

Meanwhile the team and I prayed fervently as we were all well aware of the disaster before, and all had to come into confession and repentance for allowing ourselves to be misled and deceived. None of us wanted a repeat performance of such a trauma!

She kept asking me, did I need a rest, and I said I did, but was totally unfit to travel and could not pack a shopping bag, let alone a suitcase! Many felt that I should ultimately go to Switzerland but with a prayer warrior, and enough stalwarts in the ministry agreed this, so I decided to sit on it and await God's perfect timing when I was well. I knew however as I spoke to Rufus that I really had to get before the Lord and confess and repent disobedience of His order to *'come apart and rest awhile'* (Mark 6:21) in March 1992. I knew too that when I received that strong word it was at the culmination of so much total exhaustion, and because of the events which overtook me it had been really unwise to set it aside.

I always had the very real excuse, that people with their persistent demands wouldn't let me. But whom did I fear, God or man?

Rufus and I were engaged in a very important ministry on the Friday evening with another team member. We had certainly done plenty of praying outdoors! I pulled off my boots and took a shower, dressing in my white linen. It always seemed so silly in the autumn or winter, but there we are, it had been His orders.

Whilst showering I was weeping with a broken and contrite heart for my disobedience at not withdrawing when told. Before we commenced ministry I got down on my knees and repented with Godly sorrow. I felt great release and after I had received forgiveness I heard so distinctly,

'And when I heal you, don't take off again!'

I shared this with those present and they all laughed, knowing what I am like. However, I was before God in a new way and that evening before we commenced I cancelled out my Clinic for a whole month, writing 'Pearl away' in the appointment book. I had no idea where I was going or what on, but I meant business, for I was sure that my Father did! The ministry finished in the small hours of the Saturday morning. Whilst it had taken place a message was left on my answerphone from a faithful prayer warrior, one of a triplet who pray for me in Stoke-on-Trent. This lady has for many years given me some words which I have been able to check out as of the Lord on more than one occasion.

She gave me the Word she had received, also saying that for eight weeks the Lord had got her out of bed from 2 am to 4 am with a desperate need to intercede for me. Was I alright? I explained the despair of my physical disability. She asked me about unforgiveness and I asured her that I had indeed examined my heart for any unforgiveness. In fact I had done this often knowing what a torment unforgiveness can be. I find it easy to forgive, this has never been a problem to me, to bless and love those who despitefully use me. Following Derek Prince's advice on a tape heard a decade ago when he stated, 'You have a vested interest in forgiving all those who have hurt you.'

I took this to heart. Rosa went on to say, 'You see Pearl, the Lord spoke to me about this recently and asked me if I forgave with *all* my heart. I was like you, responding to the query of carrying a hidden unforgiveness, and I was sure I was clear in that regard, but alas, I was not.'

I told her I would get before God, and I did on my knees. As I prayed I recalled hearing a tape by Marion Daniel, on which she said that not forgiving anyone is wanting them to get their just desserts, it was wanting them punished. At the time my spirit quickened and I wondered, but set my wonderings aside. I was not vindictive, I was sure. Later that night I found myself standing in front of the many files stacked under my stairway. I extracted one. It was the file of a highly illustrious body of lawyers, and contained some highly incriminating evidence concerning someone who devastated my life some ten years previously and defrauded me in many ways. I removed the papers and flicked through them. Also amongst this batch was a letter written on hotel notepaper, which had been quite vital in my defence of certain accusations wrongfully brought against me by this person. Ultimately they were dropped on the evidence of this letter. I had kept it 'just in case' it should ever happen again.

In Penang some eight years ago whilst praying for me Dr Joy asked me over and over again if I had any papers or letters with that particular name on in my house, because previously he was insistent I discarded everything with this name on. At the time I did not believe that this legal file could be part of what he meant. Now, without a doubt I knew it was! I began to shred the evidence into the waste paper basket. It was raining really hard outside and in the quietness of the small hours I could hear the rain beating down on the courtyard which encircles three sides of the property. Going to the outside bin would have drenched me, so I thought I would remove it all in the morning. Having done all this I made a coffee and sat at my desk tidying up a few things I needed to do. I did not feel like sleep. I was praying in the Spirit all the while; it was about 1.30 am.

Finally, I knew I should get to bed as I had a long drive to Romsey the next day. As I passed the waste paper basket, the letter on yellow parchment, torn up on top of the other papers stared up at me. A voice said, 'I wouldn't throw that one away if I were you, take it out and stick it together.'

I wrestled as I regarded it, 'No you don't, Satan, and what is more, even if I get soaked I'll take it out to the dustbin now.'

I did get really drenched. I was also drenched with the Holy Spirit and I returned indoors, feeling so peaceful and took my one hundred and forty sixth consecutive Holy Communion, I knew that something very important had been accomplished.

During the breaking of my bread He said to me, 'Do you not trust me to defend you and what is more get you acquitted if the time ever arises? Allow me to take care of every worry in your life and I will continue to bless you.' I slid down between the sheets feeling very contented and re-assured. I told Him I was sorry about my reluctance to dispose of the papers, and that I had seen the truth of this *'with **all** your heart,'* at last.

As I am writing this I know that it will be a witness to many who have been self-deceived in this area of forgiveness, and covered a sore when they were not totally healed and had not forgiven with *all* their hearts.

So it was I was sitting with Marion lamenting that God did not heal me and that I felt hardly able to continue so great was the despair. She looked hard at me, and said, 'Look, I have to go and say goodbye to a lot of people here. Go back to your team and stay in that group and I'll come and get you.'

Ultimately she returned and collected me, taking me to a smaller hall. She pulled out a chair and placed it near the wall by a radiator, drawing up a chair closely in front of me, and putting her hands on mine. She spoke quietly, 'Phew, the anointing, it's so strong.'

I replied, 'I know I can feel it, I want to be well.'

I wept copiously and unashamedly again. Marion was regarding me strongly under the anointing. She whispered, 'What is it? What is it?'

I knew she was talking to the Holy Spirit, as I do when I am ministering sometimes. We were in close eye contact, as she said, 'Treachery? Treachery? It's like I'm getting treachery. Have you been a victim of treachery?'

I simply have no words to describe what happened in my brain, my gut and my heart at that moment of revelation. I groaned quietly repeating over and over again, 'That's it, that's it, it's treachery, that's the word, that's it, it's treachery. It's the root, you've got it, that's it.'

I told her that I had indeed been the victim of appalling treachery and that I knew it was at that precise moment I got sick. Yes, I was tired, even exhausted, my immune system was depleted in many areas, but I could still walk and run and refuel quickly. I was not burned out as I was now. Marion continued, and I gasped because she knew absolutely nothing of my background.

'Do you know Pearl, you have been sent an angel of light, and you have had so much treachery around you.

I'm going to cut you off from this treachery and any further visitations of angels of light.'

She prayed fervently. My head slumped forward as she prayed. It was a long powerful prayer, she did not cut any corners. Then this is what happened –

The muscles in my body all moved and corrected themselves, I felt long and leggy. My eyes came into focus, my dried out eye sockets moistened, I felt light. I stood up, moving my legs like a newly born foal. I wanted to stretch out my legs as though I had just discovered them. I cried out, 'It's done, I'm healed, that's it, it was treachery, that was the root, I'm healed, Praise God! Praise God! O thank you Father.'

I hugged her, I ran into the other hall to the team, crying 'I'm healed, I'm healed, it was treachery, I was sent an angel of light.' Everyone groaned.

We all knew it was true. We had prayed against backstabbing and betrayal, but treachery is a very different thing.

Dear Marion spoke to me later, saying that the word treachery had never cropped up in her long ministry, what exactly did it mean? We discussed it, agreeing to look it up when we got home, to find the exact meaning. I went through several dictionaries and the Webster's Collegiate. I was praying as I searched for deep Holy Spirit revelation. Although it was late, I did not feel tired, I was so well, and I chanced phoning Marion. She had been searching too!

Treachery is in fact the breaking of faith or allegiance or confidence. It is a violation of allegiance built up in trust and confidence, an act of perfidy or treason. It is where deep and great love and trust is believed to have existed, whereby you would trust that person with your life, and your secrets, your confidences. It is the breaking of special allegiance, like high treason, as in the betrayal of the king. It is in fact the Judas spirit.

King Jesus was betrayed by someone he loved deeply, his close friend and disciple who dipped his hand in the dish and shared the bread and the wine with Him. Judas was guilty of treachery, he was a traitor. In Jesus' hour of need he ratted on him, and ran and gossiped with those who were only too ready to kill him. Forgetting all that they had shared, the trials and the joys as children of the Father, the wonderful teachings and friendship, built on trust and close association, he traded that for thirty pieces of silver.

Jesus said,

> 'Woe to that man by whom the Son of Man is betrayed! Good were it for that man if he had never been born.'
> (Mark 14:21)

The Holy Spirit showed me that thirty pieces of silver can mean anything or any position a person hopes to gain by treachery. It may not be financial reward, but some sort of recognition. As I received all this revelation, I realised one thing above all, that Jesus my Saviour understood what it was to be a victim of treachery, that He had felt the pain of all this with me and for me. He showed me too by His Spirit that stockpiling or burying an unforgiveness of the past, it does not matter how cleverly or deeply you do it, will make you a sitting duck for further treachery!

It happened twice to me a decade apart, but I can see quite clearly now that the first treachery which resulted in that first ME some eight years ago came in on the identical channel of a virus following a treachery which totally depleted my immune system and altered my body chemistry, allowing the invasion of the Angel of Death. Now all the resultant misery of the first treachery which left me as an open target for destruction has been dealt with. It has been taken away and nailed to the cross. Hallelujah!

Whilst praying all this through I was shown two things by the Holy Spirit which fit the letters ME.
1.   ME = Maiming entity.
2.   ME = Masquerading entity.

An entity is a being, an independent, separate or self-contained existence. Also, something that has separate and distinct existence and objective or conceptual reality.

To maim = to commit felony or mayhem upon. To mutilate, disfigure or wound seriously, so as to cause lasting damage. Maiming implies the loss or injury of a bodily member through violence, to cripple, to cut off an arm or leg impairing completeness, function or beauty.

How many times have ME patients including myself said, 'I feel as if I have no arms or legs, or that my limbs do not belong to me.' (Like a phantom spirit after surgical removal of a limb and the patient still gets pain in a limb which is not there?) Do you see what I am getting at? Women also have medically recognised phantom pregnancies and will actually produce breast milk for a baby that is not in actual fact conceived.

I looked up 'mayhem'. It means wilful and permanent deprivation of a bodily member resulting in the impairment of a person's fighting ability. How that spoke to me, because I was certain of one thing, as were many who prayed for me. Satan was hell bent on disabling me and crippling my activities against the kingdom of darkness, and as we know he is not above using another member of the Body of Christ to do it!

I have to conclude that ME is an evil entity, an End Time entity, linked with death. It causes physical and chemical bodily functions which are real and can be medically recorded. It is caused by a *shock* to the total bodily function resulting in a central nervous system going haywire and masquerading as a physical phenomena when it is not.

The effect of the ME entity which both maims and masquerades, is to be able to reproduce clinical signs and pathological changes in the physical body, giving a clear, clinical and medical diagnosis, for what is in fact a spiritual problem. Satan desires to confuse both the patient and the physician, the path lab and everyone involved, and alas has succeeded to a greater extent in so doing. I trust that reading and understanding what I have written will go towards putting a stop to his deceptive antics.

As I have been delving into the problem of ME I have

discovered that maintenance and support of the physical body and therefore boosting the immune system, is very advantageous as a precursor to the deliverance, because by that time the patient is convinced that all that can be done physically has been done, and only deliverance remains. Approaching the problem from this direction for patients who have laboured long in its clutches, brings that wonderful end of tether co-operation with the Holy Ghost!

People who have it are often accused of malingering or of pretending to be ill. To malinger is to feign sickness to avoid battle, to avoid military duty. The unwilling captive soldiers of Christ are being maimed by this entity, so they cannot fight the good fight! As with all diseases it can attack those in the world, the unsaved, but time and again I see singled out for this attack Christians active in Christ, or those on the threshold of being born again.

How often have I heard from someone unsaved, 'Well, I was just beginning to look at the Bible, because of all that is going on in the world, then I got this ME and could not concentrate or read.'

Dr James van Zyl said in his booklet *The Lord's Table and Healing* that in taking Holy Communion daily he and his wife Meg have found that their ability to discern spiritual things has increased. He writes,

> 'The gift of the discerning of spirits and the revelation gifts are so important in these last days. We need to be as wise as serpents and as gentle as doves, as we all know how hard the devil is trying at present to bring deception into the Body of Christ. We know that what we are experiencing now is due to our obedience to the revelation of breaking bread that God has given us. We do not believe that we have the full revelation yet, but we are prepared to be obedient to Him as He reveals each successive step to us, and we know He will show us more. Hallelujah!'

Amen, amen, amen to that! I believe even as a newcomer to faithful daily Holy Communion, I'm getting revelations through obedience. I believe my own deliverance has come as a result of this, and the revelations I have penned on this overlock, this intertwining of the spiritual and physical in the case of ME are just such a revelation.

May what I have written cause you to ponder upon the question of forgiveness with *all* your heart. I said earlier of hair going white overnight from shock, shock also turns people blind, and many women having regular monthly menstruation are known to suddenly cease following mental or physical trauma, even though they are not of the age to cease. The demon anorexia so closely linked to death does just that!

I believe as I conclude this book, that there may well be more revelation to follow, but I trust that what I share to date will enable many disabled soldiers to return to full time service in God's army.

As for me, I am like a new born lamb, sniffing the air, enjoying the use of my limbs, the improvement in my eyesight and the renewal of my energy. It is so wonderful.

Rosa said to me on the telephone, God wants you gloriously healed for your wedding, He does not want you as a sick bride, but totally dependent on Him. I find that very exciting!

If you decide to write to me as a result of reading this book, **please do not forget to enclose large SAE for reply**, for we now only reply to those who do so!

May the Lord richly bless you as you seek His face on what I have written.

Pearl Coleman
The Christian Clinic for Environmental Medicine
Lane End, Highlands Lane
Westfield, Woking
Surrey GU22 9PU

C000051041

THE GREAT WAR COOK BOOK

May Byron,

introduction by Eleri Pipien

AMBERLEY

This edition published 2023

Amberley Publishing
The Hill, Stroud
Gloucestershire, GL5 4EP

www.amberley-books.com

British Library Cataloguing in Publication Data.
A catalogue record for this book is available from the British Library.

ISBN 978 1 3981 2288 8 (paperback)
ISBN 978 1 4456 3400 5 (e-book)

Typeset in 10pt on 12pt Sabon.
Typesetting and Origination by Amberley Publishing.
Printed in the UK.

Acknowledgements

Thanks go to Campbell McCutcheon (*CMcC*) and John Christopher (*JC*) of Amberley Publishing for the use of their collections of images and to the Discovery Museum of the Tyne and Wear Museums, Newcastle for their cooperation in providing an image from their circus animal photograph collection.

- E. P.

Every spare piece of land was taken over for growing vegetables. Here, mostly women can be seen planting a railway embankment. (*CMcC*)

Introduction

Baker: 'What's wrong with the little chap?'
Mother: 'I give it up. I've given him a bun – I don't know what more 'e wants. I can't get 'im to realise there's a war on.' (*CMcC*)

The First World War was a turning point both tactically and for civilian life in the countries involved. The availability of food was used as a tool by both sides to force each other to surrender and led to Britain's first taste of government-led, nationwide food restrictions. Food control was tentative at first, with more measures added as the war progressed, until the introduction of rationing shortly before its conclusion. As a consequence, by the time of the Second World War, there was already a template of food and information control to follow and the government knew how to act right from the start. The First World War, as a time of great change and uncertainty, forced people to learn how to live in a different way, including how to cook cheaply and most of all, creatively.

Although we are familiar with the literature inspired by the First World War – everything from the poetry of Wilfred Owen to comedy such as Blackadder Goes Forth – it is still the Second World War that holds our attention. We are acquainted, not only with its events, but also with the images produced at the time. The Ministry of Information, used throughout the Second World War, was responsible not only for ensuring through censorship that Britain's enemies did not gain any strategically sensitive information, but also that the British population was kept calm and educated about Home Front matters. This form of propaganda was designed to uplift the spirit of the British, make them feel empowered and create a feeling of cohesion and unity. Today, these images have made a return for much the same reasons in the face of the recession, and 'austerity nostalgia' has become a national obsession. Our resurrection of war-time principles has involved learning to cook wholesome budget meals, with various celebrity chefs and cooks teaching us how to do this. Yet as food shortage was a fundamental problem during the First World War, this style of cooking was not just an option, it was a necessity.

Preparing Birmingham's 900,000 meat cards in the Council House. (*CMcC*)

Diner (choking): 'Quick! Water! Crumb in me throat.'
War Waiter: 'Ah, Sir, if only the well-to-do would leave bread for the less fortunate.'
(*JC*)

THE "IDLE" OF HIS COUNTRY.

War Lord: 'Why don't you do something? Don't you know the people are short of bread?'
Von Tirpitz: 'Nonsense! Why, nobody could have a bigger 'loaf' than I'm having!'

Alfred Von Tirpitz was Grand Admiral of the German Fleet from 1911 – 1916. He felt the German Navy was unable to take on the Royal Navy head-on and advocated unrestricted submarine warfare to break the British blockade of German ports, which had been causing severe food and communication problems. The construction of German submarines could not keep up with demand, however, and in 1916, he resigned. (*JC*)

German U-boats, including the one that sank the *Lusitania* (*second left*). (*CMcC*)

A QUICK CHANGE OF FRONT.

Punch magazine makes fun of Germans in Britain becoming more British than the British during the war. (*CMcC*)

The reality for a lot of Germans living in Britain was that they faced distrust and hostility even if they tried to blend in. Many German shops were attacked and ransacked following air-raids. (*CMcC*)

The Defence of the Realm Act (DORA) came into effect in August 1914 'for securing public safety'. This vaguely termed Act gave the government the power to prevent anything which was deemed to 'jeopardise the success of the operations of His Majesty's forces or to assist the enemy'. One of its clearer aims was to ensure that food shortages never happened. These were more guidelines than enforceable rules, however, and those with enough money could easily obtain and hoard more food. Poorer people and labourers were soon starving and malnourished, a problem that was not repeated in the Second World War. At the same time, the Royal Navy was aggressively patrolling the North Sea and also had in place a blockade of enemy ports in order to starve them into submission. They partly succeeded, with large parts of Germany suffering from malnutrition and the Austrian population facing starvation. However, in 1916, Germany retaliated by unleashing unrestricted submarine warfare. Prior to this point, Britain was able to import food from Australia, New Zealand, America and Canada (who put in place their own food restrictions in order to maintain the supply), but with this U-boat campaign, Merchant Navy ships were no longer safe. On average, U-boats were destroying 300,000 tons of shipping a month and in February 1917 alone, 230 ships were lost. Britain was facing severe shortages.

Created in 1916, the Ministry of Food was tasked with making Britain more self-sufficient. It worked hard to ensure that agricultural resources were better distributed and formed the Women's Land Army (WLA) to

Members of the WLA ploughing a field. (*CMcC*)

Potato queue. People were relying heavily on the potato, using it in place of flour and to bulk out meals. (*CMcC*)

work on the extra three million acres of land taken over for farming. By 1916, the demand for men on the Front was so high that conscription was introduced. Women – particularly young, single women who had no ties or responsibilities – were encouraged by David Lloyd George, then Secretary of State for War, and Emmeline Pankhurst, the leader of the Suffragette movement, to help the war effort by taking on the jobs that were usually done by men. Women became public transport drivers and conductors, they worked in munitions factories, took on clerical roles and farmed the land. Women had been able to work on the land previously through volunteer organisations such as the Women's Legion and the Women's Defence Relief Corps, but in 1917, the Board of Agriculture set up the WLA, a civilian organisation which paid its members. They recruited women from all walks of life to work in the fields and forests of Britain and by 1918 there were 250,000 women working the land, 23,000 of whom were members of the WLA. It was not enough and finally, in early 1918, rationing was imposed. May Byron published her 'Rations Book' the same year, joining the thousands of women who wished to help the war effort, although as a married woman, her role was limited. A seasoned author already, she turned her writing skills to compiling recipes that could be achieved with the limited resources available to the housewife.

Food demonstration showing the use of potatoes instead of flour. (*CMcC*)

Dairy products, meat and sugar were rationed and other popular ingredients were in short supply. It became a summary offence to waste wheat, rye or rice and the government considered making any food waste a punishable offence. The Ministry of Food was keen to cut back on consumption of bread in particular, as the majority of Britain's grain had been imported and was now in short supply due to the submarine blockade. They therefore issued a number of posters urging the British on the Home Front to not waste bread by cutting back by two slices a day. Housewives were also encouraged to make War Bread with GR flour, which was a less refined wheat flour, with other grains added, such as rye or barley. It was supposed to stay fresh much longer than the bread bought from the baker, enabling families to eat less bread without worrying that their loaf would go stale before they had finished it. May provides a recipe for this War Bread and bulks out her loaf with potatoes. She also comments on its longevity, stating that while bought bread goes stale after only twelve hours, her homemade War Bread stays fresh for a whole week. Food posters issued by the government made no mention of shortages or the threat of defeat, but instead stated that if you could save on bread, for example, you could 'defeat the U-boat'. These posters were designed to make the British at home feel that they could actively help win the war.

For those on the Front Line, the food situation contributed to the dire living conditions in the trenches. At the outbreak of war, each British soldier was given ten ounces of meat and eight ounces of vegetables a

German Pirate: 'Gott Straße England!'
British Potato: 'Tuber über alles!' (*JC*)

day, which dropped to six ounces of meat a day by 1916. By the end of the war, meat was only permitted once every nine days. Some soldiers, fed up with their meagre rations, would hunt, fish and forage whenever they could, and some even planted vegetable patches in disused trenches. Inefficient food transportation meant that supplies often reached the trenches stale or spoiled. Although the kitchen staff did the best they could with the poor quality and insufficient quantity of food, the meals produced were extremely unappetising, consisting mainly of weak soups and stews – the most frequently made of which, was pea soup with chunks of horse meat. Additionally, the kitchen staff had to make all the meals for their battalion in the same two large vats, and carried it to the Front Line in pans, petrol tins and jars through the communication trenches, so by the time it reached the men, it was cold and it all tasted the same. Despite Britain providing 3,240,948 tons of food to their soldiers, and the army attempting to provide the 3,574 calories to each soldier per day on the recommendation of dieticians, the soldiers were frequently hungry and dissatisfied with their food. The poor food also cause outbreaks of illness – in 1916, for example, there was a shortage of flour, so bread at the Front was made from ground parsnips that caused diarrhoea. The Home Front shared rationing with the soldiers, yet experienced little of the intense misery of the trenches.

Although the First World War drastically changed British cooking, it was not the first food-upheaval we had faced. Until the eighteenth century, the majority of the population had lived in the countryside, with great reliance on the land for food and work. The Industrial Revolution made a majority of rural living redundant and caused a mass migration to towns and cities, where people worked in factories instead of farming. The food of the working-classes became mass-produced instead of fresh and many regional dishes were lost. With industry came the rise of the middle classes, who were eager to climb the social ladder and, with the aid of publications such as *Woman's World* magazine, they were able to emulate the upper classes without the expense and the aid of servants. The upper classes were the main employer of good quality cooks and when the First World War reduced the lifestyle they were used to, these cooks either made the move to work in large hotels, or found themselves unemployed. Added to food shortages and rationing, this meant that Britain's quality culinary traditions had to be put to the side and were forgotten.

The state of British food was not helped by the rigorous rationing imposed during the Second World War, which continued for nine years after the war was over. Rationing actually meant that the British population on average was healthier than before, due to a carefully balanced diet with less fat and sugar. However, the post-war years saw a population deprived of sugar and indulgent foods compensating for the long years of rationing. Tooth decay, obesity and heart disease soared. The reputation of British food was so bad following the Second World War that George Orwell felt compelled to write an essay in defence of it, entirely unsuccessfully as we are still suffering from much the same reputation today.

The British attitude to food in the twentieth and twenty-first centuries has largely been shaped by the world wars. Rationing forced us to eat healthily and sparingly and when it came to an end, we over-compensated, causing severe health concerns. Combined with our current austerity measures, this has given rise to the subject of cheap-but-healthy cookery. Our on-going nostalgia for wartime culture has led us full-circle as we look to ration-cookery for inspiration.

"Go away! We have no bananas!"

Banana rationing, Second World War. (*CMcC*)

Similarly, those writing cookery books during the Second World War could draw inspiration from their First World War counterparts, reusing or adapting their recipes. But where did May get her inspiration from? Did she draw on traditional British recipes, or did she create her own? The main challenge she faced was limited means for experimentation – how could she devise recipes, try new things out and perfect ideas while experiencing rationing? It is likely that old recipes were simply adapted to suit the types and quantities of ingredients available, with an interesting twist given to make up for the shortages (making marmalade with carrots or parsnips for example, pp. 220–221). She also appears to have collected recipes from other people and publications, as she mentions that she has never made sugar-beet syrup before, but provides several recipes in the book. Her first austerity cook-book, May Byron's *How to Save Cookery Book*, published in 1915, contains some of the same recipes, indicating that she recycled her ideas, altering them to suit the ingredients available with rationing. Both her wartime cookery books were in a similar vein and, much like the recipes of the celebrity chefs today, show readers how to be economical in the kitchen while still creating tasty meals.

'A lesson on food economy by the Mayor of Keighley. The town of Keighley set a fine example of loyalty to the Food Controller's edicts.' (*CMcC*)

It is evident that May was taking full advantage of the war-time climate to sell her books as they were published following the implementation of DORA and rationing. Before the war, an austerity cook-book would have been impossible to sell as the content would have been suited to the working-classes, yet they would have been least likely to waste their money on buying a cookery book. The food restrictions were, to an extent, a social leveller and meant that the middle and upper classes would need to change the way they thought of and prepared food (as most had lost servants to the front line) and, of course, they had the disposable income to spend on buying a book teaching them how to accomplish this. This genre of cookery-book, encouraged by the wartime environment, has been seen in abundance since, with television personalities, cooks and chefs all taking it on. Fanny Cradock in the decades following the Second World War; Mary Berry, who has been writing about food since the 1970s; and the Hairy Bikers and Jamie Oliver, whose presence is highly publicised and on-going, have all given tips on how to create good meals for less.

Unlike the cookery books of today, which have big glossy pictures and clearly laid out recipes, with the steps listed one by one, May Byron's is unillustrated, short and delivered with a matter-of-fact attitude. It is her 'Preliminary Remarks' and short introductions to each section which hold the most character and are both informative and amusing to read. May does not shrink from giving her opinion and almost scolds her readers into the right mind-set: that of hard work, skill and imagination. Also unlike our celebrity chefs and cooks, May does not try to make cooking fun, quick or easy, stating instead in her opening sentence that cooking with rations will be difficult, yet she encourages her readers to take on the challenge with 'a sense of cheerful enterprise' as she very much does in this book. She is eminently practical, but she also has a sense of humour, sharing with us her thoughts and the occasional anecdote. She recalls, for example, hearing a man complain that he was eating so much fish to replace meat in his diet that he had 'become an aquarium'.

Wife of Profiteer: 'Er – can you tell me if – er – really *nice* people eat herrings?' (*CMcC*)

The recipes themselves take into account the shortage of butter and other fats for cooking, eggs, sugar, meat, bread, cheese and milk, using as little of these as possible. Although she makes clear her distaste of vegetarian food, most of her recipes are padded out with vegetables, pulses, rice or cereals. She also takes care to try to keep her recipes nicely balanced and often comments on their nutritional value. However, despite her horror of waste and disapproval of indulgence, she describes puddings as 'indispensable' and does not consider the option of doing without. In

What does "S.O.S." mean?
Shortage of Sugar!

Bamforth postcard depicting the consequences of sugar shortages. (*CMcC*)

fact, she states that 'one is tempted to tear one's hair above a reeling brain' while trying to think of something to make into a pudding. We would now not go such lengths to produce puddings in such circumstances, but May makes it clear that just because there is a war on, there is no excuse for letting standards slip. This attitude permeates her book and it is with such determinedly optimistic practicality that she writes.

Although May was published more than 100 times in her lifetime, very little information remains about her. We know that she was born Mary Clarissa Gillington in Wenbury, Cheshire, in 1861, the oldest of four siblings. In 1892 she published a collection of poems with her sister Alice and the same year married George Byron. During her career as a writer, she published biographies and works of poetry, children's fiction and cookery under her maiden name, her married name and the pseudonym of Maurice Clare. She was best known for her revised editions of J. M. Barrie's Peter Pan books for a child audience of varying reading abilities, but her other works were also generally highly thought

The government urged the public not to be wasteful throughout the war – May was also particularly scornful of wastage and constantly gives tips on how to use up leftovers, for example, using the water that vegetables, cereals, or pulses have been cooked in as the basis for soups. (*CMcC*)

of. Her series of biographies describe 'A day in the life of' various great authors, poets, composers and other famous personalities and although they were well received, they confused some critics, who could not tell if they were works of fiction or based on research. Her poetry appeared in both dedicated books and in newspapers and a poem entitled 'At Bay' in her collection Wind on the Heath was described as 'a cry, not from the heart of a woman, but from the heart of Woman'. This describes a passion not seen in her cookery books, but it is evident from the volume and variety of work produced that she was a very creative and dedicated individual.

Her cookery books covered everything from puddings to cooking for the ill, and in addition to her How-to-Save and Rations books she also wrote a wartime supplement for her Vegetable book. She describes her cookery books as a series and she certainly covers most forms of British cookery at the time. As her wartime cookbooks coincided with food-shortage measures, it seems that she was also a canny business woman. However, other than what can be gleaned from her publications, little remains about her life and personality. Her Rations Book though, was written in such a conversational manner, directly to her readers – in a way that few authors use now – that throughout the course of the book, we really get a sense of who she was. She was an opinionated woman, determined to 'make the best of a bad job,' and full of advice for the struggling housewife.

Out of her collection of recipes, some are familiar and have stood the test of time, but many will be completely alien. There are not only recipes for such modern favourites as Cornish Pasties, Shepherd's Pie and Chocolate Pudding, but also for dishes that we will have never heard of, such as Stewed Calf's Feet, Mock Crab and Mattress Pudding. May might be a little too fond of currying ingredients and the recipes involving offal might turn the modern stomach, but her book neverthe-less provides a valuable insight into the diet and mind-set of the British public on the Home Front.

– Eleri Pipien.

In rare cases, circus animals were also used to plough the land – elephants and camels were used in the place of horses to pull heavy loads. (*Discovery Museum*)

Different classes of women were employed in more hard physical labour than ever before. They had taken over many traditionally male roles – in both rural and urban settings. These women are carriage cleaners. (*CMcC*)

Basil: 'Mummy, aren't we exceeding the speed ration?' (*JC*)

CONTENTS

CHAPTER I

PRELIMINARY REMARKS

CHAPTER II

MEAT

CONTENTS

WAR-TIME PIES, VARIOUS

CONTENTS

CHAPTER III

FISH

CONTENTS

CHAPTER IV

SOUPS

CHAPTER V

EGGS AND CHEESE

CONTENTS

CHAPTER VI

POTATOES AND OTHER VEGETABLES

OTHER VEGETABLES

CONTENTS

CHAPTER VII

CEREALS

PORRIDGES

B

CHAPTER VIII

PUDDINGS, PASTRY, AND SWEET DISHES

CHAPTER IX

BREAD, CAKES, AND BISCUITS

CONTENTS

CHAPTER X

VARIOUS : NUTS, JAMS, BEVERAGES, HAYBOX COOKERY, WEIGHTS AND MEASURES, ETC.

CONTENTS

CHAPTER I

PRELIMINARY REMARKS

I AM not going to minimise the difficulties which lie in wait for the rationed housewife. The making of bricks without straw is notoriously a hard job ; and the concocting of palatable dishes with a deficiency of those ingredients which we were wont to use so freely, is not at all an easy task. No amount of imagination will make baked haricots the least bit like roast mutton. No extent of make-believe will turn vegetable stock into good beef gravy. The question of nutriment is one thing, that of texture and taste quite another. Of course, professional optimists will say it is very good for you *not* to have this, that, or the other ; they will chill your blood by talk of proteins and calories and carbohydrates, and will declare that all you really need for health is to be found in split peas and sago. I have even seen tapioca recommended as a *substitute* for fat ! But nobody ever yet tried to fry potatoes in tapioca.

In this book, however, " there is no deception, ladies and gentlemen," as the conjuror says. I am not intent on assuring you that " everything is for the best in the best of all possible worlds " ; I am out to help you, frankly, to make the best of a bad job. Nearly all the most valuable component parts of our usual daily food are either very scarce or very dear. We must see what we can do with the quality and quantity vouchsafed to us. There is no reason why we should not rise to the occasion, and make a success of things. If necessity is the mother of invention, let us justify our existence by our skill. If makeshifts are the order of the day—at least let us have satisfactory makeshifts.

1

To this end we shall be obliged to take more trouble and more thought, much more, than of old ; and a sort of Robinson Crusoeish interest will invest our experiments in these days of dearth. Never a thrifty nation, we have dwelt for half a century in a fools' paradise, believing that " to-morrow shall be as this day and much more abundant." Now, when faced with the crude incontrovertible fact that we live in an island, and that nearly all our food has been coming from *outside* that island, there is no doubt that the present rude awakening should—in the long run—be very much to our advantage. " It's an ill wind that blows nobody good." To begin with, a fools' paradise is a weakening and demoralising habitation ; to go on with, we are now compelled, willy-nilly, to learn the use and value of expedients, of substitutes, of skilful cookery—in a word, of brains. I conjecture that, sooner or later, we shall emerge from this dire emergency a great deal cleverer than we were before ; having acquired all sorts of knowledge, and exploited all manner of possibilities, which we should have regarded with a stare of blank bewilderment in 1913.

So, not with a long face, but with a sense of cheerful enterprise, let me proffer you the following suggestions. It hasn't been at all easy to discover them ; but a feeling of adventure in unknown lands has carried me through. And I don't put them forward as a confirmed vegetarian, or an anti-carnivore, or a pulse-eater, like Daniel at the court of Nebuchadnezzar. For—to indulge in a momentary confidence—farinaceous foods are odious to me, and pulse foods pretty nearly poisonous, and most vegetables unattractive, to put it mildly. So my hearty sympathy is extended to others in like case, and I have borne them largely in mind, when collecting the recipes in this volume. There are plenty of books for the vegetarians. This one is intended as a sort of stand-by in what the Apostle calls the " present distress."

Of course, the fundamental idea of rationing was standardisation, equalisation : *i.e.*, that nobody shall have more than anybody else. Equally of course, like all theories of standardising and equalising, it won't work out in practice—even for a single day. Because, not only does the " heavy manual worker " obtain a larger ration ; not only does the producer, or capturer, of certain foods secure more in that way ; but the small household has to tackle a much harder problem than the large one. As usual, " to him that hath shall be given," and the large family is, in many cases, conscious of no difficulty at all : rolling in coupons, and getting on supremely all right, beloved of its butcher and butterman ; whilst the households numbering from one to three persons have a desperate struggle to make ends meet on meat-ends and scraps. It is, therefore, of these last that I have chiefly thought in compiling this book : the people with very few coupons. Their perplexities are multiplied in inverse ratio to their tickets. No amount of arithmetic (which is notoriously unreliable), as regards fewer people wanting less food, will alter or ameliorate the question of how small households are to manage. This is a question only to be solved by good management.

With reference to meat, bacon, fowl, etc., I do not state the prices or exact amounts rationed and obtainable, because these vary as time goes on. I can only generalise.

FATS are a very serious crux. I most emphatically advise that butter and margarine rations (at present four ounces a week per head) should be only used at table, especially at breakfast, and never encroached upon for cookery, unless you happen to have an extra good supply. For tea, the less one eats the better, and one can make shift with jam (when procurable), or with treacle, or with one of the " fake " honeys —real honey being exceedingly expensive.

Butter and Margarine, therefore, we will rule out. If you find them mentioned in any recipe, it is purely by inadvertence, and you must substitute something else.

The question is, what ?

Fat is particularly necessary, because it is what supplies *energy* to the human body—four times as much energy as bread does. Goodness knows, most of us could do with a bit more energy, but I daresay you have noticed how marvellously energetic some very fat people are—the last thing one could expect of them.

Well, certain foods, of course, furnish more fats than others, as follows (per cent) :

Lard	..	.. 95	Pork	.. 40	Eggs		.. 9
Butter		.. 85	Cheese	.. 30	Salmon		.. 9
Margarine		.. 84	Mutton	.. 25	Herrings		.. 4
Suet	..	.. 82	Nuts	.. 22	Milk		.. 4
Bacon	..	.. 60	Beef	.. 20			

Cocoa butter would probably top the list.

I have already suggested that some coupons should be used for the purchase of suet and of fat for rendering down into dripping. In roasting or baking meat, you must be careful not to use up the dripping by putting potatoes, onions, or Yorkshire pudding into the pan. Save every scrap you can : remove and render every bit of fat from the meat when cold. It is possible for a very small household, by care and thrift, to keep a little dripping of sorts in hand. Dripping can still —very seldom—be bought, but you don't know what it is made of.

Lard and "lard substitute" (which seems to me to be cotton-seed oil, hitherto largely employed in fried fish shops) are also precious when obtainable. Preserved Suets, such as "Atora," seem to have disappeared from the market : so it is of no use considering these. We must, therefore, fall back upon that new and much-discussed substitute—Cocoa Butter.

Cocoa butter is the fat which results from cocoa nibs during the process of converting them into cocoa. It is not so digestible as butter or margarine, but considerably richer. It has always existed as a vehicle for certain medical preparations. As a medium of cookery it has been hitherto unknown. Of course, the crude stuff, as we buy it by the pound, is nothing like the highly-refined article used by the chemist.

The problem is, how to get rid of the cocoa flavour. It is all right when you are using the cocoa butter for cakes or puddings, though, even then, one grows rather tired of its persistent chocolateness. But how to make it useful for salt dishes and for pastry ?

A great deal has been written on this subject, and most people end by confessing that you never do *quite* obliterate the cocoa. Even if the taste be practically gone after repeated clarifying, the smell is slightly there. The bother is, that clarifying makes it set so hard. It is then suggested that you should add to it, in the liquefied state, any lard, oil or dripping you can spare, to soften it. But who *has* any lard, oil or dripping to spare ?

Until cocoa butter can be softened into a malleable condition, it is too hard for pastry : it makes the pastry hard when cooked.

If you use it (after clarification) for frying, shred it or flake it into the pan, and add a little salt.

For puddings and cakes it is all right, until you get tired of it, and remember that it is much richer than margarine, or even than suet, so can be employed sparingly.

The various vegetable fats, such as " nutter," seem to have disappeared off the market. Remains only that treasure of the careful cook—

Salad or Olive Oil.—This, if good, is very dear ; and, if bad, is hateful. It is the best frying medium (especially for salt dishes) which can be found ; and can be used again and again if it is not allowed to become smoked or burned. (It is less liable to burn than lard or dripping.) It can be clarified by letting it heat through slowly at the side of the stove, and then putting in some thin slices of potato, which will remove all impurities. Of course, any crumbs or particles should be removed : there are not likely to be any if you use a frying basket.

It is most important for such articles as require deep boiling fat, that you should be able to use your oil, or whatever it is, again and again. Olive oil is exceedingly expensive, but not when you use it repeatedly. I recommend that you reserve it for *salt* frying, and use cocoa butter, clarified or not, for *sweet* frying.

If you can add a little olive oil to the cocoa butter, in frying, you will do well, because the oil will soften and modify the cocoa butter.

A good many people have written to the newspapers, explaining how you can double your butter or margarine by beating it up with milk : half-a-pound to half-a-pint. I have tried this plan, and I cannot conscientiously recommend it. It takes a mighty long time : it *apparently* doubles the bulk of the butter by incorporating that much milk—but the result is like a cream. It sinks into bread and does not, consequently, go so far as a more solid article. Its increase is a deceptive matter, to my thinking. Still, some folks believe in it, so I can only state my own experience. Other plans are suggested, which will be found below.

The fat which is skimmed off stock when cold, answers admirably for frying anything of a salt or savoury nature. It can also be run down along with mutton dripping, and helps to soften and improve the mutton dripping, which is otherwise rather tallowy.

All odds and ends of cooked fat should be clarified and kept for use ; never let any go to waste.

To *clarify fat*, cut it into pieces and put them in a saucepan with half a pint of cold water ; let them boil gently for one hour, stirring from time to time. Then remove the lid and let the water boil till it has all evaporated, this will be shown by no steam rising when you stir. Let it stand a few minutes to cool and then strain it into a basin.

To *clarify dripping*, pour it while hot into a basin containing some cold water. When it has hardened, remove the top, scrape it underneath and it is ready for use. Dripping should be examined every second day or so.

NOTE.—Whenever the word " fat " is mentioned throughout this book, it means *whatever kind of fat you can lay your hand to*—rendered-meat-fat or dripping, lard, lard substitute, olive oil, preserved suet, fresh suet, bacon fat, or cocoa butter.

TO CLARIFY COCOA BUTTER

Cocoa butter should be clarified before using it for salt dishes or frying. Many recipes have been put forth, but the following are the simplest :

1. No. I

Break up small, or grate, or flake, the cocoa butter into a basin ; pour on sufficient boiling water to cover it ; set in a cool place. Next morning, drain off the water, again break up the cocoa butter, which will have set hard, and repeat the process. After this second time of clarifying, the taste and smell of cocoa should be almost imperceptible.

2. No. II

Place one pound of cocoa butter in a pan with one flat dessertspoonful of salt, and one breakfastcupful of water (or lime water). Let it come to the boil ; then place at the side of stove and let simmer for two hours. Remove, and when cold, drain off the water.

3. No. III

Boil the cocoa butter as in No. II., and when it is cold break up and pour boiling water on it as in No. I. I have found this a successful plan. But I doubt that one ever *wholly* gets rid of the chocolate taste. Some of the finer makes of cocoa butter are more susceptible to treatment than others ; but one must be thankful for so excellent a fat, flavour or no flavour.

4. No. IV

Another method is to use as much water as possible. Break up two and a half pounds of cocoa butter, put it into one and a half quarts of water, let come to the boil; add one ounce of carbonate of ammonia. Mix four ounces of cornflour smooth in a little cold water, stir this into the cocoa butter; remove pan from fire and stand it in a larger pan with cold water. Whisk it as it cools. This will incorporate some of the water and render it easier to spread.

5. No. V

And yet another way is to boil the cocoa butter, broken up, in a double-saucepan (or in a large jam-pot placed in a saucepan of boiling water), and then strain it through butter-muslin.

TO INCREASE OR AUGMENT BUTTER

6. No. I

Wash four ounces of butter or margarine in cold water; drain, and work into the butter half a teaspoonful of salt. Then add four ounces of cooked sieved potatoes, still warm but not hot, and go on beating till they are thoroughly incorporated with the butter. Leave it in a cool place, and when cold, shape into pats.

7. No II

Cream the butter in a basin, add an equal quantity of cooked sieved potatoes and a little salt. Beat well until thoroughly blended, then put aside to cool.

8. No. III

Take eight ounces of margarine, and cream or gently melt it; dissolve one dessertspoonful of gelatine in a little milk (warm); add one breakfastcupful of milk, and mix all with the margarine. Continue to beat until the mixture sets firm, and form into pats.

9. No. IV

Mix one ounce of cornflour smooth with a very little milk, deducted from half a pint, the rest of which must be brought to the boil ; then add the cornflour, and boil, stirring well, for ten minutes. Remove and let cool ; do not let it film over on the top. Meanwhile cream six ounces of butter with a wooden spoon, and mix it very gradually into the milk, etc., when the latter is nearly cold, with salt to taste. Beat well till thoroughly blended, and keep in a cool place.

SUGAR is another case in which actual standardisation is impossible ; because some people desire to make their tea into a regular syrup with it, and others hate tea that even dimly tastes of sugar. So that the regulation rationed half-pound each is far too little for some households, and abundance for others. While on this point, let me assure my readers, from personal experience and that of many friends, that if they once had the self-denial to do without sugar in tea for one week, they would find the habit broken for ever. They would do very well without sugar till Doomsday. For it is, after all, only a habit ; and the idea of sugar in tea is, in the East—whence tea comes to us—considered a sheer barbarism ; as much so as sugar in stout would be considered here.

However, be this as it may, it is best to save your sugar for puddings and for the sweetening of fruit dishes especially, which are most unpleasant to a cultivated palate if saccharine or glucose is employed. For the sweetening of puddings and such-like, there are various proprietary preparations with quaint names—there are saccharin, saxin, etc.—there are the " fake " honeys, made from wax and glucose—there is glucose itself, which is a product of maize ; and, very sparingly, one can invoke occasional jam or treacle.

Again, there is a thin syrup made from sugar-beet—I give some recipes, pp. 10, 11—and it appears to involve a lot of labour, but may be quite worth while in the long run. I

C

have not tried it myself.   Some people make a similar syrup from parsnips.

Glucose (or corn syrup) is about two-thirds as sweet as cane sugar.   It is made, I believe, out of starch derived from maize.

Saccharin is derived from coal-tar ; so are many other proprietary articles.

Date stones, simmered in a little water, will produce a thin sweetish syrup.

SUGAR-BEET SYRUP

10. No. I

Sugar-beet syrup is rather a bother to make, and will not keep longer than a month, and then only in an air-tight vessel.   You can't possibly " hoard " it ! Still, any port in a storm.

Peel and scrape the sugar-beets ; when you have got them absolutely clean, cut them up into thin strips, place in a pan with enough water to cover them, and boil for two hours ; then simmer for eight hours.   Then strain off the juice, and bottle, and cork it closely.

Chop up the drained strips very small, and dry them in a moderate oven.   They are said to be usable in puddings instead of raisins, but will need soaking.

11. No. II

Having washed and thinly peeled the beets, slice them up, and place in a large earthenware jar with a lid.   When the jar is half full, pour in cold water almost to the top, put it in a moderate oven, and leave it there for twenty-four hours.   Then strain off the liquid, and add, for every pint, a large tablespoonful of glucose.   Place all together in a ssucepan over a good heat, stir till the glucose is melted, then let boil fast for thirty minutes, or until the mixture thickens,

12. No. III

Wash the beetroot, peel it thinly, wash it a second time ;
dry it well in a clean cloth, chop it up fairly small, and weigh
it. Cook it slowly for three hours, skimming frequently ;
then add half a pint of cold water for every pound originally
weighed, and simmer two hours longer ; strain through a
sieve.

A second boiling can then be made ; put to the beet
two pints of cold water for each pound, and boil for five
hours. This will be nothing like so good as the first liquid,
but still usable.

13. No. IV

Wash and peel the beets as if they were potatoes, slice
them into a casserole (with lid), with enough water just to
cover them, and simmer them in the oven until a thick
brown syrup results ; probably in about five hours.

Sugar-beet itself can be used, boiled and mashed, or
sieved, for puddings, and for preserves. See also p. 219.

CHAPTER II

MEAT

MEAT—including butcher's meat, game and poultry, bacon and ham, tinned and cooked meat, brawn, sausages, etc., and also, what are quite as important, suet, bones and " offal "—tripe, liver, heart, etc.

Well, you must buy the cheapest pieces (so long as they are nutritive) if yours is a small household ; if you have a large family, you will probably find joints (carefully doled out and dished up) will serve you best, for you will then, in addition to the meat, obtain bones and dripping.

If you cannot manage joints, I advise you occasionally to sacrifice some coupons to buy bones, which must be thoroughly well broken up and used for stock.

Suet should also be bought ; it is just as valuable as meat. Fat for rendering down into dripping is equally precious, although in pre-war time it was an extravagance to buy fat for dripping at the price of meat.

Tinned and cooked meats do not afford anything beyond what you see of them ; I mean you will get no bones, dripping, or stock. And they are expensive in coupons. Sausages are welcome—if one can be certain of their age and quality.

Bacon—back, streaky, hock, or gammon—is a priceless possession *if you boil it* and use it cold. By this means you secure stock, bones eventually, the fat skimmings off the stock (practically lard) and an excellent and wholesome piece of meat. Rashers, in these days, are sheer recklessness ; so is fried ham. Save for certain exceptional cases. You will find a few rasher recipes later on.

Fowl is not an economical purchase, however cheaply

you may happen to obtain it, because it is very much less nourishing than either butcher's meat or bacon. The same remarks apply to game. Rabbits are better value, if procurable fairly easily, but of no great worth from a food standpoint. Goose and duck are superior to fowl, from their fattier nature. One has to take all these points into consideration, when fats are so scarce.

METHODS FOR MAKING THE MOST OF MEAT

However much we may deplore the fact, there is a limit to the methods one can employ—especially under present conditions. Roughly speaking, they are as follows:

For larger Joints, or whole Fowls, Rabbits, Game, etc.—
Roasting or Baking.
Boiling or Steaming.
Braising or Stewing.

For smaller quantities, and for cold meat cookery—
Grilling or Boiling.
Frying.
Stewing.
Mincing (for rissoles, etc. Minced meat is better used as an ingredient of a larger dish).
Chopping (for curries, or for pies, with ordinary crust or potato crust).
Thinly slicing (for various dishes).

By whatever fancy name one may call a dish, it is bound to come under one of the above heads. So you will see that for small quantities of meat, whether fresh or cooked, your resource must be to make them into grills, stews, pies, rissoles or croquettes, curries, etc., etc. And the more vegetables you can employ without swamping the · meat, the more economical your dish will be. The favourite form of treatment recommended by all experts, is stews.

Stews may be made very nice or very nasty, according to the amount of care you give them.

The first point is to fry your meat *quickly* and *slightly* before putting it into the stew-pot or casserole. This hardens the outside just sufficiently to keep in the flavour of the meat ; it also improves the flavour. You can use the fat in which it is fried, for the subsequent thickening with " roux " for the liquid in which it is stewed ; nothing need be wasted.

Second—having put the meat into the stew-jar to keep warm, put your vegetables, cut up small and neatly, into the frying-pan, and toss them until they begin to brown. Then dredge in your flour, allowing three-quarters of an ounce of flour for every three-quarters of an ounce of fat, and let it slowly cook till it is a good brown ; then very gradually stir in your stock (or water), one pint for every three-quarters of an ounce of flour ; let it boil ; skim, and put into the stew-jar. Stew very slowly, maintaining an even, regular heat all the while.

The result will be wholesome, appetising, and well-flavoured.

A casserole or covered earthenware jar is better than any tin or iron pot, because it retains heat and flavour to a wonderful degree.

A hay-box is also useful, because of its even maintenance of heat and saving of fuel. But you *must* have a coal fire or gas fire to begin with, because no boiling or frying can be done by means of a hay-box.

The most economical and (to some extent) the most tasty way of cooking meat is, undoubtedly, to stew it in a casserole. This retains all the essential juices of the meat (as of any vegetables which may be cooked with it), ensures its being tender, and is in all respects praiseworthy.

And yet one can get most dreadfully fed-up with stews !

So that, where and when you can afford to cook an old-fashioned joint in the pre-war way, do it occasionally, if only for a change. Variety is *everything* in cookery ; and a constant unremitting course of casserole and hay-box cookery is therefore not to be recommended. " The life is more than meat " ; and while not sharing the British workman's repugnance to stews, one can sympathise with his deep desire to " get his teeth into something," however leathery it might be.

Rissoles are generally termed so when they are salt; croquettes are the same thing, sweet ; *i.e.*, small balls of various ingredients, fried in deep fat. The inside should be moist, and the outside crisp. Dry stuff and wet stuff are equally to be avoided. You can use up almost anything in a rissole, provided it is minced finely, well mixed, and well seasoned. Whatever solid ingredients you use, should be *hot* when mixed ; if need be, heat and thicken a little stock, and warm up your ingredients in that. Vegetables should be riced or sieved, meat passed through the mincer. Scraps and leftovers of boiled rice, of maize " mush," of polenta, of oatmeal porridge—last drops of sauce, will all come in handy. Don't forget seasoning of salt, pepper, minced parsley, minced onion, minced herbs, etc. Having thoroughly blended everything hot, leave it to go cold. Then it will be stiff or stiffish. Shape it into balls, dip them into beaten (dried) egg, and roll them in fine oatmeal, in maize flour, or in grated crusts. Fry them (in a wire basket, if possible) in sufficient boiling fat to cover them ; and don't put too many in at once, or they chill the fat.

If cooked in a wire basket, they need not be drained on paper ; you can drain them into the frying-pan, and thus save some fat. Serve at once on a hot dish.

The average amateur method is to mix the ingredients *cold and dry*, and then bind them with a beaten egg. The result is not half so good.

For very small households of say, three people, there is nothing more appetising and nourishing than shin of beef. It is much tenderer and usually cheaper than stewing steak. Two pounds of shin at 1s. 4d. and two ounces of suet (same price) will cost you five coupons. With that, a small family should manage four dinners. One pound of the meat to be made into a steamed pudding, eked out with sliced potato, onion and carrot; a crust made of dripping or other fat, potato, and flour.

This, with plenty of vegetables, should serve for twice. Use the other pound to make a potato pie (or a paste pie, if you have a little dripping, lard, or other fat) or a casserole stew. A little well-boiled macaroni is a good ingredient, or any cold cooked haricot beans. There will be some of this left over; and it can all be cut up and curried, or made into rissoles, or treated in any of the simple ways which you will find in this book.

The above is a mere suggestion as to how things may be done; but it shows that you will have seven coupons (hypothetically) left over for bacon or anything else.

Again, a leg of mutton may be produced in three or four forms, as follows:

14. LEG OF MUTTON—THREE DINNERS FROM

A leg of mutton, if properly apportioned, will furnish three hot dinners for a small family (without counting the various ordinary ways of re-heating cold meat, such as hashes, curries, rissoles, etc.) This can be done either as follows: (1) Cut off the fillet end and bone it, replace the bone with veal stuffing, and roast it. (2) Cut a thick slice from the remaining portion, fry it to a good brown, and stew it in a casserole with turnips, onions, carrots, and herbs. (3) Roll up the knuckle end in a thick paste (should be a suet paste, but use what fat you can), tie it up in a floured cloth, and boil for three hours. Serve with baked or boiled onions.

Or thus: (1) Cut the leg right in two, with the knuckle end the largest. Bake the fillet end along with potatoes and Spanish onions (which should be parboiled first). (2) Cut a thick slice from the knuckle end, divide it into small equal strips, flour them and dip in beaten (dried) egg, and fry. Tomatoes or tomato sauce will be nice with these. (3) Boil rest of shank end with carrots, turnips, onions, and a bit of celery, and serve masked in parsley sauce. There will probably be enough scraps left from these three dishes to make a fourth. The liquid from the boiled shank should have all the bones (broken) added to it, and be boiled up again. It will make excellent stock, and with pearl barley, rice, or spaghetti, will supply a fine family soup.

Curries are a very admirable method for disposing of odds and ends. The hateful word hash, suggestive too often of dull insipidity and lack of invention, is not included in this book, save here in this paragraph.

Curries, bolstered up with vegetables, rice, and potatoes, have a savour and flavour which endears them to most people. And they need not be super-currified to ensure this result.

Minced meat is now too precious to be treated otherwise than as an ingredient in other dishes. Accustomed as you are to regard cold cooked meat as something to be camouflaged and got rid of, you will be amazed to find what an interest a very little of it lends to an otherwise " bald and unconvincing " dish.

As regards " offal," tripe, heart, liver, etc., that should be treated with equal reverence to other meat. No longer served in a plain, unvarnished condition, but tinkered up and made attractive in a variety of pleasing ways, and induced to go as far as it possibly can. I recommend sheep's hearts, calves' feet, calves' heads, ox tail, tripe, and liver, as eminently satisfactory to deal with, but *they must be above suspicion* as to condition. Anything horrider than " high " liver you will never wish to see.

15. LOIN OF MUTTON—SEVERAL DISHES FROM

Procure a piece of loin of mutton between two and three pounds (I am presuming that you are three in household), remove any fat that can be spared. Divide it into three pieces.

(1) Bone the first piece, which is for braising, flour it, and brown it in a stewpan in two ounces or so of the fat. Put it into a casserole, with seasoning of salt, pepper, and nutmeg or mace; add half a breakfastcupful of heated stock, and any vegetables you may fancy, cut up fairly small; such as onion, turnip, and carrot. Tie up in muslin two cloves, six peppercorns, a spray of parsley, some celery odds and ends, or celery seed, and a teaspoonful of minced fresh herbs or mixed dry ones. Place this with the rest in the casserole, cover, and cook very slowly. When the meat is tender, remove the muslin bag, sieve the vegetables and liquor, and serve them over the meat; or, at pleasure, serve them as they are. Anything left over, including the seasoning (and of course the bones) will come in for soup.

(2) Bake the second piece of loin, with Yorkshire pudding made with dried eggs. The most economical way to bake it is in a double tin; if you have not got one, cover whatever baking tin you use with another, the same size or a little larger, so as to retain all the heat and steam while the meat is cooking. It is the same idea as paper-bag cooking, only much better because you get more heat. The oven should be very hot for the first ten minutes; then you require to lower the heat and let the meat do very slowly. Just at the last, remove the cover and brown the joint.

(3) The third piece can be either boned, and stuffed with a simple forcemeat; or it can be steamed, and served with plenty of parsley sauce and vegetables. Or it can be boned, and the meat (browned in a little of the fat) can be made into a small mutton pie with potato short-crust; or into a mutton pudding, using the fat to make a suet crust.

(4) There will be enough odds and ends over to make a fourth dinner at least; consisting of rissoles, or potato pasties, or curry, or shepherd's pie. (5) And there should be enough stock, with the remains of these four days' meals, to result in an admirable soup.

16. BRISKET, BRAISED—SEVERAL DISHES FROM

(1) Take two to three pounds of brisket, and place in a casserole, on top of chopped fried onions, tomatoes, and carrots, with salt, and a teaspoonful of vinegar ; add enough stock of any sort to cover the vegetables but not the meat. Cover and cook very slowly indeed for two hours. Pulse, well soaked overnight, or cereals, can then be added ; such as two ounces of rice, or four ounces of haricots ; and another hour should see the whole dish ready to serve.

(2) Second day ; make some of what is left into curry, with boiled rice. (3) Third day ; mince, and serve with macaroni and tomato sauce. Or mince, enclose in mashed potato balls, and bake, smeared with a little fat.

17. BABOTIE

One onion, one cupful of milk or white stock, one thick slice of bread, six sweet almonds blanched and pounded, two eggs, any sort of meat minced, one small spoonful of curry-powder, a little bit of fat, pepper, and salt. Set a slice of bread to soak in the milk, pound the almonds, fry the onion after cutting it up very small, beat two eggs, and add to them the milk which remains from the cupful, part of which was used for soaking the bread ; mix these ingredients well together, and add the minced meat, curry-powder, fat, salt, and pepper. Rub a pie-dish with a lemon or some vinegar, put in the mixture, and bake for one hour in a hot oven.

18. BACON PIE

Mash some potatoes, and place them in a pie-dish in layers ; between each layer place thin slices of bacon, a little chopped onion, and either parsley or sage cut very fine, and some pepper ; moisten with stock, or water, or milk, as you proceed. Let the last layer be of potatoes, over which place little bits of bacon fat. Bake in a hot oven for about one hour.

19. BACON BATTER

Have twelve sound mushrooms cleaned and trimmed, place in a deep pie-dish and strew with minced sage and onion, salt and pepper. Lay two rashers of bacon on these; then add a second layer of mushrooms, seasoned as before, and two more rashers. Have ready a batter made with one (dried) egg, four ounces maize flour, one tablespoonful suet or other chopped fat (but this may be omitted), salt to taste, one breakfastcup milk. Pour this in, and bake one hour. To be served in the same dish.

20. BEEF, BOILED, WARMED UP IN FLEMISH FASHION

Fry three onions cut in slices; let them cook slowly without getting brown. Cut the cold beef in pieces about an inch square, put in the pan, adding some stock, flour, pepper, and salt, a spoonful of vinegar, and a small quantity of sugar; just before serving add a little fat.

21. BEEF, LEG OF, STEWED

Take about two pounds of fresh leg of beef and cut it small, removing any skin or gristle. Put it in a pie-dish, with a little flour dredged upon the pieces of meat, and a good pinch of salt. Cover it with cold water to top of dish, cover all closely with a dish, and let it cook gently in the oven for three hours. Add more water if it sinks. This can be eaten along with plain suet pudding, and is particularly satisfying and nourishing.

22. BEEF AND LENTILS

Fry some beef steak cut small, or some slices of underdone cold meat, with some onions, pepper, and salt. Have ready one pound of lentils boiled and mashed; make a wall of them on a dish, and place the fried meat, etc., inside. If preferred, tomato sauce can be served with the beef.

23. BEEF MINCED WITH TOMATOES

The remains of any cold beef minced fine; fry two or three onions cut in rings, and two tomatoes in slices; add the minced beef (about half a pound) and one pint of stock, pepper and salt to taste ; stir well ; make a wall of mashed potatoes on a dish, and pour the contents of the saucepan in the middle.

24. BEEF MIROTIN

Cut a small onion into very thin slices and fry in fat. When it begins to colour, stir in a tablespoonful of flour. Then add a breakfastcup of brown stock, pepper, salt, a pinch of sweet herbs, and two tablespoonfuls of tarragon vinegar. Stir till the sauce has boiled two or three minutes, and is of the right consistency, then strain it into another saucepan. When cold, put in some thin slices of cooked beef. Set the saucepan by the side of the fire, let the contents get warm, without boiling. When nearly simmering, add some sliced gherkins. The longer the mirotin takes to warm, the better it will be.

25. BEEF RAGOÛT

Fry an onion in some dripping ; add to it one pint of stock thickened with one tablespoonful of flour, salt, pepper, and a pinch of clove powder. Have ready about half a pound of minced cold beef, and stir ; just ten minutes before serving add to the ragoût one pint of hot boiled and peeled chestnuts, and mix well. Serve very hot.

26. BEEF, STEWED SHIN, WITH MACARONI

Take two pounds of shin of beef, cut it up in even pieces, and place in a stewpan with three pints of cold water. Let cook very slowly until nearly boiling, and then simmer gently for four or five hours, covered closely. Break up into two-inch lengths four ounces of macaroni, and parboil it, then add it to the stew quite half an hour before serving. Add pepper, salt, and a teaspoonful of minced parsley. An economical and nourishing dish.

27. BEEF, STEWED SHIN, No. I

Cut up half a pound of shin (or leg) of beef, one sheep's kidney, and one onion ; dredge the meat with flour, and

place in a casserole which has a close-fitting lid. Add two
sticks of macaroni broken small, and half a pound tomatoes
cut up (fresh or tinned), or tomato sauce to taste. Season
with pepper and salt, put in just enough water to cover;
place casserole in moderate oven for two hours.

28. BEEF, STEWED SHIN, No. II

The whole shin is required for this; if you can obtain it,
it will be good value, being exceedingly nutritious. The
shin-bone should be sawn across (but not the meat) in three
separate places. Put it in a stewpan with water *nearly* to
cover it, and let it heat through till just on boiling, then add
a head of celery cut up, four onions, a bouquet of herbs,
and seasoning of salt and pepper (or two teaspoonfuls peppercorns in a muslin bag). Cover up closely, and let cook slowly
for three hours, when cut-up carrots may be added at pleasure,
and cut-up turnip. Stew one hour longer and serve. Some
of the liquor may be thickened to make a sauce, and seasoned
with made mustard and ketchup of any kind.

29. BEEF, BRAZILIAN STEW

Take one pound of shin of beef, cut it into dice, dip the
pieces into about two tablespoonfuls of vinegar. Stick one
clove in an onion, take one carrot, one strip of celery, and add
half a pint of water. Put the whole in a jar and cook slowly
in a cool oven, or stand the jar in a saucepan of water.

30. BUBBLE AND SQUEAK

Slices of either cold boiled beef or of roast beef can be used.
Fry the slices of meat gently in a little fat, and arrange them
nicely round a centre of fried greens; these should be boiled
till tender, well drained, minced, and then placed in a frying-
pan with a little fat, a finely sliced onion, and seasoned with
pepper and salt. When the onion is done, the greens are
ready to serve.

31. BULLOCK'S HEART

Soak the heart, which must be thoroughly cleaned and emptied, in warm water for an hour and a half. Have ready a saucepan of boiling water, in which plunge the heart; let it boil up, and then only simmer slowly for two hours. Drain it, and either leave it till next day or until quite cold. Dry the heart inside and out with a hot cloth; fill the inside with sage-and-onion stuffing; sew it up, so that the stuffing keeps in; put some dripping on the top, and bake it in a very hot oven for two hours. If it acquires too much colour, place a piece of paper on the top. It must be basted very often, and sent to table very hot, and with a sauce tureen of gravy.

32. CALF'S FEET, BOILED

Take two calf's feet, the rind of a lemon, mace, cloves, mignonette and pepper to taste.

Boil till bones drop out. · Then place pieces of meat on the dish it is to be served in. Boil liquor till it clarifies, and reduce to just sufficient to serve each piece. Last of all sprinkle with chopped parsley. Sufficient for four persons.

33. CALF'S FEET, STEWED

Divide two calf's feet into even pieces, place them in a stewpan with one sliced onion, a little thyme and parsley and bayleaf, a saltspoonful of mace, salt and pepper; pour in a pint of water, and simmer very slowly for two to three hours. When nearly ready to dish up, stir in one table-spoonful minced parsley, and two tablespoonfuls crumbs (soaked and drained pieces). Shake up the pan well.

34. CALF'S HEAD, STUFFED

Take half a calf's head, bone it, and fill with following stuffing; three ounces crumbs (soaked and drained crusts), one tablespoonful minced parsley, half a teaspoonful of mixed herbs, grated rind of half a lemon, nutmeg, pepper, and salt to taste. Bind with one (dried) egg. Roll up the head in a cloth, tie it, and place in boiling water containing two carrots, two turnips, two onions, and a bouquet of herbs. Let simmer for two hours, or until all is cooked. Serve masked in parsley sauce.

35. CHICKEN RISSOLETTES

Cook two ounces of rice in half a pint of weak stock, until the rice has absorbed the liquid. Then fry a slice of onion in two ounces of fat, without allowing it to brown; add one ounce of flour and a saltspoonful salt. Cook until well blended, and pour in half a pint of milk, or good stock, or tomato purée; stir till it boils; then remove the onion, and add half a cupful of the sauce to some finely minced scraps of chicken. Into the rest of the sauce put sufficient rice to make it stiff enough to form into balls; add one beaten yolk. Turn both the rice mixture and chicken out on plates and set aside. When sufficiently cool, form the rice into balls, with a hollow in the top of each, which must be filled with the chicken, and covered with rice. Roll twice in flour and beaten (dried) egg, let stand for a time. Fry in deep fat.

36. CORNISH PASTIES

Have a nice piece of potato short crust ready, roll it out not too thin. Cut up small any remains of cold meat, potatoes, onions, carrots, turnips—place a little of each on half the rounds of pastry, sprinkle salt and pepper over, fold the other half of pastry over, and pinch edges together. Make a couple of slits in top with knife, pour just a little cold gravy in, and place on greased kitchen paper in hot oven till pastry is cooked.

37. CORNISH PIE

Cut up one pound of pork or any other fresh meat; also cut up one pound of apples and one pound of onions; lay these all in a pie-dish with some pepper and salt, and a very little water or stock. Cover with pastry, and bake for an hour and a half,

38. COW-HEEL, No. I

Scald one cow-heel, but do not let it boil. Take it from the saucepan, split it, and simmer gently for four hours in two quarts of water. Dish up the cow-heel, pour over it some parsley sauce, and serve very hot.

NOTE.—The liquor must be saved either for soup or jelly.

39. COW-HEEL, No. II

Scald one cow-heel; boil it for an hour in very little water; take it out and dry it well; cut it into pieces about two inches long; dip them in chopped parsley, and then in batter, and fry them a nice brown.

40. CURRY, BAKED

Fry a sliced onion in a little dripping or other sound fat. Have a small slice of bread (or baked crust) soaked in a little water. Beat two dried eggs into one teacupful of milk or milk and water: add six sweet almonds grated, and the bread. Stir to this as much minced meat as you can spare (eight ounces is the proper quantity), with a little lump of margarine, chestnut-size, and one tablespoonful curry. Grease a pie-dish, sprinkle the juice of a lemon in, put the curry in, and let bake it for thirty minutes in moderate oven. Boiled rice should be served separately, as a vegetable.

41. CURRY CROQUETTES, BAKED

Have eight ounces of rice boiled in a pint of water, along with one finely-chopped onion, one teaspoonful of curry powder, half a teaspoonful of salt. Meanwhile mince any cooked mutton odds and ends, up to eight ounces, add a little minced thyme and parsley; and mix this into the hot rice as soon as it is done. Shape the mixture into balls: roll them in maize-flour; brush with a well-beaten dried egg, set in a baking-tin, and bake brown. A nice brown gravy, or a sharp sauce, will go well with this dish.

D

42. DOLMAS (SPANISH)

Chop some mutton or beef very fine ; add one large onion, also chopped (after being boiled), pepper, salt, and some boiled rice (about as much rice as meat). Take some cabbage leaves and put them in boiling water for two minutes, dry them and put the meat into them, and roll up the leaves like small sausages ; then stew them in thin stock. Take the rolls up carefully, place them on a dish, keep them hot, thicken the gravy with a little cornflour, and pour round the dolmas.

43. FAGGOTS

Put one pound of pig's fry into a saucepan with half a pound of onions and enough cold water to cover. Bring to the boil, let boil fifteen minutes, then remove the fry. Continue to boil the onions till they are tender, then put them, with the fry, through the mincer. Mix in six ounces soaked stale bread, one tablespoonful of sage (finely minced fresh, or powdered dry), one teaspoonful of pepper, one and a half teaspoonfuls of salt. Place the mixture in a baking-tin, strew with some little bits of fat and a little of the water in which the fry was boiled ; put into a moderate oven, and bake forty minutes. The mixture can be cut into oblongs or squares, either before or after baking.

44. FOWL, BRAISED

This is a good method when a fowl is not in its first youth. Truss it for boiling, and put it in a casserole or stew-pan, on top of a sliced onion and carrot, and a slice or two of salt pork, and a rasher or two of bacon. On top of the fowl place another slice of fat meat, seasoning, of peppercorns (eight or so), cloves (six), mace (a saltspoonful), salt half a teaspoonful), thyme and parsley to taste, two or three bay-leaves, and a pint of water. Put greased paper, cover closely with lid, and simmer steadily for two hours. Strain off the gravy and thicken it before serving.

45. FOWL AND RICE

Any pieces of cooked fowl can be used thus : Boil one pound of rice in stock, add salt, pepper, and mace to taste ; when it has absorbed almost all the liquor, line a greased baking-dish with it, place the pieces of fowl in, cover with the rest of the rice. Pour a very little stock over, smooth the top, and cook in a slow oven until quite set.

46. FOWL, STEWED

Procure an untrussed fowl, and cut it up into as many small joints as possible. The legs, thighs, wings, and breasts are divisible into two pieces each, and the back into three. Have a medium Spanish onion finely minced and stewed with two ounces of fat, and salt and pepper, for an hour or so. Place the pieces of fowl in this, let cook gently for thirty minutes, then transfer to a (heated) casserole, and let them finish cooking, if need be, in the oven. Add the juice of half a lemon, and serve in the casserole.

47. FRENCH TOAST

One pound of shin of beef, half a pint of soaked and drained bread, half a pound of tomatoes. Mince the beef, mix with the breadcrumbs and tomatoes chopped up (previously scalded to remove skins), bind with one beaten (dried) egg. Press into pillow form, place in a baking-tin, cover, and bake for one hour. Remove cover, put a little fat on the top, and let it bake until brown. Make a nice gravy.

48. GOOSE, MOCK

Take half a pound of pig's liver, one pound of potatoes, one good-sized onion, a little flour, four or five leaves of chopped sage. When you have washed and wiped the liver, slice it and add a little salt and pepper ; dredge a very little flour over the pieces, and put them in a pie-dish, with a little onion between the layers—the onion should have been half cooked and well chopped. Half fill the dish with water, and

mash the potates (with a little dripping or margarine *ad lib.*)
to make a crust. Bake the " mock goose " for about forty-
five minutes in a good hot oven.

49. GOOSE, POOR MAN'S

Take half a pound of liver ; wash, wipe, and slice it evenly ;
dredge it with a very little maize or barley flour ; season
with pepper and salt ; place the slices in layers in a greased
pie-dish, and between each layer put minced parboiled
onion mixed with minced sage. Have the dish half-way
full of water ; and cover the top with sliced parboiled potatoes
(one pound will be required) ; a little fat should be sprinkled
on top if possible. This is said to taste just like goose.

50. HARE, BAKED

Have the hare skinned, cleaned, and washed. Make a
forcemeat of soaked, drained (stale) bread, suet or fat, parsley,
onion, etc., and stuff the hare. Sew up and truss ; if you
can spare any slices of fat bacon, put them over it ; if not,
wrap it in a greased paper, and bake for an hour or so.

51. HARE, HARICOT

Fry the inferior joints of a hare in one tablespoonful of fat.
Add to them one turnip, one carrot, and one shallot or small
onion, sliced ; a little thyme and parsley, and seasoning of
salt and pepper, also a pint of stock or water. Place in a
stew-pan or casserole, and simmer for two hours.

52. HARE, JUGGED

Have the best joints of hare cut up into small even pieces
or joints about three inches long (the inferior joints can be
used otherwise). Wash and dry them, fry them in one tablespoonful of fat. When nicely browned, place them in a
casserole, with pepper and salt to taste, five or six cloves,
a bayleaf, a pinch of cinnamon, the juice of one lemon, and
two pints of good stock. Put a greased paper over, and
cover with lid ; cook for two hours.

53. HEAD, POTTED

Take half a sheep's head, removing the brains; wash the head thoroughly, and soak it for an hour or two in warm water; then break it up and lay it in a pan with just sufficient water to cover it well; bring to the boil, skim well, and simmer steadily, closely covered, till the bones will slip from the flesh. Now lift the meat out, remove the bones, cut into dice, seasoning it as you do so, with the following mixture; two teaspoonfuls of salt, one of freshly ground black pepper, one of powdered allspice, and, if liked, a saltspoonful of cayenne. Return the meat to the pan, allow it to simmer uncovered for a few minutes, then pour it, with its liquor strained, into a wetted basin or mould, putting in with it the tongue, which should have been cooked separately, and leave till set. If liked, the liquor may be sharply boiled up to reduce it, while the meat is being cut up.

54. IRISH STEW

This popular dish is made with onions, potatoes, and with sliced breast, jointed scrag, or neck of mutton. Very few people succeed with it. The point is, to parboil the onions and potatoes (separately) for fifteen minutes each, and drain off the water, before slicing them thickly and placing in the casserole. The bottom layer should be onions, next potatoes, the next meat; season each layer of meat with salt and pepper, and pour in a little cold water three-quarters of a pint to three pounds of potatoes. Cover closely and bake in quiet oven, or place on stove to simmer very slowly, for three hours.

55. JAMAICA FRITTERS

Take a small slice of cold meat, about one ounce, one dried egg, the equivalent of half a slice of bread in soaked, drained stale bread. Mince the meat finely. Beat the egg, add to the bread some minced parsley and onion, or any other flavouring. Have ready boiling fat in frying pan.

Drop the mixture in by tablespoonfuls, turn when sufficiently set, so as to brown both sides—or it may be made in one large fritter, filling the bottom of the pan. Any sort of meat or fish may be used. The above is enough for two persons.

56. KIDNEY PUDDING

Take half a pound of fresh ox-kidney, cut it up in small equal cubes, dust with salt and pepper. Have six ounces of flour mixed with three ounces of chopped suet or other fat; add one beaten egg (dried) and enough water to make the whole into a thickish batter. Mix in the pieces of kidney; place all in a greased (or rinsed) basin, cover and tie down, place in boiling water; let boil quickly for three hours.

Double the above quantities can be used at pleasure, and a little finely minced onion and parsley can be added.

57. KIDNEY AND ONION SAVOURY

Take a Spanish onion, cut out the centre, and insert a kidney which has been carefully washed and skinned. Bake in rather a hot oven, basting frequently with fat; serve with thick brown gravy.

58. LEEK AND PORK PIE

Cut up small one bundle of leeks, wash, and place them in salted boiling water. Let boil twenty minutes, and drain thoroughly. Cut up one pound of salt lean pork in small equal pieces, boil for twenty minutes in enough water to cover; then empty meat and liquor into a deep greased pie-dish; add the leeks, half a breakfastcupful of soaked drained crumbs, one beaten (dried) egg, and mix thoroughly. Cover with a potato crust (see No. 486) and bake for one hour in moderate oven.

59. LIVER AND BACON

Cut up one pound of bullock's liver into thin slices, and half a pound of bacon into small strips. Lay a piece of bacon on top of each strip, roll up tight, and skewer it. Have

some hot fat ready in the frying-pan and cook the rolled
pieces until they are a nice brown. A thick gravy and a
wall of mashed or riced potatoes are correct with this dish.

60. LIVER AND ONIONS

Cut up one rasher of bacon into small squares and fry it ;
put in one large onion thinly sliced, and when this has browned
add eight ounces of calf's liver, cut up into strips or slices
a quarter of an inch thick. Let these cook slowly until well
browned both sides and thoroughly cooked ; transfer them,
with the onion, to a hot dish. Thicken the liquor in the
frying-pan, add gradually a little stock of any kind ; continue to stir until it boils and browns ; add pepper and salt,
pour it over the liver, and serve at once.

61. LIVER AND POTATO TURNOVERS

Boil some potatoes, dry and floury ; mash them smoothly,
make into a paste with a dried egg, adding a little salt and
pepper. Roll out and cut into rounds about five inches
across ; prepare a stuffing as follows : Finely chop or mince
some boiled liver, add a few breadcrumbs, season with a
little chopped onion and powdered eggs, lay a little mixture
on each round, fold over and wet the edges of one half to
make it adhere to the other, and bake in a quick oven.

62. LIVER, STUFFED

Take a calf's liver, and stuffing (sage and onions). Make an
incision through the centre of the liver to the depth of half
its thickness ; now put the knife into the opening, and, by
holding it flat, cut round on each side. This will make a
pocket to hold the stuffing. Bake in a hot oven, well basting
with good dripping.

63. MEAT CAKE

Mince half a pound of cold underdone meat ; add two
ounces of breadcrumbs, the same of cooked rice—or macaroni
cut small ; beat a dried egg into a cupful of gravy mixed with

half an ounce of flour. Add salt, pepper, fried onions, a
teaspoonful of celery sauce, a few tinned mushrooms, or
anchovy sauce, or mixed pickles. Grease a cake-tin, coat it
well with grated crust crumbs, pack in close, cover with
breadcrumbs and bake about an hour.

64. MULLIGATAWNY STEW

Fry four onions sliced small and a head of garlic of a
light brown, then put them into a stewpan with the meat,
which should be fowl or any white meat. Three spoonfuls of
curry powder and two of flour mixed together, likewise a
spoonful of lemon juice and cayenne pepper to your taste.
Pour over it a pint of boiling water and let it simmer slowly
for a short time, then add a sufficient quantity of broth made
without vegetables to make a tureen of mulligatawny. The
ingredients must then stew together an hour. To be served
with a dish of rice as for curry. Cold fowl can be dressed
this way extremely well.

65. MUTTON, BREAST OF, STUFFED AND BAKED, No. I

Have a piece of breast of mutton; put into warm water,
and simmered slowly until the bones can be removed (but
not enough to cook the meat entirely). Carrots, turnips,
salt and pepper should be placed with it. Meanwhile prepare
a stuffing, according to amount required, with (soaked and
pressed) crumbs, finely-minced onion, parsley, and thyme,
and a little chopped fat, such as scraps of bacon. Put the
meat on a flat board, remove the bones, dredge with salt
and pepper, and spread evenly with the stuffing. Then roll
and tie it, and bake until tender and a good brown.

66. MUTTON, BREAST OF, STUFFED AND BAKED, No. II

Have a breast of mutton boned, and substitute for the
bones (which must be broken up and used for stock) a turkey
stuffing of crumbs, grated lemon-peel, thyme, parsley, chopped
fat of some sort, and seasoning of salt and pepper. Spread
this an inch thick, roll up the meat the short way, tie or

skewer it, and bake, allowing thirty minutes for a pound
Baste now and then.

67. MUTTON CASSEROLE

Mince any scraps of cold roast mutton, up to eight ounces ;
add one teaspoonful each of chopped parsley and of capers,
one medium onion (boiled) and chopped, salt and pepper,
half a pint of good stock or brown gravy. Place in a casserole and cover with one pound of potatoes mashed with a
little fat. Place in a hot oven, until the potatoes are golden
brown.

68. MUTTON CHARLOTTE

Slices of cold cooked mutton, however few, will make this
appetising dish.

Have a greased pie-dish, put some grated crusts or dried
soaked crumbs at the bottom, then a little mutton, then
some slices of tomato ; sprinkle with minced onion, salt and
pepper. Repeat, from the breadcrumbs, as before. The
last layer must be tomatoes, thinly strewn with crumbs.
Bake for forty-five minutes.

69. MUTTON KEDGEREE

Chop (not mince) any kind of cold mutton scraps, up to
six ounces in weight. Have one ounce of rice boiled and
drained. Put one ounce of fat in a stewpan, melt it, fry a
small minced onion till it is golden brown ; stir in the meat,
and let fry for three or four minutes ; add the rice, with
seasoning of salt, pepper, and nutmeg. Have ready two hard-
boiled eggs ; chop up the whites, and stir them to the rice,
etc. Pour on to a hot dish. Pass the yolks through a wire
sieve, and strew them into the kedgeree, with some finely-
minced parsley. Put the dish in the oven for five minutes or
so, and serve. Any other odds and ends of meat, game, or
poultry can be treated as above.

70. MUTTON AND MACARONI

Boil two ounces of Naples macaroni in fast-boiling salted
water, drain thoroughly ; butter six small moulds thickly

and line them with the macaroni, coiling it round the bottom and sides. Take any remains of cooked mutton, remove skin, fat or gristle, mince finely, and mix with a third its quantity of bread crumbs. Also pepper, salt, a dessert-spoonful of chopped parsley, a seasoning of chopped herbs. Beat up a dried egg in a little thick gravy, add to the meat. Turn the mixture into the moulds, cover with greased paper, and steam for twenty minutes. Turn out the moulds on a very hot dish, pour good thick tomato sauce round, and serve.

71. MUTTON, MINCED

Take half a dozen ripe tomatoes, the size of an egg, break them up into a lined saucepan, with an ounce of fat, a chopped shallot, two cloves, a few herbs, a pinch of salt and of sugar, and a gill of gravy. Let simmer until cooked, then rub through a sieve, make a roux of an ounce of butter and a large tea-spoonful of flour, add the purée, and boil up well ; put in any scraps of cold mutton, cut in dice, keep the mixture well under boiling point for an hour. Then bring it barely to the boil, and dish up in a pile garnished with boiled macaroni.

72. MUTTON OLIVES

Take slices of cold roast mutton, trim neatly, dust on one side of each pepper, salt, and a little allspice. Put a small piece of stuffing on each and roll up, tying firmly with cotton. Place the rolls in a baking-tin, pour some good gravy over, cover with greased paper, bake for half an hour. Make a mound of mashed potatoes on a dish, arrange the olives round, thicken the gravy and pour round.

73. OX-BRAIN FRITTERS

Boil an ox-brain in fast-boiling water for half an hour. When quite cold, cut it in pieces, and fry in batter until it is a golden brown.

74. OX-CHEEK

Wash a cheek well, but do not soak it ; put it on the fire with plenty of cold water, and with two pints of split peas that have soaked all night ; onions, carrots, turnips, celery, salt and pepper, are also added, but not at first, as the cheek and peas will require four hours' boiling, and the vegetables not more than two. Dish up the cheek, lay the vegetables round it (all except the peas), and serve very hot, with a sauce tureen of liquor from the saucepan. The liquor with the peas makes a very good soup for the following day.

75. OX-CHEEK MOULD

The remains of an ox-cheek cut into slices, and laid in a mould with pepper, salt, powdered herbs, and hard-boiled eggs cut in slices. Proceed with these ingredients, and a few slices of boiled ham or bacon, until the mould is full ; have half an ounce of gelatine dissolved in one pint of the liquor in which the cheek was boiled ; add it to the meat, etc., in the mould, until it is quite full ; bake one hour in a hot oven. When cold, turn it out of the mould, and serve.

76. OXTAIL, STEWED

Have the oxtail cut into small equal pieces, place in a saucepan with two quarts of water, seasoned to taste with salt and pepper. Let boil, and then simmer three or four hours. Then put in any vegetables you like, such as carrots, onions, green peas, parsley, etc., and let boil for another hour.

WAR-TIME PIES, VARIOUS
77. CURRY PIE

Minced meat mixed well with the same quantity of stale bread soaked in warm water, a small onion minced, a little curry powder. Put all, well mixed, into a pie-dish, over the top put a beaten dried egg, bake, turn out, and serve with rice, tomatoes, macaroni, or fried onions.

78. HARICOT PIE

Pour boiling water on one pint of haricots ; leave to soak overnight ; boil for about one hour next day. Have one large onion and four ounces of bacon (say, two rashers) finely chopped, place in a pie-dish, with a teacupful of water ; cover with the beans, adding chopped parsley, pepper, and salt. Make a potato shortcrust, cover the pie, and bake a nice brown.

79. SQUAB PIE, DEVONSHIRE

Take a pie-dish, put at the bottom a layer of sliced apples, strew over them a little sugar, then a layer of fresh mutton (well seasoned with salt and pepper). Then another layer of apples. Peel some onions and slice them, lay them on the apples, then a layer of mutton, then apples and onions. Pour in a pint of water, cover all over with a potato crust, and bake.

80. SQUAB PIE, KENT

Take one pound of the best end of the neck of mutton, cut it into small pieces, flavour with salt and pepper, and put a layer of it at the bottom of a pie-dish ; next add a layer of sliced apples and onions, with about a dessertspoonful of brown sugar, then another layer of mutton. Cover with a good pie-crust, and bake.

81. POOR MAN'S PIE

Have half a pound of beef " pieces," nice and fresh ; stew them very gently until quite tender. Cut it up small. Make a plain short-crust with two ounces of dripping or other fat, enough to line and cover a shallow (greased) pie-dish. Have four potatoes and one onion (if parboiled, so much the better) cut up and mixed with meat. Place meat and vegetables in dish ; season with salt and pepper, add some of the stock that the meat was stewed in. Cover with paste, and put into a gentle oven for an hour.

82. SAUSAGE POTATO PIES

Take half a pound of sausages, place in a quarter pint (half-breakfastcupful) of boiling water, let simmer for twenty minutes, take out, skin, and cut each in two. Have two pounds of potatoes boiled, mash them, and beat them with about half a breakfastcupful of milk until they are very light. Then lay each piece of sausage upon a tablespoonful of potato, and cover it up roughly with more potato. Place in a greased tin, and bake to a nice golden brown, which should take about twenty minutes.

83. SEA PIE, No. I

Have one pound of shin of beef cut into equal pieces, and dredge with a little flour of any kind, seasoned with salt and pepper. Cut up one carrot, one turnip, and one onion into small cubes. Place all in a wide earthen jar, and pour in enough cold water to cover meat and vegetables. Let it come slowly to the boil, and then stew very gently for an hour. Then have ready a paste, made with six ounces of flour, pinch of salt, half a teaspoonful of baking-powder, and three ounces of chopped suet or other fat. Moisten it with cold water. Cover top of stew with this crust, put lid on, and replace in oven for one-and-a-half hours. Serve in the casserole.

84. SEA PIE, No. II

Take eight ounces of shin or neck of beef, cut into equal pieces; dip (but do not soak) each piece in vinegar. Have one large onion and one carrot sliced, at the bottom of an earthenware pot; next put in the meat, then half a pound cold boiled sliced potatoes, and any cold cooked haricots or green peas. Add salt and pepper to taste, pour in a pint of stock or cold water to taste. Let it come to the boil, then simmer gently for one hour. Put a suet crust on, and let it cook two hours more.

85. SHEPHERD'S PIE

Any sliced cold meat will do for this. Have ready a seasoning of salt, pepper, and finely-minced parsley and thyme. Place the meat in a pie-dish, alternately with layers of sliced parboiled onion and sliced cold potatoes. Pour in one gill of stock of any sort, or water. Cover with mashed potatoes that have been beaten with pepper and salt, a little

hot milk, and a little fat, dripping for preference. Smooth
the potato with a wide knife, and place in a moderate oven
until it turns a golden brown.

86. TRIPE PIE

Take cold stewed tripe, and place it in a pie-dish, with
the jellied liquor ; add salt and pepper, and a little bit of
uncooked ham if possible ; also a few little bits of fat, and a
few spoonfuls of brown stock, or gravy. Cover with a potato
crust (see No. 486) and bake in a good oven till the pastry
is done.

87. PIGEON PIE

For this, the pigeons (four at least will be required) should
be stuffed with a forcemeat of soaked drained stale bread,
fat of some sort, finely minced parsley, pepper and salt.
Steak is usually added, at top and bottom, to supply gravy,
but is too extravagant now. Still, if you can manage a little
leg or shin of beef in the bottom of the pie-dish, it will make
a more nourishing dish. Hard-boiled yolks are also usual,
but can be dispensed with. Put the pigeons breast downwards in the dish, and pour in half a pint of stock. Cover
with a potato crust if you cannot manage a short crust.
Puff paste was the pre-war usage.

88. PIGEON PUDDING

For this, two pigeons will suffice ; and steak is commonly
included, (see above recipe), and a chopped kidney is an
improvement. The pigeons should be each divided into
four pieces, and the meat (if any) cut up small, and all should
be dredged thickly with flour of any sort, salt, and pepper.
Place the pieces in a basin lined with suet crust, or potato
crust ; pour in a teacupful of good stock or gravy. Cover
with paste, tie over with scalded floured cloth ; boil gently
for two hours.

89. PIGEON, STEWED, No. I

Take 2 pigeons, and cut them in half, down the middle of
back. Cut up half a pound of shin of beef (if you can spare

it) into little equal pieces ; place in a casserole, with pepper, salt, and a sliced onion, and just enough water to cover. Simmer until tender—probably two hours—thicken the liquor and serve in same dish.

90. PIGEON, STEWED, No. II

Take a piece of dripping or other fat, about as large as an egg. Dredge it with flour, salt and pepper, and put it inside the pigeon. Have sliced vegetables in a casserole— onion, turnip, potato, and any others to taste. Put the pigeon upon these, add a little stock, and simmer for an hour. Remove pigeon, dredge it with flour, and put it in the oven until brown. Strain off the liquor from the casserole (the vegetables can be sieved for purée), season with salt, pepper, and mushroom ketchup ; pour it over the pigeon upon a hot dish.

91. PIG'S FRY, BAKED

Cut up a pound of pig's fry, lay it in a pie-dish, chop finely two onions and a few sage leaves, season to taste, mix these ingredients and sprinkle over the meat. Cut up a pound and an half of part-boiled potatoes, and cover over the meat with them ; fill the dish with water or stock, bake for two hours and a half in a moderate oven.

92. PIG'S TROTTERS

Place two pig's feet in cold water (salted), and when it just boils, remove, scrape them, and place in a saucepan with just sufficient hot water to cover them. Put in one onion, one carrot, one small turnip, all sliced ; salt and pepper to taste, a saltspoonful of ground mace, a small teaspoonful of powdered or chopped fresh thyme. Let all simmer slowly until the trotters are quite tender. Take out and serve (hot or cold) ; if hot, with peas pudding. Reserve the liquor for stock.

93. PILAU

Put one breakfastcupful of rice to soak in cold water for an hour ; then drain off the water, and put the rice into a double boiler, with two breakfastcupfuls of stock and half a smallish onion. Let simmer until the rice has absorbed all the stock. Meanwhile, stew half the contents of a tin of tomatoes, add salt and pepper, and a little fat. Mix this with the rice. Have pieces of cold cooked fowl or turkey lightly fried, put them into the centre of the rice, let stew for twenty minutes, and serve, retaining the rice around the meat.

94. PORK AND BAKED BEANS

Soak one pint of butter beans or haricot beans in cold water overnight. Next day wash and rinse them, then boil until they are just soft enough to prick with a fork. A teaspoonful of bicarbonate of soda should be added. Then rinse them in boiling water, and put half of them into a large stew-jar. Have ready half a pound of salt pork, score the rind half an inch apart, put it into the beans, and put the rest of the beans on top. Mix one teaspoonful of salt, one teaspoonful of mustard, and one teaspoonful of sugar (or treacle) with hot water, and put it over the beans ; then pour in enough boiling water to cover them. They must be kept covered with water, and you must replenish it if it sinks ; but towards the last hour of cooking you may bring the pork to the top, so that it gets browned ; but do not leave the cover off. Bake in a moderate oven for not less than eight hours.

95. PORK CHOPS, BAKED

Put the chops in a baking-tin, and cover them with slices of apple, tomato, and onion—about one pound of the first two, and half a pound of onion will suffice for four chops ; add pepper and salt, and about a tumblerful of cold water. Cover up with another tin or flat dish, and bake in hot oven for about one hour and a half.

96. PORK AND HARICOT BEANS

Take one quart of haricot beans and soak them all night in water ; next morning put them into boiling water in a saucepan, and boil them slowly for half an hour, or longer ; take them out and drain them ; have ready an earthenware jar with a lid ; put three-quarters of a pound of pickled pork into the jar, and one onion cut in quarters ; add the beans and enough cold water just to cover the whole ; bake the pork and beans in the oven for four hours with the lid on, or until they both are perfectly tender. Dish up the pork in the middle of a dish, and cover with the beans.

97. POTATO PUFFS

Mince some cooked meat, and flavour it, according to taste, either with pickles or mushrooms cut small ; moisten with stock or gravy, mash some potatoes, roll them out with a very little flour, cut them into the shape and size of a saucer, place the meat in the centre of a potato saucer, cover over with a similar piece, pinch the corners together, and fry them a light brown in some boiling fat.

98. POTATO AND MEAT ROLLS

Have enough cold potatoes as will fill a breakfast cup when mashed, mix in a little dripping, work into a smooth paste with a little milk, roll out half an inch thick, and cut into squares. Have ready any scraps of meat or bacon, or odds and ends of vegetables, finely minced, seasoned with salt and pepper and a few drops of sauce ; put a little upon each square, and bake a golden brown in a good oven.

99. RABBIT, BOILED WITH RICE

Have a young rabbit boiled gently for thirty minutes, then remove the meat from the bones. To a breakfastcupful of (hot) boiled rice, add a lettuce shredded small, one little leek chopped finely (white part only), half a teaspoon each of finely minced parsley, onion, and lemon peel ; salt and pepper to taste. Mix well, then stir in the pieces of rabbit meat. Place the mixture in a scalded cloth, and let boil slowly in the rabbit stock, which must well cover it, for about two hours, not longer. For a small rabbit, one and a half hours will suffice.

E

100. RABBIT, CURRIED, No. I

Cut up the rabbit into joints, dry, and flour them. Have one onion and one apple peeled and chopped. Heat one ounce of fat, add the onion, rabbit, one dessertspoonful of flour, and two teaspoonfuls of curry powder; fry a light brown. Add the apple and one breakfastcupful stock. Let simmer one and a half hours, or until the meat is tender. Add salt to taste, and a few drops of lemon juice or vinegar. Serve at once.

101. RABBIT, CURRIED, No. II

Take a rabbit, cut up, fry the pieces a light brown, with sliced onion and strips of bacon. When they begin to colour, dredge in flour, with curry-powder *ad lib.*; add stock and salt. Let all simmer gently till done. (The flour and curry-powder may also be mixed smoothly into the stock.) Serve with a wall of plain boiled rice around. Some people add slices of apple.

102. RABBIT, JUGGED

Cut up a rabbit into joints, place in a deep stew-jar, with two large sliced onions, parsley, pepper, salt, and a very little mace. Add any bacon bones and bits of bacon that you can spare. Fill up with enough water or stock to cover all. Place lid on, and let cook about three hours in a slow oven. The liquor can be drained off, thickened, and put back to the meat, before serving.

103. RABBIT AND ONION SAUCE

Blanch the pieces of rabbit for ten minutes in boiling water. Put them into a saucepan with an onion stuck full of cloves, thyme, parsley, pepper, and salt. Cover with boiling water. Let them simmer about three-quarters of an hour. Serve on a dish piled, with plenty of onion sauce poured over them.

104. RABBIT, STEWED

Cut up a rabbit into small pieces; fry it in some dripping with a sliced onion and tomato. When the rabbit is done through, take it out of the frying-pan, and place it in a clean saucepan; add some stock, lemon peel, spice, herbs, pepper, and salt to the ingredients in the frying-pan; boil these for an hour, and then strain them over the rabbit in the saucepan; thicken it with flour, simmer for half an hour, and serve very hot with sippets of fried bread.

105. RICE MOULD WITH MEAT

About three-quarters of a pound of any cold meat (if chicken or veal, a little cold ham or bacon as well), finely minced; add to it three ounces of boiled rice, one onion scalded and chopped, one teaspoonful of chopped parsley. Salt and pepper; mix well; add two dried eggs well beaten, and two tablespoonfuls of gravy. Pour into a greased basin, and steam for one hour. Thicken some stock with fat and flour, add one teaspoonful of sauce, turn out the shape, and pour gravy over.

106. RICE MOULD SAVOURY

This is a very tempting and nutritious dish. To half a teacupful of rice boiled in milk, add two ounces of minced cold mutton, one ounce of ham, one hard-boiled egg minced, one tablespoonful of chopped parsley, one beaten dried egg, pepper and salt to taste. If not moist enough, add a little milk. This may be baked in a pie-dish or steamed in a mould.

107. RICE SAVOURY

Boil a breakfastcupful of rice for twenty minutes; drain it; grease a pudding basin, and place in it a layer of rice, and as much as will stick to the sides of it as well. Have ready any cold meat, minced and seasoned with spice, pepper and salt; place this on the rice in the basin, and cover it over with the remainder of the boiled rice. Steam it for an hour. When cold, turn out and serve, garnishing the dish with parsley.

108. RICE PIE

Boil a breakfastcupful of rice in stock or water for twenty minutes (rice must always be put into boiling liquid) ; drain it ; grease a pie-dish, and put in a layer of rice ; on this lay some cold meat chopped very fine, one onion and some parsley (also chopped), pepper and salt ; fill up the pie-dish with the rest of the rice, carefully pour in a cupful of stock or gravy, place some little pieces of fat on the rice, cover the rice with a dish to prevent its getting hard, and bake for one hour or rather less. It ought not to be brown on the top.

109. RISSOLES AUX HERBES

Minced cold meat of any kind. Place in a greased pie-dish, with a thick sprinkling of common and lemon thyme, pepper and salt, and a very little gravy ; strew breadcrumbs thickly over, place dabs of fat on the top, and bake for half an hour in a quick oven.

110. SAUSAGES, CURRIED

Have one pound of sausages fried ; add one teaspoonful each of curry powder and flour ; mix smooth with a little water in the saucepan, simmer for ten minutes, and pour off all upon a hot dish.

111. SAUSAGE DUMPLINGS

Mash some potatoes with milk, make them into a thick crust with some flour, roll up one sausage into each piece of potato crust (after taking off their skins), and bake in a tin dish until the potatoes begin to colour, which will be in about one hour.

112. SAUSAGES AND LENTILS

Soak one pint of lentils in cold water for twelve hours. Drain them, and put them in a saucepan with one cut-up carrot, one stick of celery, one piece of parsley, one teaspoonful of salt, and three pints of cold water. Let all simmer for two hours closely covered ; then take out all the vegetables.

Melt half an ounce of dripping in a saucepan, stir in two table-spoonfuls of flour, add a small onion minced fine, and let this colour to a pale brown. Drain off to this all the liquor from the lentils ; stir and boil a few minutes. Now add the lentils, and let them boil ten minutes more. Meanwhile fry one pound of sausages, and, having arranged the lentils on a large heated dish, place the sausages on top. This is a tasty and nourishing dish.

113. SAUSAGE RAGOÛT

Fry two onions and two tomatoes in a saucepan ; add to them one pound of pork or beef sausages and one pint of stock, thickened and flavoured. Let all simmer for an hour and a half. Have ready a wall of mashed potatoes or boiled rice on a dish, and place the contents of the saucepan in the centre.

114. SAUSAGE SURPRISES

Take half a pound of sausages, prick them, and cook them for twenty minutes in a quarter of a pint of boiling water. Skin them and cut them in two. Have ready two pounds of hot mashed potatoes, mixed with a quarter of a pint of milk and a little dripping (a little finely chopped parsley is an improvement), with salt and pepper to taste. Lay each piece of sausage in a tablespoonful of potato, and cover it with potato ; let these be laid in a greased baking-dish and baked a good brown.

115. SAVOURY PUDDING

Half a pound of stale, soaked, drained bread, three dried eggs, three ounces of flour, three ounces of suet or fat, one ounce of fine oatmeal, one pint of cereal stock, a small shallot, chopped very fine, a little salt, a pinch of sweet marjoram, and enough lemon to give a flavour. Mix all thoroughly well together, not too moist ; turn into a basin or (better) a floured cloth, and boil or steam for three hours.

116. SCALLOPED MEAT

Mince some cold meat very fine. Have ready some mashed
potatoes ; place a layer of them at the bottom of a scallop
shell, with the meat in the middle, seasoned according to
taste, and moistened with either gravy or milk ; cover up
with more mashed potatoes and little pieces of fat, and bake.

117. SCRAP ROLLS

Take any pieces of cooked meat (two or three different
sorts if you happen to have them) ; mince through the
machine ; season with pepper, salt, and herbs or parsley,
according to taste. Make a crust with cold boiled potatoes,
flour, and milk ; place little pieces of the seasoned meat inside
the crust, which must be cut according to the size you wish ;
roll up tightly, and bake in the oven for one hour.

118. SHEEP'S HEARTS, BAKED

Clean some sheep's hearts, place in boiling water, and let
simmer twenty minutes. Remove, and fill with veal stuffing.
Let them grow cold, then roll up each in a piece of paste
(made with lard if you can get it) and bake about twenty
minutes.

119. SHEEP'S TROTTERS, BAKED

Boil six sheep's trotters until the bones can be easily
removed ; replace the bones with veal stuffing, of which four
ounces will be required. Fry half a sliced onion in two ounces
of fat ; add a teaspoonful of minced parsley, plenty of pepper
and salt, and one breakfastcupful of stock. Put the trotters,
floured thickly, into an open casserole ; add one teaspoonful
of vinegar to the contents of the pan, and pour it over the
trotters. Sprinkle with a few crumbs, and if possible, a little
grated cheese. Place in a good oven, and serve in casserole
when nicely browned.

120. TOAD-IN-THE-HOLE

Mince any kind of meat ; season well with pepper, salt,
one onion minced, and parsley chopped, also two large

tomatoes sliced. Place this in a buttered pie-dish; make some batter several hours before it is wanted, and just before you require the "toad" cooked, add the batter, and bake in a quick oven for an hour and a half.

121. TRIPE BOILED IN MILK

Boil one pound of tripe in water, *i.e.*, place it in cold water until the water boils; take it from the saucepan, and cut it in small pieces. Cut four large onions in slices, and put them in a saucepan with the tripe and one pint of milk; let it simmer for two hours (it must boil), then dish up the tripe, and keep it hot. Cut the onions very small, thicken the milk with a dessertspoonful of flour made smooth first in cold milk; put back the onions into the milk, let them boil up, and then pour over the tripe and serve very hot.

122. TRIPE, CURRIED, No. I

Prepare the tripe as above. While it is simmering, fry one large onion and one apple in some dripping, adding one ounce of flour, one dessertspoonful of curry-powder, pepper and salt; then add half a pint of the liquor in which the tripe simmered, and stir until it becomes nice and thick; into this put the slices of tripe, a pinch of brown sugar, and a strip of lemon-peel, and let all simmer together for two hours. Serve very hot, with a border of boiled rice.

123. TRIPE, CURRIED, No. II

Curried tripe is both economical and nutritious. Take two or three large onions, and fry them in dripping till tender. Chop them very fine, or, if preferred, pass through a sieve, and dredge with a dessertspoonful each of curry powder and peaflour mixed. When quite smooth, add gradually one pint of stock and stir till it boils. Now take one-and-half pounds of boiled tripe, cut it into pieces about one inch square, and put it into the sauce. Let all stew together for one and a half hours. Have ready some well-boiled rice, make a pile of it on the dish, pour the tripe into the centre and serve. Squeeze a little lemon juice over the whole.

124. TRIPE FRICASSEE, No. I

Take the whitest tripe you can get, and cut it in long pieces; put them into a stewpan with a little good gravy, a few breadcrumbs, a lump of butter, a little vinegar to taste, and a little mustard if you like it. Shake it up altogether with a little minced parsley, let it stew slowly till done.

125. TRIPE FRICASSEE, No. II

Take the whitest *and* thickest tripe, cut the white part in thin slices, put it into a stewpan with a little white gravy, lemon-juice, shred lemon-peel, and a tablespoonful of white wine. Take two dried eggs and beat them very well; put to them a little minced parsley, and two or three (minced) chives if you have any. Shake it altogether over the fire till it is as thick as cream, but don't let it boil for fear it curdle. Garnish with sliced lemon, or mushrooms. This will eat like chicken.

126. TRIPE, STUFFED

Have a piece of tripe large enough to double; wash and trim. Prepare a stuffing of sage and onions, crumbs (soaked and strained pieces), pepper and salt, according to requirements. Lay this on half the tripe, double over the other half, and sew the two together round the edges. Place in a greased tin, put three rashers of bacon on top, and bake for an hour or so. Remove the tripe to hot dish, thicken the liquor in the tin, browning it, pour it over the tripe, and serve.

127. (VEGETABLE) MARROW PUDDING

Peel a young vegetable marrow, cut in half, remove seeds from either half, and replace them with any odds and ends of ham, bacon, or meat, finely-minced along with onion and parsley, with pepper and salt to taste. Place the pieces together again, roll them up in a thin suet crust, and boil for three to four hours.

CHAPTER III

FISH

FISH has now too often to be our *pièce de resistance* ; it seems poor fare after the Roast Beef of Old England—even after the lamb of Canterbury, N.Z. It is very dear, but still it can be had. The red oily fishes are the most nourishing, and as a rule the cheapest ; but unfortunately they are often unsuitable for delicate digestions. They include herrings (fresh, pickled, bloaters, kippers, red), sprats, mackerel, and salmon.

To these may be added so-called sardines, which (whatever they may have been named in their native jungle) are tinned in oil, extremely nutritious and tasty. They are dear ; but it is cheaper to buy a large tin, which will serve a small family for two meals. Pilchards, or herrings (with tomato), tinned prawns—and of course tinned salmon—can also be made to provide two or three dishes each tin. So can tinned cod's-roe (larger sizes), which makes particularly dainty fish croquettes along with potato sieved or riced.

Eels are oily and nourishing, but not to everybody's taste.

Freshwater fish for the most part is dull stuff unless provided with a veal stuffing. The earthy taste peculiar to freshwater fish can be obviated by several methods, of which, for the average housewife, the easiest are : (1) careful cleaning as soon as caught, or (2) by washing and cooking in an acid— such as vinegar or lemon juice.

There are many sea-fish which in palmier days we disdained, but which are really quite decent if one takes a little trouble over them. Amongst these are sea-bream, fresh haddock, skate, ling, and the now very expensive hake. I believe lemon-sole contains less nourishment than any other fish.

Clarified cocoa butter is satisfactory for frying herrings, whose powerful taste and odour overcomes that of the cocoa. I have also found it all right for fried fish-cakes ; and I should suppose that cocoa butter, used as suet, would do very well for fish stuffings.

Remember that a little nice sauce goes a long way towards redeeming the character of the least interesting fish. I heard of a man the other day who said he had *become an aquarium*, and was sick of the very name of fish. But indeed this might have been rectified. A little pickle, or beetroot in vinegar, the plainest of parsley sauce, a few drops of anchovy essence —are invaluable when one can't afford the better sauces.

While on the subject of fish, let me recommend you to make liberal use of bloater paste. It is cheap, and intensely appetising ; it lends a flavour and a savour towards stolidly farinaceous dishes. Salmon-and-shrimp paste is useful, but does not go half so far. Anchovy paste is best of all, but also dearest of all.

It is inadvisable to have fish trimmed or filleted at the shop. By doing it at home, you obtain the bones and trimmings for fish stock.

Fish Stock is made of bones, trimmings, heads and tails, lobster-shells, shrimp-shells, prawn-heads, and any other scraps, provided they are perfectly fresh, and do not belong to " red " fish, such as herrings, sprats, salmon, etc. It must be cooked a shorter time than meat stock, and used more quickly, as it has a tendency to go bitter. A few vegetables can be included, cut up small ; also a little parsley, bayleaf, lemon-rind, salt and a few peppercorns, may be used to flavour.

The pieces should be well washed and cut up quite small, then place in *cold* salted water, and brought slowly to boiling point before skinning and adding the vegetables, etc. Let simmer about one and a half hours ; then squeeze in the juice of half a lemon, and strain.

The liquor is very useful, not only for soup and for stewed

or casseroled fish, but for fish sauce, using it when possible instead of milk.

RULES IN SELECTING FISH

1. Fish which is fresh, is firm, and the eyes are bright.

2. When stale, the eyes are sunken and dimmed by a film, and the flesh is flabby.

3. The smell of fish when fresh is scarcely apparent.

4. Mackerel, herrings, sprats, whitebait, and smelts should be bright and silvery.

5. If the colour has departed, the fish is stale.

The most economical method of cooking fresh fish, is boiling or stewing, whole or in slices.

The most extravagant, probably, is filleting. The most appetising, is baked and stuffed. The most popular, perhaps, is frying.

There is no need to employ egg and breadcrumbs for the last purpose. Milk and flour—or vegetable stock, or cereal stock, and flour—any kind, but oatmeal is excellent—will do perfectly well; and grated baked crusts will also supply the place of crumbs.

As regards the various ways of " making up " cold left-over fish, they are much the same as those employed for meat; and are always appreciated if nicely done.

A point often ignored, however, in the making of fish cakes, is that you can add almost any vegetable (riced or sieved), and improve the thing. Parsnips are especially suitable.

When fish is to be boiled, remember the water must be boiling, and slightly salted, and flavoured with vinegar, before the fish is put into it. The water must be kept boiling for five minutes, then drawn aside and simmered until the fish is done.

128. BRILL, BROILED

Wash, trim, and well dry the brill. Prepare in a deep dish a marinade as follows : three tablespoonfuls of salad oil, the juice of half a lemon (or its equivalent in good vinegar), pepper and salt ; all well mixed. Dip the fish in until well coated with the mixture, brush some of the marinade over a grill or gridiron, and broil the brill over a clear fire for ten minutes ; then turn it over, and let cook another twelve to fifteen minutes.

129.   BREAM (SEA), BAKED

The fish must be well washed inside and out, and gently dried with a cloth.   Make a forcemeat of dried grated crusts (or plain biscuits powdered), one teaspoonful of chopped mixed herbs, a little onion, pepper and salt ; moisten with good stock, mix thoroughly, and stuff the fish, binding carefully with narrow tape.   Roll the fish in maize, oat, or barley flour, put it in a baking-tin with two tablespoonfuls of stock, and three little bits of margarine or dripping on top.

Bake for thirty minutes, with frequent basting, in a moderate oven.   An ordinary veal stuffing may be used if circumstances permit, made with suet ; this will make the dish more nutritious.

130.   BREAM (FRESHWATER), BOILED

Clean and trim, but do not remove scales.   Wash and dry well, dredge with maize or oatflour ; place on an oiled gridiron and grill slowly for thirty minutes.

Anchovy sauce should be served with it.

131.   COD CASSEROLE

Cut a small onion into small slices and put it in a saucepan, containing a pint of white stock ; then add a stick of celery, a blade of mace, a few thin strips of lemon peel, one or two pieces of parsley, and a little salt and pepper ; when the milk has boiled draw the pan to the side of the stove and let it simmer very gently for twenty minutes.   Melt two ounces of fat in a saucepan, then scatter in gradually an equal quantity of any flour, and mix to a smooth paste ; strain the stock and pour it by degrees to the paste, and stir until the sauce has boiled and thickened ; add a teaspoonful of tomato ketchup. Remove the skin from a piece of cod (preferably the middle cut) weighing about two and a half pounds, put it into an earthenware casserole and pour the sauce over it ; cover it with a piece of thick greased paper, cover and put the casserole into a moderately hot oven for half an hour. When the fish is done, remove the paper, scatter some finely chopped parsley over the surface and serve the fish at once. The sauce for fish served in a casserole can be varied considerably, the tomato ketchup can be replaced by a large teaspoonful of anchovy essence, and garnish of shrimps can be used instead of the parsley. Just before serving, a squeeze of lemon juice should be stirred into the sauce. A thick brown sauce can be substituted for the white.

132. COD CUTLETS

Take thin steaks or slices from the tail end ; have them well washed and dried an hour before they are cooked. Mix one teaspoonful each of minced parsley, and of onion scalded and minced, with a little salt, pepper, grated nutmeg, and fine oatmeal, or maize flour ; moisten with a little milk, and lastly add a few drops of anchovy essence. Dust the cutlets with any flour, and coat them on both sides with the mixture ; then dip in crumbs (grated dried crusts) and fry in boiling fat.

Serve with sauce.

133. COD'S HEAD, BAKED

Wash and clean a large cod's head and shoulders. Place it in a baking-tin, and sprinkle well with bits of dripping. Bake for about an hour ; frequent basting will be needed. Remove fish to hot dish, strain liquor into a small pan, add one tablespoonful of chopped parsley, two tablespoonsfuls of vinegar, pepper and salt to taste. Let heat thoroughly, and serve as sauce with the fish.

134. COD ROCK

Slice an onion, and put it into a saucepan with a little fat until it is soft, but not browned. Have ready some cold boiled cod, freed from skin and bone, and flaked as small as possible. Add it to the minced onion, with pepper and salt and three cold potatoes mashed very fine. Stir well, and add a little fat. Serve it raised roughly on a dish, and garnish with narrow strips of pickled beetroot.

135. COD'S ROE, No. I

Take a good fresh roe, wrap it in butter-cloth, and put it into salted boiling water in a fish kettle. Let it boil gently for thirty minutes ; then take it out, but leave the cloth on until it is almost cold. When it is completely cold, skin, and slice it in pieces about half an inch thick. Dredge the slices with flour of any kind, and fry crisp in boiling fat.

136. COD'S ROE, No. II

Boil the roe for fifteen minutes in salt and water and a little vinegar. When cold, cut it in slices. Moisten and flour each slice, and fry for about ten minutes. (See also tinned cod's roe, p. 49.)

137. COD SOUNDS

Soak six cod sounds in cold milk and water all night. Next day boil them slowly in fresh milk and water or stock for two hours. Make some egg sauce, put the sounds into it, and serve with a wall of mashed potatoes round, or with boiled parsnips cut small.

138. COD STEAK, BAKED

Take a cod steak weighing one pound to two pounds. Wash, dry, and trim, tie it up into shape, dredge it with maize or barley flour, and place in a greased pie-dish or baking-tin. Have ready two tablespoonfuls of crumbs (soaked and pressed), mixed with two teaspoonfuls of minced parsley, one teaspoonful minced mixed herbs, salt and pepper to taste, and two ounces chopped suet or other fat. Shred this thickly on top of the fish, cover with a piece of greased paper, and bake for about twenty minutes.

139. COD (SALT), CURRIED

Wash and dry two pounds of salt cod, cut up into small equal pieces. Have two ounces of finely-minced onion fried in two ounces of margarine or other fat until light brown. Add half a large apple thinly sliced and two teaspoonfuls of carry powder. Stir for four or five minutes, then put in the fish. Season with salt and pepper, gradually add one gill of broth or meat stock. Place all in a stewpan and let cook gently for an hour, stirring occasionally.

140. COD (SALT), STEWED

Wash and dry three pounds salt cod. Cut it up in smallish equal pieces, dip them in oat or maize flour. Have ready two ounces of minced onion fried in two tablespoonfuls salad oil and two ounces of dripping (or other good fat). When the onion is pale brown, put the fish into the frying-pan, and let it cook for six to eight minutes, with gentle stirring. Then gradually add one teacupful of warm broth (or Oxo) and one wineglassful of sherry or Marsala. Add a very little cinnamon, and season with pepper. Place all in a stew pan, and let stew slowly for twenty-five minutes, with the lid not quite closely on.

141. CRAB, BROWNED

Clean and grease a crab shell. Mince all the crab meat with some parsley, one small onion, and two or three mushrooms ; brown these in a saucepan with some fat, and add pepper and salt. Keep stirring until it is quite hot. Put the mixture into the shell, cover with breadcrumbs and little dabs of fat, and bake about twenty minutes (until the breadcrumbs are brown) in a very hot oven. Serve in the shell.

142. EELS, FRIED

Skin the eels, remove backbones, wash and dry well, cut in 3-inch pieces ; dust with salt, pepper and grated nutmeg. Roll in maize or barley flour, fry for five minutes in boiling oil or lard.

143. EELS, JELLIED

Have two pounds of skinned and cleaned eels, cut up into two-inch lengths, and boil for twenty minutes in water, slightly salted, containing one bayleaf, one sliced onion, and about one teaspoonful of vinegar. Then drain them, remove the bones without breaking the flesh, and place the pieces in a mould, with a hard-boiled egg or two, thinly sliced. Strain the water in which the eels were boiled, measure it ; boil up again, skimming carefully, and stir in a quarter of an ounce of isinglass for each half-pint of the broth. As soon as the isinglass is dissolved by stirring, let boil fast for five minutes ; remove and let it cool off, and before it sets, fill up the mould with it. Serve when quite set and cold.

144. EEL, STEWED, No. I

Have the eel cut up in small pieces. Place in a saucepan enough milk-and-water to cover it, flavoured with one sliced onion, a little thyme and parsley, one bayleaf, pepper and salt, and any odds and ends such as bacon rinds, meat trimmings, etc. Let this liquor boil, then put the eel in. When it has simmered half an hour, remove eel to hot dish, strain off liquor, return it to the pan and boil up again ; thicken with a little flour mixed smooth, stir well, let boil, pour over eel and serve.

145. EEL, STEWED, No. II

Cut up an eel in three-inch pieces, dip them in maize or other flour, and put in a stew-pan with a little (meat) stock, salt to taste, an onion stuck with cloves, the thin peel of a lemon, and a glass of red wine. Let stew gently for half an hour ; then remove the eel to a hot dish, squeeze a few drops of lemon juice into the liquor, and strain it over the eel before serving.

146. EEL, STEWED, No. III

Cut up a skinned eel into pieces two inches long ; stew it gently in good stock, flavoured with pepper and salt, herbs, and a spoonful of mushroom ketchup, also a strip of lemon peel, for one hour and a half. When the eel is done, dish it up, and strain the gravy over it. Serve very hot.

147. HADDOCKS, BAKED, No. I

Have two middle-sized haddocks filleted. Put half of the fillets into a greased baking-tin, strew thickly with flour (any kind), minced parsley, salt, and pepper ; put the rest of fish on top, and season as above. Sprinkle with little bits of good fat, and bake for thirty minutes in a moderate oven.

148. HADDOCKS, BAKED, No. II

Cut off the heads and fins of two or three haddocks, and put into a stew-pan, with an onion, salt, pepper, and two anchovies cut up fine, a little flour, two tablespoonfuls of French white wine, and a little ketchup. Boil this all well up together, and when the fish has been skinned and cut into pieces, lay them in a deep pie-dish ; pour the above sauce over them, and bake in an oven. Strew the bottom of the dish with breadcrumbs and some more on top, having seasoned well with pepper and salt and a little grated nutmeg.

149. HADDOCKS (FRESH), FILLETED

Have two middle-sized haddocks filleted. Place two of the fillets in a greased baking-tin, and sprinkle them with fine oatmeal or grated baked crusts, with chopped parsley, pepper, and salt to taste. Then put in the other two fillets, and treat them the same, but more thickly. Put little bits of margarine or dripping on top of the fish, and round the sides of the tin. Bake thirty minutes in a moderate oven.

150. HADDOCK WITH SAUCE

Fillet two fresh haddocks ; boil the skins, heads, bones, etc., with seasoning and some parsley ; strain off the liquor

F

and season it with milk and flour. Have one egg whisked up in a tureen or deep dish, and some finely chopped parsley. Take the fish fillets, and when the liquor is boiling, place them in it and boil for ten minutes ; gently stir some of the sauce into the tureen among the egg and parsley, taking care not to let it curdle. Add the fish, with the sauce that remains, and serve very hot.

151. FINNAN HADDOCK SAVOURY

Soak a finnan haddock for four hours. Skin it and remove all bones, and break the fish into flakes, slice a small onion and two tomatoes, chop up a little parsley, season with pepper, stew in a little fat till quite soft, then add the fish and cook for ten minutes.

152. FINNAN HADDOCKS, STEAMED

Instead of boiling a finnan haddock the usual way, lay it in a deep basin or dish, and *pour boiling water upon it* to cover it completely. Cover it up with a dish, lid, or thick cloth, and leave it for ten minutes. At the end of that time it will be better done, tenderer, and infinitely more digestible than if cooked the old way. Smear it with fat, and a dash of pepper, and serve on a very hot dish.

153. HAKE, STEAMED

Put about three-quarters of a pound of hake into a small casserole, with two tablespoonfuls of milk, and stand the dish on a saucepan of boiling water. Let it steam in the milk until tender. Drain off the milk into a little saucepan, mix smooth one teaspoonful of cornflour in a little cold milk (or water), add one teaspoonful of tomato sauce, salt and pepper ; stir into saucepan, let boil, and serve as sauce.

154. HERRINGS, BAKED

Take six fresh herrings, which must be scraped, washed, and cleaned, the heads and tails removed, the fish split, and the bones and roes taken out. Lay the fish at the bottom of an earthenware jar, with the roes in the middle. Strew over them one thinly-sliced small onion, six peppercorns, six whole allspice, a saltspoonful of salt ; pour in sufficient vinegar to cover the fish (half a pint should be plenty), tie down with doubled brown paper, or cover with a close-fitting lid, and bake for thirty minutes. To be served cold.

155. HERRINGS, BOILED

Clean the herrings, and having removed the eyes, put the tails through the eyeholes, and let boil slowly in water containing half a teaspoonful of vinegar and a teaspoonful of salt.

156. HERRINGS, BROILED

Split and bone the fish, dust them with pepper and salt, lay them flat open on a gridiron, and broil quickly, cooking both sides. Place in heated dish. Have ready the following sauce : One tablespoonful of chopped parsley, one teacupful of vinegar, one ounce of fat.(melted), salt and pepper to taste —and pour it over the fish.

157. HERRINGS, MARINATED

Clean the fish well without washing. Open them so as to remove the backbone, and season them well with salt, pepper, and onion chopped very fine. Roll them up tight, and place them in a jar, and pour over them some vinegar and water in equal quantities ; tie over the jar with paper, and bake in rather a slow oven for an hour. When they are cold, pour over them a little cold vinegar. They may be pickled in the same way as mackerel (see Mackerel).

158. HERRINGS, POTTED

Take six fresh herrings, wash, dry, and split them open, removing heads and backbones. Dust them with flour, pepper, and salt, chopped parsley or powdered mace. Roll them up tightly with a small piece of fat in the centre of each. Place them in a pie-dish, pour over half vinegar and

water, but not to cover them. Cover the pie-dish, and bake
in a slow oven; then remove cover and let them brown a
little. Two bay leaves may be put in the pie-dish instead
of mace.

159. HERRINGS (RED), BAKED

Soak the red herrings in water for twelve hours. Scale,
wash, and dry well; lay the herrings in a dish, and rub them
well with a mixture of pepper, salt, and a teaspoonful of
mixed spices. Place in a deep baking dish, pour over vinegar
and water (equal proportions), enough to cover, put in three
or four bay leaves, lay a paper on top, and bake for half an
hour in a moderate oven.

160. HERRINGS (RED), BROILED

Soak the fish as above, dry, bone, and split them. Prepare a marinade of three tablespoonfuls of salad oil, two
teaspoonfuls of finely-minced herbs, pepper, and salt: all
thoroughly mixed. Dip the fish into this and broil them
over a clear fire, brushing them once or twice with the marinade, and turning them twice at least.

161. HERRINGS (PICKLED), BOILED

Clean the fish, remove head and tail, and soak for forty-
eight hours in cold water, which must be frequently changed.
Hang the fish up to drain. Wash thoroughly, and put them
in a saucepan of cold water. Bring it to the boil, then throw
away the water, replace it with cold, then bring it to the
boil again, and let simmer gently for a quarter of an hour.

162. HERRINGS AND POTATOES

Wash and boil some potatoes in their skins, carefully, so
that they do not break or get too soft. Drain them, peel,
and slice them rather thickly. Keep them hot. Fry lightly
a chopped onion in one ounce of fat. Dust in some flour,
add three tablespoonfuls of vinegar, salt and pepper, and a
bay leaf, and not quite a pint of water. Put the pan to

simmer at the side of the stove. Take two red herrings, wash them well, cut them lengthways, and remove the bones. Cut up the flesh small, and let it simmer in the sauce for a few minutes. Put in the potatoes next, stirring carefully so as not to break them. Then add two ounces of fat and one gill of milk, and stir all well over the fire till it reaches boiling-point.

163. HERRING, SAVOURY ROE

Take some soft bloater roes, place them in a slightly-greased dish, and bake for about ten minutes in a moderate oven. Then mash them well with some fat and season to taste. A little cayenne pepper is an improvement. Spread the mixture over some rounds of toast, lay a fried egg in the middle, sprinkle a little minced parsley over, and serve hot.

164. JOHN DORY, BAKED

Remove the head, clean and trim the fish, lay it in a fire-proof dish, with a sprinkling of pepper and salt and two ounces of margarine or dripping cut small. Let it bake for twenty minutes in a moderate oven. Fry four chopped mush-rooms, lay them evenly on the fish, bake ten minutes more, and serve in the same dish.

165. LOBSTER, BASHAWED

Take any remains of lobster and cut them up. Chop up a piece of onion about the size of a nut, and a little parsley. Mix all together with a little anchovy sauce and cayenne pepper. Cut up in small pieces a bit of fat and mix, and then put all into the shell of the lobster. Cover over the top with bits of fat, and shake a few raspings on the top. Bake for about ten minutes, or a little more, and serve hot.

166. LOBSTER FRITTERS

Chop up the meat, with the red part and the spawn, of two large lobsters, very fine, with finely-grated crumbs and a little fat, and season with pepper and salt, and a very small quantity of chopped sweet herbs; make this into a paste with a beaten egg, and having formed it into pieces about two inches in length and an inch thick, dip them into a good thick batter, and fry.

167 LOBSTER RISSOLES

Take one tin of lobster; mix the fish with equal weight of mashed potatoes, pepper, salt, and a little liquor of the lobster if not sufficiently moist; form into flat cakes, and fry in boiling fat until nicely browned.

168. LOBSTER, SCALLOPED

Line your dish well with lobster (tinned or fresh), put some breadcrumbs next, then lobster, and so on, alternately with little bits of fat, salt and red pepper. Cover well with breadcrumbs, and then put little bits of fat all over, and pour vinegar over all. Bake for about half an hour or more, or brown nicely before the fire. You can heat it up a second time, pouring in milk or gravy or anything to moisten. One tin of lobster makes two small dishes. Serve very hot.

169. LING, STEWED, No. I

Make brown, in a casserole, one ounce of minced onion, two ounces of dripping, and one tablespoonful of flour. When coloured, put in fillets, steaks, or slices of ling—fillets for preference—along with three bay leaves, a pinch of minced or powdered thyme, half an apple, finely chopped, and six or eight peppercorns. Let cook slowly for eighteen to twenty minutes, and add gradually one wineglass of white wine and one teacupful warm (not hot) stock. This results in a delicate and tasty dish.

170. LING, STEWED, No. II

Cut up three pounds of ling into eight steaks or fillets, coat them with maize or oat flour. Have ready in a frying-pan one ounce of chopped onion and a small quantity of parsley fried in two ounces of fat. When the onion browns, add the fish, and fry until each side is a golden brown. Then put in a little thyme, three bay leaves, half an apple finely minced, one wineglassful of sherry, and about the same of stock (these should be added gradually). Salt and pepper. Let simmer quietly for twenty minutes. Serve at once.

171. MACKEREL, PICKLED, No. I

Six rather small mackerel, four bay leaves, four cloves, one level teaspoonful of peppercorns, one pint of vinegar, thyme, parsley, fennet (if possible), salt and pepper.

Fillet the mackerel, wash and dry, strew over them the herbs finely minced, and a little pepper and salt. Put in a dish with a little fat, and bake till cooked. Try with a skewer and see if they are done. Boil the vinegar, bay leaves, cloves, and peppercorns together for ten minutes. Stir in a teaspoonful of extract of meat, and when cold, strain over the fish. Let it stand for several hours before serving, then drain, put on a clean dish, and garnish with parsley.

172. MACKEREL, PICKLED, No. II

Having cut and split the mackerel, cover them with a little thyme, parsley, and shallots, chopped fine; then fry the fish carefully. When done, pour over them some vinegar boiled with black pepper, a few cloves, and three or four bay leaves; this liquor is not to be poured upon them until it is cold.

Another mode is to cut the fish into pieces, and to cover them with a mixture of black pepper, nutmeg, mace, and salt, reduced to a fine powder; then fry them brown in oil, and when cold put them into a jar, and fill it with strong vinegar previously boiled. This is a rich preparation. The quantities of spices required for six middle-sized mackerel is: three nutmegs, six blades of mace, and an ounce of black pepper. A good handful of salt should be used.

173. MACKEREL, STEWED

Cook three smallish onions in half a pint of water in a stew-pan. When they are done, put in two pounds of mackerel, with pepper and salt to taste, and let cook till partly done. Then add one teacupful of brown vinegar and the same of treacle, which have been previously well mixed (a little gingerbread crumbled into this is an improvement), and let the whole mixture simmer until the fish is done. The pan will require occasional shaking to prevent sticking. This dish is to be served cold.

174. MULLET, BAKED, No. I

The red mullet is the only one worth using, the grey mullet being somewhat poor and coarse. Grease sheets of white paper, sprinkle them with a little salt. Clean the mullet, wipe them dry, and roll each in a separate sheet. Broil them, and send them to table in the papers, and serve with them a tureen of good sauce.

175. MULLET, BAKED, No. II

Wash and clean, but do not scrape hard. Dip each fish into a preparation of salad oil and minced parsley, salted and peppered. Wrap each separately in greased paper, lay in a baking-tin, place in a good oven for twenty minutes. Serve at once in the paper cases.

176. MUSSELS, BOILED

Remove the heads and boil the mussels in their own juice, with a seasoning of chopped parsley, garlic (or onion), and fat. Strain the liquor over the mussels before serving. No water is needed.

177. PERCH, BOILED

Wash the fish in tepid water, clean and trim it thoroughly; scrape off scales. Put it into a pan of boiling water deep enough to cover it, with five or six chives or spring onions and a handful of parsley. It must boil (according to size) from ten minutes to half an hour. Serve with parsley sauce.

178. PERCH, FRIED

Clean, wash, scale and dry two middle-sized perch. Lay them in a marinade of oil, pepper and salt, (see Brill, Broiled) for thirty minutes. Drain, and roll in oatflour containing a little powdered thyme, grated nutmeg, pepper and salt to taste. Fry in boiling fat ; and when they are golden brown, drain and serve with piquante sauce.

179. PLAICE, BAKED, No. I

Remove the black skin from a good plaice, butter a fire-proof dish well, sprinkle lightly in some very fine bread-crumbs, a little finely chopped parsley, onion, pepper, salt, and if at hand two or three chopped mushrooms. Lay the plaice on this, sprinkle the same mixture over it and bake for twenty minutes. Serve very hot on the dish on which it was cooked.

180. PLAICE, BAKED, No. II

Roll small fillets of plaice, lay them in a casserole, and cover them with parsley sauce. Put cover on casserole, and bake in moderate oven for forty minutes or so.

181. PLAICE, BAKED, No. III

Take a large plaice, grease it all over thickly, sprinkle with breadcrumbs, chopped onions, parsley, pepper and salt, and bake for an hour. Serve with the gravy that comes from it.

182. PLAICE, WITH TOMATOES AND ONIONS

Butter a pie-dish, put in a thick layer of sliced tomatoes and onions, then a layer of plaice filleted and skinned, then another layer of tomatoes and onions ; sprinkle bread-crumbs, cheese, and a little fat over them. Bake for three-quarters of an hour.

183. SALMON, BAKED

Take the required number of slices from the middle of a salmon and wipe with a clean cloth, sprinkle them with salt, pepper and finely chopped parsley, then place side by side in a greased baking tin, lay small pieces of fat on the top, and put in a well heated but not fierce oven. Bake for three-quarters of an hour, basting frequently. Serve on a hot dish and pour the following sauce over :

A teaspoonful each of chopped mushrooms and salad oil, a small bunch of parsley, thyme, a little salt and a few pepper-corns. Stir over the fire a few minutes, then add four large tomatoes cut in slices and a teacupful of stock. Stir till the tomatoes are dissolved, and pour over the fish very hot.

184. SALMON CECILS

The contents of one tin of salmon freed from bone, a few potatoes mashed very smooth, a hard-boiled egg cut into small pieces, some chopped parsley, pepper and salt to taste, a little anchovy sauce, and sufficient of the liquor in the tin to moisten the whole ; knead into little flat cakes, and fry until both sides are nicely browned.

NOTE.—This recipe can be applied to any cold fish.

185. SALMON CROQUETTES, No. I

Take half a pound of tinned salmon, pound it, rub it through a fine sieve. Have ready in a stewpan one ounce of mar-garine or dripping stirred until smooth with one tablespoon-ful flour ; add one teacupful milk. Stir all the time until it boils ; let simmer ten minutes ; add the fish, with pepper and salt, and one well-beaten egg. Stir fast until all is well mixed, then pour on to a dish until cold ; shape and fry.

186. SALMON CROQUETTES, No. II

Turn salmon out of tin and prepare as in No. I. Mix into it six ounces of well-boiled rice, a small onion minced, a dessertspoonful (or more to taste) of chopped parsley, pepper, salt and a beaten egg. Beat thoroughly till the mixture is well blended, shape into small rissoles or croquettes, and fry in boiling oil until they are a good pale brown.

187. SALMON, CURRIED

Have a pound tin of salmon drained of the liquor and broken small. Slice a small onion and fry it in two ounces of dripping or margarine. Add two teaspoonfuls of curry powder, and stir in gradually a teacupful of warm stock. Let it simmer for ten minutes, then add the salmon and when it has stewed gently for a quarter of an hour, serve inside a border of rice.

188. SALMON CUTLETS

Half a pound tin of salmon mashed with a fork, one cup of hot mashed potatoes, with salt and pepper to taste ; form into cutlets, dip in egg and breadcrumbs, and fry in deep lard or in oil.

189. SALMON MAYONNAISE

Open a tin of salmon and remove the bones. Make the following sauce : Boil one egg hard ; pass the yolk through a sieve ; add to it a teaspoonful of unmade mustard, a small spoonful of sugar and salt, cayenne pepper to taste ; add a quarter of a pint of oil, stirring all the while ; then some anchovy and Worcester sauce, a tablespoonful of vinegar, and lastly a wineglassful of milk. Pour this sauce over the salmon, cover it with young lettuces cut very fine, and place over them the white of the egg cut in rings, and two tomatoes, or a small beetroot, also cut in slices.

190. SALMON PUDDING

Pour off the liquor from a pound tin of salmon. Remove the bones and skin, and shred finely, using a silver fork. Add salt and pepper, four tablespoonfuls of melted-butter sauce, one breakfastcupful of soaked and drained bread, one beaten (dried) egg. Mix well. Place in a greased pie-dish, press down tightly with a fork ; stand the dish in a pan of hot water, and place in a good oven for about twenty minutes. For sauce, boil one breakfastcupful milk in double boiler ; thicken with one tablespoonful of cornflour mixed smooth in two tablespoonfuls of cold water. Add one table-spoonful clarified cocoa butter, the juice of half a lemon, one dried beaten egg; and stir it until it thickens. Then, having warmed up the salmon liquor, add it to the sauce last of all.

191. SALMON STEWED, No. I

Remains of cold salmon, or a pound tin of salmon, two eggs hard-boiled, cut into slices. Put the salmon and the eggs into half a pint of stock, thicken with flour, and add one ounce of fat, salt and pepper; stir until it boils. Make a wall of mashed potatoes on a dish, and pour the contents of the saucepan into the middle of the mashed potatoes.

Lobster is excellent done in the same way.

192. SALMON STEWED, No. II

Slice the fish thickly and place in a large casserole, along with a small sliced onion, sliced carrot, sliced half-lemon, three bay leaves, and two or three sprigs of parsley; salt and pepper to taste. Cover the fish with vinegar and water (in equal proportions) and leave it for four or five hours. Place the casserole on range or gas, and let it come to the boil very gradually. When it boils, remove from fire and let all cool off slowly. When cold, serve on another dish, with salad of any sort.

193. SARDINES, CURRIED, No. I

One box of sardines; strain off the oil into a small frying-pan; add to this a dessertspoonful of curry-powder previously mixed with cold water. Thicken the oil with a little arrow-root, previously mixed with water. As soon as the curry and oil make a sauce about as thick as good melted butter, the sauce is ready. Pour this over the sardines, and place them in the oven long enough to get heated through. When quite hot, serve with pieces of toast.

194. SARDINES, CURRIED, No. II

Prepare the sardines as above ; put them on toast in the oven while you prepare the following sauce : Rub a saucepan with a clove of garlic ; place in it the oil in which the sardines were tinned. When it boils, put into it one teaspoonful of curry-powder and one teaspoonful of flour, made smooth with a little stock which has been seasoned with onions, and boil, stirring all the time until sufficiently thick ; add the juice of half a lemon, and pour the sauce over the sardines in the oven. Serve very hot.

195. SARDINES, DEVILLED

Split the sardines, take out the backbones, and spread each fish with mustard, salt, pepper, and lemon juice. Leave them for half an hour, and then fry them in the oil in which they were tinned, in which also fry some slices of bread, and in dishing up place the sardines on the toast, and serve very hot.

196. SARDINES, GRILLED

Remove the skins and bones from twelve sardines, and place them in a pie-dish in the oven, covered over, just to heat through. Pour the oil from the sardines into a saucepan ; thicken with flour ; add half a pint of stock, one teaspoonful of Worcester sauce, salt, and cayenne. Beat one egg with one teaspoonful of mustard and one of vinegar, pour the sauce boiling hot on the egg, etc., stir a moment, and then pour it over the sardines. Serve very hot.

197. SARDINE SALAD

Bone some sardines, breaking them as little as possible ; lay them in a bowl, and place over them some lettuces cut small and some cress. Boil two eggs hard ; mash the yolks with salt, pepper, mustard, and cayenne ; add gradually the oil from the sardine tin and the juice of a lemon, pour it over the salad, and ornament the top with the white of the eggs cut in rings and two tomatoes in slices. A few chopped capers laid on the sardines under the lettuce are an improvement.

198. SARDINE TOAST

Put some sardines in a covered pie-dish in the oven. Fry some toast in the oil from the tin, lay the sardines on the toast, shake a little cayenne and salt over them, and send to table very hot, and a cut lemon with them.

199. SKATE, CRIMPED

Clean, skin, and slice the skate in long pieces. Roll them up and tie with string, place in well-salted boiling water, which must boil fast for twenty minutes or so : the fish should then be done. Drain, remove string, serve at once with shrimp sauce.

200. SKATE, FRIED

Take some very fresh skate, divide it up into long strips, and separate these into pieces of equal size, two inches long. Roll in oatmeal flour and fry for six or seven minutes in boiling fat. Dust with salt and serve with sliced lemon.

201. SPRATS, BAKED

Clean some sprats, place them in a pie-dish with some whole pepper, salt, and a few bay leaves spread over them; cover them up and bake them for about half an hour; let them stand in the liquor which comes from them until quite cold, and then pour vinegar over them.

202. SPRAT CROQUETTES

Cold sprats, freed from skin and bone. Add the same weight in cold potatoes, mash and mix until quite smooth, make into round balls, cover with flour, and fry in boiling fat until well browned.

203. SPRATS, FRIED

Flour each fish, and lay them on a frying pan which has been standing on the range until it is quite hot, and before laying in the fish sprinkle it well with salt ; lay the sprats in rows, turn once, and serve with cut lemon. Fresh herrings can also be done in this way, and will be found much nicer than when fried in fat.

204. SPRATS FRIED IN BATTER

Make some batter; wipe some sprats and dip them in the batter, fry a nice brown, and serve very hot.

205. SPRAT PIE

Sprats (divested of their skin and backbones) which have been cooked. Mince them and mix with chopped parsley, pepper, salt, a little fat, and stock enough to moisten them; lay in a pie-dish, and fill it up with mashed potatoes. Bake in the oven for one hour.

MIXED FISH DISHES

BOUILLABAISSE

This celebrated dish *can* be made with cod only, and with mackerel only; but, correctly speaking, it consists of a variety of fish. I give first the correct Marseillaise form, and then one of a somewhat simpler nature.

206. 1.—BOUILLABAISSE MARSEILLAISE

Take the meat from a one-pound lobster, cut it into six even pieces. Skin and trim two very fresh eels, cut them into two-inch pieces. Take a very small sea bass (or other firm-fleshed fish), clean, wash, trim, remove head, and cut flesh crossways in six equal steaks. Place all above on a plate in a cold place. Have three tablespoonfuls of oil heated in a saucepan; add two chopped onions and three chopped leeks. Let these brown gently for ten minutes, stirring occasionally. Put in three tablespoonfuls of flour, mix well for two minutes while cooking; then add one pint of tomatoes (tinned or fresh, crushed), one pint of water, the heads of the various fish, and the eel skins; one tablespoonful of salt, half a teaspoonful of white pepper, half a teaspoonful of saffron, two crushed beans of garlic, and three sprays of parsley. Mix all with a spoon for three minutes ; then let boil briskly for forty minutes, mixing now and then. Remove, strain the liquor into another pan, boil it up again, replace the fish in it. Mix lightly, cover pan, let boil gently for thirty minutes. Remove fish, and arrange it in a large deep dish, pour liquor over ; arrange six little slices of toast around, sprinkle with half a teaspoonful of minced parsley ; serve at once.

207. II.—BOUILLABAISSE ANGLAISE

Take a variety of fish up to two pounds weight in all ; they must be quite fresh. A mixture of large and small fish is quite in order ; some shellfish should be included. Dory, haddock, gurnet, brill, whiting, hake, lobster, mussels, may be suggested. The larger fish should be in slices or steaks, the smaller ones whole, the lobster cut lengthwise. Fry an onion or a leek in good oil in a saucepan ; then put in the fish with a teaspoonful of flour, a little salt and pepper, and enough water just to cover it. Add two skinned and chopped tomatoes, one crushed garlic bean, a pinch of saffron, a spray each of thyme and fennel, and two bay leaves. Let boil fast for fifteen minutes. Add a teaspoonful of finely-minced parsley ; remove from fire. Have some slices of bread laid in a deep dish, place the fish on these, and strain the liquor over all.

VARIOUS FISH DISHES

208. FISH BATTER

Any cold fish that has been slightly boiled and is quite firm ; take out the bones, season with pepper and salt, and dip in batter made as follows : A quarter of a pound of flour, made very smooth with one tablespoonful of salad oil and a quarter of a pint of tepid water ; add to this the whites of two eggs beaten to a stiff froth ; make this some time before it is wanted, and beat it quickly from time to time ;

dip the fish into it, and fry in boiling fat until it is nicely brown.

NOTE.—This batter is very superior to ordinary batter, and is equally good for meat or fruit.

209. FISH CAKE, No. I

The remains of cold fish, a few mashed potatoes, a little chopped parsley, a few breadcrumbs, pepper, salt, and anchovy sauce. Work these together until no lumps remain ; make into a flat cake and fry until nicely browned. Make a sauce with a little fat, salt, a squeeze of lemon, and a wineglassful of stock thickened with flour ; pour this over the fish cake, and serve very hot ; or the sauce can be served in a sauce-boat separately.

210. FISH CAKE (STEAMED), No. II

Take one and a half pounds of any white fish, boil it, remove any bones and skin, and shred up the flesh very small. Mix it with half a teacupful of crumbs (soaked and drained pieces), anchovy essence, salt and pepper to taste, one ounce of fat of some sort, two well-beaten (dried) eggs, and nearly a teacupful of milk. Blend thoroughly, pour into a plain greased basin, put a greased paper on top, and steam for forty-five minutes.

211. FISH CAKES, No. I

Break up very fine any remains of cold fish, having carefully boned and skinned it. Pass through a sieve any cold potatoes, and mix an equal quantity of them with the fish. Moisten with any melted butter left over, or with a well-beaten egg ; add a few breadcrumbs to make the mixture firm. Season with pepper and salt. Make the mixture into balls or small round cakes. Roll in milk and flour, as for frying fish, and fry a light brown.

212. FISH CAKES, No. II

Pull to pieces with two forks the remains of any cold fish, carefully removing all bones and skin. Mix some well-

G

mashed potatoes and a small piece of butter with the fish, season with pepper and salt to taste, adding a little cayenne. Form into small cakes and fry in hot fat to a golden brown colour, and garnish with fried parsley.

213. FISH CHOWDER

Take one ounce of bacon, cut it into dice, and fry for five minutes with a small thinly-sliced onion. Place both in a saucepan, along with six (raw) potatoes peeled and chopped small, one carrot, washed and chopped. Pour in enough boiling water (or stock) just to cover them, and let cook until the contents are tender. Then mix smooth two table-spoonfuls of flour (any sort) with a teaspoonful of cold milk, and thicken the liquor with it. Add one breakfastcupful of milk and one pound of fish of any kind, boned, and cut up small. Let cook for ten minutes or so, or until the fish is done. Serve at once.

214. FISH CURRY

Take two pounds of cod, hake, or other fish, and fry in two ounces of dripping. Take it out, and fry one sliced onion until brown. Add half a tablespoonful of curry powder, one tablespoonful of grated cocoanut, one ounce of flour, a pinch of salt, the same of sugar, and a breakfast cupful of stock. Let boil for a quarter of an hour, then separate the fish into large flakes, and add it to the mixture ; let simmer for five minutes, add one teaspoonful of lemon juice, and serve at once.

215. FISH CUSTARD

Take any cold fish, remove all bones and skin, lay it in small pieces in the bottom of a pie-dish, with a little salt and pepper. Mix a dessertspoonful of flour smooth in a teacupful of milk ; add one beaten egg and a piece of fat about as big as a walnut, creamed but not oiled. Pour it over the fish, and bake half an hour or so in a moderate oven.

216. FLEMISH FRICANDEAU OF FISH

One pound of chopped fish (cod, haddock, and a few shrimps) ; add quarter of a pound of bread crumbs soaked in stock, quarter of a pound of fat, two dried eggs, pepper, and salt. Make into the shape of a loaf and bake half an hour ; serve with caper sauce.

217. KEDGEREE, No. I

Boil two tablespoonfuls of rice, add any fish previously cooked (salmon or turbot best) ; it should be well picked from the bone in shreds ; beat up an egg and stir it in just before serving, but don't let boil after the egg is added. Serve with egg sauce.

218. KEDGEREE, No. II

Take half a pound of cold fish, break it into flakes, and remove all the bones. Then take three ounces of cold boiled rice, two hard-boiled eggs, cut the whites into dice and put them with the fish and rice into a saucepan with one and a half ounces of fat, pepper, salt, and nutmeg. When well heated, put it into a dish, and squeeze the yolks of eggs through a sieve over the top. Then put it into the oven to brown.

219. KEDGEREE, No. III

Boil two ounces of rice till tender and let it remain till cold. Mix with it a teaspoonful of curry powder and some pepper and salt. Melt two ounces of fat in an enamelled saucepan, break two dried eggs into it and add the rice and stir until it is stiff, which will be in a few minutes. Have a large square of toast ready on a hot dish and pile the kedgeree on it. Sprinkle chopped parsley on the top, and serve very hot. The remains of a cold finnan haddock, removed from the bones and mixed with the kedgeree, make a very tasty supper-dish.

220. FISH MACARONI

Take any cold fish ; free it from skin and bone ; add seasoning of salt and pepper and a little chopped parsley ;

have ready some boiled macaroni; mix the fish with it in a pie-dish, adding a little stock and fat; grate crusts thickly over the top with dabs of fat, and bake in a hot oven about three-quarters of an hour.

221. FISH MOULD, No. I

Cold fish freed from skin and bone; weigh it, and take half the weight of cold potatoes; mash them through the masher, and mix with the fish cut very small; add some fat, one teaspoonful of anchovy sauce, pepper, and salt. Grease a mould, press the fish, etc., into it, and bake for one hour in a hot oven with the mould covered over; turn on to a hot dish, and sprinkle thickly with chopped parsley.

222. FISH MOULD, No. II

Have one breakfastcupful of cooked fish (of any kind) shredded, and bones carefully removed. Whisk two eggs well, add half a teacupful of milk; stir in the fish, a breakfastcupful of crumbs (soaked, drained crusts), a little minced parsley, seasoning of salt and pepper. Mix well, steam in a greased mould for one hour. Serve hot. Sauce should be poured over the mould—a piquant sauce for preference.

223. FISH MOULD, No. III

At the bottom of a wetted mould put a little aspic jelly (or flavoured gelatine). Next put a layer of cooked fish, either shredded or in small pieces, also some sliced hardboiled eggs and minced parsley; when this has set, put in more jelly. Have ready the following: One beaten yolk of egg, one tablespoonful salad oil, salt and pepper, one teaspoonful of tarragon vinegar, one tablespoonful of white vinegar, well blended. Stir into the above, more eggs, fish, and jelly, until the mould is full up. Steam for half an hour, put aside to grow cold. Turn out and garnish with parsley.

224. FISH PASTY

Make a short crust ; line a baking-tin, put pieces of filleted or cold fish, a very thin layer of veal stuffing and a good thick gravy ; cover with crust.

225. FISH PIE, No. I

To half a pound of cooked fish (shredded) add half a pound of cooked macaroni (broken into two inch lengths). Add pepper and salt to taste, one ounce of fat of some sort a beaten (dried) egg, half a pint of hot milk, and a few drops of lemon juice. Sprinkle with grated crusts or oatflour, strew with minute pieces of fat, and bake until the mixture is well set and nicely coloured.

226. FISH PIE, No. II

Take half a pound of any cooked fish, or a half pound tin of salmon. Remove bones and shred the fish very small. Mix with the following : one teaspoonful each of chopped parsley and of grated lemon-rind, one hard-boiled egg minced finely, pepper and salt to taste, and two tablespoonfuls of any sauce left over from the fish when previously served—white sauce for preference. If you have no sauce, bind the mixture with a very little flour and milk. Have ready half a pound of paste of any kind, formed into a square. Put the fish mixture into the middle of this, and bring the corners to meet in the middle, or make a triangular " turn-over " of it. Bake in good oven.

227. FISH PIE, No. III

Fresh-water fish—either roach, jack, or eel, one pound of onions, half a pound of rice, three eggs, quarter of a pound of fat, paste.

Boil rice. Lightly fry onions, cut into small pieces. Boil eggs hard, then slice them, and bone fish. Fill pie-dish, first with layers of rice, then onions, fat, fish, and eggs. So on. Cover in with paste, and bake. Very good, hot or cold

228. FISH PIE, No. IV

One pound of cold boiled fish (no skin or bone). Stew in two ounces of fat very gently ; steep one thick slice of stale bread in boiling stock, add to it the fish and fat, then beat these ingredients in a mortar ; add pepper and salt, and two eggs well beaten ; place the mixture in a greased tin ; bake for an hour in a quick oven.

229. FISH PIE, No. V

Remove all skin and bone from any kind of fish (cooked), break into small pieces mixed with minced onion, previously fried in fat, add pepper, salt, and mustard, tomato sauce, and half a well-beaten (dried) egg, and pack into a pie-dish. Cover with mashed potatoes, brush over with egg. Bake for three quarters of an hour.

230. FISH PIE, No. VI

Put three quarters of a pint of milk into a saucepan with half a small onion, two cloves, a few thin strips of lemon-peel, and two or three pieces of parsley and some salt and pepper, and let simmer gently for twenty minutes. Make a paste in a saucepan with an ounce and a quarter of fat, and an ounce and a quarter of flour. Strain the milk and mix it gradually with the paste, thus making a thick sauce ; ascertain whether more pepper and salt is required, and add a teaspoonful of anchovy essence. Grease a pie-dish and place a layer of cooked fish which has been divided into flakes into it, and cover it with some of the prepared sauce, a few shrimps and a little chopped parsley ; then put more fish, and the remainder of the sauce, and some shrimps and parsley as before. Have in readiness some smoothly mashed potato which has been well seasoned with salt, pepper and nutmeg, and mix in some milk, fat, and an egg, then beat it until it is light and creamy, cover the fish with this, mark the top with a fork, and after pouring a small quantity of warm fat over the surface of the potato, bake the pie in a quick oven until it is evenly browned.

231. FISH À LA PORTUGUAISE

Take at least one pound of sliced or filleted fish, wash, dry, and place in a deep pie-dish. Strew it with pepper, salt, and chopped thyme to taste ; dredge it with a little flour of any kind. Have ready two onions and three tomatoes, sliced and fried ; put these on top of the fish, with one tablespoonful each of salad oil and of vinegar, and half a pint of stock. Sprinkle in a few little scraps of dripping or other fat, and cook in a very hot oven until the fish is brown, which will be at least an hour. Serve in the same dish.

232. FISH PUDDING, No. I

Any cold fish freed from skin and bone ; add to it a quarter of a pound of chopped suet, a quarter of a pound of bread-crumbs, pepper, salt, and a little good gravy ; mince one onion and some parsley very small ; add it to the fish, etc. Beat up two dried eggs and work them into the other ingredients, press all into a mould, and steam it for two hours and a half.

233. FISH PUDDING, No. II

Take one pound and a half of cooked fish, half a teacupful of milk, one ounce of melted fat, a little anchovy essence, a teaspoonful of chopped parsley, pepper and salt. Break up the fish as finely as possible in a bowl, and add the rest—the eggs and milk last. When all is well mixed, put it in a greased mould, and let it steam for three-quarters of an hour. For a baked fish pudding, use an equal amount of well-mashed potatoes, and about twice as much milk and fat as is mentioned above.

234. FISH RICE, No. I

Save the liquor in which cod or any other fish has been boiled. On the following day fry some onions and tomatoes ; add the fish stock and a bunch of herbs, and enough rice (about one breakfastcupful to one quart of liquor) to take up

the stock. When the rice is nearly done, stir in any remains
of cold fish, freed from bone, and serve very hot.

235. FISH RICE, No. II

Boil four ounces of rice until it can be mashed smooth ; and
before it cools mix into it any remains of cold fish, finely
shredded. Of course all bone and skin must be removed ;
this is better done while the fish is still warm. Add salt,
pepper, minced onion, and parsley, to taste. Blend
thoroughly, put into a basin. When cold, turn out upon a
dish ; a little sharp sauce can be poured over it.

236. FISH SCALLOPS

Take any cold fish remaining from the previous day, carefully remove all skin and bones, and break it as small as
possible with two silver forks (steel ones will injure the
flavour). Mix in any cold sauce left over, or use half a pint
of milk and two ounces of fat ; add soaked, drained breadcrumbs to thicken it, and salt, pepper, and mace to taste.
When all is well mixed, take some scallop-shells, or saucers,
butter them well, and put in the mixture. Scoop a little
hollow in the centre at the top, and put in a very small quantity of anchovy sauce. Dust over with very fine grated
crumbs, and drop some tiny bits of fat over. Bake in a
moderate oven, and serve very hot. These will be found
most savoury and appetising. A little chopped parsley may
be added at discretion.

237. FISH SOUFFLÉ, No. I

Mix the remains of some cold fish with a little mashed
potato and two well-beaten dried eggs and sufficient milk to
make a thin batter ; pour into a well-greased mould ; steam
for half an hour.

238. FISH SOUFFLÉ, No. II

Take half a pound of white uncooked fish, remove the
bones, and pass it through a wire sieve. Put one ounce of

fat into a saucepan, and mix it well with two ounces of flour which has been dried and sifted, and pour in gradually rather less than half a pint of hot milk. Stir quickly until the sauce is smooth and thick. Let it simmer for five minutes, then add two beaten (dried) eggs, and strain it into a basin. Add the fish to the sauce, season with salt and pepper. Grease a small china soufflé dish, nearly fill it with the prepared fish; cover with greased paper and steam very gently for fifty minutes. Serve the soufflé in the mould with a little chopped parsley over top.

239. FISH AND SPAGHETTI

Break up small four ounces of spaghetti, place in boiling water, boil for twelve minutes, and drain. Have any remains of cold cod or other fish well shredded and put into a pie-dish, mixed with the spaghetti. Beat two eggs very thin, blend with one breakfastcupful of milk, add a little pepper and salt, pour over the mixture, and bake for thirty minutes.

240. FISH, STEWED

Slice and fry one pound of tomatoes and one pound of Spanish onions (sliced cold potatoes may also be added). Put in any cold fried fish, broken small, and at least half a pint of stock, thickened and seasoned. Let simmer till thoroughly hot, and serve.

241. TWICE LAID

Take the remains of cold salt fish. Tear it into flakes; mix it with double its quantity of mashed potatoes. Moisten with milk; season with pepper and salt; roll into balls; dip them in egg; roll them in flour, and fry them brown. Drain and serve on a folded napkin.

242. FISH TIMBALE

Flavour one and a half gills of white stock with half an onion, a small blade of mace, a few thin strips of lemon peel, and some celery, salt, and pepper. Then thicken it with

one and a half ounces of any flour, which has been smoothly
mixed with a small quantity of cold milk and water, and stir
until it is very thick ; then add one and a quarter ounces of
fat, blend thoroughly, and rub the sauce through a gravy
strainer into a basin, pressing the onion well to extract the
flavour. While the milk is simmering, pass one pound of
raw white fish through a fine mincer, season it lightly with
sauce, pepper and nutmeg, and mix it with the prepared
sauce ; then add two unbeaten eggs, beating first one and
then the other into the mixture. Butter a china soufflé
mould and line it evenly with boiled rice, then fill it with fish
and put a layer of rice over it ; tie a thick piece of greased
paper over the mould, place an inverted saucer or small
plate on it, and steam gently for three-quarters of an hour.
Turn it carefully from the mould, garnish with a little chopped
parsley scattered over the middle, and surround it with some
good white sauce flavoured with either lemon and parsley
or essence of shrimps. Macaroni or spaghetti can be used in
place of rice to line the mould.

CHAPTER IV

SOUPS

SOUPS are not a national institution with us, as they are with other nations. We don't care for them, and that's the plain truth. Yet they can be made extremely palatable ; and they are a means of conveying nourishment, and vegetable salts, and animal juices, which otherwise would certainly be wholly wasted. They are also (when properly concocted) very satisfying. And as we have got to live on something, they supply an amount of bulk, or perhaps I should say they take up a certain amount of cubic space in the body, in a manner which nothing else can quite replace.

But soup need not be—it often is—mere tasteless wish-wash. It can be good, appetising, substantial fare. I maintain that soup to be the best which combines the greatest number of nutritive ingredients. For instance, a good bone stock, in which peas, haricots, rice, or other such materials have been cooked ; which is subsequently enriched and flavoured by the addition of vegetables, herbs, bacon-rind, and any other suitable substance, and is then passed through a sieve. Of course, it then may be called a purée, not a soup : but what's in a name ? You will assuredly find your household clamouring for more.

If I dared refer to bygones, I would also mention that eggs, and milk, and wine, can all be pressed into the service and go to make the soup of double-extra food value. But we must confine ourselves to the solemn facts of the present.

The chief of these facts are that (1) you must never throw away anything which can possibly help to eke out your soup, and (2) you must not let your stock go sour by keeping it too long. This especially refers to summer. It is far better to make soup little and often, than to run any risks with it. The more vegetable matter it contains, the more likely it is to deteriorate, and even boiling-up will not prevent this. No pieces of vegetable should be left *in* stock when it is put to cool. They must be strained off if they are not sieved.

The words "soup" and "broth" are very loosely employed. The most up-to-date significance of "soup" is, as already mentioned, what would formerly have been termed "purée," *i.e.*, all the ingredients are sieved when tender enough, and re-heated before serving. This makes the soup very thick and nice. Broth, on the other hand, has the vegetables, etc., floating loose in it. Some people prefer it thus ; personally, I regard it as an untidy, slipshod method. But it is a matter of taste. Clear soups are not to be encouraged in these days. We want something more "stodging."

There is practically nothing (except sweet things) that cannot be used for soups. All the things that people throw away, scraps and odds and ends of meat, bones, and bacon-rinds, and cheese-rinds, outside leaves of vegetables, peelings of vegetables and apples, bits of crust, etc., etc., etc., can all be put into a pot with some water, boiled, simmered for three hours or so, seasoned with salt and pepper, sieved and re-heated ; behold, a particularly attractive soup !

Again, the water in which any cereal or any dried pulse food has been cooking—rice, macaroni, haricots, split peas, etc.—forms an admirable basis for soup. Most likely you have always thrown it away before. Don't waste it any more.

Rice, sago, tapioca, semolina, pearl barley, and macaroni are excellent for thickening ; so are potatoes, and artichokes, and parsnips (cold cooked, sieved or riced). Rice, pearl barley, and sago should be well soaked before adding to soups. Half a teacupful of either will suffice for three quarts of soup. Herbs of some sort should never be omitted. If the vegetables are fried first and added to the soup with the fat they were fried in, so much the better.

Vegetable soup is not in itself a perfect substitute for soup from bones (whatever the scientific experts may say). But it can be made very tasty and satisfactory.

All bones should be broken up small with a hammer, and used *before they can get sour*. Don't save them up, but put them on at once in the water, keeping the pan covered, and boil fast until they become perforated with little holes (this may take hours). Then drain off the stock, and *keep the bones*—the Government wants them.

The water in which ham or bacon has been boiled is invaluable for stock.

Fish trimmings and bones can also be made into stock. But fish soups are not popular in Britain. Fish stock will supply the place of milk in making fish sauce.

Whenever *milk* is indicated in the following recipes, either fish stock or cereal stock can be substituted. Milk is dear and scarce. If, however, the soup is for children, you should try and give them real milk in it (or what passes for that seldom-seen liquid).

Grated cheese is a great improvement to soup. But, unhappily, there is none to be had, as ordinary cheese is too scarce, and Parmesan is at fancy prices—10s. a pound or so.

Keep soup or stock in earthenware, not in metal, vessels.

To conclude : in making tasty soups out of formerly unconsidered trifles, you have a chance to show how clever you are. It really is a most interesting job to prove this ; you try, and you'll see !

243. ARTICHOKE SOUP

Take some liquor that ham or bacon has been boiled in (if not too salt) ; add to it an onion and some pepper, six pounds of artichokes, and let them boil until quite tender ; take them out ; pass them through a sieve into a basin, adding as much of the stock in which they were boiled as will make the purée of the right thickness. Return to pan and boil up.

244. BARLEY SOUP

Two quarts of stock, a quarter of a pound of pearl barley, parsley, four onions, salt and pepper. Simmer gently for four hours; sieve, reheat, and serve.

245. BELGIAN POTAGE

Cut two white onions in halves, finely slice and place in a saucepan with three finely sliced fresh leeks, an ounce of fat and brown for fifteen minutes, stirring quite frequently meanwhile. Add four finely-sliced peeled raw potatoes, moisten with two and a half quarts stock, season with a teaspoonful salt, a half teaspoonful pepper, and a saltspoonful grated nutmeg, mix well and let boil for forty-five minutes. Add a teaspoonful of freshly-chopped parsley, lightly mix, pour soup into tureen and serve.

246. BREAD SOUP

Cut up four onions and four tomatoes, and fry them in dripping. Add as much water or thin stock as required, also herbs, pepper, and salt. Let it boil about two hours. Cut up some pieces of stale bread, put them in a tureen, put some of the stock to the bread; stand it close to the fire with the lid on for ten minutes, then add the rest of the soup.

247. BOUILLABAISSE (AS SOUP)

Take some fresh-water fish—perch or roach. Boil twenty minutes; free them as much as possible from bones; strain the water in which they were boiled, and return the fish to it, with two or three onions, two tomatoes, a few cloves, allspice, whole pepper, cayenne, anchovy sauce, one ounce of parsley, and two bay leaves. Boil one hour, strain the liquor, add the fish, and simmer gently for a few minutes, care being taken not to break the fish. Place a thick slice of bread in a tureen; soak it with the liquor. Take out the fish, serve in a separate dish, and fill up the tureen with the rest of the stock.

248. CARROT SOUP

Take three pints of stock, and add the following : one onion finely minced and four carrots grated, fried in one ounce of fat ; one ounce of rice, one teaspoonful of maize flour ; herbs and parsley to taste ; bacon rinds and scraps. Boil up, and add salt and pepper to taste, let simmer one and a half hours ; put through a sieve, re-heat, and serve.

249. CAULIFLOWER SOUP

Break up a sound medium cauliflower, and put it into a quart of boiling stock (any sort). Boil again, and let simmer for an hour. Then rub the soup hard through a sieve, return to pan. Mix one tablespoonful of cornflour smooth in a little water, and add to soup. Stir continuously until it boils and thickens, then add pepper, salt, and nutmeg or mace to taste, one teacupful of hot milk, and one table-spoonful of grated cheese. Serve immediately.

250. CELERY SOUP

Take a head of celery, which need not be a very good one fit for the table ; cut it up roughly, and place in a pint of boiling water (salted). Boil for three-quarters of an hour. Meanwhile boil half a Spanish onion in one pint of milk ; thicken with one tablespoonful of flour mixed smooth in a little cold water, and subsequently let boil for ten minutes. Rub celery and onion through a sieve, replace, with their liquor, in one of the pans. Season with salt, pepper, and mace ; serve very hot.

251. CHESTNUT SOUP

Boil one pound of chestnuts till they burst open. Throw them into cold water, peel them, crush them into a paste (moistening with a little milk when desirable), put them through a fine sieve. Set them in an earthenware pan with an onion already cooked in a little fat. Add a teaspoonful of sugar, a saltspoonful of salt, a little pepper, a light hint of spice, and as much white stock or milk as will make up the requisite amount. Stir continually, and when it boils, add a spoonful of rice-flour made smooth in cold milk.

252. CUCUMBER SOUP

Take two cucumbers, peel, slice, and seed them. (Be careful not to let your fingers come in contact with the peeled flesh of the cucumber, or it will turn bitter). Place in three pints of boiling cereal stock, and simmer until thick enough to sieve. Return to pan and thicken with one and a half ounces of cornflour melted in one ounce of fat. The soup, boiling, must be gradually poured to this, stirring continually until it has boiled again. Then put in salt and pepper to taste, one ounce of fat, and one yolk beaten up with one teacupful of milk. The soup must not boil after this is added, or the egg will curdle. Serve at once.

253. CURRY SOUP

Fry two large onions. Add one pint of stock previously flavoured with vegetables; thicken with one teaspoonful of curry powder and two dessertspoonfuls of flour mixed with cold water. Strain through a sieve. Boil a teacupful of rice, and add it to the soup about five minutes before dishing up.

254. FISH SOUP

Take the liquor in which codfish has been boiled, and add to each quart half a teacupful of tapioca, a carrot, half a head of celery, and a little parsley. Cut the vegetables up very small and boil until they are cooked. Then thicken with flour. Add pepper and salt to taste, and serve.

255. FLEMISH SOUP

Boil equal parts of potatoes and turnips in water, with one onion and a head of celery, pepper, and salt. When the vegetables are soft, pass them through a sieve. Return the soup to the fire, and as soon as it boils add some chopped parsley.

256. ITALIAN SOUP

Warm one quart of stock in which a cow-heel has been boiled. Cut up the meat into small dice, and add two tablespoonfuls of boiled sago. Put the cow-heel and sago into the stock, and let it boil. Place one tablespoonful of grated cheese into the tureen, pour the contents of the saucepan over it, and serve.

257. HARICOT SOUP

Soak one pint of haricots overnight. Next day, place in a saucepan with three pints of stock or water, and two rashers of bacon. Cut into thin strips (or some broken-up bacon bones). Add a boiled onion, sliced; two sticks of celery (or about a quarter of a head), pepper and salt. Let boil gently two to three hours, until all can be rubbed easily through a sieve. Return the purée to the pan, add a pint of milk and a squeeze of lemon-juice, and boil up for two or three minutes. Very nourishing.

258. HERB SOUP

Fry a large Spanish onion cut in rings, and two raw tomatoes; add as much hot water as required; herbs, pepper, and salt. Boil half an hour. Pass through sieve; boil up again and serve.

259. HODGE PODGE SOUP

Take a quantity of shelled green peas, with onions, carrots, and turnips, and a sprinkling of salt and pepper. Put these into a pot *with a lid*, with a quantity of stock corresponding to the quantity of soup wanted. Let it boil slowly or simmer for five or six hours. Rub through a sieve and re-heat.

260. HOTCH-POTCH

Have the liquor in which mutton has been boiled made thick with green peas, onions and leeks, grated carrots,

H

haricot beans, and two turnips ; **add** one teacupful of soaked
pearl barley when the vegetables are nearly done, and boil
for one hour.　Rub through sieve and re-heat.

261.　LEEK SOUP

Put a pint of water and a pint of rice stock (or other
cereal stock) to boil ; when boiling fast, put in four or five
leeks and an onion, well washed and chopped small.　Simmer
for an hour, rub hard through a sieve ; re-heat, and season
with salt, pepper, and mace.　Mix three tablespoonfuls
of ground rice quite smooth in one breakfastcupful of milk ;
when the soup boils, pour this in, stirring all the time.　In
about ten minutes the soup should be slightly thickened,
and ready to serve.　At the very last, stir in a quarter of an
ounce of fat.

262.　LENTIL SOUP

Soak half a pound of whole lentils in cold water all night.
Boil them in as much stock as you require soup (and keep
adding to it as it boils away) ; add onions, pepper and salt,
and also seasoning, a few pieces of pumpkin or vegetable
marrow cut small, or a few cold potatoes, to thicken.　Let
it simmer five hours.　Strain through a sieve.

263.　LENTIL FLOUR SOUP

Mince or grate one carrot, half a turnip and three outer
stalks of celery.　Fry in one ounce of fat in a stewpan for five
minutes.　Pour to them three pints of stock (any sort),
add two cloves, three or four peppercorns, and salt.　Simmer
gently for one hour.　Sieve, and return to pan.　Mix two
ounces of lentil flour smoothly in a little cold water, add
it to the soup ; boil up, stirring well ; put in half a pound
of cooked sieved potatoes.　Work the whole mixture quite
smooth, season, and serve.

264.　MACARONI SOUP

Macaroni soup is one of those which taste best when made
in the simplest manner.　After the macaroni has boiled for

ten minutes, it must be transferred to a pan containing two
quarts of boiling stock. It should then be left to simmer for
twenty minutes, after which it may be served.

265. MILK SOUP, No. I

Take four large potatoes, peel and cut into quarters, cut
up one onion, and put them into two quarts of boiling water
or white stock. Boil till done to a mash, strain through a
colander, and rub the vegetables through with a wooden
spoon, return the pulp and soup to the saucepan, and one
pint of milk, and bring to the boil, when it boils sprinkle
in three tablespoonfuls of crushed tapioca, stirring all the
time. Boil fifteen minutes, and serve.

266. MILK SOUP, No. II

Peel two pounds of potatoes, boil them in two quarts of
water, and add two leeks cut up small. When tender, rub
them through a sieve. Place them in a saucepan with two
ounces of fat, stir until the fat melts, and then add one pint
of milk, pepper and salt. When it boils, stir in three dessertspoonfuls of tapioca. Boil ten minutes, and serve.

267. MULLIGATAWNY SOUP, CHEAP VEGETABLE

Have two turnips and six middle-sized potatoes peeled and
cut into half inch dice. Add a good-sized onion, thinly
sliced, and two carrots, very finely shredded. Melt two or
three ounces of fat in a saucepan, and put in the vegetables.
Stir until they are nicely brown. Add one full tablespoonful
of rice, salt and pepper, and a heaped teaspoonful of curry
powder. Mix thoroughly. Pour in three pints of water ;
let it simmer two hours. Thicken with one dessertspoonful of
cornflour. Add one tablespoonful of vinegar. Serve very hot.

268. NETTLE SOUP

Only the very young shoots can be used for this. Wash
the nettles well ; place in boiling salted water, just enough
to cover them, with a little salt and a minute pinch of

carbonate of soda. Boil for twenty minutes, rub through a sieve. Have a little flour and fat mixed smooth in a saucepan, put in the nettle purée, seasoned to taste; thin with a little stock of any kind; boil up and serve.

269. ONION SOUP, No. I

Boil four large Spanish onions in water. When tender, take them out and cut them small. Return them to the water with one pint of milk, and add more water if necessary; pepper and salt them, add one ounce of fat, stir until it is melted, and boil altogether two hours; serve with fried toast cut into dice.

270. ONION SOUP, No. II

Cut four Spanish onions in rings, and fry them; add a thickening of flour and one pint of stock, gently stirring the ingredients for a few minutes. Add pepper and salt and a few herbs; break up some pieces of stale bread in a tureen, and soak them with liquor; mash the bread, add the remainder of the soup, and serve.

271. PARMENTIER SOUP

Cut up four or five medium-sized very mealy potatoes, with two small carrots, one pound of ripe, well-coloured tomatoes, and a small head of celery. Put into a pan two ounces of fat, and as soon as this is melted put in the tomatoes and a medium-sized onion finely sliced, let cook in the covered pan for twelve to fifteen minutes, after which pour in three pints of stock (or water), together with the potatoes, celery, etc., and seasoning to taste, and let cook gently till the vegetables are in a pulp. Rub through a sieve, re-heat and serve.

272. PARSNIP SOUP

Peel and slice one pound of parsnips, cook them brown in one ounce of fat in a stewpan; add one ounce of rice and one quart of hot stock (any sort). Simmer gently for two hours, sieve, re-heat, season to taste with salt, pepper, and

onion ; stir in, last of all, one breakfastcupful of hot milk.
Serve.

273. PEA SOUP, No. I

Take three pints of liquor in which beef or pork has been
boiled ; add two onions cut up in quarters, and some herbs.
Let this boil until the onions are soft. Have a twopenny
packet of pea powder and a teaspoonful of curry powder
made into a paste with cold water. Stir this well into the
soup for a few minutes ; let all boil together for two hours
longer, and serve.

274. PEA SOUP, No. II

Take four pints of water, one pint of dried peas, three
onions, three carrots, two turnips, a bunch of herbs, six-
pennyworth of beef bones (or stock from boiled salt beef).
Soak the peas in two or three waters for twelve hours, wash
the bones, put them in a clean saucepan with the water and
peas, add salt and pepper, skim well while boiling. Scrape
the carrots, peel the turnips, skin the onions, cut them all
in dice, add to the bones and peas, simmer very gently for
four hours. Remove the bones, season with dried mint if
liked, rub through a hair sieve if a purée is required. The
water in which a joint of salt beef has been boiled, or one
pint of bone or of vegetable stock, can be used instead of the
bones.

275. GREEN PEA SOUP, No. I

Take half a pint of shelled peas, one quart of the green
shells, one and a half pints of water, two ounces of fat, one
onion, two sprigs of mint, two lumps of sugar, half a pint
of milk, one teaspoonful of cornflour. Shell the peas, rinse
the empty shells, and with a sharp knife remove the strings.
Melt the fat in a very clean saucepan, put in the peas, the
prepared shells, the onion sliced, and toss (to absorb the
flavour of the butter), over a slow fire for a few minutes,
but do not brown. Then add the water, mint, sugar, and boil
until tender. Rub all through a hair sieve. Blend the

cornflour smoothly with the milk. Put the soup back into the saucepan, add the milk and cornflour, and stir until it boils. Season and serve.

276. GREEN PEA SOUP, No. II

Take two pounds of pea-pods (which should be young and green), wash well, and place in two quarts of boiling salted water, containing one dessertspoonful of sugar, one teaspoonful of salt, one spray of mint. Let boil for three hours ; then rub the pods through a sieve, return this purée to the pan with the rest of the liquor, add a teaspoonful of fat and a teacupful of milk, and boil up again.

277. PEA-NUT SOUP

Roast one breakfastcupful of shelled pea-nuts, skin and mill them. Stir them into two breakfastcupfuls of the liquor in which rice, macaroni, haricots, or any cereal has been cooked, and two breakfastcupfuls of milk. Add enough flour to make as thick as cream ; salt and pepper to taste, and (at discretion) a beaten egg. Bring just to the boil, and serve.

278. POMERANIAN SOUP

Soak and boil one quart of white beans until they are soft. Mash half of them in thin broth, and pass through a sieve. Add one head of celery cut small, some herbs and parsley, salt and pepper. Boil one hour longer, add the whole beans, and serve.

POT AU FEU (French)

279. No. I

(Note.—I give this recipe for completeness sake ; but it is rather reckless unless you have a lot of meat coupons. The following will suffice for eight people.)

Put two pounds of brisket into a deep pan, cover the meat with cold water, and bring it slowly to the boil. Skim off all fat. Fry two sliced onions brown ; cut up finely a small cabbage and two carrots ; add these, with salt, minced

parsley, and herbs to taste, to the brisket, and simmer quietly
for three to four hours. Serve.

280. No. II

Proceed as above, but use three pounds of brisket and the
following vegetables, all neatly cut up; one large onion,
three leeks, one small cabbage, one stick of celery, one large
parsnip, one large carrot, two or three cloves, one dessertspoonful of salt; parsley, thyme, and bay leaf. In either
case the onion should be fried to dark brown.

Remove the meat and half the vegetables before serving,
to use as next day's dinner.

281. POT AU FEU (VEGETABLE)

Have a casserole which holds three pints of cold salted
water; into this put the following, sliced; one large onion,
one turnip, three carrots, half a small cabbage. Let boil,
then simmer slowly for three hours. Then put in a bit of
toast, very hard and brown and leave it for five minutes or so;
remove it before it breaks up. This is merely to improve
the colour of the liquid. Serve at once.

282. POTATO SOUP, No. I

Wash, peel, and slice one pound of potatoes, and one
medium-sized onion. Have one ounce of dripping melted
in a saucepan, add the vegetables, but stir them so that
they do not burn. Pour in one pint of water, and half a
teaspoonful of celery seeds tied up in muslin. Cover the
pan and let the potatoes cook gently until they are soft.
Stir often. Remove the celery seeds, rub the rest through
a sieve and return to pan. Add half a pint of milk, and
seasoning of salt and pepper. Boil up and serve.

283. POTATO SOUP, No. II

Boil one carrot, one onion, one head of celery, one large
spray of parsley, and three or four leeks, with a little fat, in
just enough water to cover. Have some floury potatoes

cooked, add these to the other ingredients, and rub all through a sieve. Return to pan, and thin the purée with stock; season, and boil up.

284.　POTATO SOUP, No. III

Have two onions, three potatoes, and two ounces of bacon, very thinly sliced. Season with salt and pepper; boil in two quarts of water or stock for two hours; pass through sieve, boil up, and serve.

285.　POTATO SOUP, No. IV

Fry two onions in a saucepan; add fourteen good-sized potatoes cut in quarters, and boil them in stock until soft enough to mash; return them to the saucepan, adding pepper, salt, and a large piece of dripping. Simmer for a few minutes, and serve.

286.　PUMPKIN OR MARROW SOUP, No. I

Cut up and fry one large Spanish onion, in a saucepan with some dripping, and about six tomatoes; add a little water, and twelve pieces of pumpkin or marrow cut rather small, one sprig of thyme, and pepper and salt to taste. Boil until the vegetables are reduced to pulp. Pass through a sieve, and re-heat.

NOTE.—Wherever in these recipes tomatoes are used, tinned tomatoes or sauce can be substituted for fresh.

287.　PUMPKIN SOUP, No. II

Boil a small pumpkin, after peeling it and cutting it up into small pieces, in salted water. When quite soft, rub the pumpkin through a strainer. Melt one ounce of fat in a saucepan, with a wineglassful of milk; add the pumpkin pulp and some pepper. Stir well, and serve very hot.

288.　SEMOLINA SOUP

Peel and slice thinly two medium potatoes; chop up the outer stalks of a celery head, place in boiling stock of any sort, to simmer for one hour. Sieve, re-heat to boiling point, and gradually sprinkle in two ounces of semolina. Continue to stir until the soup boils up again, then let simmer slowly ; and at the end of thirty minutes, season to taste with salt, pepper, and mace. Add one teaspoonful of fat, and if possible a teacupful of hot milk. Stir well and serve.

289. STEW SOUP

Take the liquor in which tripe has been boiled ; add to it half a pint of split lentils (which must have been soaked the night previous), one or two turnips, a few potatoes, and a root of celery ; add pepper and salt. Let all simmer together gently for four hours, and then serve.

290. TOMATO SOUP, No. I

Take two pounds of fresh red tomatoes (or a quart of tinned ones), two ounces of crushed tapioca, two onions (medium size), a strip of celery, or trimmings, a bunch of herbs, one ounce of fat, one teaspoonful of salt, a quarter of a teaspoonful of pepper, a pint of milk, one quart of hot water.

Slice the tomatoes, peel and slice the onions, cut the celery in small pieces, tie together two sprigs of parsley, one each of thyme and marjoram, and a bay-leaf. Melt the fat in an enamelled saucepan, add the prepared vegetables, cover the pan, and cook all for five minutes over a gentle heat, but do not let them colour. Pour in the water, and cook slowly for three-quarters of an hour ; rub all through a wire sieve and return to saucepan. Wash the tapioca, and boil it in the soup until it is quite dissolved and clear, from eight to ten minutes. Lastly, add the milk and seasoning. If tinned tomatoes are used, twenty minutes instead of three-quarters of an hour will suffice for cooking them.

291. TOMATO SOUP, No. II

Fry four ounces of chopped onion in two ounces of fat, add one tin of tomatoes, let boil for half an hour, then add one

pint of stock and one teacupful of water. Salt and pepper
to taste after this has boiled. Rub the whole through a
sieve. Simmer about one hour. Thicken with rice if desired.

292. TOMATO SOUP, No. III

Cut up about fourteen large tomatoes and three large
onions; boil and mash them; add two quarts of stock,
a teaspoonful of sugar, one of salt, black and cayenne pepper,
thicken with flour, and serve.

293. TOMATO SOUP, No. IV

One tin of tomatoes, two ounces of lean ham, one small
onion, one ounce of butter, salt, and pepper, a few drops
of cochineal, and two ounces of tapioca. Slice tomatoes
and onions and ham into a saucepan, add the butter, simmer
one hour and rub through a strainer. Boil one quart of
stock, throw in the tapioca, and boil until it is clear; add
the tomato, etc., to it, season and colour it, boil ten minutes
and serve.

294. TURNIP SOUP

Boil some turnips till tender enough to mash. Fry an
onion till it is tender, but not brown. Place it in a saucepan with the mashed turnips, salt and pepper, and one
quart stock (or one pint of stock and one pint of milk). Boil
till thick, and serve.

295. VEGETABLE SOUP, No. I

Equal quantities of carrots, potatoes, and onions, a head
or two of celery, and some herbs. Slice and fry the vegetables
in a little dripping, add as much water or stock as is wanted;
put in salt, pepper, and the herbs. Let them all boil two
hours; then add a thickening of flour, mixed with a teaspoonful of mustard. Let the whole simmer for half an
hour longer, and then serve.

296. VEGETABLE SOUP, No. II

Fry a large slice of bread in some dripping; add two
quarts of stock, six potatoes, four turnips, three onions cut

in slices, one tin of mushrooms, two heads of celery, salt,
and pepper. Let the whole boil for two hours; mash the
vegetables, return them to the stock, just let them boil ten
minutes, stirring all the time, and then serve.

297. VEGETABLE SOUP, No. III

Cut up six carrots, six parsnips, six potatoes, and fry
them in dripping; add one quart of stock, boil for two hours,
and serve.

298. VEGETABLE SOUP, No. IV

Take a few sticks of celery, a large onion, a carrot, a turnip,
a pound of cabbage, cut into strips, a pint of split peas and
a rasher of streaky bacon. Boil these in a gallon of salted
water, and when the fat has been skimmed off, add a little
sugar and pepper. The bottom of the tureen should then be
covered with slices of bread, over which the soup is poured.

299. VEGETABLE SOUP, No. V

Boil some bones for six or eight hours, then strain off,
and, when cold, take all the fat off. Mince small a couple of
turnips, a tiny onion, a piece of shallot, and some outside
pieces of celery. Let the stock boil for twenty minutes, then
throw in the vegetables and a tiny bit of fat. Let boil rapidly
for half an hour, and if the stock is not sufficiently thick
with the vegetables, mix a teaspoonful of flour smoothly
with cold water and strain it into the soup. Let it simmer
at once, then strain it into the soup-tureen.

300. VEGETABLE MARROW SOUP

One slice of raw ham or bacon boiled in one quart of stock
or water; one vegetable marrow, peeled and cut into small
pieces and mashed; add a pint and a half of boiling milk
or stock to the bacon and marrow; mix well; flavour with
pepper and salt and a very little nutmeg. A bay leaf must
be boiled in the milk or stock. Remove the ham, and serve.

301. VERMICELLI SOUP

Boil for a quarter of an hour two ounces of vermicelli in one pint of stock; add salt and pepper. Add a pint of stock. Boil five minutes and serve.

302. SCOTCH BARLEY BROTH

Take one pound of scrag of mutton, chop it into even pieces, place in a saucepan with one teacupful pearl barley, one large onion sliced, and one quart of water; pepper and salt to taste. Simmer gently for two hours.

303. SCOTCH BROTH

Take six quarts of cold water, any bones of meat or a ham bone, two carrots, two turnips, two onions, one small cabbage, half a teacupful of pearl barley, half a teacupful of parsley, half a teacupful of shelled peas, a bunch of sweet herbs. Any other vegetable in season. Put the water in a large pan with the bones and the barley. Let boil with the lid on until the barley is nearly tender. Wash the vegetables, cut the carrots, turnips and onion into neat dice and the cabbage into shreds, tie the herbs together. Put all the vegetables into the pan, put on the lid, and cook for about one and a half hours. About ten minutes before sending it to table, add the parsley coarsely chopped. Season carefully and serve.

304. VEGETABLE BROTH

Vegetable broth is composed of greens or cabbage, shorn or cut into small pieces, onions, carrots, and turnips, or one or more of them as can be got, also cut into small pieces, with pearl barley boiled slowly in a portion of water corresponding to the quantity of broth wanted, to which a sprinkling of salt and pepper is added, a small quantity of dripping is also added, when that can be procured; and vegetable broth, if properly made, is a nourishing and palatable food.

CHAPTER V

EGGS AND CHEESE

This subject is particularly awkward to handle, because eggs are so very dear, and cheese so very rare. We cheerfully pay 4d. to 6d. each for so-called new-laid eggs now—in 1916 3d. seemed an exorbitant and preposterous price. Real eggs, therefore, should be regarded as on a level with meat—and of almost equal value, which, indeed, they are ; one new-laid egg is said to be equivalent to a quarter of a pound of fresh meat. They must be used as solid articles of food—poached, boiled, shirred, fried, or curried ; and never lightly used for culinary purposes.

Boiled eggs are (or should be) eaten with bread and butter. But we want to save the butter.

Poached eggs are (or should be) served on buttered toast. Butter again.

Fried eggs can only be cooked in fat of some sort. Fat is precious.

Shirred or baked eggs must be put into greased cups, etc., in order to bake them. They are not so easily digested as the rest ; and they don't go so far, in actual bulk.

Omelets are nowadays too great a luxury. It follows that *hard-boiled* eggs, included with other ingredients in a dish, will go the farthest and be the best value. Next to these I should place fried eggs.

Most fortunately for us in our present dilemma—when we are even forbidden to " hoard " eggs beyond a certain number, by putting away the usual store in water-glass—dried eggs have been invented, and are (comparatively speaking) cheap and plentiful. They are available for most culinary

purposes instead of " real " eggs ; but I have not found
them very successful for pancakes, fritters, or omelets, or such
dishes as should have the yolks and white separately beaten.
It is obvious that they could not be the ideal eggs for these.

For custards, cakes, and many puddings, custard and egg
powders are quite good enough. They don't profess to be
made from eggs ; but they will serve their purpose right
enough for the time being.

305. CAIRO EGGS

Take four hard-boiled eggs ; have ready cold boiled lentils,
seasoned with minced herbs, pepper and salt. Coat them
half an inch thick with this mixture ; then brush with milk,
roll in fine oatmeal, and bake for about ten minutes on a
greased tin in a quick oven. They can be served as they
are, with a nice gravy separate ; or halved and set upon flat
cakes of hominy or polenta.

306. COCOTTE EGGS

Take four good eggs, and four little earthenware egg-pots.
Line the dishes with a thin layer of anything you have handy
—such as scraps of meat or bacon finely minced and mixed
with chopped parsley and crumbs—or a plain forcemeat.
Break each egg and drop it into its pot ; the pots must
then be placed in a shallow pan of boiling water in the
oven, until the eggs are well poached and set. Serve in
the same dishes, with a little tomato sauce or ketchup on top
of each egg.

307. CURRIED EGGS, No. I

Take four hard-boiled eggs, one sour apple, one large
onion, one ounce of fat, one ounce of flour, one dessertspoonful
of curry-powder, one small teaspoonful of salt, half a pint
of milk or milk and water, a quarter of a pound of Patna rice.
Boil the eggs for ten minutes ; shell and lay them in cold
water, to keep white. Peel and chop finely the apple and
onion ; fry them in the fat for five minutes, using a sauce-

pan ; stir in curry powder, then the flour and salt ; lastly, the milk, and simmer gently for a quarter of an hour. Add the eggs, which should be cut in quarters. When quite hot, serve in a border of boiled rice.

308. CURRIED EGGS, No. II

Slice finely a couple of onions, and fry them a delicate brown in two ounces of fat, rub together till smooth two ounces of curry-powder, two teaspoonfuls of good vinegar, and a teaspoonful of castor sugar. Stir into it, over the fire, about a breakfastcupful of good stock and bring it to the boil. When nicely blended, break into it five eggs, and let them cook gently in this about one or two minutes. Serve at once with boiled rice.

309. CURRIED EGGS, No. III

Take six eggs, boil them for twenty-five minutes ; then place in cold water for fifteen minutes. Next, remove the shells carefully, and put the eggs in hot water to keep warm. Have some rice ready boiled (according to any of the recipes on pp. 152–4), and put it in a warm place. Fry a teaspoonful of chopped onion in a tablespoonful of fat, till it is golden yellow. Have one tablespoonful of cornflour, with one dessertspoonful of curry powder, mixed smooth in a little cold milk (or water or stock), and add it to the onion in the saucepan.; then add gradually three teacupfuls of milk or white stock. When the liquor thickens and clears, season with salt and pepper, and strain. It should be quite smooth, and golden yellow. Dry the eggs gently in a cloth, roll them in the sauce until they are completely coated ; arrange the rice on a dish, like a deep nest, and put the eggs in. Carefully fill up the nest with the rest of the sauce.

310. CURRIED EGGS, No. IV

Cut up small one large onion and one apple. Put in a stewpan with one ounce of fat. Stir over a moderate fire till slightly browned. Add one tablespoonful of curry powder and half a teaspoonful of flour. Mix well, and add a pint of water. Simmer slowly for an hour, and then add a little salt, and, if wished, a little lemon juice. Strain and pour it over either hard-boiled eggs cut in halves or lightly poached eggs. Serve with well-boiled rice.

311. DUCKS' EGGS

These are not only larger but richer than hens' eggs. One duck's egg is equivalent to two ordinary eggs. They are best when shirred (baked), scrambled, or made into omelets, with a little seasoning of chopped parsley and onion. They can also be hard-boiled and curried ; or fried and served with tomato sauce. They need very little fat for frying, being oily in themselves.

312. NORMANDY EGGS

Have half a pound of haricot beans soaked overnight, and next day place them in a pan of cold water, with three ounces of fat, and boil two hours or until tender. Drain, add salt and pepper, and toss them in one ounce of fat. Meanwhile have six eggs hard-boiled, shelled, and halved, when cold. Make a sauce with two ounces of fat and one ounce of flour, and one pint of stock of any kind, vegetable or otherwise. Season with salt and pepper, and carefully re-heat the eggs in the sauce. Place the haricots on a hot dish, hollow the centre of them, and arrange the eggs and sauce in the hollow.

313. PALESTINE EGGS

Trim and boil eight good-sized Jerusalem artichokes, and set them to cool. Boil four eggs hard and let them get cold (they can be plunged into a bowl of cold water), then cut them up. Slice the artichokes, lay them in a greased baking-dish ; strew the chopped eggs over them ; next, put a layer of sliced tomatoes ; last, a layer of grated cheese. Bake until lightly coloured, and serve very hot.

314. SAVOURY EGGS AND RICE

Take a pint of stock, and cook four ounces of Patna rice in it until tender. Colour it with a little strained tomato sauce ; cut up two slices of fried bacon into little strips, and add these. Add salt and pepper to taste. Put the rice into a shallow greased pie-dish, and when it is well pressed and shaped, turn it out upon a heated dish. Have ready some eggs, either four (hot) hard-boiled, cut in halves, or five poached, and arrange these upon the rice. This is a nice dish, but must be served hot with care.

315. TRIPED EGGS

Have six eggs hard-boiled for fifteen minutes ; place in cold water ; subsequently shell, and slice them very thinly with a sharp knife. Melt three ounces of fat with about one ounce of flour in a saucepan ; put in six small boiled finely minced onions, seasoned with salt and pepper ; gradually add two tablespoonfuls of milk, and let simmer for ten minutes or so. Then add the sliced eggs, which must not be stirred ; shake the pan gently to let them mix with the rest, and when they are heated through, in two or three minutes, pour off all upon a hot dish.

316. TURKISH EGGS

Put an onion cut into slices, with some fine herbs and butter, into a saucepan, adding a little flour, salt and pepper. When these have been on the fire a few minutes, add a glass of white French wine and the whites of six hard-boiled eggs cut into slices ; when these ingredients are well united, add the yolks which had been previously set aside, and serve up very hot.

———

CHEESE must also be regarded as a very special article of food. It must never be served as a mere luxury course ; nor should it be eaten *au naturel* with bread and salad. It should be reserved for addition to otherwise flavourless

I

articles, such as macaroni, or used along with potatoes or other vegetables *au gratin*, when a very nourishing and admirable dish is the result. In several recipes I have included grated cheese; not as a seasoning, but definitely to increase their food value. I believe that Parmesan cheese (the correct kind for grating, immensely hard and durable) is still obtainable at the big stores—at a very high price. So-called " cream " cheese (see recipes below) is available instead of butter, and is particularly wholesome, when you happen to have any sour milk. If cheese cannot be obtained, however, neither can it be replaced. There is, so far as I am aware, no known real substitute for cheese; you cannot imitate it either in flavour, texture, or peculiar food-value.

HOME-MADE CHEESE
317. I

Sour milk need not be wasted. Let it become quite thick, then stand it in a jar in a saucepan of hot water. It must heat slowly, but *not boil*, until the curd and whey are well separated. Then strain out all the whey through a cloth, pressing hard. Add a little salt, a morsel of dripping or margarine, and a very little fresh milk, to the curd, and blend them in thoroughly with a spoon until the mixture is quite smooth and fine. Shape into balls or cubes, and keep in a cool place.

318. II

Put one pint of milk in a warm place until it is sour and quite thick. Put it, loosely tied, into a piece of buttermuslin, and hang it up over a bowl for several hours to drain off all the whey. Then tighten the muslin as much as possible, and press for an hour between two plates.

319. III

Take some milk which has gone sour suddenly, and reduce it to curds and whey by boiling. Place the curd on (or in) a cloth to drain thoroughly, and when it is as dry as you can get it, press it down tightly in a small wooden box, with clean fresh hazel leaves in layers here and there. Keep a good weight on top of the curd, and turn it out when dry, which should be in two days.

In all these recipes, the milk must be *absolutely* sour, or the cheese will be tasteless.

320. BREAD AND CHEESE CUSTARD

Mix well eight ounces of soaked drained bread with eight ounces of grated cheese, salt and pepper to taste; pour in one pint of boiling milk, and let all cool; then stir in one beaten (dried) egg. Place in greased pie-dish and bake in a hot oven to a golden brown. This is extremely nutritive.

321. CELERY CHEESE

Take a sound head of celery, trim it, and place it in a saucepan containing macaroni which is nearly cooked, and add (if need be) enough *boiling* water to cover all. When the celery has cooked slowly until quite tender, remove it; strain off the water (which should be kept for stock), and replace it with a little milk; after a few minutes, mix one teaspoonful of flour smooth in a little water, and stir into the macaroni and milk (this makes it creamy), and just let it thicken. Then put the macaroni into a deep dish, chop up the celery very small and lay it on top; add a little grated cheese, a few little dabs of fat, and seasoning of salt and pepper. Place in a moderate oven and bake slowly to a golden brown.

322. CHEESE AND ONIONS

Have two pounds of parboiled English onions sliced, seasoned, and placed in a deep baking-dish. Cover them thickly with flaked, shredded, or thinly-sliced cheese— six to eight ounces will be required. Strew little dabs of fat —about two ounces altogether—on top; and bake for thirty minutes in a good oven. Serve immediately, before the cheese can harden.

323. CHEESE AND ONION PUDDING

Take a good-sized pie-dish, grease it, and place at the bottom a layer of sliced onions. Next put in a thin layer of grated cheese. Strew this with salt and pepper to taste, and a little pinch of dry mustard. Follow with a layer of onions, and so on till the dish is nearly full. Have a dried egg beaten with enough milk to fill up the dish, and bake until the onion is done, in a moderate oven.

324. CHEESE AND RICE PUDDING

Make a batter with a quarter of a pint of milk, one (dried) egg, and four ounces of flour. Beat it well, and let stand for at least half an hour. Have three ounces of rice boiled till tender, and well drained. Mix with it, one and a half ounces of grated cheese, half a teaspoonful of finely minced herbs, and seasoning of pepper and salt. Stir this into the batter; lastly, add a quarter-pint more milk, and half a teaspoonful of baking-powder. Blend thoroughly; pour into a greased pie-dish; bake about twenty-five minutes more or less in a hot oven.

325. CHEESE AND POTATOES

Cut some cold boiled potatoes in thin slices, and lay them in a greased pie-dish; over them lay cheese cut thin; then a little fat and a pinch of dry mustard, then more potatoes, and so on until the dish is full. Pour over all one pint of milk, and bake in a quick oven for one hour.

326. MOCK CRAB

Mix two tablespoonfuls grated cheese with one tablespoonful of margarine, one saltspoonful each of salt, pepper, and (dry) mustard, a little anchovy paste to taste, and a teaspoonful of vinegar. Blend thoroughly until you have got a smooth paste, and spread upon slices of bread.

CHAPTER VI

POTATOES AND OTHER VEGETABLES

THE cooking of potatoes is an immensely wide subject. Unluckily it is discounted by the dearth of fats. Potatoes are starchy foods, and without some sort of fat to accompany them, they are undoubtedly far from gay. They are eatable, but they are not interesting.

I therefore advise you to make potatoes one of your first considerations when you are salving fat of any sort. A steamed potato in its jacket is a fine wholesome sustaining thing; but a parboiled potato baked in a little fat is something to set before the king. Riced potatoes are an elegant dish in connection with gravy of some kind; but they have not the subtle appeal of mashed potatoes, which *must* have either milk, or fat, or both. As for " chips "—beloved of the working classes—these are, of necessity, almost things of the past.

Potatoes can be made presentable and delectable in so many different ways, that no other vegetable comes within a mile of them. In 1917, when we were practically potato-less, we realised how largely we depended upon that cheap and humble tuber. In vain to urge that we never had potatoes before the seventeenth century—that other nations don't bother about them; that hundreds of millions never see them; that rice, or haricots, or swedes do just as well. All these arguments may be true, yet they are not convincing. What we want is potatoes " every time." And we haven't yet used them for a fraction of their true value; no, not though potato-spirit is driving motors, impelling aeroplanes, and constituting a vital ingredient of high explosives.

You will find a lot of potato recipes here. But I have had to omit the most delectable. They simply couldn't be carried out in these days.

In this chapter potatoes are only treated as vegetables. For their use in puddings and pastry, *see* Chapter VIII. ; in bread and cakes, *see* Chapter IX.

For all ordinary purposes, it is necessary to have a good sieve or a potato ricer. Mashing with a rolling pin or any other implement never achieves the same result as one of the above, takes longer, and leaves hidden lumps. But whether you sieve, rice, or mash it, do so *while the potato is hot*. If you let it go cold first, it is much more difficult to deal with, and will make your dish heavy.

I need hardly say that potatoes should *never* be peeled before cooking. Peeling wastes not only the potato, and its flavour, but the mineral salts which lie next the skin, and 85 per cent. of all its most important qualities are literally *thrown away*. The potato must be boiled, or better, steamed, in its " jacket," after a good scrubbing.

The potato baked in its skin is a very appetising thing ; but this is a wasteful way of treating it, and I don't commend it, on that account.

To mash potatoes in the old way, with butter and milk, is undoubtedly too extravagant now. To sauter them is usually out of the question. Cooked potatoes, however, are an indispensable means of eking out one's meat, fish, bacon, or eggs ; a very little fat will do to heat them through, or they can be sieved for fish-cakes and rissoles.

As regards the *Other Vegetables*, please note that the most nourishing (after Potatoes, which are miles ahead) are Jerusalem Artichokes—(it is astounding how many folks are ignorant of these)—Parsnips, Carrots, Beet, and Onions ; the " pulse " vegetables, dried or fresh Peas, Beans, Runners, Haricots, Kidney Beans, etc. (dried are more nutritious than fresh) ; and then the rest in go-as-you-please order ; scientists never seem to agree about their respective degrees of nutriment. But beyond actual food-value, one must take into consideration the mineral salts supplied by vegetables, and by green saladings, which play a most important part in the purifying of the blood. I think it may fairly be stated that the vegetable of least value (for human beings), from any point of view, is the Turnip. But Turnip-*tops* are extremely useful and beneficial, so that it is hard to generalise.

A number of tasty recipes are set forth in the Ministry of Food vegetable leaflet—but as they nearly all involve the use of fat—our priceless fat !—or of cheese—that exceedingly rare article !—I do not quote them. An excellent piece of advice in the leaflet, however, is that with reference to cooking all vegetables " in very little water in closed vessels. Water is only used to prevent the vegetables from sticking to the pan and getting burnt ; so that the vegetables are really steamed." Half a teaspoonful of fat to one pound of vegetable has been stated as sufficient : this fat not only improves the flavour, but helps to cook the vegetable.

If cooked thus in an earthenware casserole, tightly covered, the flavour is all retained and there is no waste of anything. If you have no casserole, the vegetable can be put in a steamer. The old-fashioned plan of using quarts or gallons of water, is at once wasteful and insipid. All the mineral salts and true taste of the vegetable get washed away. You will be surprised at the difference when you have tried the little-water method.

If cereals are used as vegetables, soak them for twelve hours before cooking ; this includes rice, pearl barley, sago, tapioca, hominy, etc. Pulse (dried) vegetables such as haricots, dried peas, split peas, lentils, butter beans, etc., require twenty-four hours preliminary soaking. *Be sure to keep for stock the water in which any of the above has been boiled.* In these cases plenty of water is necessary, that the cereals or pulse may absorb it and thus swell out and become tender. Remember that if they don't swell out properly in the cooking, they will attempt to do so inside the human stomach ; a most unpleasant process.

A very important statement regarding pulse foods was recently made in *The Garden*, *i.e.*, that haricots, dried broad beans, dried peas, are much more digestible and nourishing if eaten as in Burmah—soaked for a day or two, then put, covered with a cloth, for forty-eight hours or so, in a warm place (sixty to seventy degrees Fahr.) such as a warm cupboard near the kitchen fire, and *allowed to sprout*. When little shoots about half an inch appear on them, as they should do in two days, the starch in the beans or peas is converted into maltose ; the seeds have softened, the thick outer coat comes off. They require much less boiling, and are far more readily digested. This is a valuable " tip."

Pulse food should always be accompanied with fat in some form, however little ; and bottled salad dressing, which contains oil, is a fine sauce for plain boiled haricots.

Further vegetable recipes may be found in the " Vegetable Book " of this series, and issued with a war-time supplement.

POTATOES

327. POTATO BALLS

Mix two ounces of flour with twelve to sixteen ounces of cooked sieved potatoes ; add two teaspoonfuls of minced parsley, one teaspoonful of minced herbs, salt and pepper to taste. Moisten with one beaten (dried) egg. Make the mixture into balls. Have ready any odds and ends of meat, put through the mincer, and flavoured with a little tomato sauce or curry powder. Put a teaspoonful of meat into each ball, cover, and re-shape and bake in a greased tin in a hot oven until the potato is a golden brown.

328. POTATO CAKES, No. I

Have twelve ounces of potatoes (boiled in their skins and sieved) mixed with two ounces of flour (any sort) ; add half a teaspoonful of salt and one teaspoonful of fat. Bind with a dried egg ; roll out to desired thickness, cut into small rounds, and bake or fry to a golden brown.   Serve at once as a vegetable.

329. POTATO CAKES, No. II

Take one breakfastcupful of cold sieved or mashed potatoes ; one tablespoonful of self-raising flour, mix thoroughly with the fingers ; season with salt and pepper, and moisten with enough milk to make a stiff dough.   Roll out a quarter of an inch thick, cut into rounds, and fry.   Serve as a vegetable.

330. POTATOES, CURRIED

Fry in dripping an onion, cut into thin slices.   Cut up some boiled potatoes, and fry with the onion, dredge them with curry-powder, and add a little gravy, salt and some lemon juice, if you have it.   Allow this to stew for a quarter of an hour, and serve.

331. POTATO CUSTARD

Peel some potatoes as thinly as you can, slice them very finely, and lay them in overlapping scales in a deep fireproof earthen pie-dish.   Make a custard with dried eggs or custard powder, and a little milk and stock or water.   Pour a little meat extract over the potatoes, just enough to moisten them ; sprinkle them with a very little finely minced parsley and onion.   Season the custard, pour it over the potatoes, and bake in a hot oven for thirty-eight to forty minutes.

332. POTATOES, DELMONICO

Chop cold, boiled potatoes into bits the size of peas ; make a white sauce and stir the chopped potato into it, using a generous cupful of potato to each cup of sauce.   Pour in to a greased pudding-dish, cover the top with bits of fat and crumbs, and bake about fifteen minutes in a hot oven.

333. POTATOES, DUCHESSE, No. I

Take ten ounces of mashed potatoes, and beat up with them, while still hot, three ounces of Spanish onions boiled very soft.   Add one and a half ounces of fat, one tablespoonful of milk, one dessertspoonful of grated cheese, one beaten egg (dried).   Mix all these well while hot.   When the mixture is cold, roll it out on a floured pasteboard, to about one inch thick ; cut it into rounds or ovals ; dredge these, and fry them a golden brown, in dripping, over a low fire.

334. POTATOES, DUCHESSE, No. II

Prepare a potato purée. Divide into six equal parts. Spread a little flour on a corner of a table, roll each piece of potato in the flour, then give to each a nice heart-shaped form ; nicely criss-cross their surfaces with a knife.   Butter a small pastry-pan with a teaspoonful of fat, arrange the potatoes over, and lightly grease their surface.   Place the pan in a hot oven and bake for ten minutes, or until of a fine golden colour.   Remove from the oven, and with a skimmer lift them up and place on a heated dish, and serve.

335. POTATO DUMPLING

Beat up some dry floury cooked potatoes until they are perfectly smooth, then mix with them one quarter of their weight in fine flour, season with salt, and form into a moderately firm paste with an ounce of fat, melted in a little warm water or stock.   Put the mixture into a greased basin and steam over plenty of boiling water until the dumpling is quite firm and light, then turn it out carefully on to a hot dish, garnish it with sprigs of parsley, and send to table very hot, with some pleasantly flavoured sauce or gravy as an accompaniment.   Or, if preferred, instead of sauce or gravy, some stewed mushrooms, baked tomatoes, or fried onions, etc., may be served with the dumpling.

336. POTATO DUMPLINGS, No. I

Mash one pound of steamed potatoes, keep them hot in a saucepan, stir in one well-beaten dried egg and one tablespoonful of milk.   Then mix in thoroughly one breakfast-

cupful of flour and one teaspoonful of baking-powder, and
leave the mixture to cool. Make it into small dumplings.
Put the dumplings for fifteen minutes in (slightly salted)
boiling water, drain, and serve them. A sharp sauce is an
excellent addition.

337. POTATO DUMPLINGS, No. II

Have eight large potatoes steamed in their jackets, peeled,
and rubbed through a sieve while warm. Let them grow
cold, then add three ounces of flour, and one ounce of fat,
melted till soft but not oiled. Add one beaten (dried) egg,
salt, pepper, and nutmeg to taste ; beat well ; then stir
in one teaspoonful of baking-powder. Form the dumplings
into small balls, and place them in boiling stock or water.
They must boil fast for twenty minutes or so. Lift out and
drain, and serve at once, with a good gravy or sauce.

338. POTATO FRITTERS

Take one pound of hot sieved potatoes, and work into it
one beaten (dried) egg, three ounces of flour, pepper, and salt,
and nutmeg to taste. Form into fingers about one inch wide
by three inches long ; fry in boiling fat, drain, and serve.

339. POTATOES HASHED

Grease an omelet pan and put into it cold boiled potatoes
chopped rather fine ; sprinkle with a little salt, scatter bits
of fat over the top, and pour over a little white stock
or hot water. Cover and cook slowly until thoroughly heated
through. Turn out carefully into a hot dish without stirring.
Care needs be taken that the potato be not browned, but the
stock and fat absorbed.

340. POTATOES WITH HERRINGS

Well wash and boil some potatoes, taking care not to let
them break or get too soft ; then drain off the water, peel
and slice them fairly thickly, and keep them hot. In the
meantime put a chopped onion into a stewpan with an

ounce of fat, and fry until lightly browned ; then dust in some
flour, add three tablespoonfuls of vinegar, a bay leaf, and
rather under a pint of water ; season with salt and pepper,
draw the pan to the side of the stove, and let simmer for a
little.   Well wash two red herrings, cut them down lengthways, remove the bones, cut up the flesh small, put it into
the sauce, and let it cook in this for a few minutes ; now put
in the potatoes, and stir them gently, being careful not to
break them.   Next add two ounces of fat and a gill of milk,
and stir over the fire until it reaches boiling point.   When
cooked, turn out on to a hot dish, and serve.

341.   POTATO MIROTON

Boil or steam twelve fair-sized potatoes in their skins.
Skin, mash, and season them with salt and pepper.   Mince
up a small onion, and fry it in two tablespoonfuls of fat.
When the onion is light brown, add in the mashed potatoes,
stir all well, and put in a tablespoonful of mushroom ketchup
or some similar flavouring, and two dried eggs well beaten.
Sprinkle a greased mould with breadcrumbs, and bake the
mixture in it for half an hour.   Moderate oven.

342.   POTATO PANCAKES

Have six ounces of G.R. flour in a bowl, make a hollow
in the middle, and pour into it one and a half breakfastcupfuls of water.   Beat well until you have a smooth batter.
Then add six ounces of grated raw potato, one ounce of grated
or minced onion, salt and pepper to taste ; mix thoroughly.
Let stand for an hour, mix in one teaspoonful of baking
powder, and cook as for other pancakes.

343.   POTATO SAVOURIES

Boil and mash some potatoes ; moisten with milk or white
stock ; add a seasoning of salt, pepper, chopped herbs, and
grated lemon-rind.   Have some small patty-pans greased
and dusted with fine crumbs ;   fill these with the potato

mixture, lay a little bit of fat on the top of each, and brown them in a moderate oven.

344. POTATOES STEWED IN MILK

Slice some waxy potatoes. Melt two ounces of fat in a pan, add to this gradually one ounce of flour, and stir gently without allowing the flour to colour ; then add by degrees one pint of cold milk, stirring all the time ; directly this reaches the boil, put in the potatoes, which must be well covered by the liquid ; add salt, and put on the lid tightly ; then let the whole simmer gently at the side of the fire till the potatoes are cooked ; this will take about half an hour. Five minutes before serving, sprinkle in some finely minced parsley, and serve.

345. POTATOES WITH WHITE SAUCE

Put into a saucepan a small piece of fat, with a little flour, diluted with a little stock ; to which add some salt and pepper, and thicken it over the fire ; having boiled the potatoes, peeled them, and cut them into slices, pour this sauce over them, and serve hot. To vary the flavour, some minced capers or a little chopped parsley may be added to the sauce.

OTHER VEGETABLES

346. ARTICHOKES, CHINESE (OR JAPANESE)

For a pound of the vegetables, put one pint of water into a stewpan with a saltspoonful of salt, a dessertspoonful of vinegar, a teaspoonful of flour, and an ounce of fat ; stir these all over the fire till boiling then put in the artichokes, which should have been washed and scraped, and simmer slowly for fifteen minutes with the stewpan not quite covered down. Then drain, and serve with any sauces suitable for celery.

347. ARTICHOKES (JERUSALEM) AND ONIONS

Boil two pounds of Jerusalem artichokes, drain, and sieve ; add one gill of stock (any sort), and season to taste. Mix

with them two large Spanish onions, well boiled and finely
chopped. Pour the mixture into a greased baking-dish,
dust the top with grated cheese, and bake a light brown.
A little thickening of cornflour can be added at pleasure.

348. BEANS AND CARROTS

Soak eight ounces of butter beans in four pints of cold
water for a day and a night. Boil them in the same water;
add salt and pepper, mixed spice and herbs to taste, and
two onions and six carrots sliced small; also any other
vegetables, cut up small; place all in a casserole, cover,
and let simmer slowly for two hours. Towards the last, put
in a small teaspoonful of curry powder, and the same of
minced parsley.

349. BEANS AND RICE

Soak half a pound of butter beans overnight—next day
cook them for two hours, or until tender. Have one ounce
of rice boiled in vegetable stock, add salt and pepper. Place
half a pound tin of tomatoes in a stewpan, with one ounce
of fat and a muslin bag of minced herbs and parsley (a
teaspoonful will suffice). Cook until the tomato can be
sieved. Blend it with the rice and butter beans, and serve
very hot.

350. BEAN ROAST

Soak half a pound of butter beans overnight; next day
cook gently for three hours, or until soft enough to sieve.
Have eight ounces of rice boiled for a quarter of an hour,
and two minced onions lightly browned in about an ounce
of fat. Add these to the sieved butter beans, along with a
teaspoonful of minced parsley, an ounce of minced bacon,
and pepper and salt to taste. Some people put in a pinch
of dried herbs. Mix well, and to moisten the mixture use the
following: Have two ounces of flour mixed smooth in a
little of the (cold) stock from the butter beans. Boil enough
additional stock to make a breakfastcupful altogether,
and add it to the paste, stirring until all is smooth. Season,

and add a tablespoonful of tomato ketchup. Boil up, and simmer from eight to ten minutes ; add to the beans, etc. Shape the whole mixture into a roll, dredge it with oatmeal, sprinkle with little bits of fat, bake on a floured tin in a hot oven for thirty minutes.

351. BEETROOT, BAKED

Put the beetroot without washing it into a slack oven, and bake for eight hours. When cold, peel and serve.

352. BEETROOT, FRIED

Cut up a boiled beetroot in thin slices, also one onion ; fry both in dripping, add pepper and salt, drain, and serve very hot.

353. BEETROOT MOULD

Boil a large beetroot, and while hot pass it through the masher ; mince a raw onion ; add it to the beet with pepper, salt, and one ounce of fat. Place in a greased basin or mould with a cover over, and bake for one hour.

354. BEETROOT RAGOÛT

Boil a good-sized beetroot ; fry an onion, and season with salt, pepper, and a teaspoonful of vinegar ; add the beetroot cut into small pieces and one cupful of milk or stock, thicken with flour, and serve very hot.

355. BEETROOT SAVOURY

Fry a large onion in rings ; cut up a boiled beetroot in large dice. When the onion begins to colour, add the beetroot, pepper and salt, and three tablespoonfuls of tarragon vinegar. Serve very hot.

356. BEETROOT STEWED, No. I

Make some thickened stock very hot on the fire ; add a small parboiled and skinned beetroot cut in thin slices, a spoonful of vinegar, and some pepper and salt. Let all boil until the beet is tender, but not mashed at all—about one hour. Serve very hot.

357. BEETROOT, STEWED, No. II

Take two medium-sized cooked beetroots ; peel and cut them into dice. Put them in a saucepan with just enough hot water to cover them (about one pint), add a little salt and pepper ; let them stew slowly for fifteen minutes. Mix one tablespoonful of cornflour smooth in a little cold water, and put this, with one ounce of fat, to the beetroot, stirring well until the cornflour thickens. Serve it in a heated vegetable-dish, and sprinkle over it one teaspoonful of chopped parsley.

358. BRUSSELS SPROUTS, LYONS

Cook and well drain one pound of Brussels sprouts. Fry one tablespoonful of minced Spanish onions in one ounce fat ; when this is a golden colour, add the sprouts ; toss them in the pan for three minutes, and serve very hot.

359. CABBAGE, PIEDMONT

Boil or steam one pound of cabbage. Drain, press, and let it get cold. Cook, separately from this, eight ounces of mild onions ; let them get cold. Grease a baking-dish, sprinkle it with minced parsley. Shred in the cabbage and onions in alternate layers of each, with a seasoning of salt and pepper to each layer, a few little bits of fat here and there, and a thin layer of grated cheese. When the dish is nearly full, moisten the mixture with stock (taking care not to make it too wet) till it is level with the top of dish. Brush the top with a little melted fat, cook in moderate oven for about half an hour, and serve when thoroughly hot.

' 360. CABBAGE (RED) FLEMISH, No. I

Shred the cabbage very finely, put into a saucepan with a piece of dripping for each cabbage, two large onions, two apples cut in slices, a spoonful of stock or water, a spoonful of vinegar, pepper, salt, and Demerara sugar. Cover and well boil at least three hours. When the cabbage is soft, stir with a wooden spoon ; mix well ; if necessary, add more sugar. Strain before serving.

361. CABBAGE (RED FLEMISH), No. II

Cut one large or two small red cabbage in quarters; boil them with an onion cut up, two cloves, salt, pepper, and a bay leaf for an hour and a half. Strain the cabbage, and place with some fat in a casserole in the oven for five minutes. Serve very hot.

362. CABBAGE (RED) FRICASSEE

Stew a large red cabbage in some stock until nearly done; there must only be enough stock to keep it from burning. Drain it, cut the cabbage in thick slices, and fry with two onions cut in rings, and either two tomatoes or a tablespoonful of tomato sauce.

363. CARROT PATTIES

Clean, slice, and boil three medium carrots in slightly salted water until soft enough to mince. Have ready two ounces of (hot) boiled rice, add salt, pepper, and nutmeg to taste, and half a teaspoonful each of curry powder and of meat extract. Blend thoroughly and heat up gently. Meanwhile prepare some potato shortcrust (see p. 162), roll out nearly an inch thick, and line some greased patty-pans. The crust should be pricked with a fork before you put in the carrot mixture. Sprinkle each patty with a very little grated cheese, and place in a hottish oven for twenty minutes or so.

364. CARROTS, STEWED

Slice the carrots in rings thinly, simmer in weak stock or water; when nearly soft, shake in one tablespoonful of flour, add a chopped onion, one tablespoonful of chopped parsley, salt to taste, and a very small piece of fat; simmer together till it thickens, pour in a vegetable dish and serve. The water or stock should only be sufficient just to cover the carrots.

365. CARROTS À LA VICHY

Take some young carrots (or if old ones be used they must first be parboiled) and slice them, then put them in a pan

K

with sufficient water to cover them, allowing half an ounce
of salt, one ounce of sugar, and two ounces of fat to the pint
of water, and let them boil up sharply till the water has
almost entirely evaporated, then serve sprinkled with chopped
parsley.

366. CELERY FRITTERS

This is a method of using the green parts of celery—young
leaves and green stalks—which are generally discarded as
uneatable. Wash them and mince them very finely ; about
a breakfastcupful of chopped celery will be enough. Make a
thick batter with one egg, one pint of flour, one teaspoonful
of baking-powder, salt and pepper to taste, and enough milk
to moisten the mixture ; add in the celery, and put large
tablespoonfuls of the batter into boiling fat. Fry a golden
brown, drain, and serve.

367. COLCANNON

Boil separately an equal amount of potatoes, of fresh
cabbage, and about half the amount of onion. Mash all very
finely, mix well together, with a little butter or dripping,
salt, and pepper, put in a buttered bowl and bake, well covered
up. Serve very hot.

368. COLD SLAW

This is a very popular American dish. Take half an ounce
of fat and half a tumblerful of vinegar ; warm them in a lined
pan, and shred in a tender cabbage, only using the heart.
Add a pinch of salt, two pinches of celery seed, and two
dessertspoonfuls of flour. Let the slaw simmer for a few
minutes, then add a lightly beaten egg and stir it well in.
When the mixture has cooked about five minutes longer,
take it off. To be eaten cold.

369. DARIOLES, SAVOURY

Take one breakfastcupful of soaked and drained bread-
scraps, and mix well with the following ; one medium boiled
onion finely minced or grated, one teaspoonful finely-minced

parsley, pepper and salt to taste, two (dried) beaten eggs, a little fat of some sort, and a little milk to moisten. Have ready some greased dariole tins ; half fill with the mixture ; place in good oven for about twenty-five minutes.

370. GIPSY PIE

Cut some cold boiled potatoes in slices about a quarter of an inch thick and arrange these in layers in a well-greased pie-dish with a little salt, pepper, finely minced parsley, boiled onion chopped small, and tiny bits of fat, between each layer. When the dish is sufficiently full, and the potatoes on top arranged as evenly as possible, brush over the surface with dripping, and bake in a moderate oven until the pie is bubbling hot and well browned. If you have it, a little finely chopped meat of some kind, pleasantly seasoned and moistened with good gravy or sauce, may be placed between the layers of potatoes, and the whole covered in the usual way with crust of well-made potato pastry. Some brown gravy, or a well-flavoured sauce is a great improvement to a gipsy pie, in the opinion of some people, while others prefer it without.

371. HARICOTS, BOILED

Soak one pound of haricots overnight. Have two good-sized onions cut up in rings, and browned in one teaspoonful of fat. Put the haricots to this ; add enough cold water to cover them, and let them simmer slowly for two and a half hours, or until tender. Season with pepper and salt and pour into a hot dish.

372. HARICOT MINCE

Soak half a pint of haricots overnight. Boil with a little chopped onion, until quite tender ; drain. Add to these any scraps you have got ; odds and ends of cooked vegetables, of crusts, etc. ; and seasoning of pepper, salt, nutmeg, sage, parsley, etc. Mix well, and put the whole lot through the mincer. Then place in a greased pie-dish and bake. The more scraps you put into this, the better it will be. A few

little bits of fat should be strewn on the top.   If cocoa butter
be used, the seasoning employed should disguise its flavour.

373. HARICOT MOULD

Soak half a pint of haricots overnight ;   place in salted
boiling water, let boil two and a half hours ;   drain.   Have
ready in a frying pan half an ounce of minced onion, and a
teaspoonful of minced mixed herbs, browned in one ounce
of fat, to this add the haricots, with half an ounce of maize
flour, pepper and salt to taste, one tablespoonful of minced
chutney (any sort) and half a gill of stock (any sort, but
preferably meat stock).   Let simmer twenty minutes ;   then
put in half a gill more stock, and continue to simmer till
it is absorbed.   Add half an ounce of fat and half a teaspoonful of mixed spice.   Blend thoroughly, and rub all through a
sieve.   Place in a mould that has been rinsed with cold water,
pressing the mixture well in.   When cold, unmould and serve.

374. HARICOT STEW

Soak half a pound of haricots overnight ;   drain, and boil.
They should be done in about one and a half hours.   Drain
and cool.   Have one ounce of fat browned in a pan, with a
little minced parsley.   Add the beans, let cook a quarter of
an hour.   Put in one tablespoonful of tomato sauce, pepper
and salt to taste, and a glass of white wine.   Mix well,
simmer for five minutes ;   serve at once.

375. IRISH HOT POT

One pound of potatoes, one pound of onions, half a pound
of good cheese.   Slice potatoes, ditto onions, ditto cheese,
and fry them separately.   Then line a dish with potato and
fill it with onions mixed with cheese, pepper, salt and sage.
Cover with the potato to form crust.   Bake.   To be eaten
very hot.   If left, the cheese will get hard.

376. LENTILS, BOILED

Soak a pint of lentils overnight in slightly salted water ;
leave them soaking till wanted, then place them in slightly

salted boiling water, and let cook until tender but not broken.
Fry a good-sized onion brown in a little salad oil, in a stewpan,
add a teaspoonful of flour, then put in a breakfastcupful of
stock (any sort). Boil slowly, stirring well. Then strain the
lentils (keep the water they were cooked in, for stock), and
put them in the pan, with a little salt and pepper. Let cook
gently for three or four minutes ; serve on a hot dish at once.

377. LENTILS, CURRIED

Soak half a pound of lentils overnight (twenty-four hours
is not too long) in a pint of water. Place them, water and
all, in a saucepan ; when they boil, take out half a teacupful
or so of the liquor, and mix smooth a thin paste, with a
dessertspoonful each of curry powder and of flour, and one
cube of Oxo or similar meat extract. Put this mixture back
to the lentils, mix well, and let simmer until thoroughly tender.
Serve with plain boiled rice.

378. LENTIL CUTLETS

Have one pound of lentils soaked overnight, and gently
stewed next day until tender, with just enough water to
cover them. Have a beetroot minced very small, a large
onion chopped and fried, one tablespoonful of minced parsley,
one teaspoonful of minced thyme ; pepper and salt to taste ;
two tablespoonfuls of ketchup (any kind), one ounce of dripping or other fat. Mix all above thoroughly well, bind
with one and a half (dried) beaten eggs, set aside to cool.
Shape into cutlets ; egg and flour ; fry in boiling fat or oil.

379. LENTIL MOUSSE

Soak half a pint of lentils overnight ; place in boiling salted
water, enough to cover them ; add two cloves. Boil until
tender enough to sieve, first draining off the water. When
cool, add one and a half dried eggs, a little salt and pepper,
a pinch of curry powder, and a gill of milk. Blend thoroughly,
place in a greased mould, put a greased paper on top, and
steam for an hour.

Minced onion and parsley can be added if liked.

380. LENTILS AND RICE FRITTERS

Soak half a pound of rice and half a pound of lentils over-night. Tie up loosely in butter-muslin, and place in salted boiling water. The cloth will have to be tied higher up as the rice and lentils swell. When they cease to expand, remove them and leave them to cool, still tied up. In about two hours they should be cold. Take them from the cloth, when a solid mass will be found. Cut this into thin slices, which should be dusted with pepper, salt, and powdered herbs, and fry.

381. LENTIL AND POTATO PATTIES

Make half a pint of onion sauce (using stock in which macaroni or rice has been boiled, instead of milk), and mix with it one breakfastcupful of cooked lentils, one teaspoonful of finely minced parsley, salt and pepper to taste. Make a potato shortcrust (see pp. 162–3) and line some patty-tins ; bake, and fill with the hot lentil mixture. Serve at once.

382. LENTILS, POTTED

Take about half a pound of lentils, rather more than less. Simmer them in a muslin bag until tender, in stock or water. When they are soft, beat them to a pulp in a basin, or pulp them through a sieve ; and while they are hot, add one tablespoonful of fat, half a teaspoonful of powdered or finely chopped sage, a piled tablespoonful of drained soaked bread, salt and pepper. Mix thoroughly well and bake slowly for about an hour in a greased pie-dish. Keep the water for stock.

383. LENTIL PURÉE

Soak one pound of lentils overnight. Drain them, and place in salted boiling water or stock, with a sliced onion, four or five cloves, and one ounce of fat bacon. In an hour and a half they should be tender enough to serve. Add pepper and salt, and dilute with stock of any sort to the consistency desired. Re-heat and serve.

384. LENTIL SAUSAGES

Soak eight ounces of lentils overnight; next day boil till tender enough to mash. Add three pounds of boiled and mashed potatoes, one onion chopped (and fried, if possible), pepper and salt to taste. Let the mixture cool; shape into sausages, drop into milk and flour or oatmeal; fry.

385. LENTILS, STEWED

Soak one pound of lentils overnight; place them in one quart of salted boiling water. Boil quietly until nearly tender. Have ready a little chopped onion and parsley, brown them in a saucepan with one ounce of fat and a teaspoonful of anchovy essence. Add the lentils, pour in enough stock to cover them, and stew until the lentils are quite done.

MAIZE OR SWEET CORN, GREEN

Even as its grains are much larger and of a different formation to those of other cereals, so, when cooked green, the taste of maize is of a pleasant sweetness, quite unlike any other flavour one can recall.

Strip off the husk to the inner layer, and remove the "silk"; then replace the inner layer, and tie it at the top end. In some cases, separate the grains from the cob; but this is only necessary where indicated. Short thick ears are the best.

386. MAIZE, BAKED

Prepare as above; smear the cobs with softened fat, dust them with pepper and salt, place them in a baking-dish in a hot oven, turning and basting them so that they may brown all over.

387. MAIZE, BOILED, No. I

Prepare as above, and place in boiling water, *not* salted. Boil fast for at least fifteen minutes. Serve with fat, salt, and pepper, or with white sauce or Sauce Hollandaise.

388. MAIZE, BOILED, No. II

Pare off stems, remove leaves and silk from six sound,
tender ears of green corn.   Boil in a saucepan three quarts
of water, one gill of milk, one tablespoonful of salt, and half
an ounce of fat, then plunge in the corn and boil twenty-
five minutes.   Lift up, thoroughly drain, dress on a hot dish
and serve, enveloped in a napkin, with a little melted butter
separately.

389. MAIZE, ROASTED

Cut off the stalks, remove the leaves and silk from six
ears of fresh, sound, green corn, place them in a saucepan
with two quarts of water, one gill of milk, and a teaspoonful
of salt, and boil for twenty minutes only.   Lift up with a
skimmer, drain on a cloth, then place them on a tin ; lightly
baste with a little melted fat ; then set them in a brisk oven
until a nice golden colour, being careful to turn them once
in a while.   Remove, dress on a hot dish, envelop in a
napkin, and serve.

390. MAIZE SAUTÉ (CRÉOLE)

Cut away stalks, remove leaves and silk from six fresh,
sound, white ears of green corn, then with back of a knife-
blade detach from the cobs.   Heat a tablespoonful of oil
in a frying-pan, add one finely chopped small white onion.
Nicely brown three minutes, add corn, and fry eight minutes,
occasionally tossing meanwhile ; add two finely chopped,
peeled, red tomatoes.   Season with half a teaspoonful of salt
and half a teaspoonful of sugar ; toss well, and cook eight
minutes, lightly mixing meanwhile.   Dress on a vegetable
dish, and serve.

391. MAIZE, STEWED

Thoroughly drain a pint tin of corn, then place in a small
frying-pan with a gill of milk and half an ounce of fat,
season with half a teaspoonful of salt, two saltspoonfuls of
white pepper, and half a saltspoonful of grated nutmeg.

Gently mix, and let slowly cook for eight minutes. Remove, pour into a vegetable dish, and serve.

392. NETTLES, BOILED

Take young nettle shoots, wash and drain well, place in boiling salted water. Boil twenty to twenty-five minutes. Drain and chop ; return to pan and thicken with a little fat, a little flour (two teaspoonfuls to the pound) and stock ; season with salt and pepper ; serve very hot.

393. NETTLES, FRIED

Wash the young nettle-tops thoroughly in salted water. Put into a very little boiling water, salted ; some people add a pinch of soda bicarbonate. Boil fast for thirty minutes ; then squeeze dry, chop, season, and make into small flat cakes (using a little sieved potato to bind the nettles if need be). Fry, and serve with fried eggs.

394. NETTLE PUDDING

Take half a gallon of young nettle-tops, wash them thoroughly. Clean, prepare, and chop one good-sized onion or leek, one broccoli head, or the same bulk in Brussels sprouts, and two ounces of rice. Mix all well with the nettles, season, tie them up in a muslin bag, and place in salted boiling water. Boil till all is thoroughly cooked, and serve with a little good gravy.

395. NETTLES, STEWED

(Only very young nettle-tops must be used.) Wash one pound of nettle-tops very thoroughly ; boil and chop them up. Place in a stewpan in which one tablespoonful of barley flour has been browned in two ounces of fat, and a teacupful of stock added. Mix well, stew till re-heated, and serve.

Nettles may also be cooked exactly like spinach. They should be picked first thing in the morning.

396. ONION PIE

Take four Spanish onions, peel and slice ; boil in salted water for five minutes ; place in a casserole with two ounces of fat. When they are nearly soft, take them out; have ready sufficient sliced parboiled potatoes to fill the casserole in alternate layers with the onions. You must begin with potatoes at the bottom, and end with potatoes at the top. Season each layer well with salt and pepper, cover, and bake for an hour or so in a moderate oven.

397. ONIONS, SAVOURY

Put four peeled Spanish onions into salted boiling water; cook for five minutes; then put into a casserole, with one ounce of fat, and let cook slowly until quite soft. Take out the inside of each onion so as to leave a firm outer shell, and mince finely what you have removed; then mix it well with two ounces of either mashed potato, boiled rice, cooked porridge, or semolina—one ounce each of fat and of grated cheese, salt and pepper to taste. Moisten with a little stock. Fill the onion shells with this mixture, replace them in the casserole, and reheat through. Serve at once.

398. ONIONS, SUPPER

Peel and wash eight or ten large onions, throw them into a large saucepan of boiling water with two ounces of salt; let the onions boil one hour exactly—take them up with a wooden spoon on to a flat dish, put an inverted pie-dish over, and drain the water away. Serve with potatoes baked in their skins.

399. PARSNIP PIE

Take cooked parsnips (hot) and mash them up with a little fat, pepper and salt. Let them go cold; then mix with minced parsley to taste, and cold cooked rice, and any vegetables (chopped or sieved) left over; place in a pie-dish, moisten with stock or gravy, and cover with a potato crust.

400. PEAS, GREEN, À LA FRANÇAISE

Put one pint of shelled green peas into a casserole or pan containing half a pint of boiling water; add one teaspoonful of sugar, and pepper and salt to taste; a head of cabbage lettuce, a spray of parsley, and four or five tiny onions. Let boil for thirty minnutes; remove the lettuce and parsley (which can be used for some other dish, such as Haricot Stew, or Parsnip Pie, or for soup), and put half an ounce of fat to the peas. Let simmer slowly for five minutes; pour off contents of pan into heated vegetable dish, and serve immediately.

401. PEAS, JUGGED

This is one of the best ways to cook peas, whether fresh, dried green, tinned, or bottled. Shell a pint of peas, put them into a clean two-pound pickle-bottle or any jar with a closely fitting top, adding a tablespoonful of fat, a teaspoonful of powdered sugar, a saltspoonful of salt, a dozen mint leaves, and, at discretion, a very little black pepper. Cover the vessel tightly, and immerse it, to the extent of half its depth, in a pan of boiling water. Set the latter on the fire and boil briskly. Examine in half an hour; the peas, if very young, should be done by then; if old, they will of course take longer.

402. GREEN PEAS PUDDING, No. I

Have half a pint of shelled peas boiled and sieved, and mixed with four ounces of sieved cooked potato. Add salt and pepper to taste, a teaspoonful of finely-minced onion, and one ounce of fat. Mix thoroughly; bind with a dried egg; place in a greased pie-dish, and bake for thirty minutes.

403. GREEN PEAS PUDDING, No. II

Make a batter with a breakfastcupful of flour, two breakfastcupfuls of milk, one (dried) egg, salt and pepper, a pinch of powdered mint, and one teaspoonful baking-powder) Add to this, half a pint of cooked peas (either fresh or tinned. pour into a greased pie-dish, and bake until well set and slightly browned.

404. PEAS PUDDING

Soak for twenty-four hours a quart of dried peas, tie them rather loosely into a cloth, put them down in cold water to boil slowly till tender—good peas will take at least two hours and a half. Rub through a sieve, adding a dried egg, an ounce of fat, some pepper and salt, and beat them well for about ten minutes. Flour the cloth, and tie the pudding tight as possible, and boil an hour longer.

SALADS

405. APPLE SALAD

Two cupfuls of sour apple, half a cupful of celery, half a cupful of blanched walnuts, four tablespoonfuls of salad dressing, one teaspoonful of sugar. Salt and pepper on nuts.

406. DANDELION SALAD

Very young dandelion shoots should be used. Wash well and shred finely; add a very little finely-minced onion and mint. Mix a little brown sugar with vinegar containing a pinch of raw mustard; pour some of the liquor over the dandelions, enough to moisten; serve immediately.

407. HARICOT SALAD

One pint of white haricots, well boiled. Sprinkle over them one teaspoonful of salt and half a teaspoonful of pepper; add a very finely chopped onion or a few drops of shallot vinegar, one tablespoonful of vinegar, two tablespoonfuls of oil, and a sprinkling of very finely chopped parsley.

408. NUT, CRESS, AND CELERY SALAD

Take a shallow bowl, and arrange watercress in a wreath around the centre. Put inside this some finely sliced celery, and in the very middle put some skinned and thinly cut walnuts. Pour over this a salad dressing. Thin slices or cubes of apple may be added at discretion. Lemon juice should be squeezed on apple to keep it white.

409. TOMATO SALAD

Take some good ripe tomatoes, cut them into slices with a sharp knife, lay them in a salad bowl with a few finely

sliced rings of Spanish onion or a dozen young spring onions.
Season with pepper and salt and a pinch of sugar, sprinkle
with chopped parsley, and pour a salad dressing over.

Add, at pleasure, thin slices of cold cooked potato, a few
chopped capers, or a little grated cheese.

410. VEGETABLE SALAD, MIXED

Take half a pint each of shelled broad beans and of peas,
cook, and drain, and add to them one breakfastcupful of
parsley sauce, well seasoned. Let the whole go cold. Have
a glass bowl lined with very thinly sliced alternate cucumber
and beetroot ; put in a few spring onions very finely minced.
Add the beans, etc., and (at pleasure) use radishes, mustard
and cress, for garnishing.

411. VEGETABLE SALAD, COLD COOKED

The remains of a cold cauliflower, pulled into small heads ;
a small carrot sliced finely ; a teacupful of haricot beans
or green peas ; thin slices of cold potato ; any scraps of cheese
which can be grated. Arrange symmetrically and pour a
dressing over.

412. WINTER SALAD, No I

Take some white haricot beans, French beans, potatoes,
beetroot, and onions. Blanch all the vegetables separately,
cool, and drain them. Chop the onions, and put them
in the corner of a cloth ; dip this in cold water, and press the
water out of the onion. Do this two or three times, which
will render the onion more digestible. Cut the potatoes
and beetroots in half-inch discs. Put all into a salad-bowl,
adding some chopped chervil ; season with salt, pepper, oil,
and vinegar, and mix the whole well.

413. WINTER SALAD, No. II

Take a stick of celery and a little endive, cut and shred
them up in short pieces ; mix in two tablespoonfuls of russet
apples cut in dice after peeling and coring. Cover these

with half a pound of grated nuts of any kind, and pour a thick dressing over all.

Note.—A large number of other salads will be found in the "Vegetable Book" of this series.

414. SIMPLE SALAD DRESSING

Blend equal quantities (say a quarter of a teaspoonful each) of salt, pepper, and dry mustard. Add one dessert-spoonful each of oil and of vinegar, and one tablespoonful of milk. When these are thoroughly mixed, stir in one tablespoonful of honey.

415. SWEDES, MASHED

Take two pound of swedes; wash and peel them, and slice. Boil for an hour; then drain, mash and season with salt and pepper, and add two teaspoonfuls of fat and a tea-cupful of milk (or any sort of stock). Beat thoroughly, heat up again; serve at once.

416. SUCCOTASH, No. I

Have green maize freshly cut, and take the cobs cleanly out of the outer leaves, etc. ; add an equal quantity of soaked butter or haricot beans. Put them into a saucepan with only just enough water to cover them ; let them stew till perfectly tender, then pour off the water, and pour in the same amount of milk. Let the vegetables stew a little more, then add pepper and salt and a teaspoonful of cornflour mixed smooth in a little cold milk, and a lump of fat about as big as a large walnut. Mix well, let all boil up once, and serve very hot.

417. SUCCOTASH, No. II

Scrape, wash, and score in quarter-inch slices a quarter of a pound of salt pork. Cover with boiling water, and let simmer five or six hours, or until nearly tender ; add one pint of freshly shelled Lima beans, and more water, if needed. When the beans become tender, add one pint of grated (green) maize pulp. Cook about fifteen minutes, and add two tablespoonfuls of fat, and salt if needed. Pour the succotash into the serving-dish, slice the pork according to its scorings, and serve at once. This dish is particularly good prepared with dried beans and either dried or tinned corn. If dried vegetables be used, let soak overnight in cold water. To remove the pulp from the ears of corn without the hull, with a sharp knife cut down through the centre of each row of kernels, then with the back of the knife press out the pulp, leaving the husk on the cob. For a change, add a cup of reduced tomato pulp, seasoning accordingly; or an onion may be cooked with the beans, and removed before the dish is sent to table.

418. TOMATOES WITH SAVOURY CUSTARD

Mix together one pint of tomatoes (tinned), one-fourth of a cup of soaked drained bread, one tablespoonful of finely-chopped onion, one teaspoonful of sugar, and salt and pepper to taste; pour into a greased baking-dish. Beat two dried eggs, add half a teaspoonful of salt, a teaspoonful of sugar, and a cup and a half of milk; pour over the tomato mixture, and bake in a slow oven until set (about three-quarters of an hour).

419. VEGETABLE CURRY, No. I

Take some boiled and sliced carrots and turnips, some cooked peas, French beans, little squares of cooked vegetable marrow, some cauliflower or broccoli—in fact, any cold cooked vegetables which may be to hand. Place them in a stewpan with a little dripping, and put on the edge of the stove, so that the dripping may be melting and the vegetables warming, while the curry sauce is prepared. For the sauce, fry two sliced onions, then mix with them one dessertspoonful of curry-powder, and fry for two minutes. Pour into the stewpan three-quarters of a pint of stock and cook until the onion is quite tender. Mix one dessertspoonful of arrow-root with some water to a paste; stir into the sauce, and simmer for eight to ten minutes. Add five or six drops of

lemon juice. Pour on to the vegetables, stir gently, make
thoroughly hot, and serve in the centre of a wall of boiled
rice.

420. VEGETABLE CURRY, No. II

Cut onions into thin slices, and fry a good brown ; add
breakfastcupful of stock in which a teaspoonful of curry has
been mixed. Let all boil together for twenty minutes, stirring
the whole time ; then add the vegetables—previously parboiled—and let all simmer for an hour. Potatoes, peas,
beans, carrots, and turnips may be used. Broad beans
alone make a delicious curry.

421. VEGETABLE FISH, No. I

Boil one breakfastcupful of milk ; thicken it with two
ounces of ground rice. Add salt, pepper, a pinch of mace,
one small minced or grated onion, and a little fat of some
sort. Mix well, and let cook, stirring often, for ten minutes.
Have ready three boiled potatoes, pass them through ricer,
stir them at once into rice, turn out the mixture on a dish
to set cold. Then cut in slices, egg and flour them, fry.
Serve with anchovy sauce, parsley sauce, or sauce piquante.

422. VEGETABLE FISH, No II

Boil a quarter of a pound of ground rice in one pint of
mixed milk and water ; then add two potatoes boiled and
mashed, one saltspoonful of mace, about one teaspoonful
of pulped onion or onion juice. Mix all pretty stiff, and
spread it out to cool, about one inch thick. When cold, cut
it in slices, breadcrumb and fry it, and serve with a sharp
sauce.

423. VEGETABLE GOOSE

Soak and well drain any scraps of bread. Season with
salt and pepper and one teaspoonful of powdered, or finely-
minced fresh sage. Add one tablespoonful of barley flour,
and mix all well with two tablespoonfuls of milk. Put into a
greased baking-tin, strew plentifully with shredded dripping

or other fat ; place in good oven for twenty minutes or so. Remove from tin, cut into squares, pile on a hot dish ; serve with onions or leeks, or with apple sauce.

424. VEGETABLE RAGOÛT

Take the remains of cooked vegetables, the larger the variety the better, and cut them into small pieces, then season these pleasantly with salt and pepper and put them in a well-greased stewpan ; toss them over the fire for a minute or two, after which moisten them with a little gravy, or some suitable sauce, and allow them to get thoroughly hot, giving the pan a gentle shake every now and then to prevent them burning or sticking to the bottom. Do not stir during the process of reheating, as the ragoût presents a much more dainty appearance if the vegetables are kept unbroken. When thoroughly hot, pile up the ragoût in the centre of a well-heated dish, and serve at once.

425. VEGETABLE TURKEY

Have one pound of lentils soaked overnight, and boiled next day until tender. Grease a pie-dish, and line it throughout with lentils. Have ready a turkey stuffing, which can have dried eggs substituted for fresh ones, and any other fat for suet. Place it so as to fill the rest of the dish, and put the remainder of the lentils on top. Strew with a few bits of fat, and bake three-quarters of an hour or longer. To be served at once.

426. VEGETABLE MARROW, STUFFED

Cut off a thick slice from the top of a young marrow, and scoop out the seeds ; stuff the inside with any forcemeat most convenient or merely breadcrumbs and herbs. Rub a saucepan or casserole with a blade of garlic, and, when you have put on the top which was cut off the marrow, lay it carefully in the pan (it should only just fit), pour upon it half a pint of stock, and add herbs, pepper, salt, and a little bit of onion or a clove of garlic ; lastly, a tablespoonful of

L

vinegar. Cover the pan closely, and let the marrow simmer slowly for two hours. Dish up carefully, and pour the sauce through a strainer over the marrow.

427. VEGETABLE MARROW MOCK WHITEBAIT

Parboil a medium-sized vegetable marrow; cut it up into slices about the size of whitebait ; roll these on a floured cloth ; get them as dry as possible. Have ready a pan of boiling fat, deep enough to cover the slices completely ; fry them a golden brown. Drain them, pile them on a paper serviette. Serve with sliced lemon (or salad dressing).

CHAPTER VII

CEREALS

UNDER this heading are included those invaluable articles of food, most of which are the staple diet—sometimes almost the only diet—of whole nations.

Maize or Indian corn, with its preparations, hominy, semolina, maize-meal, flaked maize, etc. ; wheaten preparations, such as macaroni, vermicelli, wheat semolina, etc. ; oaten preparations, oatmeal, oatflour, rolled oats, etc. ; rice, rice flour, flaked rice, etc. ; barley preparations ; and for purposes of convenience I will add sago and tapioca (although as a matter of fact, sago is the pith of a palm, and tapioca is the hardened juice of the cassava tree). There are also Force, Grapenuts, and a variety of similar proprietary articles.

In these islands we have never used cereals to a thousandth part of their food value ; partly, I think, because they require a little more trouble in cooking successfully than the average person cares to give. But now we shall be only too glad to fall back on them. The bother is, so many of them come from overseas. The beautiful macaroni and spaghetti that we used to buy so cheaply, we shall very likely never see again. It was made of Rumanian wheat from the Danubian provinces, which has a peculiarly glutinous quality. We are now having to make shift with Canadian and Japanese macaroni, spaghetti, vermicelli, etc. ; " and good they are, but not the best."

The main value of cereals lies in their starch and fat. One does not associate fat with these dry things, but it is present, especially in maize and oatmeal.

As the food value of bread and of potatoes mainly consists

in starch, it is as well to know what excellent substitutes for bread and potatoes can be provided, if need be, by other materials.

	Per cent. starch.		Per cent. starch.		Per cent. starch.
Sugar	.. 98	Oatmeal .. 60		Green Fruit	
Tapioca, Sago,		Peas, Beans,		and Beans	17
Arrowroot	85	Lentils (dried)	60	Bananas	14
Rice	.. 79	Dried Fruits	60	Fresh Fruit	12
Flour	.. 75	Treacle	.. 55	Milk	.. 5
Barley Meal	73	Bread	.. 57	Nuts	.. 5
Maize	.. 66	Potatoes	.. 21		

So, you see, three pounds of potatoes are equivalent in starch food value to one pound of bread.

But three-quarters of a pound of tapioca, sago, arrowroot, or rice; or one pound of oatmeal, beans, peas, or lentils, are equivalent in starch food value to one pound of bread.

And you can get the equivalent of one pound of potatoes in four ounces each of either rice, sago, tapioca, or arrowroot; or in five ounces each of either maize, barley meal, oatmeal, beans, peas or lentils.

Add to this, the amazing increase in bulk and weight of *cooked* cereals (three ounces of rice, for instance, will expand to one pound by the time it has absorbed enough water to cook it. See "Mixture Breads" in Chapter IX.), and you will perceive how enormously valuable cereals are.

But they *must* be well soaked and cooked to be digestible, and well seasoned and flavoured to be palatable.

In the case of hominy, soaking overnight is necessary; pearl barley should also be soaked (boiling water poured on it) for at least two hours before cooking. The actual boiling should not be scamped; and in every instance, you should use a double-boiler or its equivalent—a jam-pot standing in a pan of boiling water—unless you are prepared to stir all the time, or risk having your preparation stuck to the pan and burned.

Cereals are the only valid substitute—of sorts—for bread and for potatoes. There are many which we hardly know in England, such as millet, buckwheat, and rye (the latter is very little used), but which might well be included in our bills of fare. The recipes in this chapter only refer to cereals used in *salt* or savoury form. You will find them in *sweet* form in the chapter on puddings (No. VIII.) and on Bread and Cakes (No. IX.). Porridge, which is eaten by some with salt and by others with sweetening, figures here in considerable variety.

Vermicelli is like a baby macaroni—very minute tubes. It may be used for anything for which one uses macaroni.

Semolina is employed very largely for that popular Italian and Spanish dish, polenta. It is highly nourishing and (properly flavoured) most palatable. We mostly are acquainted with it only as a nursery pudding.

For further particulars and recipes regarding cereals, I will refer you to Chaps. VIII. and IX. ; I advise you to do all you can with these cheap and invaluable foods.

PORRIDGES

Note.—Porridge, for many, is an indispensable article of breakfast. Many others take it for lunch, and in the country it is frequently a supper dish. The above usually means oatmeal porridge, or rolled oats in one of the proprietary forms.

Oatmeal porridge is very nutritious ; slightly too blood-heating for some people ; can be eaten with either sugar (or treacle) or salt, the latter being the Irish method ; and, when milk is plentiful, can be made with milk instead of water, which of course doubles its nutritive quality. It has two drawbacks :

(*a*) That it really requires *some* milk along with it ; and milk is so very scarce just now.

(*b*) That it often " stodges you " at the time of eating,

and leaves an amazing void about two hours later, so that you feel as if you had had no breakfast.

I don't know how to remedy these disqualifications.

However, remember, in making porridge:

(1) That it is best to use a double saucepan, or else a big jam-pot placed in a saucepan of boiling water, with two pieces of wood to rest the pot on, so that the water can get all round it, otherwise you will have to keep on stirring all the time.

(2) That the water must be boiling fast before the meal (whatever it is) goes in.

(3) That the meal should not be shoved or shot in *en masse*, but gradually sprinkled in, a very little at a time.

(4) That a pinch of salt improves the flavour of anything and—I may say—everything.

(5) That unless the porridge is properly cooked enough, it is worse than useless—because it will disagree with you vilely.

(6) That unless you serve it very hot, it is a most unappetising affair.

This last clause particularly refers to oatmeal porridge which has been cooked overnight and re-heated. Rolled oats are much more quickly prepared.

There are, however, a number of other porridges, including the "corn-mush" or maize-meal porridge so popular in Canada and the U.S.A. I give recipes for some of these.

428. SCOTCH OATMEAL PORRIDGE

Put three breakfastcupfuls (one and a half pints) of boiling water into a double saucepan, with half a teaspoonful of salt. Let it boil again, then sprinkle in one breakfastcupful of coarse oatmeal very gradually. Do this with your *left* hand, so that you may stir continually with your right; the handle not the bowl of a wooden spoon should be used. Be sure to get the mixture quite smooth by stirring well and brushing out lumps. When the porridge boils, cover it up and let it boil gently for two hours. It may require more (boiling) water.

NOTE.—Any cold cooked porridge can be utilised for stuffing or forcemeat (instead of breadcrumbs) for cakes (mixed with barley flour enough to stiffen), and for " cutlets." Maizemeal porridge is practically the same as polenta.

429. BARLEY PORRIDGE

Have ready one pint of salted boiling water ; throw in two tablespoonfuls of pearl barley and one of oatmeal, and boil for one hour. Then mix into this four tablespoonfuls of barley kernels, and let cook at least twenty minutes.

430. HOMINY PORRIDGE, No. I

Put eight ounces of hominy to soak overnight in half a pint of water. Next morning, place in a double-boiler with the water it was in, half a pint of milk, and a pinch of salt. It will take about one and a half hours to cook ; so must be used for lunch, not for breakfast. Once cooked, it can be (1) re-heated, (2) sliced and fried, (3) made into puddings, (4) or cakes.

431. HOMINY PORRIDGE, No. II

Soak a teacupful of hominy overnight in a breakfastcupful of cold water. Next day, put on to boil with two break-fastcupfuls of cold water, slightly salted, and boil for one hour.

432. MAIZE (OR INDIAN) MEAL PORRIDGE, No. I (ALSO KNOWN AS CORN-MEAL MUSH)

Put two and a half pints of water into a double-boiler, add one dessertspoonful of salt. When it boils, gradually stir in three teacupfuls of maize-meal, and mix it very smooth. Let it cook for three hours. If to be served for breakfast re-heat next day for half an hour. This porridge, like hominy porridge, can be re-heated in different ways.

It is usually served with syrup or treacle.

433. MAIZE-MEAL PORRIDGE (CORN-MUSH), No. II

Have ready one pint (two breakfastcupfuls) of boiling water, put in a small teaspoonful of salt; sprinkle in, very gradually, two tablespoonfuls of maize-meal. Stir with a wooden spoon while you put the meal in, and continue to boil and stir for half an hour. Unless the mush is in a double-boiler, you will not be able to leave it until the half hour is up, when the pan must be moved to the side of the range for another half hour, but must continue to simmer and move, and will want occasional stirring.

434. MAIZE-MEAL PORRIDGE (CORN-MUSH), No. III

Have ready one pint of fast-boiling water; stir into it four to six tablespoonfuls of maize-meal. Add one teacupful of milk, and salt to taste. Boil until the maize is thoroughly cooked, which should be in about half an hour, but may take an hour.

435. FLAKED MAIZE PORRIDGE

Boil one pint of milk with one tablespoonful of sugar. Sprinkle in three heaped tablespoonfuls of flaked maize, stirring gently all the time, and let boil quietly for twenty minutes.

436. PEASE PORRIDGE

Have one pint of fast-boiling water, sprinkle in two heaped tablespoonfuls of pea-flour; stir well and quickly, get it perfectly smooth. Boil for an hour or more, and season with salt. A lump of dripping or margarine improves it.

437. RICE FLOUR PORRIDGE

Mix two tablespoonfuls of rice flour with half a teacupful of milk-and-water, and pour it into one pint of slightly salted boiling water. Boil for a quarter of an hour, stirring well. A bit of margarine will improve this.

438. ROLLED OATS PORRIDGE

Have ready one pint (two breakfastcupfuls) of boiling water; salt it and sprinkle in 1 breakfastcupful of rolled oats. Stir well, and let boil fast for twenty minutes. More (boiling) water can be added if the porridge gets too thick.

439. SAVOURY PORRIDGE

Have ready one pint of boiling salted water, sprinkle into it three tablespoonfuls of rolled oats; let boil for twenty minutes, stirring now and then. Add a walnut-sized lump of margarine or other fat, and one teaspoonful of any good vegetable extract. Continue to boil and stir for five minutes; season, and serve. A little very finely minced parsley may be added at pleasure.

440. SEMOLINA PORRIDGE

Put two piled tablespoonfuls of fine semolina to soak overnight in one teacupful of water. Next morning, put the semolina into three teacupfuls of cold milk-and-water, and boil for twenty minutes, adding a small pinch of salt.

HOMINY

-NOTE.—Hominy is the coarsest-ground form of maize, as cornflour is the finest, and semolina the medium. Flaked maize (which I have found admirable as a substitute for flour in puddings) is differently prepared, and easier to cook than hominy, etc., it needs no soaking. But hominy must be well soaked overnight before cooking, and well cooked before you can make any use of it. It is very nice for a change.

See previous directions for hominy porridge, which is the basis of the following dishes.

441. HOMINY SAVOURY BALLS

Take a quart of well-boiled hominy while hot, and make it into balls about the size of an orange; roll them in breadcrumbs, then in a beaten dried egg mixed with two tablespoonfuls of cold water. Crumb them again and fry in deep fat and drain well; then roll them in grated cheese, and serve in a hot vegetable dish. Salt and pepper to taste may be added before shaping the balls.

442. HOMINY CHEESE

Stir four ounces of grated cheese into eight ounces of cooked hominy; season with salt and pepper; add minced parsley and minced parboiled onion to taste, and a teaspoonful of fat. Mix thoroughly, place in greased pie-dish, bake for twenty minutes in good oven.

443. HOMINY CUTLETS

Take one breakfastcupful of cooked hominy, with pepper, salt, minced parsley, and a teacupful of drained soaked crusts; add one ounce of creamed fat, and a beaten dried egg. Mix thoroughly, shape into cutlets, dip in milk or stock, dredge with fine oatmeal, fry.

MACARONI

NOTE.—There is not very much variety about the salt and savoury dishes to be made with macaroni. But they are very nourishing, comparatively cheap, and as a rule most easily digested. Of course cheese is an almost invariable ingredient; but a little tomato sauce makes the macaroni appetising, if you have no cheese. Breadcrumbs are often strewed on top; but this is unnecessary. Butter can be done without; so can milk. The macaroni will still be quite nice. Fried chopped bacon is an admirable addition.

444. HOME-MADE MACARONI, No. I

(Macaroni made as below will not keep beyond three or four days.)

Put one pound of barley flour in a basin, make a "well" in it, and put in three beaten eggs, a pinch of salt, and a little tepid water (about three tablespoonfuls), enough to moisten into a dough. Work this well, let stand for five minutes, and cut in half. Roll each half until it is very fine, soft, and pliable; do not roll heavily. Roll out very thin, dust it with flour, and cut with a sharp knife into fine strips. Lay these separately to dry for fifteen minutes. Any other kind of flour can be used if preferred.

445. HOME-MADE MACARONI, No. II

Proceed as above, but when the dough is well worked, cover it up with a cloth, and leave it for about a quarter of an hour ; next, roll out very thin, and place to dry on a cloth for another quarter of an hour. Then dust it with a little semolina, and cut into thin strips. Have boiling salted water ready, and boil twenty-five minutes.

446. MACARONI AND CHEESE

Boil three-quarters of a pound of best macaroni in three quarts of water, with a teaspoonful of salt, for forty minutes. Drain on a sieve, return to the saucepan, season with half a teaspoonful of salt, half a teaspoonful of white pepper, and a saltspoonful of grated nutmeg, adding one ounce of good fat and two ounces of grated cheese ; carefully mix with a fork until well amalgamated, and transfer to a deep dish. Nicely brown a very finely chopped white onion in a frying-pan, with a tablespoonful of butter, for eight minutes, frequently mixing meanwhile ; then pour over macaroni, and serve.

447. MACARONI CURRY

Melt two tablespoonfuls of fat in a lined pan ; cook two slices of onion in it to a light straw colour ; mix in two table spoonfuls of flour, one tablespoonful of curry-powder, a little pepper and salt, and last, very gradually, stir in a breakfast-cupful of milk. When all is boiling smoothly, pour it over one breakfastcupful of macaroni which has been cooked till tender in (salted) boiling water, and afterwards rinsed in cold water. Heat up all again in the pan, and add two tablespoon- fuls of tomato pulp.

448. MACARONI MILANESI

Put one-fourth of a cup of dripping into the frying-pan, and, when melted, sauté in it an onion sliced thin, a stalk of celery cut in cubes, and a sprig of parsley; stir to keep from burning, and when of a golden brown, add a tin of tomato; season with salt and pepper, and let simmer about half an hour, or until the watery juice is evaporated. Meanwhile cook half a pound of macaroni in boiling salted water; let boil about twenty minutes or until tender, but in perfect shape; drain and rinse in cold water, then set in a hot place. Press the tomato sauce through a sieve fine enough to keep back the seeds, but coarse enough to let the pulp pass through (it should be of the consistency of thick cream). Dust a hot platter with Parmesan cheese, cover with macaroni, pour over sauce; add grated cheese, then more macaroni, sauce, and cheese, until all is used; then with a spoon and fork gently turn the macaroni over and over until it is thoroughly mixed with the sauce; add a generous sprinkling of cheese to the top, and serve. Mix quickly, so that the macaroni may be served hot.

449. MACARONI MOCK TRIPE

Put half a pound of macaroni, broken up small, into a saucepan full of boiling water. Let simmer till it is fully swelled and quite tender, which may take one and a half hours. Have ready a Spanish onion, sliced and cooked (in as little water as possible), and kept hot. Boil half a pint of milk and water (in equal parts), put in a walnut-sized lump of fat, and one dessertspoonful of cornflour mixed smooth with a little cold water. Let this thicken for five minutes; add salt and pepper; stir the macaroni and onion into it, and serve at once.

450. MACARONI AND MUSHROOM SAVOURY

Put half a pound of macaroni into boiling salted water, let cook for half an hour. Have ready four ounces of well-cleaned mushrooms, simmered with one ounce of fat and just enough water to cover them, in a casserole for a quarter of an hour. Take half a pint of milk, and take out two tablespoonfuls, which must be mixed smooth with half an ounce of cornflour. Remove the mushrooms from the casserole, and keep them warm ; meanwhile add the milk and the cornflour paste to the liquor in the casserole ; let it boil, and then simmer for five minutes. Have a small onion finely minced, and a rasher of bacon chopped small ; fry them. Grease a deep basin, line it with the macaroni ; put in the mushrooms, bacon, onion, and sauce from the casserole, all thoroughly mixed ; cover with the rest of the macaroni and with a greased paper. Steam for one hour, and serve in the sauce basin. This dish is well worth the extra trouble entailed in making it.

451. MACARONI QUENELLE

One ounce macaroni, four ounces breadcrumbs, two beaten dried eggs, half a pint of milk, one teaspoonful of minced parsley, salt and pepper to taste ; two ounces of fat melted, two tablespoonfuls of minced ham. Boil the macaroni till cooked, cut into small pieces, boil the milk and pour in the breadcrumbs, soak five minutes, then mix all the other ingredients into it. Steam in a well-greased mould for one hour, turn out and serve with either mushroom or caper sauce.

452. MACARONI AND VEGETABLES

Boil four ounces of macaroni in water till tender ; drain and cut into convenient lengths. Boil eight ounces of onions till rather more than three-parts cooked ; drain and slice them. Take eight ounces of tomatoes, dip them a minute into boiling water, then skin and slice them. Butter a pie-dish, dust it with fine breadcrumbs and grated cheese, with a sprinkling of finely minced parsley ; put a bottom layer of the macaroni, moistened with a little milk, and dusted with a little cheese and parsley ; then a layer of onions, and a layer of tomatoes, each similarly moistened and flavoured ; finish up with a layer of macaroni. Stew this with four ounces of grated cheese, three ounces of breadcrumbs, a little minced parsley, and about one ounce of fat broken up small. Put

into a hot oven for twenty minutes or so, to become nicely
and evenly browned.

453. OATMEAL DUMPLINGS

Mix four ounces of grated suet with one breakfastcupful
of fine oatmeal, one minced onion, one dessertspoonful of
minced parsley, salt and pepper to taste. Blend thoroughly
with the fingers ; moisten with cold water until a stiff dough
is obtained. Scald a pudding-cloth, dredge with fine oatmeal,
and put in the dumpling, giving plenty of room for it to expand
to almost twice its size. Place it in a pan of boiling water
and let boil fast for nearly two hours. Serve at once.

454. POLENTA

Boil one quart of fresh milk in an enamelled saucepan ;
add a pinch of salt, and stir in very gradually five or six
ounces of fine semolina. Let boil very gently for about
fifteen minutes, stirring well (or it will stick), till it becomes
a thick paste. Pour this into a greased baking-tin, let it get
cold, then cut it up in fingers ; pile them neatly in a baking-
dish. Pour a little melted fat over, so as to cover each piece,
then cover all with a thin layer of grated cheese, and bake a
golden brown.

455. SEMOLINA CREAM

Have a pint of boiling milk ; add four ounces of semolina,
slightly flavoured with nutmeg ; stir well till it thickens ;
add three ounces of grated cheese, and continue to stir.
When it is very thick, take it off the fire, stir in one beaten
egg, and place it on a dish till cold ; then cut it in slices, pile
it in a baking-dish, cover with grated cheese, sprinkle with
fine crumbs, strew with little bits of fat, and bake to a light
golden brown.

456. SPAGHETTI À L'ITALIENNE

Have ready boiling a pan of three quarts of water, to
which has been added one tablespoonful of salt. Put in,

stirring it gently so as not to break it, one ounce of Italian sphaghetti. Boil twenty-five minutes, and thoroughly drain off the water. Place the spaghetti in a frying-pan, with a full tablespoonful of fat, and one tablespoonful each of salt, pepper, and grated nutmeg. Shuffle and toss gently over the fire for four minutes. Add a bare half pint of hot tomato sauce, mix gently with a fork and add two ounces of grated Parmesan cheese, mix for a minute more, and pour upon a hot dish. Serve at once.

457. VERMICELLI RISSOLES

Boil half a pound of vermicelli in one pint of milk till tender. Mix into this one hard-boiled egg pounded small, two ounces of grated cheese, a little salt, pepper, and nutmeg. Place the mixture on a dish to cool, and subsequently shape it into rissoles; flour, or egg and breadcrumb them, and fry in boiling fat.

RICE

NOTE.—Boiled rice, properly cooked, is a thing one very rarely meets. A stodgy unappetising cannon ball of wet pulp, *tied up in a cloth*, is what the working classes indulge in. I have therefore given a large number of recipes, which vary considerably in detail, but should not vary in result.

Once you have got the well-boiled rice, any rice left over can be used in a number of little ways, to impart variety to other dishes. Mixed with sieved boiled potato, made into balls and fried; with a little minced parsley and onion, pepper and salt, at discretion. Or, flavoured with celery salt, made into potato shapes and served as a vegetable. Or, mixed with slices of hard-boiled egg, and moistened with milk, and flavoured with a hint of anchovy or of grated cheese, baked *au gratin*. There need not be any waste of rice that is properly cooked. It is only the miserable wet stuff that requires to be disguised in various half-hearted ways.

There are several ways of cooking rice, each of which has its own points of merit. " As a rule rice-growing people prefer the rice-grains less tender than do those of Northern climes, just as the Italians prefer macaroni in a state which by many would be called an under-done condition." But soft or not, all wish rice dry. The quantity of liquid that the grain will absorb depends upon the variety of the rice, the season in which it was grown, the time it has been kept, and the liquid used. These things affect, also, the time of cooking. Rice will absorb in cooking from two and a half to four times its bulk of liquid. When three cups of water or thin stock would suffice, three and a half or four cups of milk are required.

Rice must be thoroughly cleaned before cooking. It may be washed in several waters, being rubbed, meanwhile, between the hands, but one of the most satisfactory ways is to blanch rice. Put the rice over a hot fire in a large saucepan of cold water, and stir, occasionally, while it is heating; let it boil five minutes, then drain on a sieve and pass cold water from the top through it. The rice is now beautifully white and clean and the grains do not adhere to each other. To cook, return to the fire, covered with the hot liquid, whatever this be, in which it is to be cooked, let cook rapidly, until nearly all the liquid is absorbed, then finish cooking over hot water. If the liquid be milk, cook from the first (after blanching) in the double boiler.

458. TO COOK RICE, No. I

Give the rice a thorough good washing in four or five waters; then place in a pan, allowing to each breakfastcupful of rice one pint of water and half a teaspoonful of salt. Cover it, and let boil till all the water has boiled away. Then stand it on the side of the range, move the cover ajar, and let it steam till it becomes quite dry.

459. TO COOK RICE, No. II

Have a pan of fast-boiling water, say one quart. Put one breakfastcupful of rice into it; leave the lid off, and continue to boil till the water has boiled away. Then steam at the side of the stove.

460. TO COOK RICE, No. III

Wash the rice well, throw it into plenty of boiling water, adding a teaspoonful of salt. Boil it fast until tender but not broken; drain through a colander, run cold water through it to separate the grains and heat it again in the oven.

461. TO COOK RICE, No. IV

Put half a pound of rice into one quart of cold water; when it has boiled for twenty minutes, put it to drain in a sieve, after which dry it before the fire to get rid of all superfluous moisture, stirring from time to time, and serve very hot.

462. TO COOK RICE, No. V

Wash the rice thoroughly, cook, in four times as much water, directly over the fire. Use a tightly covered saucepan, that the steam may be absorbed by the rice. Have the fire less brisk at the last part of the cooking than at first.

463. TO COOK RICE, No. VI

Cover the blanched rice with a relatively large quantity of salted boiling water and let cook rapidly in an uncovered saucepan until the grains are tender; drain off the water, cover the saucepan with a cloth and let stand on the back of the range to dry. Serve in a hot dish.

464. TO COOK RICE, No. VII

Put one gill (half a breakfastcupful) of rice, well washed, in a clean tin canister with a lid that fits tight. Add to the rice a pinch of salt and half a breakfastcupful of cold water. Fix the lid on, and stand the tin in a pan of boiling water. In half an hour the rice ought to have absorbed the water in the tin, and to be nicely cooked with the grains all separate. (A pound canister would probably be best, to leave ample room for the rice to expand.)

M

465. TO COOK RICE, No. VIII

Put one teacupful of well washed rice into two teacupfuls of cold water. Boil until the water is absorbed, then let the rice steam until quite dry.

466. TO COOK RICE, No. IX

Take half a pound of rice, wash it in cold water in a colander, put it into two quarts of salted boiling water. Let cook quickly with the lid off, removing any scum that rises, until the rice is tender—a quarter of an hour or so. Drain, and dry the rice in gentle heat, until the grains are well separated.

467. RICE AND CABBAGE

Boil a large cabbage; drain it; place it in a hot clean saucepan; add one teacupful of hot, boiled rice, pepper, salt, and a large piece of dripping; mix and stir well on the fire, and serve very hot.

NOTE.—This is very economical, as the remains of either cold cabbage or cold rice can be used. It is best to cut the cabbage quite small before adding the rice.

468. RICE CHEESE

Have four ounces of rice boiled in some vegetable stock till it is tender but not broken. Drain it well, and of course save the stock for future use. Add one and a half ounces of dripping, three ounces of grated cheese, and salt and pepper to taste. Serve very hot, heaped on a hot dish.

469. RICE (CRÉOLE), No. I

Place in a saucepan one medium, chopped onion; pour in one tablespoonful of melted fat, and fry six minutes, stirring meanwhile; add six ounces of raw rice, and cook on range five minutes, stirring meanwhile; add three peeled and finely chopped red tomatoes and one pint of stock. Season with a teaspoonful of salt; mix well. Cover pan, and as soon as it comes to a boil, set in oven thirty-five minutes. Remove, dress rice on a hot dish, and serve.

470. RICE (CRÉOLE), No. II

Chop fine a white onion; sauté with half a cupful of raw ham, shredded rather fine, in one-fourth of a cup of fat; cook about ten minutes, then add a cup of blanched rice and three cupfuls of stock; simmer twenty minutes, then add four tomatoes, peeled and cut in slices, and one teaspoonful of salt. Cover, and finish cooking in the oven or in a double-boiler.

471. RICE CROQUETTES, PLAIN

Half a cupful of rice, half a teaspoonful of salt, one cup of boiling water, one dried egg, one cupful of hot milk, two tablespoonfuls of fat.

Blanch the rice as on p. 152, cook in a double-boiler, with the water, milk, and salt, until the rice is tender and the liquid is absorbed; stir in the beaten egg and the fat; let cool, and finish as usual.

472. RICE CROQUETTES, SAVOURY

Half a cupful of rice, one cupful of stock, one egg, two cups of tomatoes, half a cupful of grated cheese, a slice of onion, one tablespoonful of fat, a sprig of parsley, quarter of a teaspoonful of pepper, two cloves, quarter of a teaspoonful of salt.

Cover the rice with cold water and bring quickly to the boiling-point; let boil for five minutes, then drain, rinse in cold water, and drain again. Cook the tomatoes with the onion, parsley, and cloves fifteen minutes, and pass through a sieve; add to the rice with the stock, pepper, and salt, and cook over hot water until the rice is tender and the liquid absorbed, then add the cheese, fat, and beaten egg. Spread on a dish to *cool* (do not let it become too cold,) then shape and finish as any croquettes.

473. RICE, CURRIED

Take two breakfastcupfuls of rice, put into a saucepan in three pints of cold water, and set over a hot fire to boil quickly. When the water boils, let it continue five minutes ; then drain the rice through a colander, rinse it with cold water, and put it back into another pan, which must contain three pints of boiling water, one teaspoonful of salt, and juice of half a lemon. Stir occasionally, and add more hot water if it boils away. Let it boil fast till the rice is tender, then stir in three tablespoonfuls of creamed fat and one tablespoonful of curry-powder. Serve at once.

474. RICE WITH EGGS, SAVOURY

Boil a quarter of a pound of Patna rice in one pint of good stock. Mix with it sufficient tomato sauce to colour it, two tablespoonfuls of grated cheese, and salt to taste. Reheat until it is sufficiently reduced to take a shape. Meanwhile put one ounce of fat in a frying-pan, and fry four good eggs in it ; trim each into a nice round. Press the rice in a shallow buttered mould, as firmly as possible, and quickly unmould it in a heated dish. Arrange the eggs on top of it, garnish with bits of parsley, and serve at once.

475. RICE WITH FRENCH BEANS.

Having boiled a breakfastcupful or so of rice, and got all the grains clear and separate, fry it lightly in a little fat, add enough tomato sauce to moisten it with the beaten yolk of one egg and two good tablespoonfuls of grated cheese, Mix thoroughly and set this rice as a wall round the centre of a hot dish. Place in the middle some French beans, boiled, drained, and seasoned with fat, pepper, and salt.

476. RICE, GOLDEN

Put one quart of water in a pan, with the following seasoning : one small whole onion, one bayleaf, one head of garlic, ten cloves, five cardamoms, half a teaspoonful each of cinnamon, mace, and salt, and saffron sufficient to colour all. When the water boils, add six ounces of rice ; let it boil till tender ; drain it, steam it, and serve it piled upon a hot dish, garnished with fried onions, and fried almonds, at discretion.

477. RICE, ITALIAN

Melt one ounce of fat, in a stew-pan. Take one onion about the size of a golf ball, mince it very finely, and fry it. When it is a golden yellow, stir in four ounces of hot, well-boiled rice. Work it well with a fork, at the same time shaking in two heaped tablespoonfuls of grated cheese. Serve it piled on a flat dish, garnished with sliced hard-boiled eggs.

478. RICE, MILANESE

Take half a medium-sized onion, chop it small, and cook it in two tablespoonfuls of fat in a hot stew-pan; don't let it get brown. Then add half a breakfastcupful of rice and about one quart of hot water (or white stock). When the rice has soaked up all the liquid, and is cooked quite tender, add a little salt and pepper, and two tablespoonfuls of grated cheese; mix this in gently with a fork, and serve it as a vegetable, with a little more grated cheese on top. A sauce may be served with it.

479. RICE PILAF

Mix one cupful and a half of stock, with one cupful of stewed and strained tomato. When boiling, add one cupful of well-washed or blanched rice and half a teaspoonful of salt; stir lightly with a fork occasionally, until the liquor is absorbed, then add half a cupful of fat and cook over hot water until tender; remove, cover, and stir with a fork before serving.

480. RICE, WITH PARSLEY OR CHIVES

Cook half a cup of blanched rice in boiling salted water until tender (an aluminoid dish will be found useful for this purpose); add two tablespoonfuls of fat and one teaspoonful of finely chopped parsley or chives; mix gently so as to avoid breaking the grains. Serve as a vegetable.

481. RICE SAVOURY, No. I

Take about four ounces of rice, and place in about one pint and a half of salted cold water along with three large

Spanish onions finely chopped. Let it stew quietly for at least two hours; if the water boils away, so that the rice is in danger of burning, add a little more hot water. When the rice is quite tender, stir in two ounces of fat, and serve very hot.

482. RICE SAVOURY, No. II

Set a cupful of rice over the fire in three pints of cold water; let come quickly to the boiling-point, and boil five minutes; then drain through a colander, rinsing with cold water. Return to the fire with a quart of boiling water, one teaspoonful of salt, and the juice of half a lemon; shake the pan occasionally, lest the rice burn, and add a little more water if necessary, or set on an asbestos mat or in a pan of cold water. When tender, stir in very carefully one-fourth of a cup of fat, creamed with a tablespoonful of curry-powder.

483. RICE AND SHRIMPS

Chop finely enough onion to make half a tablespoonful and fry it in three tablespoonfuls of fat. Add one and a half tablespoonfuls of cornflour, mixed with two teaspoonfuls of curry powder, salt and pepper. Stir till all is thoroughly mixed. Continue to stir, and gradually add two breakfastcupfuls of milk. Let boil; then add one breakfastcupful of warm boiled rice, and nearly twice as much of shelled shrimps. When all is well heated through, serve at once.

484. RICE VALENCIENNES

Finely chop a medium white onion, and lightly brown in a saucepan with two tablespoonfuls of oil for five minutes; add six ounces of raw rice, and brown eight minutes, frequently stirring meanwhile. Moisten with a pint of stock and two gills of tomato sauce, add three tablespoonfuls of cooked green peas, half a teaspoonful of salt, three saltspoonfuls of white pepper, and a saltspoonful of Spanish saffron. Mix well, cover pan, and set in oven forty-five minutes; remove, dress on a vegetable dish, and serve.

CHAPTER VIII

PUDDINGS, PASTRY, AND SWEET DISHES

THEY are indispensable in every decent English household. The question arises, of what shall we make them ? Milk is scarce and dear; suet ditto; dried fruits are almost non-existent; pastry of the good old sorts is practically *hors de combat;* we ought not to use wheat flour more than we can possibly help.

Well, you can still have *some* milk puddings; cocoa-butter can replace suet for boiled or steamed ones; rhubarb and fresh fruits must be largely used; and potato-paste, though only a makeshift, is much better than no paste at all. Dried eggs and egg-powders are invaluable; jam still is made and sold. And there are plenty of bottled fruits, which even if rather acid in themselves, are very good when accompanied with a custard-powder custard. Sweetness can be imparted, as I have already pointed out, by various means (see pp. 9–11). Dates, when procurable, stoned and chopped, do very well instead of raisins. Soaked drained crusts or stale bread make a quite satisfactory basis for a vast number of dishes. And potatoes are an invaluable stand-by in emergencies.

Amongst the following recipes you will find a considerable variety of puddingified concoctions. Sometimes, I allow, looking round on a depleted larder, one is tempted to tear one's hair above a reeling brain. But a few moments' calm reflection will convince one of the folly of such a proceeding; at the same time such reflection may provide one with a pudding.

Let milk (baked) puddings cook very slowly; to ensure

their being properly done, to retain as much as possible of the milk (which evaporates if cooked too fast), and to preserve the flavour. See "Rice Pudding, Economical," No. 538.

"Barley-kernels," sold in packets, are a pleasing variety from the hackneyed rice, semolina, sago, etc., and are particularly wholesome. So (properly soaked) is pearl barley.

Fruit can be sweetened by honey, or treacle, or any of the substitutes now being sold. Saccharin has a peculiarly nasty effect on fruit. In the case of rhubarb and gooseberries, chopped dates are a good sweetener. A pinch of bicarbonate of soda, or a pinch of salt, helps to lessen the acidity of the fruit. So does cooked sago. A (dried) egg or (powder) custard is invaluable in this respect.

Except for special dishes, it is *extremely wasteful to peel apples.* With them, as with potatoes, the most valuable properties lie next the skin. Their beauty, in fact, is skin-deep; and then their utility begins. They should be either *very* thinly sliced, peel and all, and the core removed; or they should be stewed in a little water until tender enough to rub through a sieve. By this means you waste nothing except the cores and pips, and save the flavour of the skin, besides all that would have been wasted in parings. If, however, for some special dish it be absolutely necessary to peel the apples, stew the parings and cores in a little water, and strain it to the apples subsequently; this improves their flavour fiftyfold. Or you can boil the strained water with a little sugar, till it turns pink; thicken with cornflour, and pour into a wetted mould.

Dried fruit is best cooked as follows : Wash the fruit and place it in a casserole : it should only occupy a quarter of the space. The other three-quarters should be filled up with boiling water. Leave the fruit to steep, for twelve to twenty-four hours. By that time it should have absorbed most of the liquid, and swelled out, fresh and fragrant. Drain off any of the liquid left, make a syrup of it with a little honey or sugar; let cool, and pour over the fruit in a glass dish.

All fruit-stones should be broken and the kernels extracted to use (milled or ground) for flavouring; a very little goes a long way, because these fruit kernels contain prussic acid.

Fruit is particularly valuable now that we are eating so much constipating pulse and cereal food.

NOTE.—Many excellent puddings, etc., not included here (see "Pudding Book" of this series), can be adapted for present use.

(1) By substituting "alien" flours in the following proportions:

For baked puddings, instead of all-wheat flour, use one-third of wheat flour, one-third of maize flour, one-third of (cooked) whole rice.

For boiled puddings, one-third of wheat flour, one-third of maize flour (or flaked maize), one-third of uncooked ground rice.

Maize flour, or maize semolina, or flaked maize should be used instead of wheat flour, or halved with it, whenever possible. It imparts a rich and delightful colour to the pudding, and is very nourishing. If you don't use maize, use barley flour. Oat flour is too pronounced in taste, except for articles to be fried, when the taste is altered by frying.

(2) By substituting cocoa-butter, or good dripping, for suet, butter, and margarine. Some people use sago instead of suet for steamed puddings, ounce for ounce; but of course sago, though nourishing, is not *fat*, and all it does is to lighten the texture. And some people use grated raw potato (twice as much as the right amount of suet), to which exactly the same remarks apply.

(3) By substituting dried eggs (there are countless varieties of these) for real eggs. This will not answer, needless to say, for any dish requiring the yolks and white whisked separately —such as anything in the nature of a méringue or soufflé.

(4) By substituting chopped dates for currants, raisins, or sultanas—which are practically obsolete.

(5) By substituting any of the various " sweeteners " for real sugar ; and by using jam, honey, or treacle where possible.

(6) By substituting milk and water for all milk ; the water in which macaroni, rice, etc., has been cooked, comes in very handy because it is already nutritious.

(7) By using potato-pastry instead of all-flour pastry, and by employing potatoes wherever you can, in place of flour. We are only, slowly and reluctantly, beginning to guess at the great usefulness of potatoes.

(8) By using all your old scraps and crusts of bread, where " breadcrumbs " are mentioned in the recipe. Dry crumbs (for frying and for dishes *au gratin*) can be provided by baking and powdering the crusts ; crumbs for all moister purposes, by soaking the stale bread in boiling water, leaving it some hours, and *squeezing* it dry in a cloth.

485. BARLEY SHORTCRUST

To eight ounces of barley flour, add a pinch of salt and half a teaspoonful of baking-powder. Rub in four ounces of fat, and mix with as little cold water as possible.

486. POTATO SHORTCRUST, No. I

Rub three ounces of fat into eight ounces of flour ; then mix in half a pound of potatoes, boiled in their skins, peeled, and mashed, sieved, or riced, half a teaspoonful of baking-powder, a pinch of salt, enough milk and water to mix into a stiff paste. Roll out about a quarter of an inch thick.

487. POTATO SHORTCRUST, No. II

Mix two ounces of flour (household), two ounces of barley flour, and two ounces of riced potatoes. Lightly rub in three ounces of fat ; add a pinch of salt, quarter of a teaspoonful of baking-powder, and enough cold water to moisten to a stiff paste, which must only be rolled out once.

488. POTATO SHORTCRUST, No. III

Mix eight ounces of cooked riced or sieved potato with four ounces of barley flour and four ounces G.R. (household) flour and a pinch of salt ; rub in four ounces of fat ; add one teaspoonful of baking-powder. Mix with a little water into a stiff paste.

NOTE.—Many people find that ground rice, or even puffed rice, can be successfully used in pastry-making (with or without potato) instead of G.R. flour ; or half and half of rice and flour.

489. ALEXANDRA PUDDINGS

Boil six apples and mash them through a sieve ; add to them one ounce of fat, a pinch of salt, a breakfastcupful of breadcrumbs, two (dried) eggs, a little grated nutmeg, and half a cupful of milk. Sweeten to taste. Mix perfectly ; then pour into wetted cups, and bake for half an hour. Turn them out, and serve.

490. APPLE BATTER PUDDING

Pare and core some apples, and put as many into a pie-dish as will stand close together. Make some batter with two tablespoonfuls of flour, three-quarters of a pint of milk, and one egg well beaten ; sprinkle the apples with sugar and lemon juice ; add the batter, and place immediately in a hot oven for an hour and a half, when the batter should be quite set, very light, and nicely browned.

491. APPLE AND EGG PUDDING

Beat an egg well, add one gill of milk or water, seven table-spoonfuls of flour, two tablespoonfuls of sugar, one saltspoon-ful of salt ; mix well together. Pare and cut into pieces three middle-sized apples ; stir them into the batter. Boil in a cloth for one hour and a quarter ; if in a basin, ten minutes longer.

492. APPLE PUDDING, GRANDMOTHER'S

Take half a pound of plain flour, three ounces of minced suet or fat, three ounces of cold boiled potato, a little salt, one pound or more of apples. Peel, core, and cut up the apples, rub the potato in the flour (as you would butter), add the chopped suet and salt. Wet with a little water, roll out on to a floured board. Grease a pudding-basin, line it with the crust, put the apples in with a little sugar, wet the edges, and put on the top crust. Flour a thick pudding-cloth, tie down, put into boiling water, and boil for three hours. This can be made the day before wanted, and not boiled till the next day, when it will turn out a nice biscuit colour. Can be made two days before boiling, but no longer, as the potato turns sour. Same crust can be used for all boiled puddings.

493. APPLE AND RICE PUDDING

Boil some apples until quite tender, and some rice in a separate saucepan—in the proportion of two pounds of apples to a teacupful of rice. Butter a pie-dish, and spread the rice and apples in alternate layers (adding sugar and grated lemon rind) until the dish is full. The last layer must be rice. On this place little pieces of fat, and bake with a plate over the pie-dish for quite an hour. Can be eaten either hot or cold.

494. APPLE AND TAPIOCA PUDDING

Peel six apples ; remove the core, and fill up the cavity with moist sugar and powdered nutmeg, and on the top of each apple put a small piece of cocoa-butter. Place the apples in a pie-dish, and strew round them a small teacupful of raw tapioca, sweetened with sugar. Fill the dish with water, and let the contents bake slowly in a slack oven for two hours.

495. APPLES, SCRAPED

Take one pound of good *eating* apples, peel them, and scrape them finely with a sharp knife into a glass dish. Have ready, not too hot, a nice (powder) custard, flavoured with sugar and vanilla, and pour this at once over the apples, as they discolour at once while exposed to the air. Let them be well covered with the custard. This is a most delicious and wholesome dish.

496. APPLE SHAPE

Boil about two pounds of sour apples with a little water until they are quite tender ; pass them through a sieve ; sweeten and flavour to taste. Dissolve overnight one ounce of gelatine in one pint of cold water ; add this to the apple pulp ; place all on the fire, and boil it for twenty minutes or longer, stirring all the time. Place in a wetted mould, and turn out when cold.

497. APPLE FOOL

Boil some apples as above. When mashed, add sugar and lemon juice to taste, and mix with one pint of hot milk. To be eaten cold.

498. ARROWROOT PUDDING

Mix half a teacupful of arrowroot with half a pint of cold water ; put one pint of milk into a saucepan with two ounces of sugar and a stick of cinnamon ; pound six bitter almonds, and add them to the arrowroot and cold milk. When the milk in the saucepan boils, put the arrowroot, etc., into it, stirring all the time ; boil for ten minutes, and place in a wet mould. Serve when cold.

499. AUSTRALIAN PUDDING

A quarter of a pound of suet or other fat, one pound of flour, one teaspoonful of baking-powder, a pinch of salt, and the grated rind of a lemon. Stir these ingredients in a basin ; mix a breakfastcupful of milk with a teacupful of black treacle ; stir into the flour, etc. ; place in a greased basin, and steam for three hours and a half. Turn out and serve.

NOTE.—Whenever treacle has to be used, it should be warmed first.

500. BREAD PUDDING

This is an excellent method of using up hard stale pieces, both crust and crumb. Lay them in a large bowl or pan, pour boiling water over them, cover them with a clean cloth, and leave them overnight. Next day strain off all moisture and add (to one pound of bread) a quarter of a pound of grated suet or good dripping, a quarter of a pound of dates or stoned raisins, two ounces of brown sugar, a pinch of salt, a little cinnamon or nutmeg at pleasure, and enough flour—very little will be required—to help bind the whole. Either a dried egg or a very little warmed golden syrup will help to bind the mixture. Bake in a greased baking-tin.

501. BROWN BREADCRUMB TRIFLE

Put through a fine sieve any stale brown bread, till you have at least two breakfastcupfuls of fine crumbs, which pile on a dish. Put over about a breakfastcupful of some moist juicy jam, such as strawberry, which will soak into the crumbs. When it has fairly soaked in, mask the whole in a (powder) custard. This is exceedingly good if the crumbs are well saturated.

502. BROWN BETTY

Thinly slice enough large tart apples to make two breakfastcupfuls; they need not be peeled. Put a layer of then at the bottom of a greased baking-dish, sprinkle with a little sugar, cinnamon, and shredded clarified cocoa-butter. Put next, a layer of soaked bread, well squeezed dry; repeat in alternate layers until the dish is nearly full. Let the top layer be bread, strewn with bits of cocoa-butter. Cover with a dish of equal size, and bake in moderate oven for forty-five minutes; then remove cover and let brown quickly. Gooseberries can be treated as above.

503. CAROLINA SNOWBALLS

Boil some rice in milk until quite soft; prepare some large apples as for apple dumplings, and having placed as much of the rice on a small cloth as will entirely cover the apple like a crust, tie each up closely, and boil for two hours.

504. CHOCOLATE MOULD

One pint of milk, two tablespoonfuls of cocoa, two tablespoonfuls of cornflour, two tablespoonfuls of sugar.

Mix the cocoa and cornflour to a smooth paste with a little
cold milk ; bring the remainder to boiling point, and add the
sugar ; then pour slowly on the paste, stirring all the time ;
return to the saucepan and cook very slowly ; stir all the
time, as it easily sticks.   Pour into a wet mould.

505. CHOCOLATE PUDDING

Shred and warm three ounces of cocoa butter, and add two
beaten (dried) eggs.   Then mix in four ounces of cocoa,
two ounces of flour, two ounces of ground rice, and one
teaspoonful of baking powder.   Beat well, place in mould,
and steam for one and a half hours.   A hot custard is nice
with this.

506. DATES IN CUSTARD

Stone enough dates to cover the bottom of a glass dish,
and put half a blanched almond in each ; pour over them
one pint of (powder) custard and serve cold.   This is particularly nutritious.

507. DEVON "STIR-UP" PUDDING

One cupful of flour, one apple cut up, one tablespoonful
of currants, one tablespoonful of suet chopped, half a teaspoonful of baking-powder, and a pinch of salt.

Mix all together to a stiff paste with a little water, and
steam in a basin for one and a half hours.   Serve with a sauce
of treacle and milk in equal parts—heated, but not boiled.
This pudding is also excellent when made with rhubarb,
gooseberries, or any sort of fruit.   The above quantities
make a small pudding sufficient for two or three persons.

508. ELIZABETH'S PUDDING

Have ready one pound of soaked stale bread, squeezed
dry and broken up with a fork ; prepare one pound of stewed

rhubarb, sweetened with two ounces of sugar (or any other stewed fruit). Mix with the bread one dried egg, a pinch of salt, and two ounces of suet or other fat. Put half this mixture in a greased pie-dish; pour in the rhubarb; place the rest of the bread mixture on top. Set in a moderate oven for one and a half hours.

509. GINGER PUDDING

Shred and warm one ounce of cocoa-butter, heat it along with half an ounce of sugar and one (dried) beaten egg. Add three ounces of boiled sieved potatoes, two ounces of flour, one flat teaspoonful of ginger. Mix well, and add one dessert‑spoonful of treacle, and a quarter of a teaspoonful of carbonate of soda. Add enough tepid water to mix into a thick batter, and steam in a basin for two hours.

510. HOMINY SNOWBALLS

Take one pint of milk, and two tablespoonfuls of soaked hominy. Put it into a double boiler. Let it simmer for two and a half hours, then turn it into teacups to set; when cold, unmould, and serve with jam.

511. LEMON CURD WITHOUT EGGS

Take eight ounces of peeled swede turnip, place in boiling water and cook until tender enough to rub through a sieve. Have ready, and add, half an ounce of fine sago which has been soaked in cold water overnight, three to four ounces of sugar, half an ounce of ground rice, a pinch of salt, the juice and grated rinds of two lemons. The ground rice should go in last. Cook over a gentle heat until the mixture thickens and the sago clears. Place in glass jars and cover closely.

512. MACARONI PUDDING

Take two ounces of macaroni and break it into half-inch pieces; wash it. Have a pint of milk, flavoured with one ounce of white sugar and the peel of half a lemon, brought slowly to the boil in a lined saucepan. When it boils, put

in the macaroni, which must simmer until it is quite tender
—which will be half an hour at least.   Add a little more milk
if it boils away too soon.   Take off the mixture and let it cool,
then stir in one well-beaten (dried) egg, and let the whole be
baked about ten minutes in a slow oven.

513.   MAIZE PUDDING, No. I

Have ready half a pint of fast-boiling water, in a double-
boiler, add a teaspoonful of salt, and gradually sprinkle in
(stirring continuously) two tablespoonfuls of maize meal.
Let boil gently for thirty minutes ; frequent stirring will be
needed.   Pour it into a pie-dish, mix in one (dried) beaten
egg, one breakfastcupful of milk, sugar or honey to taste,
and a little nutmeg.   Place in a moderate oven, and bake
for thirty to forty-five minutes.

514.   MAIZE PUDDING, No. II

Mix one tablespoonful of sugar with one breakfastcupful of
flaked maize ; add a pinch of salt ; place in a pie-dish.   Pour
a pint of boiling milk in, and bake forty-five minutes in
moderate oven.

515.   MAIZE AND APPLE PUDDING

Stir one teacupful of maize meal with a pinch of salt
into one pint of boiling milk and let cook gently, with frequent
stirring, for thirty minutes.   Remove from fire, and beat
in with a fork two tablespoonfuls of treacle and one ounce
of fat, or half an ounce of cocoa butter, and a pinch of soda
bicarbonate.   Have ready one pound of apples stewed
(without peeling) in as little water as possible, and rubbed
through a sieve.   Put half the cooked maize in a greased
fireproof dish, then put in the apple ; cover with the rest
of the maize, and bake for thirty minutes in a moderate oven.

516.   MATTRESS

Two teacupfuls of flour, two ounces of dripping, one teaspoonful of baking powder, one (dried) beaten egg, and
enough milk when added to the egg to fill a teacup.

N

Rub the dripping into flour, add the baking powder and sugar, and mix. Beat the egg, add the milk, and mix together. Bake on shallow tin from twenty to thirty minutes. Spread with jam and serve.

517. NUT PUDDING

Have ready four ounces of boiled rice, and mix into it a pinch of salt, a tablespoonful of sugar, a teaspoonful of grated lemon rind or a few drops of lemon essence, and two ounces of minced or milled nuts. Place in a greased baking-dish, and cover with half a pint (powder) custard. Place in a moderate oven for thirty minutes; when the pudding has been cooking about twenty minutes, strew it with two dessertspoonfuls of minced nuts or grated coconut.

518. NUT CUSTARD PUDDING

Boil a pint of milk and water, put in two ounces of broken macaroni, cook until quite tender. Place in a greased dish, and strew in one tablespoonful of sugar, a half lemon rind grated, a pinch of salt. Pour on top a breakfastcupful of hot (powder) custard, and strew this with some minced nuts, at least a tablespoonful. Bake in a moderate oven until the nuts brown a little.

519. OATMEAL PUDDING

Put into a greased pie-dish a little less than half a tin of Swiss milk, diluted to one pint with water; add a pinch of salt, two ounces of rolled oats, and one tablespoonful of chopped dates. Let soak in a warm place for one hour, stirring up occasionally. Then strew some shreds of fat and a little nutmeg on top, and bake two hours or so in a moderate oven.

ONE-ORANGE PUDDINGS
520. No. I

Place half a breakfastcupful of cold boiled rice at the bottom of a glass dish; peel one orange, and slice it thinly crossways, with a silver knife, on top of the rice ; dredge with one ounce of castor or granulated sugar ; spread another halfcupful of boiled rice over the orange. Make a quarter of a pint of custard powder, and when it is cooling, pour it over the rest. Set by for two hours or until quite cold and set.

521. No. II

Have three ounces of flaked maize made into a smooth paste with a little cold water. Boil a pint of milk, pour it to the maize, and put back all in the saucepan. Add a pinch of salt, half an ounce of fat, one ounce of sugar, and the grated rind of one orange. Let boil for five minutes or so, continually stirring. Place in a greased dish and bake for thirty minutes.

522. No. III

Put four ounces of sago to soak overnight in three breakfastcupfuls of cold water. Turn all into a greased dish next day, add a teaspoonful of salt, and place for an hour in moderate oven. Then remove, and add the grated rind and juice of one orange, and either two tablespoonfuls of sugar or one of sugar and one of honey. Mix well and replace in oven for thirty minutes more.

523. No. IV

Put two ounces of sago to soak overnight in two breakfastcupfuls of water. Next morning boil up all together, add a pinch of salt, a tablespoonful of sugar, and the grated rind and juice of one orange. Let cook a few minutes longer, until quite thick and clear. Pour into a wetted mould, and when cold unmould.

In Nos. 2, 3, and 4, lemon can be substituted for orange with good effect.

With any of the above puddings, a hot or cold (powder) custard is advisable.

524. PLAIN STEAMED PUDDING

Mix half a pound of G.R. flour with a quarter of a pound of grated raw potato, a pinch of salt, and a teaspoonful of baking powder. No fat required. Moisten with sufficient water, or milk, or both, to make a firm dough. Boil or steam in greased mould or basin, two or three hours. Serve with sweet sauce, jam, or treacle.

525. POTATO PUDDING, No. I

Boil and mash four large potatoes ; add to them a pinch of salt, two ounces of moist sugar, a quarter of a teaspoonful of vanilla essence, one ounce of fat, and two dried eggs.   Pour into a greased mould, and bake for half an hour in a quick oven.   Turn out of the mould, and serve with sweet sauce.

526. POTATO PUDDING, No. II

Mix eight ounces of cooked sieved potatoes with two ounces of household flour, two ounces of barley flour, two ounces of soaked drained stale bread, three ounces of shredded cocoa butter or suet, three tablespoonfuls of treacle, half a teaspoonful of carbonate of soda. Beat thoroughly till well blended, using a little milk to moisten. Steam for three hours in a greased basin.

527. POTATO PUDDING, No. III

Mix with eight ounces of cooked mashed potatoes, two ounces of fat, sugar to taste, a pinch of salt, the juice and grated rind of one lemon, and two dried eggs. Blend thoroughly, and place in a greased pie-dish (with potato-crust round edge if liked), bake for 30 minutes.

528. POTATO PUDDING, No. IV

Take half a pound of boiled and sieved (or riced) potatoes, put them into a deep bowl, and form a " well " in the middle, as if you were going to make bread. Have ready the following : four ounces of maize meal (or maize semolina) soaked in half a teacupful of milk, or in half a dried egg. Melt one ounce of cocoa butter, and stir into it two teaspoonfuls of cocoa. Put all these into the middle of the potato, along with one tablespoonful of treacle and one teaspoonful of baking powder, and beat all together until thoroughly well mixed. Then place in a greased pie-dish, and put into a moderate oven for 30 minutes.

529. POTATO PUDDING, No V

Mash eight ounces of potatoes ; add two ounces of fat, the grated rind and the juice of one lemon, sugar to taste, two dried eggs, and a teacupful of milk. Bake in a dish (with pastry round the edge) for half an hour.

530. POTATO AND APPLE PUDDING, No 1

Mix a pinch of salt with four ounces of G.R. flour, grate in two ounces of cocoa butter (clarified), add four ounces of cooked riced potatoes, and mix well ; moisten with as little water as possible. Roll out half an inch thick, and line a greased basin with it. To fill, take two large apples peeled and chopped small, one tablespoonful of treacle or corn syrup, rind of half a lemon grated, and one tablespoonful of crumbs (any sort). Put half the apples in the lined bowl ; sprinkle them with half the other ingredients. Put a round of the potato crust. Place greased paper over and steam for three hours.

531. POTATO AND APPLE PUDDING, No. II

Take twelve ounces of apples, stew (but do not peel) and pulp them through a sieve. Have ready twelve ounces of potatoes, steamed, peeled and sieved ; mix well into the potato one tablespoonful of sugar, one tablespoonful of fat, one tablespoonful of milk, vanilla or almond essence to taste, and a pinch of salt. Roll out and line a greased pie-dish with part of this mixture, put in the stewed apple, sweetened to taste, and put the rest of the potato paste on top. Put the pudding in a good oven until it is a nice golden brown.

532. POTATO AND APPLE PUDDING, No. III

Boil till tender one pound of apples (wiped but not peeled), and pass them through a sieve. Mix with them half a pound of cooked sieved potatoes, two ounces of sugar, a pinch of salt, half an ounce of fat (any sort), one dried egg, and a little grated lemon rind (or ginger if preferred). Place in a greased pie-dish, in a moderate oven, and bake for 30 or 40 minutes.

533. POTATO AND APPLE PUDDING, No. IV

Boil and mash one and a half pounds of sour apples ; boil three potatoes, and add them through the masher to the apples ; mix well, add four ounces of sugar, a cupful of water, and the grated rind of one lemon ; one or two eggs can be added, but are not necessary. Beat well, place it in a greased basin or mould, and steam for an hour and a half.

534. POTATO AND LEMON PUDDING, No I.

Mix two ounces of ground rice and a pinch of salt, with eight ounces of cooked riced potatoes. Place in a basin, make a hollow in the middle, and put into it one and a half ounces of creamed or melted fat, one beaten dried egg, one tablespoonful each of treacle and of milk. Beat all thoroughly ; lastly, add one teaspoonful of baking powder. Place in a greased dish, and bake for three-quarters of an hour in a moderate oven.

535. POTATO AND LEMON PUDDING, No. II

Boil one teacupful of milk, put in one ounce of fat and melt it, add one beaten (dried) egg and a pinch of salt. Stir in one pound of cooked sieved potatoes, one tablespoonful of treacle, the grated rind of one lemon. Beat thoroughly, bake in a greased pie-dish in a moderate oven to a good brown.

536. POTATO AND LEMON PUDDING, No. III

Have ready one pint of (powder) custard ; add a pinch of salt ; stir in eight ounces of cooked sieved potatoes, and mix well, beating continually. Add half an ounce of fat, three ounces of chopped dates, and the grated rind of half a lemon. Bake in greased pie-dish in moderate oven.

537. RICE CREAM

Take a large heaped tablespoonful of ground rice, and rub smooth with a little cold water. Put one pint of milk in a saucepan, sweeten, and flavour with vanilla or lemon essence. When the milk is hot, add the ground rice, and stir well until it boils. Serve cold. This is an excellent accompaniment to any stewed fruit, especially rhubarb. It can either be poured over the fruit or served alone in a glass dish.

538. RICE PUDDING (ECONOMICAL)

Wash sufficient rice to cover the bottom of a pie-dish about half an inch deep. Add one pinch of salt, and two teaspoonfuls of sugar. Pour boiling water in, enough to cover the rice and leave plenty of room to swell. Place in a moderate oven until the rice has swelled ; then put in enough milk to fill the dish three-quarters full, give a good stir, and add whatever flavouring is desired, and bake until set. This takes much less milk.

539. SAGO FRUIT, No. I

Have one breakfastcupful of sago boiled in five breakfastcupfuls of water ; when it is quite clear, put in four tablespoonfuls of jam, raspberry or black currant for preference. Pour into a mould which has been rinsed with cold water. When cold, unmould, and serve with a (powder) custard.

540. SAGO FRUIT, No. II

Put into a casserole, three ounces of fine sago, one pint of topped-and-tailed gooseberries, sweetening to taste (or chopped dates), and one breakfastcupful (or a little more) of cold water. Cover closely, bake slowly, and remove when all is firm. This is better served cold.

541. SEMOLINA PUDDING

Boil half a pint of milk, sprinkle in one ounce of semolina, with two teaspoonfuls of sugar, and stir until the mixture is quite free from lumps ; then let it cool a little, and stir in one well-beaten dried egg (but this is not essential), and bake in a slow oven, in a greased pie-dish, for about half an hour.

Fine sago or crushed tapioca can be treated the same way.

542. SUGAR-BEET PUDDING

Take six ounces of sugar-beet, wash well and peel, place in boiling water sufficient to cover, let simmer for two hours. Remove from water, chop small, and place in a covered casserole with a very little water, and let cook until soft enough to pulp through a sieve (or cook it to a similar condition by any of the methods on pp. 10, 11).

Add to the sieved beet the following, well mixed : two ounces of cooked sieved potatoes, four ounces of G.R. flour (or half G.R. flour and half ground rice), and a quarter of a breakfastcupful of fat ; with a pinch of salt, and the grated rind and juice of half a lemon. Very little moisture will be needed, but if there is any of the sugar-beet liquor left from the *second* cooking, use some of that (about half a teacupful), otherwise use some from the first boiling. Last of all, moisten one teaspoonful of carbonate of soda and add. Blend thoroughly, place in a greased basin, and steam three hours.

543. SWISS PUDDING

Boil one pound of apples (wiped but not peeled) in a very little water until tender enough to put through a sieve. Have three ounces of sugar, or of treacle, mixed with three ounces of shredded clarified cocoa butter, six ounces of soaked strained crusts, a pinch of salt, and the same of cinnamon. Place half of this at the bottom of a greased pie-dish, put in the apples, then add the rest of the mixture ; strew a few

little bits of fat or cocoa butter on top.   Let bake about
an hour in a moderate oven.

544.   TREACLE PUDDING

Two tablespoonfuls of golden syrup, or treacle, two tablespoonfuls of chopped suet or fat, six tablespoonfuls of flour,
one teaspoonful and a half of baking-power, one egg.

Mix flour, suet, and baking-powder and pinch of salt.
Stir in treacle, beaten egg, and a little milk.   Place in a
greased basin, cover with paper, and steam for about two
hours.

545.   TRENCH PUDDING

Have two tablespoonfuls of rice boiled in half a pint of
milk and water, until the liquid is absorbed and the rice tender.
Mix in two ounces of shredded cocoa butter (or suet) and one
dried egg, with a few chopped dates or a little sugar, and
steam them in a greased basin.

546.   VEGETABLE MARROW TART

Take a small marrow, stew it quite tender, mash it up with
fat and sugar to taste ;   add a little flavouring of lemon
peel, spice, and ginger, and beat a dried egg well in.   Line
a dish with potato-crust and, when the pastry is baked, and
has gone cool, fill it with above mixture, and put it back
for a minute in the oven.

CHAPTER IX

BREAD, CAKES, BISCUITS

BREAD is the most important article of all. At the moment of writing we are not rationed in bread; but any day we may be.

The saving in flour, health, and happiness which can be effected by good home-made bread is unbelievable until you have ocular demonstration of it. We don't know, most of us, what good bread is. We have lost the power of perception and discernment, because we have been grumblingly content to put up so long a while, year in and year out, with a mysterious compound *called* bread (but exceedingly unlike the genuine thing), which was supplied by bakers. Some bakers' bread is worse than others. But it is very rarely that you hear of a household changing its baker. It just grumbles and—goes on.

With one's own bread, not only is great economy the immediate result—because it is so much more nourishing and satisfying, and keeps fresh so much longer, than the miserable shop stuff which is dry at twelve hours old—but you can vary it to suit your own requirements; with less or more potatoes, less or more moisture—with a little lard or fat if that can be spared—with a little sweetening of fruit (fresh or dried) if desirable.

You can vary it in shape and in size; even in colour, by the admixture of more maize, rice, oat, or barley flour (but G.R. flour will not stand *much* more admixture). And if you are rationing your house in flour, as every patriotic Briton should do, you will find that you are quite surprisingly to the good in the amount of flour left over after breadmaking.

I save five pounds out of twelve pounds of my flour rations every week.

Also you will find that minor digestive ailments disappear. The people who grouse about " War Bread " are those who only know *the bakers' version of it.*

But some will say, " All very well, but it is a troublesome job, and I haven't time." Others will hint that a dark secrecy envelops the operation of breadmaking, and that only the initiated can hope to succeed.

This is pure fallacy. It is a job which cannot, from its inherent nature, be done right off. You can sandwich its details between the labours of the busiest day. And as regards what *you* have to do, that is perfectly plain sailing. Any trifling discrepancies as regards the yeast, the G.R. flour, the temperature of the weather and the oven, you will speedily learn to recognise and get even with. . . . I wish every woman knew the pardonable pride and joy of seeing big beautiful loaves cooling off upon the table, and smelling the delicious odour of home-made bread all over the house.

For further particulars, see pp. 187–191.

Bread must never be wasted—not a scrap of it. To waste bread now is a culpable and a criminal act. As has already been stated, any crusts or broken bits must be soaked and then well squeezed as dry as possible, used for puddings, rissoles, and any of the numerous purposes for which we formerly employed fresh crumbs. Or they must be dried hard in the oven, pulverised, and used where dry crumbs are a desideratum.

Bread should not be used when you can possibly supply a substitute. At breakfast, for instance, it can be reduced to a minimum by substituting sufficient potatoes (sliced cold cooked potatoes, fried if possible, or any of the recipes in Chapter VIII.) or " cutlets " of cold boiled hominy, oatmeal, rice, maize-meal or lentils; or plenty of porridge of some sort (see Chapter VII.) ; anything, in short, which supplies bulk of a farinaceous kind. There are also a

large number of hot breakfast cakes, which are used continually in Canada and the U.S.A., and are all exceedingly
satisfying.

The same remarks apply to luncheon.

Bread should not be used at tea at all, if you can make
shift with simple little cakes or biscuits (see Chapter VIII.).
One is not hungry at tea as a rule ; most people simply eat
from force of habit. *Don't eat unless you are absolutely hungry* : that is " the way to be healthy, wealthy, and wise."

Bread at dinner is a needless superfluity.

As regards the various " alien flours " of which excellent
bread can be made, you will find them dealt with in the recipes
seriatim. However, please note the following :

Wheat flour is the only flour (except rye) which " rises,"
i.e., responds to the action of yeast. Therefore, if you mix
it with any other flour (it is pretty well mixed already !) you
must remember that that other flour will only rise by the
wheat-flour lifting it along with itself, and you must make
your calculations accordingly.

Barley flour imparts a dark, somewhat dirty-looking
tone to a loaf. It is very nutritious, but inclined to promote
biliousness if one is inclined that way. It is the moistest
flour I know.

Maize flour has a drying effect, and gives a lovely yellow
colour to the loaf. The flavour is pleasant.

Oat flour is dryer still. It whitens the loaf, and imparts
a delightful oaten flavour.

Rice flour whitens the loaf, and is very drying.

Boiled rice, boiled oatmeal and *boiled maize-meal* are useful,
if not ideal, adjuncts. They absorb a lot of dry flour in
the kneading process ; but they greatly increase the *bulk*
of a loaf, if not its quality.

Potatoes (boiled in their skins, peeled, mashed, sieved, or
riced, and added to the dough—or to the yeast—while still
warm), moisten the loaf, lighten it, increase the bulk, and
improve the taste. The correct proportion of potatoes to

flour has been the subject of Ministerial experiment; I give the result. Personally I find that one pound of potatoes to three and a half pounds of flour is an excellent admixture; but one and a half potato is also very good.

G.R. Flour.		With Potatoes.		Makes Bread.
7 lbs.	..	—	..	9 lbs.
7 lbs.	..	1 lb.	..	10 lbs. 9 ozs.
7 lbs.	..	2 lbs.	..	11 lbs. 10½ ozs.
7 lbs.	..	3½ lbs.	..	12 lbs.
7 lbs.	..	7 lbs.	..	14 lbs. 9 ozs.
7 lbs. (Wholemeal)		7 lbs.	..	13 lbs. 7½ ozs.

The old recipes for wheat-flour bread do not quite hold good now. The millers, or the bakers, or both, are allowed to mix the wheat flour with a percentage of " alien flours," barley, maize, oats, rice, and beans. Sometimes they use one, sometimes another, sometimes several; and consequently the flour varies from week to week, and the housewife never knows with what particular " aliens " she has to cope. But the net result—striking an average—is this :

(1) Less moisture is required for mixing and kneading; I should say, as a rule, nearly half a pint less than what is indicated in recipes for pure wheat flour. Barley flour is so moist and sticky in its tendency, and potatoes also contain so much moisture, that if you employ the usually stated amount of moisture, you are likely to get a dough which is most difficult to knead, and turns out pasty in the baking.

(2) Less kneading, according to some experts, is required. I don't know that I agree with this. It is quite easy to knead too little; it would be hard to knead too much. Especially now that the wheat flour is so mixed with the other flours that won't respond to the action of yeast, it is more than ever necessary that the yeast should be thoroughly incorporated. It is therefore advisable to stick to the good old-fashioned twenty minutes for kneading—(this signifies from start to finish—from the time you actually begin to

mix the flour into the risen yeast-and-potato in the
" well ").

(3) The rising of the dough is very, very slow. No wonder ;
think what a lot of " alien " flour it has got to shove up by
hook or crook. Of course, its rising varies with the weather,
the temperature, and the condition of the yeast ; but still
it is very slow. If, however, it has been properly kneaded,
the second rising, in the tins, will not be unduly prolonged.

(4) The time of baking is, as a rule, longer now than
formerly ; but this also varies very much.

I have been experimenting with various admixtures of
" alien " flours for a year ; and very nicely most of these
experiments turned out. But during that period, the G.R.
flour has become more and more coloured, or discoloured, until
now you cannot at a little distance distinguish it from
wholemeal flour (which is also considerably diluted with
beans, etc.). Of course, however, the wholemeal flour has
a different texture. . . . Well, I have come to the conclusion that it is no longer safe to try any admixtures of
one's own, lest one should upset the balance and not have
enough proportion of wheat flour—in which case the dough
cannot rise. The only safe extra ingredient, at the moment,
is potatoes. Except in the case of " mixture breads," which
see (p. 195).

Potatoes are a distinct improvement in every way. Not
only do they, as already mentioned, increase the bulk, but they
improve the taste and colour, and they lighten the texture.

They should be boiled or steamed in their skins ; then you
must remove the skins, and mash, sieve, or pass the potatoes
through a ricer. The last is the quickest. Anyhow, get them
perfectly free from lumps.

Opinions vary as to *when* you should add the potatoes ;
though all agree that they should be warm (not scalding hot)
when you add them. Some put them into the flour before
making a " well " for the yeast ; some mix them with the
dough while kneading. I follow a third course. " The middle

way is the safest," says the old proverb, and certainly I think
this is as safe as any. I mix them into the creamed yeast-and-
sugar after the tepid water has been added to it; and pour
the whole lot into the " well." No flour need be stirred in to
make a " sponge "; the potatoes suffice. Sprinkle some flour
over the top, and cover up with a cloth.

NOTE.—The stalest loaf may be revived and made eatable,
by treatment as follows. Plunge it for a minute into fresh
cold water; and *immediately* place it in a *very hot* oven.
It should begin to steam, and when it has finished steaming,
it should (theoretically) be ready to take out. But the time
varies with different breads.

YEAST

NOTE.—It is advisable, if not absolutely necessary, to
understand *something* about yeast; otherwise one is working
in the dark.

Yeast is a plant, " a collection of living, one-celled organ-
isms "—though most people are unaware of this. It grows,
by perpetual budding out of itself; this is what raises the
flour. Like any plant, it needs certain favourable conditions
for growth, and these conditions are mild warmth, a certain
amount of moisture, and suitable food. The favourite food
of the yeast-plant is sugar; which it finds, or rather manu-
factures for itself, in wheat flour. It digests this sugar,
so to speak, and turns it into carbonic-acid-gas and alcohol,
which, in their efforts to escape from the glutinous walls of
the cells enclosing them, expand, inflate, or swell the dough,
as the yeast grows and grows. It is a most interesting and
mysterious process.

If you let the yeast (at any stage) stand in a draught,
which all plants hate, it will deteriorate. If you check the
growth of the yeast at the wrong moment by too fierce
a heat, or too intense a cold, it will die; just as any plant
will. It *does* die, at a certain moment, when it has done
its duty by raising the dough. The heat of the oven

eventually kills the yeast; the size of the air-cells which it has evolved remains fixed; the alcohol and carbonic gas are driven off; in other words, the bread is properly raised, aerated, and baked. Several other things happen; but this is the simplest way of stating it.

If, however, the dough is left too long before baking, its condition will change. The alcoholic fermentation produced by the yeast will be followed by a break-up of the alcohol into acetic acid and water (just as wine changes to vinegar), and the bread, when baked, will be sour. This souring is more likely to happen in warm weather.

But as the longer time of fermentation or rising that you can allow, will secure the best bread, if it be necessary to leave the dough a good while, " cut it down " once or twice after it has doubled in bulk. This lets out some of the gas and improves the flavour. " Cutting down " is the clean cut, with a sharp knife, across, north to south, and east to west, mentioned in the general formula for bread-making.

Yeast may be (1) that known as brewer's or liquid yeast, which is the best, but which *must* be used fresh, and is rather hard nowadays to come by. Or (2) compressed, formerly known as German, yeast, which is now more than twice its old price; this will keep two, sometimes three days, but is much the best when fresh. It should be of a light even colour like good dripping, with no dark veinings in it. (3) Home-made yeast, which is invaluable when you can't procure either of the others; only, note well, you must *start* your home-made yeast with No. 1 or No. 2. I give several recipes for this. It is of most use to those who have to make bread often and to a considerable amount. It won't keep longer than three days open, but may be good for six weeks, bottled; and you can always start a fresh supply from a little of the old stuff. Having once obtained the yeast plant, you can go on propagating it for ever.

A piece of dough held over unbaked, will serve as leaven for a new lot, and some people swear by it; but I don't recommend it, because obviously the chances are that it will make the bread sour.

In these hard times we must not run the least risk of wasting any of our materials. We must try and make sure that we are giving our bread the best possible conditions ; so that every scrap of it shall be eatable, wholesome, and enjoyable.

The right proportion of yeast to be used is stated so differently by different experts, that the subject might well bewilder an amateur. You may, however, be sure you are safe in allowing one ounce of compressed yeast to three and a half pounds of flour, or one and a half ounces to seven pounds of flour. Two ounces is said to suffice for fourteen pounds of flour. But I had rather be on the safe side by using a little more.

One ounce of compressed yeast equals about two-thirds of a breakfast cup of liquid (brewers') yeast ; or about half a pint of home-made yeast.

547. HOME-MADE YEAST, No. I

Put a heaped tablespoonful of dried hops, and a pinch of salt into a bowl, pour on one pint of boiling water (water in which potatoes have been boiled is best) ; let this grow cold, then strain and boil it up again, all but a tablespoonful or so, which you can use (cold) to mix to a smooth paste one heaped teaspoonful each of flour and of sugar. When the liquid boils, pour it over the sugar, etc., stirring continually. Bottle, cork closely, and set in a warm place. It should ferment on the third day. A breakfastcupful will suffice for three and a half pounds of flour.

548. HOME-MADE YEAST, No. II

Wash and chop up three good-sized potatoes, without peeling them. Put them, along with one and a half handfuls of dried hops, into four and a half pints of cold water, and bring to the boil. When the potatoes are done enough, mash them well, and let all cool down to lukewarm or blood heat. Then stir in smoothly one and a half handfuls of sugar and two large handfuls of flour, also one ounce of compressed yeast (but this last is only needed the first time you start making it), which should be creamed with a little sugar and lukewarm water. Pour all into a jar, and set in a cool place. Before using, shake it up and strain it through a gravy strainer or a piece of muslin. Half a pint will raise seven pounds of flour.

Some of this yeast must always be kept to begin the next lot with (instead of buying more compressed yeast).

("Handfuls" is rather vague; but as bread-making matters are usually run by men, I should say that "handful" was about a large tablespoonful.)

549.　HOME-MADE YEAST, No. III

Take eight or nine good-sized potatoes; peel, and boil them along with a large handful of hops tied up in muslin; have enough water to cover them completely. Strain off the water when the potatoes are done, remove the hops, mash the potatoes, put them back, with the water, into the saucepan, mixing thoroughly. Then put in two table-spoonfuls of flour, half a cupful of granulated sugar, and one tablespoonful of salt. Stir well, and dredge in more flour, until you have a thin batter. Let cook for four or five minutes, then add two ounces of compressed yeast (creamed). Mix all well, pour off into an earthenware jar, let stand ten or twelve hours in a warm place, stirring every four hours. Then cover closely and put into a cool place.

550.　HOME-MADE YEAST, No. IV

Have one and a half pints of water boiling in a pan. Add a full teacupful of hops, tied up in butter-muslin, and one and a half pounds of potatoes. Boil these till the potatoes are tender, then press them through a colander, and add one breakfastcupful of wheat flour, one and a half teacupfuls of

Demerara sugar, one teaspoonful of ground ginger, one ditto salt. Take two and a quarter ounces of ordinary yeast, melt it in a little warm water, and mix it with the other ingredients. Leave the mixture in a cool place for twenty-four hours, then mix in as much cornflour as will enable you to roll it out into a paste. Roll out the paste, cut it into small rounds with the top of a flour-dredger or a wine-glass, and dry them on a dish, taking care that both sides become thoroughly dry and hard. They must then be wrapped in butter-paper and put away in closed tins in a dry place. For bread-making, one and a half ounces of this compressed yeast can be used to seven pounds of flour; dissolve it in half a pint of warm water, adding a good teaspoonful of brown sugar, and let it stand in a warm place for five minutes or so; when the yeast rises to the top of the water, it is ready for use.

HOW TO MAKE WAR BREAD OF G.R. FLOUR IN 1918

NOTE.—I have explained this (really very simple matter) most carefully and at considerable length, so that it may appear quite plain sailing. After you have done it once or twice, you will be able to do it almost mechanically, fitting in the various bits between your other jobs. It will present no more difficulty than doing up your hair in the morning. Every woman knows that some days her hair *won't* be done up satisfactorily. Even so, some days bread-dough turns obstinate and is slow in rising. In both cases, Patience is a virtue.

THE MIXING

Take three and a half pounds of G.R. flour [if you have no means of weighing, remember that four (heaped) breakfastcupfuls are about equal to one pound of flour; one pint of flour weighs fourteen ounces] and set aside half a pound of it on a plate. Put the three pounds in an earthenware pan, or large bowl, and mix well into it one teaspoonful of salt. Stand the bowl in some place where the flour can get warmed through ; either in front of the fire, or out in the sun (on a chair), or in the gas oven. Stir it up now and then, that it may get warmed right through. Meanwhile weigh one pound of potatoes (a little over will not hurt, but if you can't weigh them, say five medium-sized ones). Scrub them, and boil or steam them ; when they are done, put them through a sieve, or through a ricer, or mash them quite free from lumps. Let them cool off a little, so as not to be scalding hot ; but on no account let them be cold.

Put one ounce of fresh compressed yeast into a bowl, cream it with one dessertspoonful of sugar ; and mix into it about two breakfastcupfuls (rather less than more) of lukewarm water. Then stir in the sieved potato, a little at a time. Don't get the yeast ready as above until the flour is warmed.

Make a hollow in the centre of the flour, with your knuckles or with a wooden spoon. (This hollow is known as a " bay," or " well," or " fountain.") Make it fairly deep and wide, but not right down to the bottom of the pan. Pour, into this hollow, the yeast and potato mixture. Sprinkle some flour over the yeast, from the sides of the hollow. Cover the pan with a thick cloth or towel, and put it in a warm place, out of a draught ; such as a kitchen chair beside the fire ; or on the fender before the fire ; or out in the sun on a chair, in summer. If you have none of these places handy, anyhow put it in the warmest, most sheltered place you have got. In about a quarter of an hour you should find that the yeast mixture has broken through the sprinkled flour, and is working and moving about with big bubbles—often making funny little noises. (But if the yeast is not very fresh, or the weather is cold, it may take longer.)

You then lift the pan to a table out of a draught. Have ready a pint of lukewarm water (you may not want it all), and the half pound of flour which you set aside at the beginning.

THE KNEADING

You now mix into the yeast in the middle all the flour from the sides, doing this gradually and deliberately, and adding more lukewarm water as you need it. It is not possible to explain in words the exact state of softness to which you must bring your dough, especially as some flour requires more moisture than others. It is better to have the dough too stiff than too wet ; but try to have it what appears just right.

You now proceed to knead it, with your clenched fists and the back of your knuckles. Bring in the sides of the dough continually towards the centre, and throw the whole weight of your body into each part of the dough which you tackle. Do not use your hands too close to each other. The object of the kneading is to distribute the yeast equally throughout the flour, and to give the bread a uniform texture, with neither holes nor pasty places, so that it shall be equally light and porous all over. Some people do their kneading on a paste-board, but it is easier in the pan.

As you knead, you will find that sometimes a little more water is required, sometimes more flour. Whichever you add, do it *gradually*—don't splash it in anywhere. You should thus, by degrees, add at least another breakfastcupful (half-pint) of tepid water, and all the rest of the half pound of flour. Be careful not to get the dough too moist ; it is better too stiff than too moist. But you may need a whole pint of tepid water.

You must go on kneading until the bread is a smooth, elastic ball, which comes right clean away from the bottom and sides of the pan. For the above quantity of flour, about fifteen to twenty minutes' kneading should be necessary.

When the dough seems just right, turn it upside down in the pan, cut it across twice with a sharp knife—north to south and east to west ; cover it up again with the cloth and return it to the warm place as before, *well out of a draught,* to rise till it is at least double in size. This may take an hour, or an hour and a half, or even more, according to the state of the weather, the freshness of the yeast, the quality of the flour, and the warmth of the place.

Have ready, out of a draught, a pasteboard, or clean table, dredged with a little flour, and two half-quartern bread-tins, or a large flat baking-tin. Whichever tins you use, they should be well warmed and greased. (Some people say, if you warm the tins properly, you need not grease them. But I don't think that applies to G.R. flour, which has a lot of sticky barley flour in it.)

Lift out your dough upon the board, divide it into two equal parts, and knead it *only just enough* to get it into the proper shape for your tins, or, round for " cake " loaves. (But if cake loaves are made where potatoes are used, the dough is apt to be too soft, and spreads out too thin.) *Only half-fill the tins.* Prick the top of the loaves sharply with a steel fork, in three or four places ; and put them into a warm sheltered place to rise again. The kitchen rack is a good place. You will find that the dough has gone much smaller while you were handling it. Let the loaves double in size and rise to the top of the tins before you bake them. This will probably take half an hour.

THE BAKING

If you use a coal fire oven, it must be very hot at the beginning. Put half a teaspoonful of flour into the oven ; if it goes brown in three to five minutes, the heat is right for the loaves. You must keep up a good heat all the time, but especially the first half hour.

A gas-oven requires to have the gas turned *full on for fifteen minutes* before you put the bread in, when you must turn it down to half. When the bread has been in for half an hour, reduce the heat much further, turning it quite low.

The baking should take about an hour ; it may be more, or a little less. The time depends chiefly on the oven, and on the weather, but also on the amount of moisture in the dough. You can tell if a loaf is done by taking it out, and tapping the bottom of it with the back of your fingers. If it sounds hollow, it is done.

If there is anything not quite right with your bread first time, you must find out whether it was the yeast, the risings, too much water, too little kneading, or the oven. But it *should* be just right.

When the loaves are done, turn them upside down, or on their sides, upon a sieve or grating of some sort, *out of a draught*, until they are quite cool. Then wrap them in a thick dry cloth, and put them on a shelf or in a bread-pan. Loaves kept as above are quite moist after several days. What is left of the bread I make one week, is beautifully fresh the following week, when I bake again. (Think of the bought bread after twelve hours !)

*   *   *   *   *

The above recipe should result in about six pounds of bread ; because, in addition to the three and a half pounds of flour, you have one pound of potatoes, also one and a half pints (equal to one and a half pounds) water ; also the creamed yeast and sugar. Of course a lot of the moisture evaporates in the oven. The bread, therefore, goes very much further than two half-quartern baker's loaves ; and it is so much nicer, wholesome, more nourishing, and better-keeping, that you wonder why the baker's loaves should be called " bread " by the side of yours.

Now, the above may appear a lengthy, complicated, and arduous undertaking. Yet I assure you that it's nothing of the sort, but ridiculously simple. You can just sandwich it in between the various details of your daily work. For instance, two or three days ago I made my bread in the intervals of (1) an hour's (very important) odd jobs about the house, (2) two hours' (very difficult) shopping and carrying things home, (3) transplanting large rose bushes to make

room for vegetables, and (4) writing parts of this book. . . .
I often remember an account of Mrs. Beecher Stowe writing
" Uncle Tom's Cabin," in bits and snatches, and simul-
taneously attending to her baby of a few months old—doing
all the housework—*and making the bread.*

Reduced to its usual cook-book formula, the above " How
to Make War Bread " would read thus :

> Three and a half pounds of G.R. flour, one pound of
> boiled sieved potatoes, one teaspoonful of salt, one dessert-
> spoonful of sugar, one ounce of yeast, lukewarm water.
> Make as for ordinary yeast bread.

And you would probably be none the wiser. . . . It is
because I am so anxious that every woman should have
home-made war bread, and that all likelihood of its going
wrong in the making should be reduced to vanishing point,
that the foregoing minute instructions have been given.

There are, of course, many other ways of making bread ;
but this is the best for the present emergency, as regards
dealing with G.R. flour.

BREAD MADE WITH BAKING-POWDER AND OTHER ARTIFICIAL LEAVENS

NOTE.—This is not so good from any point of view as
yeast-bread ; especially, because it gets dry so much sooner.
But in some cases it is Hobson's Choice.

Artificial leavens include baking-powder (bought or home-
made) and bicarbonate of soda combined with cream of
tartar (sometimes with sour milk, with treacle, or with lemon
juice).

The proportions usually given for these vary as widely
and astoundingly as do those given for yeast. But you will
find it safe to use either

> One large heaped tablespoonful of baking-powder
> to one pound of flour. The flour, salt, and baking
> powder must be well mixed together, *dry* ;

Or, one teaspoonful of carbonate of soda, and three and a half teaspoonfuls of cream of tartar, to one quart of flour (this is under two pounds, see p. 230).

As baking powder is made of bicarbonate of soda and cream of tartar, in a little rice flour, you will find it cheaper to use that instead of buying the ingredients, because cream of tartar is now so very expensive. Cream of tartar, or tartaric acid, is a deposit which forms inside wine-casks ; and there are not many wine-casks available nowadays.

One teaspoonful of soda may also be combined with one pint of thick sour milk, for one quart of flour. Never mind about treacle—it is too scarce ; or lemon juice—too dear.

Please note that (1) *Baking-powder bread is not kneaded any more than you can help*—only just enough to get it into a decent dough ; so that in this respect it is exactly opposite to yeast-bread, which likes all the kneading (at the right stage) that you can give it.

(2) That it must be *baked the minute you have mixed it*— opposite to yeast-bread again.

(3) That it is best made into *small* loaves.

(4) That the oven must be hot and the *heat kept up the same till the end.* So, you see, on all these points it radically differs from yeast bread ; and in America it is not called bread, but " biscuit."

552. BAKING-POWDER BREAD, No. I

Mix two pounds of flour with two large teaspoonfuls, *heaped,* of baking-powder ; add one teaspoonful of salt ; mix thoroughly. Some people add a teaspoonful of sugar. Pour in by degrees about two breakfastcupfuls of cold water, or more, enough to moisten the flour into a firm dough. Mix quickly, and knead as little as possible. Make it into small loaves, place in greased tins or on a flat tin, and put them *at once* into a quick oven for an hour.

553. BAKING-POWDER BREAD, No. II

Take one pound of flour, one ounce of sugar, one teaspoonful of salt, two level teaspoonfuls of baking-powder. Mix very thoroughly. Moisten with about half a pint of milk and water, knead very quickly, divide into two loaves, place in greased tins. Bake in quick oven for one hour.

554. BAKING-POWDER BREAD, No. III

Take half a pound of flour, mix thoroughly with a pinch of salt, and a good half-teaspoonful of baking-powder. Pour to this one breakfastcupful of milk, stirring well all the time. Knead quickly and lightly, handling as little as possible ; divide into four to six equal pieces, place on a flat tin (floured) in a very hot oven ; bake a quarter of an hour.

555. RICE BREAD (BAKING-POWDER)

Have three ounces of rice boiled until you can pulp it through a sieve. While it is still warm, rub in one ounce of fat to fourteen ounces of flour, to which has been added half a teaspoonful of salt, and one teaspoonful of sugar. Add two teaspoonfuls of baking powder, and mix in the rice. More liquid (milk or water) or more flour, may be added in order to make the dough of the right consistency. When it is stiff enough, shape into little rolls, and bake in a quick oven.

556. SODA BREAD

To one pound of flour, add a *small* teaspoonful each of salt and of bicarbonate of soda, and a *heaped* teaspoonful of cream of tartar. Mix thoroughly ; then add half a pint of milk, and mix quickly into a softish dough. *Do not knead.* Place in greased tin and bake immediately in a quick oven, for about forty-five minutes.

557. SODA BREAD (WHOLEMEAL)

One pound of wholemeal, one teaspoonful each of sugar and of salt, half a teaspoonful of bicarbonate of soda, one teaspoonful of cream of tartar, one ounce of margarine (or other fat) rubbed in. Moisten with milk or water ; mix to a nice dough, roll out quickly two inches thick, bake in a shallow warmed greased tin for half an hour to forty minutes.

558. LITTLE SODA LOAVES

One quart of flour, one small teaspoonful of soda, one large teaspoonful of cream of tartar, a pinch of salt. Mix the salt and soda with the flour, then dissolve the cream of tartar in a little milk, and make your dough. Shape into very small loaves, and bake in hot oven.

559. WHOLEMEAL BREAD (YEAST), No. I

Requires to be made a trifle moister than bread of G.R. flour ; also it takes rather longer to bake. To three pounds of wholemeal, allow half a pound of flour for the mixing, and one pound of sieved potatoes ; one dessertspoonful of sugar, one ounce of yeast, and two to three level teaspoonfuls of salt. Proceed as for War Bread.

MIXTURE BREADS (FLOUR-SAVING)

NOTE.—For these, the extra ingredient—*warm cooked* rice, pearl barley, oatmeal, etc.—is incorporated into the flour before the yeast is put in ; and a different procedure from that of G.R. bread is adopted, *i.e.*, you *mix and knead when you put the yeast in*, and then let rise two or three hours.

As two ounces of oatmeal (uncooked) make one pound when cooked ; and three ounces of pearl barley yield one pound, and eight ounces of rice similarly result in two pounds, it will be seen what a large quantity of bread can be produced by this means. I haven't tried these mixture breads myself ; but a great many experts pronounce them admirable. It is possible that they are better in quantity than in quality.

More salt is required in the flour—two and a half teaspoonfuls instead of one—and less sugar. A hot oven, *with the heat well maintained*, is advisable for these mixture breads.

560. BARLEY BREAD

Cook three ounces of pearl barley in two pints of water, until it can absorb no more water ; drain, and add it while warm to two and a quarter pounds of G.R. flour, warmed and well salted. Cream three quarters of an ounce of yeast with one teaspoonful of sugar ; add half a pint of (tepid) water in which the barley was boiled. Mix with the flour and barley, and make a dough ; leave to rise for two or three hours. Knead, add more flour if need be ; form into loaves, and let these rise for half an hour. Bake in a hot oven. Forty minutes should suffice.

561. MAIZE BREAD

Make a stiff maize porridge with one and a half break-fastcupfuls of maize meal, one tablespoonful of salt, and one pint of water. (See Maize Porridge, pp. 143–4.) Have ready—this is better made overnight—a " sponge," made with three quarters of an ounce of yeast creamed in one tablespoonful of sugar, and diluted with one pint of tepid water. Stir in one breakfastcupful each of G.R. flour and of maize meal, and beat it well until it is quite smooth and elastic. Put it, covered closely, in a warm place to rise. When it is light and spongy—which will not be for nine or ten hours, mix it with the lukewarm porridge ; add one and a half cupfuls more meal and three cups more flour, and, if need be, more tepid water. Knead, and proceed as for War Bread. Will take at least an hour in a hot oven.

562. OATMEAL BREAD

Put two ounces of oatmeal into one pint of boiling water, in a double saucepan, and cook, stirring well, until you have a stiff porridge. Let cool a little, and mix it into two and a quarter pounds of G.R. flour, salted and warmed. Have three quarters to one ounce of yeast, creamed with one tea-spoonful of sugar, and diluted with half a pint of tepid water. Mix into the flour and oatmeal, making a nice dough. Set

to rise two to three hours. Then knead, adding more flour
if need be ; shape into loaves, leave them to rise again ; bake
in a hot oven for about forty minutes.

563. RICE BREAD, No. I

Boil one and a half pounds of rice gently in four quarts
of water, until it is tender enough to beat into a smooth
paste, or rub through a sieve. Have four pounds of salted
flour ready warmed ; have one ounce of fresh yeast creamed
with one dessertspoonful of sugar, and set to rise in a " well "
in the flour. When the yeast bubbles, add the rice while
still warm, kneading very thoroughly ; and proceed as per
formula for War Bread.

564. RICE BREAD, No. II

Boil eight ounces of rice until soft enough to beat smooth.
It will by then be about two pounds in weight. Mix it while
warm into two and a half pounds of warm salted flour.
Cream one ounce of yeast with one dessertspoonful of sugar,
place it in the " well " and sprinkle it with flour, or mix it right
in to the flour and rice. Let stand one hour. Then knead,
and let stand for two hours. Proceed as for War Bread,
and bake in hot oven for one and a half hours.

VARIOUS BREADS

NOTE.—These recipes are included for the sake of completeness ; but unless made with pure wheat flour instead
of G.R. flour, they are not certain to be satisfactory.

565. BARLEY BREAD

(1) Mix two and a half pounds of G.R. flour, with two
and a half pounds of barley flour, one ounce of salt, one
teaspoonful of sugar, one ounce of yeast, about two pints
of tepid water (but remember that barley flour is rather
moist and sticky in itself). Proceed as for War Bread,

Or (2) One and three-quarters of a pound of G.R. flour, one and three quarters of a pound of barley flour ; one teaspoonful each of sugar and of salt ; one and a quarter ounces of yeast.

Or (3) Two pounds of barley flour to one pound of G.R. flour ; one ounce of yeast.

Or (4) Two pounds of barley flour to two and a quarter pounds of G.R. flour ; two ounces of yeast.

(It will be seen that these recipes vary very greatly as regards proportions. I may add that they have each been recommended by experts. Barley bread is largely used in Wales. I understand that it doesn't suit " liverish " persons ; just as oatmeal is, for some, too heating to the blood.)

566. MAIZE BREAD

Proceed as for Barley Bread, No. 1.

567. OATMEAL BREAD

Mix three pounds of G.R. flour with one and a half pounds of (dry) oatmeal, and one ounce of salt. Set it to warm, and make a " well " in the middle. Pour into this one and a half ounces of yeast, creamed with a dessertspoonful of sugar, and diluted with one breakfastcupful of lukewarm water. Sprinkle with flour ; and when the yeast works through the flour, knead (using more tepid water as required) for half an hour. Set in a warm place to rise, and proceed as for other yeast bread. Should take one hour in a good oven.

568. RYE BREAD

Rye is the only flour besides wheat which rises under the action of yeast. Cream one ounce of yeast with one dessertspoonful of sugar ; meanwhile have three pounds of rye meal, to which has been added one teaspoonful of salt, warming by the fire. Add half a pint of tepid water to the yeast, make a " well " in the rye-meal, and pour it in. Proceed as for other bread. It should not take so long to bake as

G.R. flour. If preferred, use two pounds of rye and one pound of wheat flour.

569. POTATO BREAD

Take the quantity of potatoes required; boil them in their skins. When done, peel them, and bruise them with a rolling-pin to the consistence of a paste. To this add as much flour as there is potato pulp, salt—at least one tea-spoonful—and yeast (creamed with sugar) in the proportions of one ounce to three and a half or four pounds of flour and potatoes. Knead them well, putting as much water as may be necessary. When properly kneaded, form into loaves, and place in the oven, taking care that it be not quite so hot as for common bread, or it will become hard on the outside before the inside is properly baked. This bread must be allowed longer time to bake than any other.

570. WHOLEMEAL BREAD, No. II

Take two pounds of wholemeal flour, twelve ounces of white flour, two large teaspoonfuls of sugar, and the same amount of salt, three-quarters of an ounce of yeast, one quart of warm water. Mix the yeast with the sugar; add in the water and salt, and gradually stir in the wholemeal flour, till all is thoroughly mixed and absorbed. Sprinkle a little white flour over the dough, and put it aside in a warm place to rise. When it has risen enough, add in the rest of the white flour, sufficient to make it into a firm dough when kneaded; make it into two loaves; put it again to rise; then bake in a moderate oven for one hour and a quarter.

FRUIT BREADS

NOTE.—These are useful and wholesome for a variety. Apples, gooseberries, and dates are the fruits most fre-quently used, because (as a rule) they are the cheapest. Chopped figs are very good, so are raisins—when one can get them—or currants.

The dough in which fruit has been intermixed takes a long while to rise—from six to eight hours.

571. APPLE BREAD

Take one pound of apples to two pounds of flour. Boil the apples to a pulp (using as little water as possible) and sieve them. Meanwhile have half an ounce of yeast creamed with sugar, and set to rise in the warmed flour. Knead the dough with the warm apple-pulp, instead of water. Set the dough to rise for a long while, six hours at least; shape into long loaves, and bake.

572. DATE BREAD

For this, yeast dough made with milk instead of water is the best. Work into it, when thoroughly risen, a little fat, say two ounces to the pound. Then add stoned chopped dates, as many as you like; eight ounces to the pound of dough will suffice. Work in the dates thoroughly, and place the dough to rise again in greased tins. It will take longer to rise and to bake than plain bread.

573. GOOSEBERRY BREAD

Cook half a pound of gooseberries in a very little water until they are soft enough to rub through a sieve. Have one and a half pounds of flour, mixed with half a teaspoonful of salt, warmed; make a " well " and put in half an ounce of yeast, creamed with a teaspoonful of sugar, and a little tepid water. Let the yeast rise in the usual way—add the gooseberries, while they are still warmish, in kneading. Leave six or eight hours to rise, and put into tins to rise again.

Sugar and spice may be added at pleasure (cinnamon, cloves, or ground ginger); and two to four ounces of lard or other fat may be added in the kneading.

CAKES AND BISCUITS

These at first sight seem a woeful extravagance in war time. But they're not really. A plain cake may go just as far, and use up very much less flour, than a plain loaf. Also, it supplies wholesome variety—and variety is wholesome in itself. Cocoa butter lends itself to biscuit-making, but is apt to be rather hard of effect in cakes. Eggs, of course, are out of the question; but egg substitutes are handy here as elsewhere.

The following recipes are very plain and simple; yet they will produce nourishing and appetising results.

Your attention is especially directed to the hot cakes and scones of true scone nature, *i.e.*, fried, not baked. These may be either salt or sweet. A very little fat suffices for them. A number of other suitable recipes are to be found in the "Cake Book" of this series, which can be adapted for present use.

574. JOHNNY CAKE, No. I

Stir one pint of scalded milk or water, or half of each, into one cup of yellow or white cornmeal, to which a teaspoonful of salt has been added. Bake in a shallow greased pan or on a griddle.

575. JOHNNY CAKE, No. II

Into one pint of meal and one teaspoonful of salt stir boiling water to make a thick drop batter; thin to a thick pour batter with cold milk; drop by tablespoonfuls on to a hot greased frying-pan and bake as griddle cakes; or cook as No. 1.

576. MAIZE CAKE

Have one pint of maize meal and half a pint of G.R. flour thoroughly mixed with two teaspoonfuls of baking powder, one teaspoonful of salt, two tablespoonfuls of sugar. Add one (dried) beaten egg, one tablespoonful of fat (creamed) and three-quarters of a pint of milk or milk and water. Put the mixture into a greased tin, and bake in hot oven.

577. COFFEE CAKE

Into two breakfastcupfuls of bread dough, mix one beaten (dried) egg, one tablespoonful of fat, one teacupful of sugar.

P

Mix thoroughly, moistening if necessary with tepid water.
Let rise, cover in a warm place, until double in size ; roll out
very lightly and quickly, an inch thick, place in a greased
flat baking tin, and let rise again.   Then spread the top
with half a dried egg, beaten up with one teaspoonful of
sugar, and some chopped nuts.   Bake in a fairly hot oven for
at least half an hour.

578. OATMEAL CAKE

Mix four ounces of fine oatmeal with eight ounces of G.R.
flour ; add a pinch of salt, any spice desired, and one teaspoonful of baking powder.   When all is well blended, moisten
with four tablespoonfuls of treacle and a little milk (tinned
will do).   Beat, pour into a greased cake-tin, and bake in
moderate oven for an hour.

579. PARKIN

Mix one pound of fine oatmeal with one teaspoonful of
salt, one teaspoonful of soda bicarbonate, four teaspoonfuls
of ground ginger.   Heat in a pan four tablespoonfuls of
milk, four ounces of fat, one tablespoonful of treacle, two
tablespoonfuls of sugar.   Pour this liquid to the dry ingredients, mix into a soft paste, bake in a shallow greased
baking-tin, in a moderate oven.   Half an hour should suffice.

580. POTATO CAKE

Take eight ounces each of G.R. flour and of cooked sieved
potatoes ; and a pinch of salt, two ounces of sugar creamed
with two ounces of fat, four ounces of chopped dates, and a
teaspoonful of baking powder.   Mix thoroughly, moisten
with a very little milk, place in a greased tin, bake in a
fairly hot oven to a nice light brown.

581. SEMOLINA CAKE

Two ounces of flour, two ounces of semolina, two ounces of
lard or dripping, one ounce of Demerara sugar, a dozen raisins,
a teaspoonful of baking-powder, a pinch of salt, one dried egg.

Mix flour, semolina, sugar, baking powder, salt together, rub in dripping, add raisins, and mix with the egg, well-beaten. Bake in greased and papered tin in hot oven.

582. BARLEY BANNOCKS

Put one pint of milk into a lined pan, add two ounces of fat and a pinch of salt. Let boil, then stir in barley meal until the whole is a thick dough. Turn out on a floured board, let cool a little, roll thin, cut into rounds, cook on a heated greased griddle over a sharp fire. Both sides must be browned. Serve at once.

583. BUCKWHEAT CAKES

Take one pound of buckwheat flour, add one full teaspoon of baking powder, a quarter of a teaspoonful of salt, two dried eggs, and cold water enough to mix all into a deep batter; beat this well—then drop the batter by table-spoonfuls into boiling fat in a frying pan, and cook over a clear hot fire. Drain and serve at once.

584. CORN DODGERS

Mix one teaspoonful of salt with two breakfastcupfuls of maize meal. Put these ingredients into a bowl, make a hollow in the middle of them, put one tablespoonful of lard or other fat into the hollow ; then pour in boiling water (about three quarters of a pint) to wet the meal thoroughly and melt the lard. Beat one (dry) egg with one tablespoonful of milk, and stir it into the meal when that has cooled off a bit. Mix thoroughly, beat well, and either drop in spoonfuls on a greased tin, or roll out a quarter of an inch thick and cut into rounds. Bake in a very hot oven for fifteen minutes, or in a hot oven for thirty minutes, according to whether the dough is dropped or rolled out.

585. CORN PONES

Mix a pinch of salt into two pints of maizemeal, moisten with enough cold water to make a soft but firm dough.

Melt one and a half teaspoonfuls of lard, stir it into the dough ; shape it into little oval cakes and bake in greased tin in hot oven for fifteen minutes, or until well browned.

586. ELLEN CAKES

Mix eight ounces of G.R. flour with a pinch of salt, three ounces of sugar, and half a teaspoonful of baking-powder. Then rub in three ounces of fat—lard will do ; flavour with a few drops of lemon essence or the grated rind of half a lemon, and moisten with a dried egg and a very little milk. Bake in little patty pans, or on a greased tin. Above quantity should make sixteen little cakes.

587. GINGER CAKE

Mix six ounces of flour with six ounces of medium oatmeal, a pinch of salt, and a teaspoonful each of ground ginger and of baking powder. Rub in four ounces of fat, or two ounces of grated cocoa butter. Put four tablespoonfuls of treacle into a teacupful of milk, and warm it, but do not boil ; then stir in two beaten dried eggs, and blend thoroughly. Moisten the other ingredients with this liquid mixture, mixing well ; bake in a greased cake-tin. It should take one and a half hours in a moderate oven. Chopped preserved ginger can be added at discretion.

588. HOMINY CAKES, No. I

Take some cold boiled hominy, and to each breakfastcupful allow one pint of self-raising flour, one teaspoonful of salt, one dried egg, two ounces of fat. Moisten with a little milk, mix well into a not too stiff paste. Shape into buns, and place on greased tin in hot oven. Cold boiled rice may be treated the same way.

589. HOMINY CAKES, No. II

Take two breakfastcupfuls of cold boiled hominy (see p. 143), seven breakfastcupfuls of self-raising flour, two well-beaten dried eggs, one teaspoonful of salt, one quart of milk. Mix thoroughly and bake immediately.

590. HOMINY CAKES, No. III

Boil one breakfastcupful of hominy (soaked) for two hours in one quart of milk. Remove, and stir in half a teaspoonful of salt, two beaten dried eggs, two tablespoonfuls of fat. Mix thoroughly, drop in little heaps upon a greased baking tin, and bake a pale brown.

591. HOMINY CAKES, No. IV

Take some cold boiled hominy, and to each breakfastcupful allow two ounces of fat, one beaten dried egg, one teaspoonful of salt, and one pint of self-raising flour. Moisten with enough milk to make a soft paste. Shape into buns, and bake in hot oven on greased tin.

Cold boiled rice may be used in the same way.

Sugar to taste may be added to any of above.

592. MAIZE ROCK CAKES, No. I

Mix four ounces of maize flour, four ounces of G.R. flour, a pinch of salt, three ounces of sugar, half a teaspoonful of mixed spice. Rub three ounces of fat; moisten with two beaten dried eggs; beat all thoroughly. If more moisture is required, use a little milk. Drop in rough heaps, using two forks instead of a spoon, on a greased baking tin. Cook for twenty minutes in hot oven.

593. MAIZE ROCK CAKES, No. II

Take two breakfastcupfuls of maize meal and one of G.R. flour. Mix thoroughly with one and a half teaspoonfuls of baking powder and a good pinch of salt. Then rub in one tablespoonful of fat, and add chopped dates to taste and a little sugar if you can spare it. Mix into a very stiff batter, drop in lumps upon a flat tin (greased), and bake in a good oven to a nice golden brown.

594.   OAT CAKES, No. I

Take a walnut-size piece of dripping or other fat, and melt it in a saucepan containing one breakfastcupful of boiling water.   Flour well blended, one large tablespoonful of brown sugar, one dessertspoonful of salt, three teaspoonfuls of ground ginger, half a teaspoonful of bi-carbonate of soda. Pour the fat and water to these ; and immediately sprinkle in two breakfastcupfuls of oatmeal.   When the dough is firm enough to knead with the fingers, and the ingredients are well mixed, roll out very thin, dusting with a little flour if need be.   Cut into shapes as desired ; bake a light brown in a moderate oven.

595.   OAT CAKES, No. II

Have one ounce of lard melted in one pint of boiling water ; add one pound of medium oatmeal, and make into a stiff dough.   Knead slightly, divide into equal portions (eight or ten), make each into a ball, roll out thinly, and cook in a greased frying-pan, or bake in a cool oven, until the edges curl up.   Put in a warm place until dry.   Store in a tin. The cakes should not brown.

596.   OAT CAKES (SOFT), No. III

Mix one pound of medium oatmeal with half a pound of self-raising flour, and one ounce of salt.   Cream one ounce of yeast, add one breakfastcupful of warm water to it, let stand till it begins to work.   Make a " well " in the meal and pour it in, and mix with lukewarm water to a thin batter. Cover, and let stand three hours or more.   Pour a teacupful at a time into a thick greased frying pan, and cook over a clear fire or on a gas stove.   Let one side cook about six minutes, then turn it over with a knife, and cook the other side about four minutes.

597.   RICE AND MAIZE MEAL CAKES

Take half a breakfastcupful each of maize meal and of flour ; one cup of cold boiled rice, two teaspoonfuls of baking powder, one teaspoonful of salt, two dried eggs, one cup of new milk.

Mix the dry ingredients well, add the mixed eggs with milk. Roll out, shape into cakes, cook on griddle ; serve hot.

598. POTATO CAKES, No. I

Take about one pound of cold boiled potatoes. Mash well with salt, add two ounces of fat, and moisten with a little milk into a thick batter. Then work in about double the quantity of flour, mixed with one dessertspoonful of baking powder. Sweeten to taste. Work until all is quite soft ; roll out, cut into small cakes, and bake in a good oven.

599. POTATO CAKES, No. II

Take an equal weight of cold boiled potatoes, pressed through a sieve, and of flour. Mix well ; rub in dripping, two ounces to the pound, and salt to taste. Moisten with a little milk ; roll out about half an inch thick ; cut into rounds with the top of the flour dredger. Put the cakes into a good hot oven till they are a golden brown ; serve piping hot. Serve with treacle.

600. WALNUT CAKES

Take three tablespoonfuls of flour, rub in two ounces of fat, add half a teaspoonful of baking powder, and eight ounces of shelled walnuts, blanched, skinned, and broken very small. A pinch of salt must then be mixed in, and two eggs. Blend thoroughly ; drop teaspoonfuls of the mixture on a greased paper or tin, and brown in a good oven.

BISCUITS

601. CHOCOLATE BISCUITS, No. I

Mix one ounce of flour with four ounces of ground rice rub in one and a half ounces of cocoa butter. Add half a teaspoonful of cocoa, four ounces of boiled sieved potatoes ;

mix well. Add a few drops of vanilla essence, and beat in half a dried egg and one tablespoonful of treacle. Lastly, mix in half a teaspoonful of baking powder. Roll out half an inch thick, cut into small rounds. Bake about fifteen minutes (or more) in a hot oven.

602. CHOCOLATE BISCUITS, No. II

Cream two ounces (melted) cocoa butter along with two to four ounces of sugar (according to taste). Stir in two ounces of cocoa, one beaten (dried) egg, and enough cornflour to make the mixture into a stiff paste. Lastly, add half a teaspoonful of baking powder. Roll out half an inch thick, cut into small rounds, bake ten to fifteen minutes in good oven.

603. MAIZE BISCUITS

Mix one breakfastcupful of maize meal with half that quantity in G.R. flour. Add one ounce of castor sugar, creamed with four ounces of cocoa butter, one beaten (dried) egg, one teaspoonful of baking powder. Moisten with half a breakfastcupful of water. Roll out a quarter of an inch thick, cut into rounds, bake about fifteen minutes in moderate oven.

604. OATMEAL BISCUITS, No. I

Mix eight ounces of oatmeal with the same quantity of G.R. flour, into which two ounces of fat has been rubbed. Add one flat teaspoonful of salt, and the same of baking powder. Mix into a stiff paste with water or milk. Roll out a quarter of an inch thick, cut into biscuit shapes, bake on a tin in a moderate oven for about twenty minutes.

605. OATMEAL BISCUITS, No. II

Mix half a pound of medium oatmeal with half a pound of risen dough. Add four ounces of fat, half a teaspoonful of salt, one teaspoonful of baking powder. Knead well into a smooth dough, roll out half an inch thick, cut into small rounds, bake in a rather slow oven.

606.   OATMEAL GINGER BISCUITS

Melt three ounces of fat with one tablespoonful of treacle. Have ready mixed eight ounces of flour and four ounces of oatmeal, with two ounces of sugar, one small teaspoonful of ground ginger, and a quarter of a teaspoonful (or rather less) of cream of tartar. Add the treacle, etc., blend thoroughly; roll out half an inch thick, cut into biscuits, bake on a greased tin in a quick oven for twenty minutes.

607.   OATMEAL WAFER BISCUITS

Mix one breakfastcupful of oatmeal, one of rolled oats, and two ounces of flour, with a quarter of a cup of sugar, one teaspoonful of salt, two-thirds of a teaspoonful of bicarbonate of soda, and enough hot water (about half a cupful) to moisten into a stiff paste. Roll out very thin ; cut into biscuits, bake on a tin in a moderate oven.

608.   OATMEAL CRACKNELS

Mix thoroughly half a pound each of oatmeal and of flour, with one teaspoonful of baking powder and half a teaspoonful of salt. Rub in four ounces of fat, till the whole is like breadcrumbs. Moisten with milk till you have a firm but not stiff paste ; mix with a knife. Turn out on floured board, knead lightly into a round, roll out thin, cut into shapes, place on a greased tin, prick with a fork, and bake till hard, in a moderate oven. Do not let the cracknels brown, except slightly underneath. Remove from oven and place in a wire sieve till cold.

609.   POTATO AND CHOCOLATE BISCUITS

Mix three ounces of ground rice with two ounces of G.R. flour, rub in one and a half ounces of fat (cocoa butter can well be used), add a pinch of salt, four ounces of cooked riced potatoes, and a teaspoonful of cocoa. Blend well, and add one teaspoonful of treacle and half a dried egg. Beat till the ingredients are thoroughly incorporated, then put in vanilla essence to taste, and a half-teaspoonful of baking powder. Mix, roll out half an inch thick, cut into desired shapes ; bake about twenty minutes on greased tin in quick oven.

610. POTATO AND OATMEAL BISCUITS

Mix two ounces of G.R. flour with three ounces of medium oatmeal, and a pinch of salt. Rub in one ounce of fat ; add two ounces of cooked sieved potatoes. Mix thoroughly, adding half a teaspoonful of baking powder. Moisten with sufficient water (about a teacupful) to make a paste firm enough to roll out a quarter of an inch thick. Cut into desired shapes, bake on greased tin for about twenty minutes in moderate oven.

611. WHOLEMEAL BISCUITS

Mix three ounces of wholemeal flour with three ounces of G.R. flour, a pinch of salt, a quarter of a teaspoonful of bicarbonate of soda, and one tablespoonful of sugar. Rub in two ounces of lard or other fat ; bind with a beaten (dried) egg and a little milk-and-water. Mix into a firm dough ; roll out a quarter of an inch thick or a little more ; cut into desired shapes ; bake on a greased tin in a hot oven.

612. BARLEY FLOUR SCONES, No. I

Rub one tablespoonful of fat into four breakfastcupfuls of barley flour : add half a teaspoonful of salt, one and a half teaspoonfuls of sugar, two teaspoonfuls of sugar : moisten with enough milk-and-water to make a stiff dough. Roll out, cut into desired shapes, and bake.

613. BARLEY FLOUR SCONES, No. II

Mix six ounces of barley flour with two ounces of fine oatmeal, one dessertspoonful of sugar, a teaspoonful of salt, two ounces of dripping or other fat, and one teaspoonful of baking powder. Moisten with warm milk-and-water sufficiently to make a firm but not stiff dough. Roll out half an inch thick, cut into any shapes desired, and cook the scones for twenty minutes in a rather hot oven.

614. BARLEY MEAL SCONES

Mix four ounces of barley meal and two ounces of G.R. flour. Rub in one ounce of dripping or other fat; then add half a teaspoonful of bicarbonate of soda and one teaspoonful of salt. Moisten with sour milk into a workable dough. Knead quickly for a minute or two, roll out half an inch thick, cut into any shapes desired; set in a hot oven for a quarter of an hour.

615. RICE SCONES

Put eight ounces of rice, one teaspoonful of sugar, and a good pinch of salt, into a saucepan, with a pint of cold water. When it boils, draw aside and let it steam two hours or so till the water is absorbed and the rice perfectly soft. Turn it on to a floured pasteboard until cold: then add enough flour to help shape it into thin scones, and bake on greased tin in good oven.

616. MAIZE MEAL SCONES

Mix into one pint of maize meal, one teaspoonful of salt, one tablespoonful of sugar, and two teaspoonfuls of baking powder. Rub in one tablespoonful of fat, then stir with cold milk into a batter which will drop stiffly from a spoon. Bake at once in a greased tin in a hot oven or on a griddle.

617. POTATO SCONES

Boil eight medium-sized potatoes in their jackets: peel and sieve, and mix whilst hot with two ounces of sugar creamed with half an ounce of yeast and dissolved in a breakfastcupful of warm milk. Beat until well mixed, then beat in enough flour to make a soft dough: let it stand until light and double in size. Roll out quickly half an inch thick, cut into squares, and bake in greased tin in hot oven.

618. WHOLEMEAL SCONES

Mix one pound of wholemeal flour with twelve ounces of barley flour, a pinch of salt, two teaspoonfuls of baking powder. Rub in two ounces of fat, and moisten with a beaten dried egg and a little milk. Make into a soft dough, knead for a minute very lightly, roll out half an inch thick, cut into shapes, bake in a hot oven, or cook on a griddle.

CHAPTER X

VARIOUS: NUTS, JAMS, BEVERAGES, HAYBOX COOKERY, WEIGHTS AND MEASURES, ETC.

NUTS

NUTS are of great food value, and are not, as a rule, used half so much as they ought to be, except by strict vegetarians. They are disproportionately dear at present : still, they are worth buying occasionally—if only for variety. They include walnuts, hazel-nuts, filberts, almonds, chestnuts (practically unprocurable), Brazils, and pea-nuts (which are not really nuts at all).

They can be employed, blanched, peeled, chopped (or better still, milled or grated) in cakes, biscuits, and puddings : in some kinds of bread : in salads : and even separately as vegetables. Not to mention " cutlets " and other vegetable make-believes.

Almond-meal, walnut-meal, etc., are to be purchased at the bigger stores : but they are distinctly expensive.

Some people cannot digest nuts at all : they result in skin eruptions, boils and swellings. This is, I presume, because nuts contain oil in too highly concentrated a form. However, to most digestions they are safe and wholesome—if properly prepared by blanching and grating.

619. CHESTNUT CURRY

Shell one pound of Spanish chestnuts, put them into a saucepan of cold water, bring to the boil, and remove the inner skin. Replace in the water and boil for a quarter of an hour, then drain off the water. Have ready the following sauce : Fry one sliced onion in a little fat ; add one table-spoonful of flour, one ounce each of curry powder and of curry paste, and mix smooth ; proceed to add and cook one sliced tomato, two teaspoonfuls of ground almonds, salt, pepper, and nutmeg to taste, and one breakfastcupful of stock (any sort). Boil up fast, and strain the liquor upon the chestnuts, or rub all through a sieve over them. Simmer the whole mixture for twenty minutes or so. Serve at once, with rice.

Half above quantities will suffice for three people.

620. CHESTNUT STEW

Boil twelve ounces of shelled chestnuts, remove inner skins. Have a minced onion and a sliced tomato fried in a little fat. Take them out, and put in one ounce of cornflour ; when it is brown, add half a pint of stock or water, and let boil. Add the onions and tomatoes, also half a small turnip, half a small carrot, and two or three mush-rooms, all chopped small, a small teaspoonful of Worcester sauce, and the chestnuts. Cover and simmer slowly for one and a half hours. Then add salt and pepper, and (at pleasure) a wineglass of claret and a tablespoonful of red currant jelly.

Serve with boiled rice.

621. NUT OMELETTE

Shell and peel the skin off one pound of fresh walnuts. Mill them, or pound into a paste. Have one teacupful of soaked drained bread, beaten into crumb, mixed with four beaten dried eggs, and seasoned with salt and pepper. Have a little fat very hot in a frying-pan, put in the bread mixture (which should be just liquid enough to pour), and cook it carefully or it will burn. When it is almost cooked, strew the walnut over it, put a plate over the pan to cover it for an instant, then roll up the omelet and serve.

This is, of course, better with real eggs ; in which case, beat yolks and whites separately, and add the latter just before frying the mixture.

622. NUT ROAST

Boil a pint of stock (any sort), sprinkle in three table-spoonfuls of semolina, and let cook for five minutes, or until it thickens. Add two teaspoonfuls of grated cheese, and stir well for five minutes more ; then remove the pan from the fire, and put in three ounces of milled nuts, two teaspoon-fuls of grated onion, one tablespoonful of tapioca (previously soaked for an hour) and half a breakfastcupful of soaked drained crumbs ; with seasoning to taste, and half an ounce of fat. Mix very thoroughly, shape into a thick roll, smear with little bits of fat, and bake thirty minutes, or until nicely browned, in a hot oven.

623. NUT SAUSAGE

Mix one breakfastcupful of milled or minced nuts with one breakfastcupful of riced potato. Add salt and pepper, moisten with one beaten (dried) egg, blend thoroughly, shape into sausages, dust with fine oatmeal, and bake a nice brown in a hot oven.

624. NUT SCALLOP

Mill two ounces of shelled nuts. Cut one pound of cooked potatoes into little cubes. Have half an ounce of fat melted in a saucepan ; stir in half an ounce of flour, continue stirring for a minute or two ; then put in a breakfastcupful of milk and water, and go on stirring till it boils. Add salt, pepper and (made) mustard to taste. Put in the nuts and potato, and one teaspoonful of grated cheese ; thoroughly blend, and pour into a greased dish. Strew the top with another teaspoonful of grated cheese, a little grated crust, and some tiny bits of fat. Place in a moderate oven ; when nicely browned and well heated through, serve at once.

625. PEA-NUTS

These nourishing articles are not really nuts at all, but are produced by a leguminous plant (hence " pea "). They should be boiled for twenty minutes, then drained and spread out on a dish for some hours until dry ; then put in a baking-tin in the oven until rather brown ; and if rubbed in a dry cloth when you take them from the oven, the skins will come off. Keep in a dry tin.

626. PEA-NUTS AND RICE

Melt three tablespoonfuls of fat in a saucepan, stir in three tablespoonfuls of flour and cook until the mixture is quite smooth. Add three breakfastcupfuls of milk and water, stirring continually. When this thickens, season with pepper and salt. Have ready some hot boiled rice (one breakfast-cupful, cooked as per any of the recipes on p. 152, etc.), two breakfastcups of chopped or minced pea-nuts, two tea-spoonfuls of salt, and pepper to taste. Mix thoroughly with the sauce, pour into a greased pie-dish, bake twenty minutes in a moderate oven.

Half the above quantities would suffice for a small family.

627. PEA-NUTS AND RICE RISSOLES

Prepare the following : four ounces of pea-nuts, roasted, skinned, and minced ; eight ounces of hot rice, boiled and drained ; four ounces of hot cooked sieved potatoes ; half an ounce of melted fat ; pepper and salt to taste. Mix thoroughly and let cool. Shape into rissoles, roll in fine oatmeal or grated crusts, and bake or fry to a nice brown.

628. PEA-NUTS, STEAMED

Shell, blanch, and skin one pint of pea-nuts ; mill them, and mix a little fat in. Have ready two breakfastcupfuls of tomato purée, one breakfastcupful of cornflour, salt and pepper to taste. Mix thoroughly for at least five minutes. Place in mould or basin, and steam for four to five hours.

629. PEA-NUTS, STEWED

Shell one pint of pea-nuts and blanch them, either by boiling water or by oven-heat ; rub off the red skins. Put them into a casserole with enough water to cover them well (about two quarts), bring to the boil ; place in a slow oven and bake for eight hours or so, or until tender. Season with salt and pepper, and serve.

630. WALNUT PIE

Line the bottom of a greased pie-dish with hot mashed or sieved potatoes ; over these, put four ounces of grated walnuts ; add salt and pepper. Heat and thicken a quarter of a pint of stock (any sort) and a quarter of a pint of mushroom ketchup, and pour over walnuts ; cover with a layer of mashed potatoes, dab with bits of fat, bake to a golden brown.

631. WALNUT ROAST

Take one breakfastcupful of blanched, ground, or grated walnuts ; add two breakfastcupfuls of soaked drained crumbs, one tablespoonful of finely chopped onion, one teaspoonful of minced parsley, and a pinch of minced lemon-thyme. Season to taste with salt and pepper. Mix thoroughly, and bind with one (dried) egg. Place in greased basin, and cook for one hour (at least) in a good oven. Serve with apple sauce and green vegetables.

WAR-TIME JAMS AND MARMALADES

NOTE.—See the remarks on sugar. If you have saved sugar from your ration, and can eke it out with glucose (one part to three parts sugar), or if you can use dates as a sweetener (for instance, with rhubarb or with apples), or if you cook the fruit in sugar-beet syrup instead of plain water, plus a little sugar, you will be able to provide yourself with jam. Readers of the " Jam Book " in this series will remember the essential principle there laid down, that it is the

Q

fruit which requires cooking, not the *sugar ;* so, that to
follow the usual method and cook both together, is great
waste of the sugar. Whereas, if you *first cook the fruit* and
then give it a boil up with the sugar, twelve ounces of the
latter per pound of fruit will be found amply sufficient.
The old-fashioned " pound for pound " is " na-poo."

The less sugar is used, the shorter time the jam will keep,
because sugar is a preservative.

In using dates as a sweetener, wash them, steep a while in a
little cold water ; stone, chop, and weigh along with the other
fruit, using the water they were in. To each pound of mixed
fruit, allow four ounces of sugar.

Where sugar for jam is out of the question, you can use
glucose (corn syrup) as follows :

To ten pounds of fruit, allow seven pounds of corn syrup ;
boil it with the fruit (after cooking the fruit first) and add
a small teaspoonful of tartaric acid, citric acid, or white
vinegar. This helps to set the jam. Let it stop boiling
two or three minutes, stir thoroughly and pour off into pots.

Another method employs one pound of glucose to one pound
of fruit (the sweeter fruits being best for the purpose).
The fruit is cooked gently until the juice runs, then boiled
up fast until soft ; the glucose is then well stirred in, and
the mixture boiled and skimmed, until it sets.

This will not keep so well as preserve made with half-
and-half glucose and sugar.

In making jam with combined sugar and glucose, put
the sugar in first and let it dissolve *slowly,* simmering, Then
add the glucose, and let it dissolve fast, *boiling.*

Treacle can be used, four and a half pounds to six pounds
of fruit. But it is only advisable for mixture jams and the
coarser fruits. I do not recommend it for choice, but for
Hobson's choice.

In using saxin, for every pound of fruit allow forty tablets
of saxin, and about one ounce of gelatine (a little less will do).
When the fruit is cooked, add the saxin, and boil for thirty

minutes; then put in the gelatine, and stir well until it is dissolved.

It is said that 1 teaspoonful of salt to every pound of fruit makes it less acid.

Raspberry or black currant jam can be diluted by mixing it with a double quantity of cooked beetroot (put through the mincer), and soaked boiled sago (allow one ounce to each one pound of original jam, and three breakfastcupfuls of the water in which the sago has been boiled), and the juice and grated rind of one lemon per pound of the original jam. Boil up all together until the jam will set. This is all right for cooking purposes, but hardly for table use.

See also the sugar-beet syrup recipes in Chapter I.; these may be used instead of water in making jam, and considerably less sugar will be needed, but it will not be so good for keeping.

632. APPLE AND GINGER JAM

Well wipe, peel, core and slice, four pounds of cooking apples. Place in preserving pan with one teacupful of water, the grated rind and juice of two lemons, and a quarter of a teaspoonful of ground ginger. Cook till nearly a pulp; then add one pound of glucose and two pounds of Demerara sugar;- boil up again until the jam will set; put into pots, and cover whilst hot.

633. APPLE AND GINGER JELLY

Take the peel and the cores of the apples, used for above, place in a covered jar, with enough water to cover them, and simmer for six hours. Strain, and to each pint allow the grated rind and juice of one lemon, a pinch of ground ginger, and twelve ounces of sugar. Boil the juice separately for forty-five minutes; add the sugar, and boil up until it sets. Place in jars, and do not cover until cold.

634. BLACKBERRY JELLY (French Sugarless)

Place the picked blackberries (four to six pounds) in a preserving pan, covered with water; boil until tender enough to strain through a muslin. Return strained juice to pan ; and add three carrots, two beetroots or one sugar-beet, and one lemon ; all coarsely sliced. Boil up until the jelly will set, remove the vegetables, pour off into jars, do not cover until cold.

635. CARROT MARMALADE, No. I

Take two and a half pounds of peeled sliced carrots (weigh after preparing), six lemons thinly sliced, with the pips removed, a heaped saltspoonful of salt and four quarts of water. Boil all together till they can be pulped through a sieve ; say about two and a half hours ; then add two pounds of sugar, and boil up until the marmalade will set.

636. CARROT MARMALADE, No. II

Take six oranges and four lemons, put them to soak for twenty-four hours in a quart of water, soaking the pips separately in a breakfastcupful of water. Peel and chop one and a half pounds of carrots, pass them through a mincer, put them with the oranges and water and boil for two hours, along with the pips in a muslin bag. Remove bag, add one teaspoonful of salt and two and a half to three pounds of sugar. Boil fast until set.

637. MIXED FRUIT JAM

Peel and slice six bananas, peel and cut up the pulp of four oranges (removing pips), thinly slice four lemons (removing pips), halve and core (but do not peel) six cooking apples. Place all in a preserving pan with eight pints cold water, bring to the boil, let cook steadily for two hours, or until all is soft enough to pulp through a sieve. Weigh and add twelve ounces of sugar for every pound of pulp. Boil up again until the mixture will set or jelly ; proceed as for other jam.

If preferred, the jam need not be sieved ; in that case the apples must be peeled and sliced.

638. ORANGE JAM

Take ten sweet oranges, peel, remove pips and white " rag," and cut into chunks, using a silver knife. Weigh, and set aside eight ounces of sugar for every pound of fruit ; if the jam is not intended for long keeping, six ounces of sugar will suffice. Add a pint of cold water, place in a preserving pan ; bring to the boil and boil until quite tender.

Stir in one ounce of gelatine dissolved in a little warm water ; then add the sugar, and boil up until the jam sets, which will not be long because of the gelatine. Do not cover the pots until the jam is cold.

639. ORANGE MARMALADE JELLY

Take six oranges and two good lemons ; clean carefully, and grate the peel into one quart of cold water. Remove any superfluous white inner lining, and slice the fruit across, in thin rounds. Place the fruit in a jar of two quarts of cold water, and the pips in a breakfastcupful of water. Leave for a day and a night. Then put the fruit and water to boil in a preserving-pan, with the strained water from the pips. Let boil for thirty minutes ; rub through a fine sieve ; replace the liquid in the preserving-pan. Then strain off the water from the grated peels, and add them to the liquid in the pan. Boil this for ten minutes, then measure, and for every pint allow twelve ounces of sugar, or eight ounces of sugar and four ounces of glucose. Stir well until the sugar is dissolved, and boil fast for half an hour or until the jelly sets when tested.

Do not cover the pots until cold.

640. PARSNIP MARMALADE

Peel and slice enough parsnips to make two pounds when weighed subsequently, place in boiling water, and boil steadily for an hour. Strain off the water, and set aside half a pint. Sieve or rice the parsnips, and return the half pint of water to the jam, along with the grated rind and juice of two lemons, and eight ounces of sugar, or six ounces of sugar, and two ounces of glucose. Stir thoroughly until the sugar is dissolved; then add the parsnips, and boil, stirring often, for thirty minutes.

BEVERAGES

641. BARLEY WATER

Pour one quart of boiling water upon two full tablespoons of pearl barley; let it steep a little at the side of the stove; then turn all into a saucepan and simmer with the thinly pared rind of a lemon, till it is as thick as desired, which may take from half an hour to two hours according to what you want. Strain off the liquor (the barley can be then used for a milk pudding) and sweeten to taste; adding any flavour preferred. One large apple can be sliced, boiled separately, and added with its liquor to the barley water before straining.

642. BLACKBERRY SYRUP

Stew the blackberries with a quarter of a pint of water to every three pounds, until the juice is drawn. Strain, and to every pint of juice add six ounces of sugar. Boil sugar and juice together for fifteen minutes, and bottle for use when cold.

643. BLACKBERRY VINEGAR

Take three quarts of ripe blackberries, crush them, pour over them two quarts of good white vinegar. Let them stand twenty-four hours, then strain through a muslin, and add the liquor to three quarts of fresh blackberries. Stand and strain these as before, and if the liquid does not seem strong enough, repeat a third time with fresh berries. Pour it into a jar, to stand in a pan of boiling water which must boil fast for one hour; then bottle it for use.

644. GINGER BEER, No. I

Take two and a half pounds of loaf sugar, two ounces of best whole ginger, two sliced lemons, and one ounce of cream of tartar. Put one gallon of water on the fire, and when it boils, add the ginger and the lemons, let it boil a quarter of an hour, then turn it into a pan, and add six quarts of water and the sugar. When cool, set it to ferment with half a breakfastcup of good yeast, or piece of compressed yeast the size of a chestnut. After it has done fermenting, which will be in thirteen or fifteen hours, strain through a muslin rag, and beat the cream of tartar and the white of an egg together, and add just before bottling.

645. GINGER BEER, No. II

Have powdered ginger, one ounce ; cream of tartar, half an ounce ; a large lemon sliced ; two pounds of lump sugar ; and one gallon of water, added together, and simmered over the fire for half an hour. Then ferment it in the usual way with a tablespoonful of yeast, and bottle it for use, tightly corked.

646. GINGER BEER, No. III

Take two ounces of cream of tartar, one ounce and a half of white ginger well beaten (not ground), one lemon shred fine, one pound and a half of sugar. Put them all together in an earthen vessel, and pour on them ten quarts of boiling water. Let stand till nearly cold, then add two tablespoonfuls of good yeast ; mix it well ; let it stand for thirty hours, then strain it through a flannel bag, pressing it well through. Bottle it, and confine the corks with twine. It will be fit for use in two days.

647. LEMON SYRUP

Rub one pound of loaf sugar upon the rinds of six lemons, until all the yellow part is absorbed, and place the sugar in a preserving pan with half a pint of cold water. Boil until the syrup is clear ; then add the strained juice of twelve lemons. Let it simmer for five minutes very carefully ; it must not boil again. Pour off into clean dry bottles ; let the syrup grow cold, and cork closely.

648. RASPBERRY SYRUP

Take two quarts of good ripe raspberries, pour one quart of good vinegar over them ; cover them closely and let them stand for two days. Then mash up the berries in the vinegar, and strain off the liquid on to two quarts of fresh fruit. Let this stand another two days, then mash and strain as before. To every pint of liquid, add two teacupfuls of white sugar. Let it simmer very gently for fifteen minutes in a lined saucepan over the fire, keeping it well skimmed. Then strain it, bottle it, cork, and cover closely ; seal the cork. This should be taken with cold water.

APPENDIX

649. BLACKBERRY AND APPLE CUSTARD

Peel some good-sized apples, core them, put them in a baking-tin with a little water and sugar, bake until done. Have ready some cooked blackberries, flavoured with a little grated lemon-rind; fill up the hollows of the apples with these, and return to the oven for a little while. Then place on a glass dish; pour over them any syrup that was formed; and cover with a (powder) custard.

650. BREAD PANCAKES

Take enough stale soaked bread, well-squeezed, to make two breakfastcupfuls. Add two beaten (dried) eggs, one teaspoonful of flour, one teaspoonful of salt, and sufficient milk to make a thin batter. Beat until very smooth; then mix in one teaspoonful of baking powder, and cook on a griddle or in a frying pan.

651. BREAD STEAKS

Cut slices of stale bread in pieces about a quarter of an inch thick, two inches wide, and four to six inches long. Dip them into ketchup and water (but do not let them soak or they will break), have ready a (dried) beaten egg, seasoned with pepper, salt, and finely minced parsley: dip the steaks into this, and fry in boiling fat. Serve with fried onions.

652. CURRIED SAVOURY TOAST

Take two dried eggs, one ounce of fat, one salt spoon of curry powder, three tablespoonfuls of milk. Heat the fat in a stewpan, add the curry powder to this when it boils and a little milk. Beat the eggs a little, add to the ingredients in the pan, stir altogether, add the three tablespoonfuls of milk and salt to taste. Directly the mixture is thick, pile it on to squares of fried or toasted bread and serve garnished with small dice of beetroot.

653. FISH OR CHICKEN WITH MAYONNAISE

This is a good way of employing an almost infinitesimal quantity of any kind of choice fish or poultry. First place in little china or paper cases a layer of broken lettuce, very lightly dressed with oil, vinegar, pepper, and salt. Next a slice of tomato. On this place a little heap of chopped chicken or turkey, flaked salmon, turbot, halibut, lobster, or crab. Over all pour some rather thick mayonnaise sauce or salad dressing, and garnish, as may be convenient, with an olive, a few strips of gherkin, and chilli, or whatever may be at hand.

654. GRAVY WITHOUT MEAT

Allow four large onions sliced to two quarts of water, a bundle of sweet herbs, a burnt crust of bread, two ounces of fat, some pepper and salt. When boiling, strain it, and add to it a tablespoonful of ketchup.

655. OATMEAL JELLY

Have two breakfastcupfuls of boiling water in a double-boiler. Have one and a half ounces of fine oatmeal mixed smooth with a little cold water, stir it in, let boil, add a pinch of salt, and thin lemon rind to taste. Cover the inner pan, and let boil about forty-five minutes, with frequent stirring. Strain through a muslin jelly-bag into a rinsed mould; put in any extra flavouring desired, and let grow cold, then unmould.

656. RICE SHORTCRUST

Mix four ounces of flour with two ounces of fat, rubbing well in; add a pinch of salt, stir in four ounces of well-drained boiled rice; mix to a stiff dough, using a little cold water to moisten, roll out and use.

657. SAUSAGE AND CARROT SAVOURY

Grate eight ounces of raw carrots, and mix with one pound of boiled sieved potatoes, eight ounces of sausage meat, a small onion finely minced, a teaspoonful of minced parsley. Mix well, then add salt, pepper, and nutmeg to taste, a teaspoonful of meat extract, and a beaten dried egg. Blend thoroughly, and moisten if necessary with a little stock. Place in a greased basin, covered with greaseproof paper, and steam for two hours.

HAYBOX COOKERY

NOTE.—There is a distinct variety of opinion on this subject—some people maintaining that they cannot be bothered with haybox cookery, because it does not abolish the use of a fire, and can only be used for dishes which have to be cooked very long and slowly, but which *must* be started and finished by means of stronger heat than a haybox can afford. Also, that unless you remove these dishes at the psychological moment, they will go bad.

Others, again, declare that they were " perishing in the snow " before they discovered the invaluable haybox; that it has made life much easier to them, saved no end of fuel, and resulted in most appetising meals.

However, this is what a haybox will and will not do. It *will* cook, most effectually, stews, soups, and such porridges as require a lengthy process; under certain conditions, it will cook suet puddings; it will cook such vegetables as are stewed *en casserole* with next to no liquid. And it will keep other things warm for several hours.

It *won't* roast or bake, boil or steam or simmer, broil or grill, fry or sauter. All these operations require strong heat, in varying degrees of intensity. So that you must cook the food by one of above methods before putting it in the haybox; and you must make it thoroughly hot, after taking it out of the box, before you can serve it.

This is how you make it—get an old cube-sugar box or other box about the same strength and size, *with a lid*. This lid must be fixed on by hinges of some sort at back, and a hasp or fastener in front. If no wooden box be obtainable, a little old tin one will do.

Line the inside with two or three thicknesses of newspaper. Then you put a layer of hay all over bottom and sides—the hay must be at least four inches thick ; and it must be covered with flannel ; and you must arrange two little nests in it (or three, if there is room), into which your casseroles or stew-jars will fit, exactly and just-so. And you then provide cushions of thick tight hay to fit over each jar in its nest, or one cushion to cover the entire top over the nests. The idea is that there shall not be the smallest chance of any heat escaping, and not the least chink or crack through which it might escape.

There are other ways of making a haybox, but the above is about the best ; and while you are about it, you may as well play for safety.

Remember (1) that you must transfer your food, whatever it is, in the casserole, straight from the fire to the haybox whilst the liquid is actually boiling.

And (2) that you must not open the haybox until it is time to take the casserole out.

To this end, you must go by a definite time-table as follows :

Dish.	Cooked on the Fire or Gas.	In Hay-Box.
Lentil Soup	¾ hour	4 hrs.
Potato Soup	¼ hour	1½ hrs.
Fish, stewed	3 minutes boiling ..	½ hr.
Irish Stew	{ ½ hour Meat— Potatoes 5 minutes }	1½ hrs.
Beef Stew with Vegetables	¾ hour	3 hrs.
Potatoes	5 minutes	1½ hrs.

Dish.	Cooked on the Fire or Gas.	In Hay-Box.
Haricot Beans, soaked ..	1 hour	2 hrs.
Boiled Rice	2-3 minutes boiling	2½ hrs.
Stewed Apples	2-3 minutes boiling	1-2 hrs.
Stewed Prunes	2-3 minutes boiling	3½ hrs.
Coarse Oatmeal Porridge	5 minutes boiling ..	All night
Quaker Oats	5 minutes boiling ..	2½ hrs.
Suet Pudding	30 minutes ..	2½ hrs.
Meat Pudding (Suet) ..	45 minutes ..	3 hrs.
Boiled Bacon or Mutton	45 minutes ..	4-5 hrs.
Vegetables—Young ..	10 minutes ..	2 hrs.
Old	18-20 minutes ..	2½-3 hrs.

The meat for stews must be absolutely fresh for haybox cookery.

Suet-puddings must be placed in a basin with a screw-down top, set in a pan of *boiling* water, and, after thirty to forty-five minutes boiling, put, pan and all, into box.

Porridge can be cooked overnight, by boiling fast for five minutes, placing in the haybox, and heating up in the morning.

Vegetables, as already stated, require very little water or stock.

You understand, the food must not be shunted or *shifted* from a pan into a jar or casserole to go into the box. Whatever it is boiling in, must go *straight in, just as it is.*

WEIGHTS AND MEASURES

2 saltspoons full	equal	1 coffee spoon
2 coffee spoons full	,,	1 teaspoon
5 teaspoons (dry) full	,,	1 tablespoon

WEIGHTS AND MEASURES—*continued*.

4 teaspoons (liquid) full	equal	1 tablespoon
4 tablespoons (liquid) full	,,	1 wineglass, or half a breakfast cup.
8 large tablespoons full	,,	1 gill
2 gills	,,	1 breakfastcup, or half a pint.
2 breakfastcups full	,,	1 pint
2 pints (4 cups) full	,,	1 quart
1 tablespoonful (liquid)	,,	½ ounce
1 heaped tablespoonful of sugar or butter	,,	1 ounce
1 breakfastcupful of sugar (granulated)	,,	8 ounces
1 breakfastcupful of butter (solid)	,,	8 ounces

Roughly speaking :

1 pint (milk or water) equals 1 pound of dry material.

The same applies to small articles such as beans, peas, nuts, and small berries.

For making roux, *i.e.*, thickening sauce, use one tablespoonful of flour and one tablespoonful of fat to half a breakfastcupful of liquid.

Remember that one breakfastcup of rice will absorb three times its amount if water be used, and more in the ˙e of milk or stock.

FLOUR WEIGHTS

1 pint of flour	weighs	14 ounces
1 quart (½ quartern)	,,	1¾ pounds
1 quartern (½ gallon, or ¼ stone)	,,	3½ pounds
1 gallon (2 quarterns or ½ stone)	,,	7 pounds

FLOUR WEIGHTS—*continued.*

1 stone (2 gallons, or 1 peck)	weighs	14 pounds
2 stones (2 stones)	,,	28 pounds ($\frac{1}{2}$ bushel)
1 bushel (4 pecks)	,,	56 pounds
1 sack (5 bushels)	,,	280 pounds